Marine Geology

Marine Geology

Ph. H. KUENEN   PROFESSOR OF GEOLOGY
UNIVERSITY OF GRONINGEN
THE NETHERLANDS

JOHN WILEY & SONS, INC., NEW YORK
LONDON

Printed in the United States of America

THIRD PRINTING, JULY, 1960

To B. G. ESCHER,
Professor of Geology
University of Leyden

Inspiring teacher and generous friend

Who first directed the writer's interest towards the problems of marine geology by insuring his appointment as geologist to the *Snellius* Expedition

Preface

The geologists of the past have not always developed their science systematically. The geology of the seas has been especially neglected, but with good reason. Most geological subjects are readily accessible, or relatively so, as respects time and money. The examination of the sea floor, however, means expensive and lengthy cruises as well as intricate techniques of investigation. Only recently have an increasing number of individual workers, oil companies, and oceanographical institutions embarked on a more intensive study of marine geology.

This neglect still prevails in teaching in spite of the fact that most undergraduates will later spend a major portion of their time dealing with fossil marine sediments in one way or another. As long as marine geology remained undeveloped, this lack of emphasis could be fully justified. However, now that great advances in this subject have been made there would seem to be ample reason for giving more attention to the geological problems of the sea.

To this end, three purposes have been in mind while this book was being written. The first was to introduce university students of geology to an important branch of their subject. The second, to provide a guide for geologists, oceanographers, and scientists in general who wish to explore the field of marine geology, and, finally, to aid the advance of research by summarizing achieved results and emphasizing the many problems still to be solved. It should be realized that this is not intended as a source book for data, but references, although not complete, will point the way to whatever detailed information the reader may require.

Throughout, emphasis has been laid on problems in the hope of stimulating the student's interest and his critical faculties. I am well aware, however, that this approach may have led me to make sweeping statements and to emphasize some subjects beyond their general significance, while neglecting others. Some subjects, such as geophysics of the sea floor, geomorphology of coastlines, descriptive petrography of recent marine sediments, and the analysis of fossil rock facies, have purposely been touched on only superficially. On the other hand I have given special attention to coral reefs, submarine canyons, and the Moluccan deep-sea troughs, having spent much time myself on these subjects.

The present volume differs markedly from other recent textbooks dealing with marine geology. Daly's *The Floor of the Ocean* is mainly geophysical; Bourcart's *Géographie du fond des mers*, geographical; *The Oceans* by Sverdrup et al., oceanographical. Shepard's excellent *Submarine Geology* emphasizes geomorphological matters and field techniques, and there is surprisingly little duplication in our texts.

Not until well along with the writing did I realize how wide and diversified is the field of marine geology. Had it not been for the generous assistance offered by several colleagues this book would never have been brought to completion. Foremost among these are C. O. Dunbar, who read the whole of the original manuscript, and F. P. Shepard, who read most of it. Both suggested a very substantial number of corrections and alterations. Others who read some chapters and gave valuable advice are P. Groen, D. L. Inman, A. N. Jeffares, Gerda A. Neeb, L. M. J. U. v. Straaten, and J. H. F. Umbgrove. To all these friends I tender my sincere thanks, hoping that they find satisfaction in the results of their advice without feeling the responsibility for the shortcomings they will likely encounter.

                                                        Ph. H. Kuenen

Geological Institute
University of Groningen
The Netherlands

Contents

Physical Oceanography

The geology of the sea floor is intimately connected with many physical, chemical, and biological problems of the oceans, and no sharp distinction can be made between marine geology and oceanography. Erosion and deposition are controlled by currents and waves. The source of sedimentary particles is largely to be sought in planktonic life, which is in its turn dependent on the character and distribution of physical and chemical conditions in the sea. Sedimentary matter, whether carried in suspension or supplied directly from solution, is distributed from its original source by the movement of the ocean waters. The topographic forms of the sea floor, the position of sea level, and tidal phenomena are of importance to geologists and oceanographers alike. Evidently marine geology cannot be successfully studied without knowledge of certain aspects of oceanography.

The science of oceanography deals with the following subjects: the physical and chemical properties of sea water; the distribution of temperature, salinity, and other variables; the movements of sea water; the interaction of atmosphere and hydrosphere; the shape of the ocean floor; the biology of the seas; the deposits on the sea floor; the erosion of coasts and ocean bed. The observation of gravity and other geophysical determinations at sea are also sometimes considered oceanographical subjects.

In this chapter emphasis will be laid on the aspects of physical oceanography that are of special importance to marine geology.

Summaries of oceanography from a biological point of view are to be found in Murray and Hjort (1912), Russell and Yonge (1928), Hentschel (1929), and Correns (1934). Treatises in which physical problems are placed in the foreground are: Defant (1929, 1940), Bigelow (1931), National Research Council (1932), Correns (1934),

Vaughan (1937), Fleming and Revelle (1939), Rouch (1939, 1941, 1943-1948), Thorade (1941), and Sverdrup (1945). The treatise by Krümmel (1907, 1911) is very complete but out of date. The excellent volume by Sverdrup, Johnson, and Fleming (1942) is of wide scope and presents a modern compilation of all subjects embraced by oceanography. The two monographs by Schott (1935 and 1942) together form a treatment of oceanography from the regional point of view. Shepard's recent volume (1948) is an able and up-to-date treatment of the geological and especially the geomorphological aspects of oceanography written by one of the most active workers in this field. A very complete list of periodicals dealing with all aspects of marine sciences is given by Vaughan (1937).

THE COLLECTING OF DATA

Although some oceanographical observations can be made from land, ships are required for obtaining most of the data. Accurate knowledge of surface currents, tides, coastal and bottom topography, maritime meteorology, etc., is of preeminent importance to mercantile shipping and to navies. Long before scientific inquiry had begun, a vast amount of knowledge had been compiled by anonymous observers on the bridges of seagoing vessels. Our information on surface currents, for instance, is based largely on observations of the drift of ships under way. All seafaring nations have hydrographic departments, many with long records of high merit. Besides the observation and scientific investigation of tides and currents, such departments have been entrusted with the arduous task of compiling charts of the coastal waters, generally showing both depths and bottom deposits. The U. S. Navy sponsored a vast program of oceanographical investigation during the second world war, and research has been pushed forward actively ever since. Other official bodies studying special aspects of oceanography comprise harbor boards, meteorological institutes, fishery boards, coast guards, beach erosion boards, etc.

Some of these government institutions have carried their surveys farther afield and extended their observations beyond coastal waters to the wide oceans. Nevertheless the deep sea would have remained practically unexplored but for a number of purely scientific expeditions. Whereas the more utilitarian investigations were mainly restricted to surface waters and to the bottom in depths reaching only to a couple of hundred meters, scientific expeditions concentrated mainly on deeper water. Now that the serious arrears in the exploration of the deep ocean have been diminished and the first curiosity appeased, scientists are turning their attention to the many important problems of shallow waters and surface phenomena.

The series of deep-sea expeditions was inaugurated by the voyage of the *Challenger* between 1872 and 1876 under the leadership of Sir William Thomson. More than eighty deep-sea expeditions have followed (Rouch, 1943). In Table 1 those that sailed between the world wars have been listed.

TABLE 1. DEEP-SEA EXPEDITIONS BETWEEN THE WORLD WARS

Ship	Year	Nationality	Investigated region
Carnegie	1909–29	U.S.A.	World cruises
Pourquoi-Pas?	1912–36	French	Atlantic-Arctic
Dana	1921–32	Danish	World cruise
Michael Sars	1924	Norwegian	Arctic
Discovery	1925–26	British	Arctic
Meteor	1925–27	German	Southern Atlantic
William Scoresby	1926–32	British	Antarctic-Atlantic
Armauer Hansen	1928	Norwegian	Northern Atlantic
Godthaab	1928	Danish	Baffin Bay
Marion	1928–35	U.S.A.	Arctic-Northern Atlantic
Willebrord-Snellius	1929–30	Dutch	Moluccas
Discovery II	1930–35	British	Antarctic
Norvegia	1929–31	Norwegian	Antarctic
Atlantis	1931–32	U.S.A.	Atlantic
Catalyst	1932–36	U.S.A.	Pacific
Hannibal	1933–36	U.S.A.	Antilles-Pacific
Mahabis	1933–34	Egyptian	Indian Ocean
E. W. Scripps	1937–40	U.S.A.	Gulf of California

These expeditions provided more or less incidental opportunities for studying oceanographic problems. A growing number of permanent marine laboratories and oceanographical stations is now engaged in extensive programs of marine research. While some concentrate on marine biology or even on a specialized aspect such as fishery problems, others have chosen physical oceanography as a special line of investigation or limit their investigations to tidal phenomena alone. A few institutions, however, have a wider field and devote themselves to the entire field of oceanography. Some of these laboratories are run by state governments or university departments; others have been founded by private individuals and are financed by donations.

Oceanographical institutions usually own motor launches or even larger seagoing vessels with which extended cruises can be undertaken. Hence the scientific staff is in a better position to study rhythmic or secular changes by visiting the same area repeatedly. Any problem requiring either a prolonged investigation or an intensive study in a limited area can be attacked only by such permanent laboratories and not by separate deep-sea expeditions. More than two hundred laboratories and other permanent bodies engaged entirely or part time with oceanography are enumerated by Vaughan (1937).

It would take up too much space to describe oceanographical instruments and methods of investigation in detail. A geologist interested in oceanographical results, however, cannot entirely ignore the methods by which the data are procured from which conclusions are drawn. Otherwise he might easily place a wrong value on the facts presented in oceanographical papers or he might expect information from his colleagues engaged on marine researches which cannot be obtained. While referring the reader to treatises on oceanography and especially to reports of expeditions for gaining detailed information, the writer will give a short description of the operations carried out on board the *Snellius* during the expedition in the Moluccas from 1929 to 1930. As geologist of this expedition he was in a position to become acquainted with this oceanographical work. In general, similar lines have been followed by other expeditions. Some remarks on recent developments will be added.

The course followed during the cruise was continually checked as accurately as possible by dead reckoning, by astronomical observations, and by taking bearings on adjacent coasts. The depth was determined by echo soundings at intervals of a few kilometers or more frequently where the bottom proved to be irregular or to slope steeply. Recent developments include the production of echographs giving continuous records. The surface temperature, salinity, and oxygen content were determined every few hours, and a self-registering thermometer provided an uninterrupted record of surface temperatures. A small meteorological station on board registered temperature, moisture, and barometric pressure of the air, and solar radiation was measured at regular intervals. When time allowed, a tow net or dredge was operated for biological purposes. Biological and geological investigations on shore were made whenever feasible, the gaining of information on coral reefs and coastal phenomena being given priority.

The main object of the expedition, however, was the occupation of oceanographic stations throughout the deep basins of the Moluccas. These stations began with a wire sounding to check the depth, to obtain samples of the deposit and bottom water, and to determine the temperature. Meanwhile surface plankton catches were made by fine-meshed nets. Next followed a so-called serial observation to procure water samples and temperature readings at a number of levels between the surface and the bottom. At deep stations, where the maximum number of samples, amounting to twelve, was insufficient, two or three series were carried through, each at increasing depths (Fig. 1). At some stations a net was lowered to a few thousand meters and raised a certain distance before being closed by a messenger. By this method catches were made at various water levels. A chemical laboratory on board was constantly occupied with the determination by titration of salinity, alkalinity, oxygen content, and nutrient salts in the water samples.

Several anchor stations were also occupied during a few days each, some exceeding 5000 m in depth. From the stationary ship, current velocities at various levels were measured. Serial observations repeated during 24 hours served as a basis for studying vertical displacements of the water strata by internal waves.

Recent additions to the equipment used for oceanographical purposes are the bathythermograph and sea sampler, instruments served from the ship underway.

Observations carried out by other oceanographical expeditions include stereophotography of waves, magnetic observations, geophysical determinations of gravity and sediment thickness on the sea floor, light transmission, and quantitative measurements of plankton and silt.

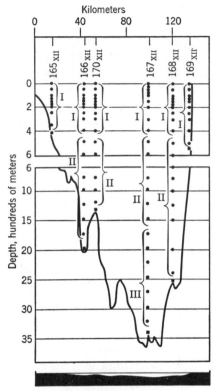

Fig. 1. Section through the Flores Trough, north on the left, depth in hundreds of meters. Vertical 100 × horizontal in upper part and 50 × in lower part. (True scale section at bottom.) Each dot denotes level at which a temperature measurement and water sample were obtained by the *Snellius* expedition. (After van Riel, 1937, Fig. 2, p. 91.)

In view of the special importance of bottom deposits to geological science, a short summary will be given of the various methods used for securing samples. A large number of different instruments have been developed. The most common type consists of a long steel tube, weighted at the upper end. When the sampler is dropped into the bottom at high speed (3 or more meters per second), gravity drives the tube deep into the soft deposit. In some types the weights are automatically detached so that the sampler can be raised more easily. This practice is wasteful, however, and is infrequent nowadays, except in very deep waters where the great weight of the sounding wire leaves a small margin of strength to pull the sampler out of the mud. When hauled up above water the sample is likely to drop out again; hence, an arrangement is generally provided for closing the lower end of the tube. With this type of sampler, cores more than 5 m long have been secured. Snappers are used for sand or gravel because these materials either drop out or are not penetrated at all by a gravity corer.

An ingenious sampler was constructed by Piggot; it has a short gun that shoots the corer into the sediment on reaching the bottom. This type has also been used with success and has yielded samples 3 m in length.

The latest spectacular improvement is due to Kullenberg, who made a great stride forward by securing samples no less than 23 m long from the deep-sea floor. The most serious trouble experienced with coring tubes is that the length of sample passing into the tube is less than the distance the sampler penetrates into the sediment, owing to the friction along the inner wall of the sampler. The new Swedish sampler contains a piston suspended from the end of the sounding cable at the lower end inside the tube. On striking the bottom the piston is held in place and the weighted tube slides down around it. The hydrostatic pressure of the surrounding water and sediment keep the sample pressed up against the piston. In this manner a sample is obtained of the same length as the distance of penetration and almost free of distortion. The great length of the samples is partially due to the exceptionally heavy weight used.

Most samplers contain an inner lining of glass, copper, plastic, etc., that is extracted with the sample inside. The inner tubes are stoppered, and in this manner the sample can be stored in the original moist condition for future examination in the laboratory.

Bottom samples can now also be taken in shallow water from ships at high speed by "underway bottom samplers" (Emery and Champion, 1948, Worzel, 1948).

A special technique that has been newly inaugurated by Ewing is submarine photography. A camera with flash bulb is lowered, and it operates automatically on reaching the bottom. Among others, Shepard and Emery obtained interesting exposures off the California coast from depths as great as 250 m. Future work by this method promises additions to our knowledge that could not be obtained by other means. Features clearly shown on submarine photographs are ripple marks, tracks, animals, pebbles, concretions, rocky scarps, etc.

Dredging has provided very important information on the sea floor. The technique is difficult but has amply rewarded the pains taken. Among the unexpected discoveries are the amazing amount of rock bottom and the presence of rounded cobbles and even boulders at depths of 1000 m and more.

COMPOSITION AND PROPERTIES OF SEA WATER

A large variety of ions are in solution in sea water. More than half of all known elements have been detected, though many such as gold and uranium occur only as slight traces. The important constituents can be classed on the one hand as atmospheric gases, especially nitrogen, oxygen, and carbon dioxide, and on the other as salt ions.

GASES DISSOLVED IN SEA WATER

It was formerly assumed that the nitrogen dissolved in sea water does not enter into new compounds during the circulation of the water, and that the percentage is not subject to appreciable variation. It has therefore seldom been determined. Further investigations are required, however, before this assumption can be accepted.

The other two atmospheric gases, on the other hand, play an active part in the metabolism of organisms, in the formation and solution of lime, and in the rotting of organic matter. Hence the percentage varies considerably from one body of water to another, and the determination becomes of fundamental importance. The surface waters are normally saturated with oxygen, the content varying between $4\frac{1}{2}$ and 9 cm³ per liter, depending on the temperature and salinity. The higher values correspond to the lower temperatures. Owing to convection, wave action, etc., the layer held in equilibrium with the atmosphere is of variable but considerable thickness.

The surface waters are also in equilibrium with the atmosphere as regards carbon dioxide. In accordance with the low percentage of this gas in the atmosphere (0.03 vol. per cent) the amount dissolved is also slight (roughly $\frac{1}{10}$ gram per liter). Yet the total amount present in the oceans is 25 times the entire stock in the atmosphere $(60 \times 10^{12}$ tons as against 2.2×10^{12} tons).[1] The chemistry of carbon in its various compounds in sea water is highly complex and cannot be treated here. The reader is referred to Sverdrup et al. (1942).

No sooner, however, are surface waters carried away from direct contact with the atmosphere by plunging currents than alterations in the amount of the two gases, oxygen and carbon dioxide, begin to develop. Photosynthetic activity of plants under the influence of light causes the extraction of carbonic acid and the delivery of oxygen. This process may ultimately lead to oversaturation with oxygen. As the sunlight penetrates only to a few dozen meters' depth with sufficient intensity to render plant life possible, the "euphotic" zone, in which oxygen can increase, forms no more than a thin film covering the ocean. At lower levels two processes tend to reduce the amount of free oxygen. In the first place animals extract this element from the water by respiration while giving off carbon dioxide. In the second place a similar exchange is produced by the rotting of organic matter.

Roughly speaking, the longer a body of water has been withdrawn from contact with the surface the lower the oxygen content will be, *ceteris paribus*. But as the original content itself is variable and as, moreover, biological processes are not of equal intensity everywhere throughout the oceans, so that varying amounts of oxygen are converted to carbonic acid in different places, no accurate value for the "age" of the water can be deduced from the gas content.

The marginal layer between two bodies of water moving in opposite directions is almost at rest, except where turbulence is strong. As the consumption of oxygen appears to be independent of the oxygen content, the more slowly a mass of water moves over a certain distance, the more oxygen will be withdrawn from it, other things being equal. Since only slight differences in gas content occur, and since large bodies of water are involved, normal diffusion scarcely influences the distribution of gases. Only diffusion by turbulent motion (eddies, internal waves, and movements of swimming animals) brings in a supply of oxygen and precludes entire depletion. Consequently a low percentage of oxygen should tend to mark such a stagnating boundary.

---

[1] Compared with the amount of carbon incorporated in limestones of the earth's crust, all the other stores of this element, even those contained in the deposits of coal and petroleum, are negligible.

The poverty of oxygen is often sufficiently marked to aid oceanographers in tracing the limits of currents in the deep sea. Nevertheless, inasmuch as low oxygen content may be due to other causes, such as high consumption, great discretion must be exercised in deducing current boundaries from gas content.

Conversely, a relatively high percentage of oxygen indicates the center of a ventilating current. The deep basins in the Atlantic, for instance, are replenished by a cold bottom current rich in oxygen deriving from the surface in the neighborhood of the Antarctic continent.

POORLY VENTILATED BASINS

That poor ventilation has an adverse effect on the oxygen content is demonstrated by the conditions in various almost completely closed basins. In the oceans or in shallow seas communicating freely with open waters outside, there is always sufficient interchange to replenish the oxygen.

Partly closed basins which have the entrance restricted by a sill may present various conditions of ventilation. If the sill is deep, the exchange of waters between the basin and open ocean takes place far below the surface. The ventilation is then fairly active and is independent of the conditions prevailing at higher levels. With a shallow sill other situations are possible (Fig. 2). (1) Where the climatic conditions tend to form water of greater density at the surface by evaporation or cooling, this locally produced water sinks and fills the deep part of the basin. An inflow of light oceanic water at the surface results, and an outflow of heavier water over the threshold (Fig. 3, A). (2) With a very shallow sill there may be room for only an incoming current so that a continuous concentration of salts must occur in such basins in a dry climate. (3) Where evaporation is less than precipitation and runoff, waters of low salinity flow out at the surface and heavy oceanic waters come in over the sill (Fig. 3, B). In the last case stagnating water may be formed behind a very shallow sill, and the resulting poor ventilation causes interesting phenomena. Only the last type of basin will be treated here; the other types are discussed later in connection with currents.

The Black Sea, many Norwegian fiords with a shallow threshold, the Kaoe Bay between the northern promontories of Halmahera, and similar nearly closed basins are insufficiently ventilated (Trask, 1939; Strøm, 1939). In the Norwegian fiords normal sea water has flowed

in from outside and filled the entire depression of the basin. This
water remains stagnant, while the surface layer is generally diluted by
fresh water coming from the surrounding land. The brackish surface

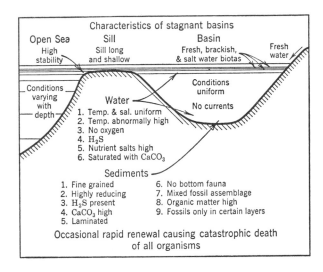

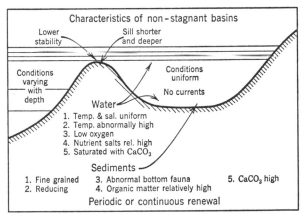

Fig. 2.   Characteristics of stagnant and non-stagnant basins. Fine lines show
equal densities. (After Fleming and Revelle, in Trask, 1939, *Recent Marine
Sediments*, Fig. 10, p. 96, American Association of Petroleum Geologists.)

water remains at the top, owing to its lower specific gravity, even
during cold weather. It creeps out slowly to sea, where it is disseminated and loses its identity. At depths the oxygen is gradually consumed, and as soon as it is all used up hydrogen sulfide begins to form.

From that time onwards organic life is excluded except for certain sulfur bacteria. The development of hydrogen sulfide in the bottom sediment begins at an even earlier stage (Fig. 4).

The concentration of hydrogen sulfide in the water varies from one place to another and depends on the degree of stagnation. In some fiords, continuous though slow convection takes place, so that a constant condition is maintained with hydrogen sulfide content increasing towards the bottom. In other places no stirring appears to occur and the amount of hydrogen sulfide gradually increases from year to year. Beyond the threshold aperiodic variations in the properties of

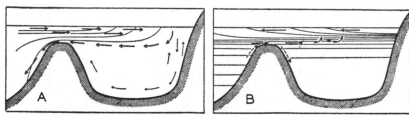

Fig. 3. *A*. Basin with local formation of basin water and outflow across the sill. *B*. Basin with surface outflow of low density and occasional ventilation by inflow of dense water across the sill. (After Sverdrup et al., 1942, *The Oceans*, Fig. 37, p. 148, Prentice-Hall.)

the ocean waters are encountered. The advent of abnormally saline and therefore heavy water at the sill may suddenly cause an influx of fresh sea water from outside. In other fiords a gradual rise of temperature and decrease of salinity are brought about in the stagnant water through turbulent mixing with the surface layer. Eventually a labile condition develops. This may also lead up to a sudden ventilation by outside waters over the threshold. In both cases the old contaminated water is raised by the incoming current and may even reach the surface, causing a general poisoning of the rich life in the upper stratum. Thus an intermittent ventilation of the stagnating fiords is brought about. The maximum content of hydrogen sulfide found in Norwegian fiords is 40 cm³ per liter.

In a few fiords a curious biological phenomenon is observed. A rich marine fauna is found leading a precarious life in a thin layer of normal sea water between the brackish surface and the contaminated deep. Floating seaweed is even found of which the bladders are filled with water instead of air so that the density is between that of fresh and that of salt water.

Variations in temperature at the surface must tend to encourage convection. Therefore, in tropical basins where atmospheric conditions are more uniform than at higher latitudes, stagnant conditions develop more readily. Thus Kaoe Bay in the island of Halmahera contains as much as 0.30 cm³ of hydrogen sulfide per liter close to

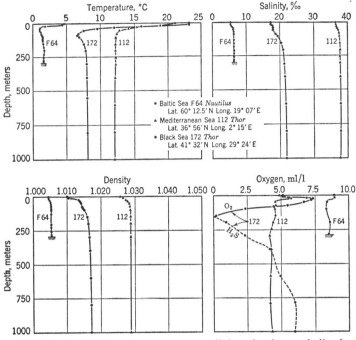

Fig. 4. Vertical distribution of temperature, salinity, density, and dissolved oxygen in different types of basin. Baltic Sea = large basin in high latitudes. Black Sea = stagnant basin. Mediterranean = large ventilated basin in area of excessive evaporation. (After Fleming and Revelle, in Trask, 1939, *Recent Marine Sediments*, Fig. 9, p. 94, American Association of Petroleum Geologists.)

the bottom at 500-m depth, in spite of having an entrance that is 50 m deep and fairly broad. A Norwegian fiord of similar topography would be well ventilated.

In the Black Sea the surface waters down to a depth of 50 m are well stocked with oxygen, but at lower levels the supply quickly diminishes. Below 150 m all oxygen has been consumed and hydrogen sulfide has developed. At a depth of 500 m the content of hydrogen sulfide is 4 cm³ per liter, this value increasing to 6 cm³ per liter down to the bottom at 2000 m.

In the deep, oxygen-free part of the water, organic matter sinking to the bottom is not decomposed in the normal manner. Carion eaters, such as crabs, are not present, so that the dead bodies are left intact on the bottom. The bottom water is not agitated by waves or currents; otherwise the oxygen would not become depleted. Hence no mechanical wear and tear takes place. There is merely the gradual disintegration of decomposable organic matter by anaerobic bacteria.

These abnormal conditions have two important results. In the first place the skeletons of dead vertebrates, especially of reptiles and mammals, which have sunk to the bottom are left intact. Ideal conditions for fossilization are thus provided. In the second place the organic content of the deposits becomes abnormally high. Even before the stage in which all oxygen in the bottom water is consumed, hydrogen sulfide begins to develop below the surface of the bottom deposit. The small supply of oxygen in the water enclosed between mineral particles is quickly used up by oxidation. In the anaerobic medium, sulfur bacteria can develop. Such deposits have a green color, and they smell of rotten eggs. Examples are found in parts of the Red Sea, where the bottom water shows less than 1 cm^3 of oxygen per liter, while the sediment contains a certain amount of hydrogen sulfide.

Where hydrogen sulfide has replaced the oxygen in the bottom waters of a basin the sediment is found to be black, owing to finely disseminated iron-sulfur compounds. The organic content of deposits in poorly ventilated basins is high and may attain 25 or even 35%.

In Kaoe Bay, where the amount of hydrogen sulfide in the water is only slight, the *Snellius* expedition found greenish deposits with a few per cent of organic matter instead of black mud (Fig. 5). The deposits of the Black Sea also deviate from the rule by showing a high percentage of lime.

The Baltic Sea occupies an intermediate position. This inland sea communicates with the North Sea by way of the narrow and shallow straits between the Danish Islands. The ample supply of fresh water from the surrounding land causes a surplus above evaporation. This surplus flows out along the surface through the straits between Denmark and Sweden, causing low salinity in the neighboring part of the North Sea. Through the deepest of the straits, the Store Belt, a current of this mixed water returns along the bottom and flows into the Baltic because it is heavier than the brackish waters in this basin. The deepest threshold, however, is only 18 m below the surface. Consequently only water of low salinity (less than half normal) can be tapped from the open sea. Eastward, the salinity gradually decreases, reaching one-tenth of normal in the Finnish and Bothnian Gulfs.

The comparatively stable stratification of Baltic waters results in poor ventilation of the bottom water. In the Bogskär Deep, hydrogen sulfide is sometimes temporarily observed, and large areas are practically devoid of oxygen and have a high content of carbon dioxide.

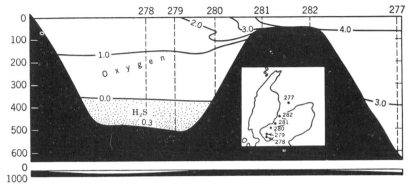

Fig. 5. Section through Kaoe Bay, Halmahera, to Pacific. (True scale section at bottom.) Showing oxygen in cc/l and development of hydrogen sulfide in depths. (Data given by van Riel, 1943.)

Hence the deposits are rich in organic matter (up to 6%). In Chapter 4 we shall return to the sediments formed in poorly ventilated basins.

SALTS DISSOLVED IN SEA WATER

The foregoing discussion has shown that no fixed relation can exist between the amounts of various gases dissolved in sea water. The same also holds for lime and plant nutrients, especially phosphates, nitrogen compounds, iron, and silica. These are supplied by the surrounding land or the dissolution of dead organisms and their skeletons. Conversely, plant and animal life extract these substances from the water to build their tissues, shells, etc.

Plants are the most important "consumers" of the inorganic substances (Fig. 6). As photosynthesis is restricted to small depths, by far the greater amounts of plant nutrients abstracted from the sea water are taken from the surface layers. Through the consumption of phytoplankton by animals and the sinking of animals and plants after death the removed substances are ultimately carried downwards. The metabolic activities of the animals and bacteria return the elements to inorganic form, especially below the euphotic zone. This drain upon the resources of the surface layers is partly made good by the contribution from rivers, but a far greater return takes place through convection, upwelling, and diffusion.

The "salt" ions dissolved in sea water stand out in sharp contrast to the substances mentioned above, because they are not concentrated appreciably in either plants or animals. Partly because of their great solubility and partly because they are not extracted from the sea water under normal conditions, the salt ions have been gradually concentrated in the oceans during the geological past and now form the brine of ocean waters.

All gradations are encountered, from fresh water, almost devoid of salts, to the waters of the Red Sea and Persian Gulf, where the concentrates formed by evaporation show salinities as high as 40‰. Yet in all sea waters the relative proportions of the various ions are constant, and so the total amount of salts dissolved in sea water can be determined by the measurement of one constituent only. The custom is to give the salinity as, for instance, 35‰, and chlorinity as 19‰.

TABLE 2. COMPOSITION OF NORMAL SEA WATER WITH SALINITY 34.3 ‰

Ions in solution	Grams per kilogram, ‰	Grams of salts crystallizing from 1 kg	
Cl^-	18.98	NaCl	27.21
Br^-	0.065	$MgCl_2$	3.81
$SO_4^=$	2.65	$MgSO_4$	1.66
HCO_3^-	0.14	$CaSO_4$	1.26
Mg^{++}	1.27	K_2SO_4	0.86
Ca^{++}	0.40	$CaCO_3$	0.12
K^+	0.38	$MgBr_2$	0.08
Na^+	10.56		

Formerly the composition of sea water was expressed as if the salts occurred as molecular compounds. Now it is assumed that the ions do not form salts until evaporation has caused them to crystallize out.

In the open ocean the salinity varies from less than 33‰ in the northern polar seas and 34‰ in the Antarctic Ocean to more than 36‰ in the tropical Pacific and Indian oceans and more than 37‰ in the tropical Atlantic Ocean (Figs. 7 and 8). At the equator it sinks again to 35‰ in the Atlantic and less than 34‰ in the Pacific and Indian oceans. The reasons for these variations are not far to seek. At the poles, evaporation is low, and abundant precipitation and the melting of icebergs contribute to dilute the sea water. Around the

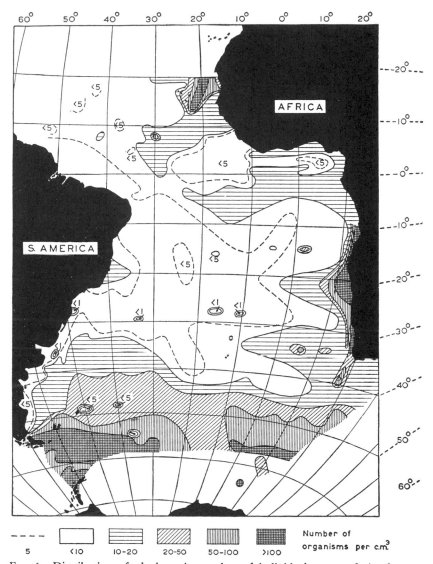

Fig. 6. Distribution of plankton in number of individuals per cm³ (surface to
tenberg in South Atlantic. A distinct relation between the two is visible.

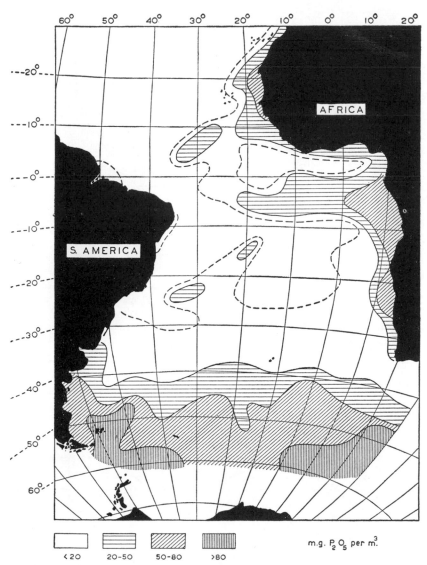

50 m) according to Hentschel and phosphates (mg P_2O_5/m^3) according to Wat-
(Redrawn after Wattenberg, in Correns et al, 1934, Figs. 36 and 37, p. 71.)

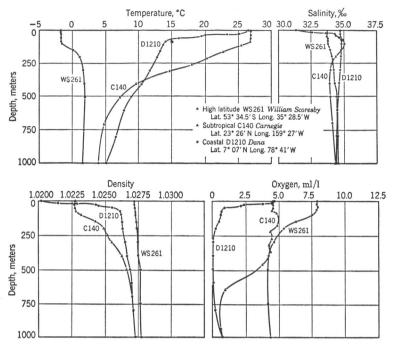

FIG. 7. Vertical distribution of temperature, salinity, density, and dissolved oxygen in the ocean. (After Fleming and Revelle, in Trask, 1939, *Recent Marine Sediments,* Fig. 8, p. 93, American Association of Petroleum Geologists.)

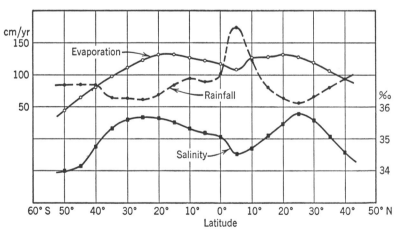

FIG. 8. Distribution of evaporation and rainfall between 40° N and 50° S over oceans. High surface salinities are found in latitudes where evaporation exceeds precipitation. Balance between rainfall and evaporation occurs at about 40° N and S and close to equator. (After Fleming and Revelle, in Trask, 1939, *Recent Marine Sediments,* Fig. 7, p. 88, American Association of Petroleum Geologists.)

windy and warm tropics, evaporation is strong and precipitation relatively low. Near the equator there is a calm belt with high precipitation and overcast skies. In inland seas with preponderant evaporation high salinity is encountered, for instance in the Mediterranean, the Red Sea, and the Persian Gulf. In the Baltic, in Indonesian waters, etc., precipitation and runoff take the upper hand and cause salinities below the average.

It may be pointed out that Sverdrup et al. (1942) give details of forty-four elements detected so far in sea water.

PROPERTIES OF SEA WATER

Salt Water versus Fresh Water. Owing to salinity, the properties of sea water are strongly modified from those of distilled water. From our point of view the most important differences are the following.

1. Increase of specific gravity. One liter of sea water weighs about 1.025 kg, depending on temperature, salinity, and pressure. The changes in specific gravity due to dilution or concentration form one of the most important characteristics of sea water. All sorts of currents are caused by differences in specific gravity that would not arise in pure water under the same conditions.

2. Lowering of the freezing point to about $-2°$ C, which allows temperatures in the oceans to sink below the freezing point of fresh water.

3. Lowering of the temperature at which the greatest specific gravity is shown to below the freezing point. Fresh water develops its greatest density at $+4°$ C, but on cooling normal sea water contracts until it starts to freeze.

4. Strong influence on life. The physiological effects of the salts in solution is so great that there are hardly any plants or animals that can live both in sea water and in fresh water.

Density of Sea Water. In accordance with the behavior of all solids and liquids, water expands on heating and contracts on cooling. But, as is generally known, water close to the freezing point constitutes a highly remarkable exception to this general rule. The contraction continues until 4° C is reached and is then replaced by expansion down to the freezing point. In consequence a lake first cools throughout its mass while it is still above 4° C, because the cooled surface waters become heavier and sink to the bottom. When the greatest density is reached at 4° C the surface layer begins to expand. Hence it remains at the top until it freezes at 0° C, and the ice formed covers a basin of uniform temperature at $+4°$ C (except for cooling by conduction or turbulent mixing).

But it is much less widely known that sea water of normal salinity does not show this exceptional property and continues to contract right down to the freezing point. Theoretically there is a temperature of maximum density, but it lies far below the freezing point and therefore is of no consequence in nature. The point at which ice begins to crystallize in sea water is about 2° C below zero. At this temperature pure ice crystals are formed, causing an increase in the concentration of dissolved matter in the remaining water. Part of this concentrated brine sinks away, part is entrapped between the ice crystals. The freezing point of the enclosed water is thus further lowered. In other words, there is an interval over which freezing takes place that varies according to circumstances.

From the above it can be deduced that the temperature of the deep sea is not restricted to values above 4° C as it is in lakes. Thermometer readings below 0° C are therefore common in polar regions and along the bottom.

The pressure in the oceans is practically equal for all points at the same depth. Differences in specific gravity in the same horizon are therefore due to variations in temperature and salinity. But these properties are perceptibly changed only at the surface. At depths, only mixing can bring about alterations in density.

The temperature of surface water can change by radiation, conduction, evaporation, or condensation. Sun and wind are the main factors causing these variations. The salinity is influenced by evaporation, condensation, river runoff, and melting or formation of ice. Charts giving the salinity or temperature show a far less regular picture than those showing the specific gravity of the same area. This is mainly due to the fact that, as soon as external factors cause an increase of the density of the water, it starts to sink, whereas, when simultaneous alterations of salinity and temperature cause opposed but equal differences in the specific gravity, the differences can reach high values without causing the surface waters to sink.

The density at the surface varies between 1.02 and 1.03, apart from separate basins with brackish water such as the Baltic Sea. The greatest densities in open water (1.027 to 1.028) are encountered in the polar seas, owing to the low temperature. The density gradually decreases towards the warm, tropical seas and finally reaches 1.022 at the equator (see Schott, Table XXI for the Atlantic and XVIII for the Pacific).

Heat Conductivity; Turbulence. The heat conductivity of water is only slightly reduced by the presence of the salts. Nevertheless, a much greater conductivity must be postulated in nature than is found in laboratory experiments. This is due to turbulent mixing in addition to pure conduction. Turbulence causes masses greater than molecules to change place, and these carry along their heat content bodily. Ultimately molecular movement must equalize the temperature between the smallest units that turbulence has placed in juxtaposition. But the distance to be traveled by the molecules is much smaller, or, differently expressed, the surface of contact between the two water bodies with a difference in temperature is greatly extended.

Observation in nature and experiment have shown that laminar flow, in which the particles follow courses parallel to the containing walls, is possible, but that roughness of the walls or increase of velocity and dimensions encourages turbulence. The water then rolls and boils in more or less independent masses that move over and along each other. The dimensions of currents at sea are always too great to permit of laminar flow.

With large horizontal eddies the conduction of heat can often attain 10^8 times the molecular conductivity. The turbulence in a vertical sense in general involves much smaller units so that values of 10 or 100 times the absolute are normal. In the event of marked differences in specific gravity the units tend to return to their original levels, and the mixing is then retarded. The more gradual the transition is, the more effective turbulent conduction will be, *ceteris paribus* (Fig. 9).

It is obvious that mixing of chemically contrasted waters is brought about by the same turbulent mechanism, and the same process influences momentum. The result is an increase of diffusion and viscosity. Values for horizontal eddy viscosity of 2×10^4 times true viscosity are normal. The influence of turbulence on viscosity and suspended particles will be discussed later.

Color and Transparency of Sea Water. The color and transparency of sea water are influenced by suspended and dissolved matter, both organic and inorganic. The clearest water is encountered in the Sargasso Sea in the central parts of the northern Atlantic. The currents passing along the coasts take up mineral particles and nutrient salts that cause profuse development of planktonic life. These flows curve around the Sargasso Sea without entering the central regions. The distance to the coasts is too great to allow of an appreciable direct supply from the land and coastal regions. The surface waters of the Sargasso Sea show a slight tendency to sink, so that no nutrition is carried to the surface and planktonic life is at the minimum. In this limpid water 50% of the blue light penetrates to 25-m depth and 10% to depths of 75 m. The color of the sea is intensive, dark blue with a tinge of violet.

In shallow coastal waters, where suspended particles of clay and plankton cause turbidity, half the light may be absorbed in the first meter. The reflected light also shows a marked change in color in such impure waters. From deep blue to lighter blue and greenish

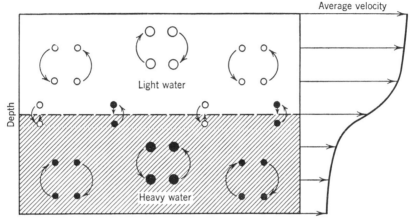

Fig. 9. Diagram illustrating processes of vertical turbulence and mixing with two bodies of water showing difference in density and moving at different average velocities. Particles moved into the opposite body tend to return, and turbulence is restricted along the boundary.

blue, the tints change to intensive green; gray, brown, reddish, and yellowish shades may also be observed (see Schott, 1942, Table XV, for the coloring of the Atlantic Ocean).

The color of the sea is also strongly influenced by cloudiness, waves, and the position of the sun both as to height above the horizon and direction with relation to the observer. The height of the sun is especially important, owing to the influence on reflection. When the angle of incidence is 90° about 4–7% is reflected, but with an angle of 30° reflection amounts to some 20%. In shallow waters the bottom also shimmers through and influences the color that one observes.

In some regions the silt suspended in the waters has a marked influence on the color. Thus the Yellow Sea is named after the vivid hue of the mud introduced by the Hwang Ho. The Amazon and Congo cause a reddish color to distances of several miles from their mouths, owing to the lateritic silt these huge tropical rivers contain. The Po and Adige carry turbidity to the coastal waters, causing the Adriatic Sea to lose its intensive blue color around their deltas.

Diatoms that thrive in untold numbers in the polar seas lend an olive-green tinge to the water. Small jellyfish may lead to a brown color, and Copepoda and algae to blood red. A milky white is also observed from time to time.

Compressibility of Sea Water. Water is generally considered to be incompressible. In comparison with gases, or when only small pressures are considered, this is approximately true. In dynamic oceanography, however, the effect of high pressures is found to be of great importance as they cause compression. Although the ensuing alterations in density are slight they play a decisive part owing to the huge masses of water involved and to the often labile stratification in which they occur.

A very important aspect is the rise in temperature due to compression, and vice versa. Where water is subject to vertical displacements without the addition or abstraction of heat, the temperature is changed. These changes of temperature are termed adiabatic. In a deep basin that is filled from over the edge by inflow of water with a constant temperature, a higher temperature will be found along the bottom than at the intake. In spite of the higher temperature this bottom water will show no tendency to rise, because every vertical movement is compensated by an equivalent adiabatic change in temperature. By expanding, a rising mass of water would automatically acquire the same temperature as the surrounding masses in the new level and finally revert to the original temperature of the inflow when it had reached the level of the rim. Hence no energy would be set free to overcome the friction due to the rising motion.

When oceanographical computations on the density of water masses are carried out for ascertaining the degree of vertical stability, the adiabatic influence must be eliminated. The concept of "potential temperature" has therefore been introduced. By this term is meant the temperature that would prevail if the pressure were released without transfer of heat. In the example mentioned above, the water in the basin would everywhere show the same potential temperature, equal to that of the inflow. Hence the adiabatic rise in temperature must be subtracted from the temperature in situ (read from the thermometer) to obtain the potential temperature.

TEMPERATURES OF SEA WATER

The specific heat of water is greater than that of any other solid or liquid, with the exception of ammonia. As water is also much more pervious to the rays of the sun than the solid crust of the earth, the temperature of the sea cannot be raised nearly as much during summer or daytime as the temperature of the thin film of rock on land, which shows seasonal or daily variations of temperature. There is also less drop in temperature at night and in the winter. The greater humidity of the air over the oceans is likewise of importance, because water vapor is highly opaque to the long heat waves emitted by dark objects. The effective radiation of the sea surface is reduced as compared to that of the solid crust. Other factors contribute to the uniformity of temperatures at sea, such as mixing by turbulence and horizontal currents.

Another important factor in this connection is that when the sea is warmer than the atmosphere the layer of air receiving vapor and heat from the water is carried upwards by convection. When the atmosphere is warmer than the sea, however, the cooled layer of air remains in contact with the water, so that both conduction and evaporation are reduced. Hence evaporation is often stronger during cold weather, that is to say during winter in middle and high latitudes, than when the air is warm. As about 90% of the heat surplus of the oceans is given off by evaporation and only 10% by conduction, the importance of factors governing evaporation is obvious.

A clear picture of the far greater uniformity of temperature at sea than on land may be gained from charts on which the yearly variations of air temperatures are shown (Plate IX of Schott's *Geographie des Atlantischen Ozeans* and on Plate X of his *Geographie des Indischen und Stillen Ozeans*). In the center of continents values of 20° to 30° C and higher are encountered, whereas at sea even 10° C is exceptional. Much the same picture is shown by charts giving the yearly variations of surface temperatures in the oceans (Schott's Plates XIX and XXIV, respectively).

This is not the place to discuss fully the influence of the seas on the climate of adjacent lands. It is sufficient to recall that a maritime climate is characterized by higher humidity and especially by smaller variations in temperature than a continental climate. One cubic meter of sea water gives off sufficient heat to raise the temperature of 3118 m³ of air by an equivalent amount. During cold weather Lake Geneva daily discharges to the surroundings heat equivalent to the combustion of 250,000 tons of coal, according to Forel.

In the tropics the temperature at the surface of the sea is close to 30° C, and in polar regions 0° C or lower. About a quarter of the area of all seas is above 25° C, and half is over 20° C. The average temperature is 17° to 18° C; in the northern hemisphere it is 19° C, in the southern 16° C.

In passing downwards from the surface of the oceans increasingly lower temperatures are encountered, except for special conditions sometimes prevailing in polar regions. In general the drop is small over the first 25 to 50 m owing to mixing by waves and currents. Then follows a swift decrease to 150- or 200-m depths. At greater depths the temperature sinks very slowly and soon becomes almost constant. Again the reader is referred to Schott or Sverdrup et al. for maps of the temperature at 200-, 400-, and 1000-m depth. At the 400-m level the maximum temperature has decreased to about 15° C. This value is found in bands to the north and south of the equator. At the equator the temperature at 400 m is 8° to 10° C. At depths of 1000 m temperatures above 10° C are exceptional. In the deep sea, uniform temperatures of −1° to +5° C prevail. It is obvious that the low temperature of the deeps is due to the high density of cold water. When dealing with the circulation of the oceans we will return to this subject.

ICE IN THE SEA

Ice floating at sea is of two different origins. The ice carried to the sea from land is fresh and forms icebergs. Apart from exceptional floes introduced by rivers, icebergs are masses of glacier ice. In northern seas, where the International Ice Patrol was established after the *Titanic* disaster in 1911, the ice tongues of the Greenland land ice provide many and large icebergs. The glaciers of Spitzbergen, Franz Josef Land, Northland, Ellesmere Land, and Alaska produce comparatively small blocks that soon melt away. Consequently the northern Pacific has few icebergs, for only a limited number are introduced through Bering Strait. The Greenland icebergs are of irregular shape and of a bluish hue. They float with about five-sixths of their mass below sea level, the proportions varying according to the air and moraine content (Fig. 10).

The glacier tongues calve all the year round, but during winter the bergs are frozen fast in sea ice. In spring they are freed and sally forth into open water. Wind and currents cause them to drift great distances. The Labrador Current, especially, carries a vast number out of Davis Strait and past the eastern coast of Newfoundland. On reaching the Gulf Stream they finally melt away. The farthest limit at which icebergs have normally been observed roughly follows the fortieth parallel. The variation from year to year of this limit is wide and depends on a number of circumstances. The distribution is influenced not only by the strength and direction of the wind and currents but also by temperature, waves, etc.

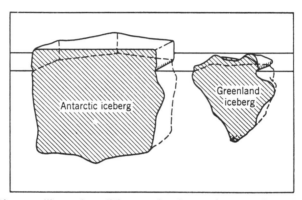

Fig. 10. Diagram illustrating difference in shape of Antarctic and Arctic icebergs. Moraine enclosed in latter.

The icebergs deriving from the Antarctic are of a different nature. Most of the Antarctic glaciers do not break up immediately on reaching the coast but push out over the shelf. Around large parts of the continent they form a fringe of ice that may be dozens of kilometers wide. The powerful centripetal winds deposit a thick covering of snow on top that entirely masks the actual glacier. The resulting cake of ice, called shelf ice, is porous and white. It breaks off in flat prismatic slabs that float away as enormous floes. Because it is much less compact than the true glacier ice of northern icebergs only three-fourths of the mass is submerged. The steep scarp at the edge of the shelf ice is termed the Ice Barrier.

Antarctic icebergs can attain truly gigantic dimensions. In 1893 an iceberg was observed off the Falkland Islands of 140-km length and with an area as great as that of the island of Corsica. The thickness of such giants is estimated at 300 to 400 m, so that the cubic content of the berg mentioned must have been similar to that of all the Swiss lakes combined.

The limits to which icebergs drift in the Antarctic Ocean is about 45° southern latitude in the Pacific and 35° in the Atlantic and Indian oceans.

By far the greater part of the ice at sea is autochthonous and is formed by the freezing of sea water. With normal salinity this takes place at −2° C. The ice from sea water has a lower salinity than the water itself because part of the dissolved salts, particularly the chlorides, escape as brine during the freezing process. This happens especially when the freezing is slow. In the course of time more brine leaks out of the ice, and finally a composition is reached rendering the sea ice potable on melting.

The reflection of radiation from ice, especially when covered with snow, is much greater than from sea water. Hence a sharp drop in temperature takes place as soon as a sheet of ice is formed over the sea. The cooled air tends to flow out from the ice, and the low temperatures consequently spread quickly. In the event of a thaw the opposite influence may cause a very rapid melting of pack ice. It has been suggested that a slight general rise in temperature would suffice to change the North Polar Sea to an ice-free ocean.

The low conductivity of ice precludes the formation of masses more than a few meters thick. By superposition of floes and the fall of snow somewhat thicker masses may be formed, but this can never lead to the production of true icebergs.

Sea ice is generally brittle, owing to wave action, tides, and wind during its formation, as also through the incorporation of air and saline waters. Along the much-exposed Antarctic coasts the ice is not permitted to become fixed or to continue growth for even a few years in succession. The thickest and most extensive sheets of ice are therefore encountered in the more protected North Polar Sea. Several drift expeditions frozen into the ice and the Russian expedition on a large floe have proved that the pack ice of the North Polar Basin is subject to comparatively swift motion. It may move from the pole to the edge of the pack ice in a few years or even in one season.

An extensive review of ice at sea is to be found in the *National Research Council Bulletin* 85 (1932) and in the *Ice Atlas* of the Hydrographic Office (1946).

MOVEMENTS OF SEA WATER

The movements of sea water can be classed under three main headings: currents, tides, and waves.

CURRENTS [1]

Causes of Currents. The forces working on a mass of water and causing it to flow are partly primary and partly secondary.

The primary forces are the cause of the movement; the secondary forces are merely a consequence of the movement and tend to alter the direction of flow. The former can again be divided into external and internal forces. The external forces are wind, alterations in barometric pressure, and tidal forces (to be dealt with later on). They do not alter in any degree the properties of the water, but the resulting flow does change the distribution of masses. The internal forces are caused by the gravity field of the earth and the differences in specific gravity of the water in consequence of non-identical salinity and temperature. Thus all factors causing a variation of density may become the cause of currents. The so-called climatic factors are evaporation or precipitation, heating or cooling, freezing or melting of sea ice.

The secondary forces are, first, the frictional forces, both external friction along the bottom and internal friction between water bodies; second, the Coriolis force, the force that is exerted in consequence of the rotation of the earth; and third, centrifugal force. Although none of these secondary forces are able to produce a movement of stationary water, they may modify the movement caused by primary forces in a very marked degree. The Coriolis force acts on all bodies moving with respect to the earth. Its horizontal component is at its maximum at the poles and decreases to zero at the equator (provided that any vertical velocity component may be neglected in this respect). In the northern hemisphere the force is directed to the right, perpendicular to the direction of the movement; in the southern hemisphere, to the left. When a current flows in a curve the centrifugal force is away from the center of the curve.

Formerly it was thought that currents at sea were possible only in consequence of differences in level, whereby the flow would be directed from the higher to the lower level. It was not until 1878 that Zöppritz first directed attention to the frictional force exerted by the wind. His treatment of the subject, however, was later found to be inadequate. In 1885 Mohn attempted for the first time to calculate currents due to differences in specific gravity and to the force of the wind. But it remained for V. Bjerknes and V. W. Ekman at the

[1] See, among others, Rouch, 1948; Defant, 1929; Bigelow, 1931; National Research Council, 1932; Correns et al., 1934; Fleming and Revelle in Trask, 1939; Schott, 1935, 1942; Sverdrup et al., 1942.

beginning of the present century to perform the first trustworthy calculations on the basis of the forces mentioned. Later, especially Nansen, Helland-Hansen, Sverdrup, and Wüst contributed to the theory and practice of calculating currents at sea. The first comprehensive treatment of the subject was given by Defant (1929).

The initial problem that had to be solved before the calculations could be carried out with success relates to friction. In the laboratory very small coefficients of friction are found in laminar flow, but as soon as turbulence develops, as it does everywhere in nature, the effect of friction is greatly enlarged, as pointed out above. The eddying movements along the margins of a current must cause a strong exchange of momentum with the surroundings: water masses belonging to the current mingle with the adjacent bodies of water, and stationary masses are incorporated in the flow. The ultimate effect is identical with that of considerable friction. Hence, as long as the average effect on greater bodies is taken into account, and not the actual movement in detail, friction appears to be greatly increased. It was previously shown that similar effects are caused in conductivity and diffusion.

In calculations involving currents at sea the effect of this increased "eddy viscosity" must be taken into account. The absolute value varies with the strength of the turbulence, and naturally this complicates the calculations. In general, one must reckon with a coefficient of viscosity that is several hundred times greater than that for laminar flow. The degree of turbulence is expressed by means of the mass of liquid that is exchanged per unit of time and per unit of area between the neighboring bodies of water (the so-called Austausch coefficient or numerical value of the eddy viscosity).

One of the most striking results of Ekman's theoretical investigation of currents was that, with a flow in deep water far from the coast driven by a constant wind (i.e., drift currents) at a constant speed, the motion at the surface is directed 45° to the right (in the northern hemisphere) of the wind. Actually Gallé found an average angle of 47° between direction of wind and resultant currents at the surface. Below the surface the direction gradually diverges farther and farther to the right of the wind and concomitantly the velocity decreases. At a depth called the friction depth, which varies with the latitude and force of the wind and does not exceed 200 m, the current is directly opposite to the surface current and has fallen to 4% of the surface velocity. If bottom friction is left out of account the average movement is at right angles to the direction of the wind. The frictional force exerted by the wind and the Coriolis force at right angles to the movement are then equal and exactly opposed in direction. This state is closely attained in nature. Yet there is some slight friction, and the resulting force plus the Coriolis force is equal and opposite to the force exerted by the wind. Figures 11 and 12 show these relations and also the case in which a slope of the surface is the motive power.

It may be assumed that, after a certain time (a few days to many weeks) after the wind has set in, a constant motion without further

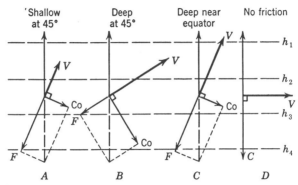

FIG. 11. Balance of forces in ocean current due to slope of surface. V = velocity and direction of current, $h_1 - h_4$ = surface contours, Co = Coriolis force, F = frictional force. (A) in shallow water: the bottom friction is large and the deflection by Co is relatively small; (B) in deep water: the friction with deeper layers is small and the deflection large; (C) near the equator: Co is small; (D) assuming no friction: the current flows at right angles to the surface slope.

acceleration has been reached. The primary and secondary forces are then nicely balanced and a dynamical equilibrium under constant conditions has been attained. Hence the larger systems of currents that are driven by constant winds should show unaltering conditions. Obviously this ideal is never attained, because all winds, even the trades, are subject to variations in strength and direction.

When the wind just begins to blow, the first movement of the water will be in the same direction as the wind, but as soon as motion of the water sets in the rotation of the earth makes itself felt. In shallow water, where the friction with the bottom is considerable, the current will be less deflected by the Coriolis force than in the ideal case. In regions like the North Sea and the Baltic, where the winds are variable, where the water is shallow, and where the surrounding coasts are at no great distance, wind-driven currents will generally follow the direction of the motive force fairly closely. In dealing with the tides of the former Zuider Zee in Holland the effects of wind will again be referred to.

Along the Pacific coast of the United States the winds blow parallel to the coast in a southeasterly direction. This causes a current with a component directed away from the coast, because of the Coriolis force directed to the right of the flow. Even if the wind were directed obliquely towards the coast the surface waters would still be gradually driven off shore and the surface of the sea would be depressed along the coast. This suction causes deep water to well up to the surface from depths of 100 or 200 m. Lower temperatures and a supply of plant nutrients therefore characterize the coastal waters off California. For reasons to be discussed later there remains a marked component in the direction of the wind.

Similar upwelling occurs along other coasts, as the west coast of South America and of Africa. The movements should not be thought of as strongly developed currents, for there is merely an upward component to much stronger horizontal flows. In the case discussed above, the vertical movement is of the order of 50 m per month and, moreover, is intermittent.

On nearing the equator the Coriolis force decreases more and more until the current approaches the direction of the wind or flows at right angles to the surface

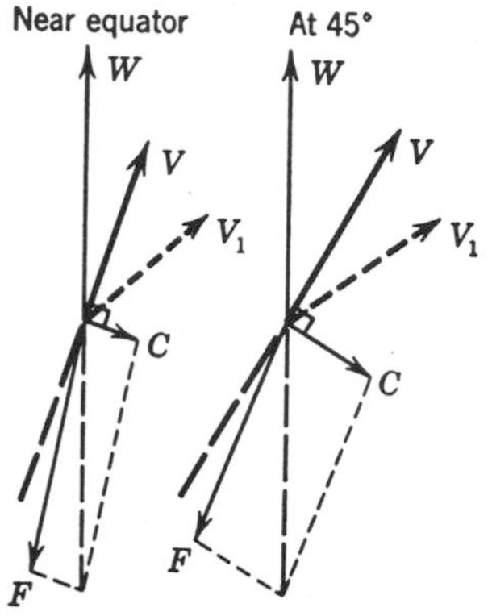

FIG. 12. Balance of forces at surface in steady drift current set up by wind. W = stress exerted by wind, F = stress exerted on uppermost water layer by that immediately beneath it owing to difference in velocity and direction, C = Coriolis force, V = direction and velocity of current at surface, V_1 = direction and velocity of layer just below surface.

contours of the sea. At the equator the influence of the rotation of the earth on the direction of the current is zero.

To give an idea of the strength of the currents developed it can be stated that a wind of force 5 of the Beaufort scale at 45° latitude will result in a current of about 15 cm per second.

In spite of the great advances made in the last few decades with respect to the calculation of currents, it has not yet proved possible to explain completely the currents produced by constant winds such as the trades and those of the "roaring forties" of the southern hemisphere. Movements are found down to considerable depths having the same direction at all levels. This does not agree with the theory advanced above and is probably due to obstructing masses of water and to macroturbulence generated by the wind.

In order to calculate currents due to unequal distribution of mass, determinations of temperature and salinity at all depths are required, preferably at several stations not situated along a straight line. It is then assumed that, below a certain depth, uniformity in pressure prevails in any level plane and consequently a state of no motion. Further uniformity of pressure at the surface is postulated. The difference in weight of the columns between two levels must yield the force to maintain the current.

If there were no friction and no accelerations the current would flow parallel to the contour lines of the isobaric surfaces with the Coriolis force at right angles and opposite in direction to the resolved force of gravity. From this assumption it may be deduced that in the northern hemisphere the lighter water lies on the right-hand side of an observer looking in the direction of the surface current; in the southern hemisphere the denser water lies to the right. This rule explains why there must be a component of the current in the direction of the wind parallel to a coast, as discussed above.

Where the data on density are insufficient in amount or accuracy to permit direct calculation of currents, a different procedure may be followed. The distribution of temperature, salinity, or some other variable is studied, and the investigator seeks to establish from a map how certain masses move. Examples will be given later when treating the circulation in basins.

The differences in density that cause currents should gradually disappear in consequence of these very currents. Therefore in the case of permanent flow, such as most density currents, external influences must act continuously to maintain the differences. These influences are the climatic factors already referred to. Many times these cause vertical movements also, although the horizontal components generally prevail. Lessening of the density at the surface has little direct influence on vertical movements, but an increase in specific gravity causes the surface waters to sink. Thus dense surface water is developed by strong evaporation at low to middle latitudes. However, as this water is warm it cannot sink to great depths. The cold deep water beneath will have an even greater density. Only in partly closed basins, that will be dealt with later, can water of exceptional density be generated by evaporation.

The chief source of deep water filling the ocean basins must therefore be sought in polar regions. In the fall and winter intensive cooling takes place and an increase of density occurs down to the freezing point at $-2°$ C. The increase may continue even when the formation of comparatively fresh sea ice adds to the salinity of the remaining water. Under these circumstances sea water with the greatest density is produced.

Circulation in the Deep Sea. A vertical section from north to south through the Atlantic Ocean will be discussed in order to illustrate some general features of deep-sea circulation. In the first place it should be noted that the section (Fig. 13) is greatly exaggerated in height, about 100 times. In a horizontal direction the properties of the water vary extremely slowly, because each level is subject to similar conditions over very wide areas. To reach a region with a different climate distances of hundreds or even thousands of kilometers must be covered. But in a vertical direction considerable variations are encountered over short distances. Radiation penetrates only to shallow depths. Gravity tends to cause a stable stratification, with the heaviest water at the bottom. For example, the vertical temperature gradient in the Pacific is roughly 6000 times as great as the horizontal, and for salinity the same rule holds. In order to show both the vertical and horizontal variations in the same figure, therefore, the vertical scale must be greatly exaggerated. Moreover, the shape of oceanic basins, relatively shallow in comparison with the enormous extensions, would in itself force us to adopt the reduction of the horizontal scale.

In the second place our section clearly demonstrates that currents may be deduced not only from calculation but also from the distribution in space of the properties of the water masses. The velocity cannot be ascertained by this method, but the direction and extension of the flow are frequently obvious. Consequently the major oceanic circulations with vertical components are known qualitatively, although quantitative calculations are not yet available.

In the third place the great predominance of the horizontal over the vertical component of the major oceanic circulation currents follows directly from our section, for even in this much-compressed representation the greater extent of the horizontal movements is still obvious.

Finally it becomes clear on inspection of our figure that the sinking currents are in general much more clearly defined than the corresponding returns to the surface. This is due to the fact that downward flow takes place in more or less well-defined currents, whereas the displacements back to the surface, that must, of course, be of exactly

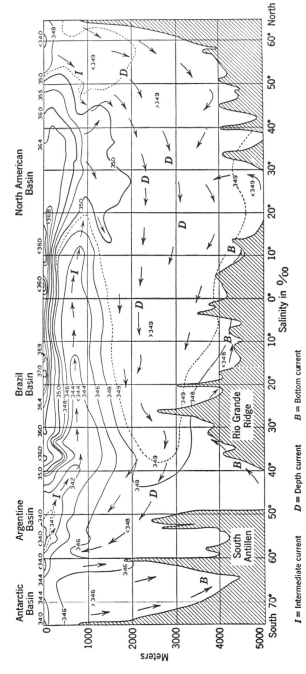

FIG. 13. Section through Atlantic from south to north, west of the Mid-Atlantic Rise, showing salinity and major circulation currents. (According to Wüst, redrawn from Schott, 1942, Fig. 57, p. 194.)

I = Intermediate current   D = Depth current   B = Bottom current equal volume, take place by mixing with overlying waters and are therefore more diffuse.

Viewing the section in more detail, the most conspicuous feature is the great deep current that sinks in the north off Greenland and may be followed southwards far across the equator. As explained above, the polar surface water in the north sinks during the winter, so that the current receives a pulsating impetus. But owing to the vast mass

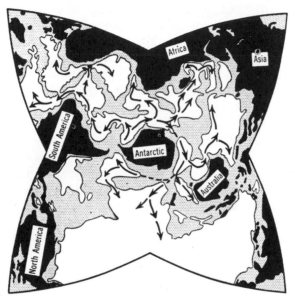

Fig. 14. The spreading of Antarctic bottom water into the deeps of all major oceans. (Redrawn from Defant, 1940, Fig. 3, p. 6.)

a continuous flow results. At 60° south latitude this great depth current loses its identity. The Antarctic winter water must be even more dense, because it dives under the depth current to form the bottom current.

In the other oceans, also, the Antarctic water flows to the deepest depressions and fills them to sill depths. Figure 14 summarizes these movements. It also shows that the apparent closure of the basins in the profile of Fig. 13 by submarine ridges is not complete. Outside the plane of the section there exist deeper passages where the water can enter over inconspicuous sills. But to reach some of these depressions, for instance to attain the basin east of the Mid-Atlantic Rise, the water must follow extended routes. It was stated above that the velocity of these currents is not accurately known, but it is assumed that several dozens of years elapse before the surface waters of the Antarctic reach the equator along the bottom. Wüst estimated that the bottom current in the Pacific flows at a velociy of 2 to 3 cm per second (1.7 to 2.6 km per day).

At a higher level the Atlantic intermediate current *I* is found. This flow comes from the Antarctic convergence at 50°–60° S and runs with a velocity of 5 to 10 cm per second at a depth of about 1000 m towards the north. It may be traced to some 30° beyond the equator. A similar flow originating in the neighborhood of Greenland and running south is much less distinct. Towards the surface there are other currents, but these have not been indicated on our section. They comprise sinking branches at roughly 30° north and south latitude. The water flows at about 600-m depth towards the equator, where it wells up to form a cool area and returns along the surface.

The reader may ask if more accurate data on the direction and velocity of the major oceanic circulation systems cannot be obtained by direct measurement. The *Meteor* expedition has indeed performed measurements at anchor stations in the south Atlantic, but the results cannot be accepted unreservedly. A ship lying at anchor in the deep sea on 7000 m of cable yaws considerably under the influence of surface currents and wind. This must cause the current meter to be dragged to and fro through the water. Also the anchor may drag. Part of the current measured is therefore fictitious, but the size of the errors thus introduced is not known, although they are doubtless considerable as compared to the slow circulation investigated.

The Indian Ocean is cut off from the direct influence of the north polar region, and the Pacific nearly so. The influence of the Antarctic Sea must therefore predominate entirely. A detailed treatment is given by Sverdrup et al. (1942). Our Fig. 15, reproduced from this treatise, gives a striking picture of the complicated currents around the Antarctic continent. The greatest surface velocities of 15 cm per second are encountered north of the Antarctic convergence. Closer to the pole, in the Antarctic region, the currents flow at only 4.4 cm per second. The rise of deep water towards the surface is of great biological, and therefore also geological, importance, because it constantly renews the supply of plant nutrients in the surface layer. The dense population of plankton in the Antarctic water is thus closely related to the type of circulation.

Roughly speaking, the block diagram in Fig. 15 is representative of the entire circumference of the Antarctic continent. At the surface the currents appear to run right round from west to east, but closer inspection shows that water from the Antarctic region is carried towards the north and out of the region both near the surface and near the bottom, while deep water is drawn into the system from the north. At any given point a number of factors are active in altering the properties of the water: cooling or heating, dilution or concentration of

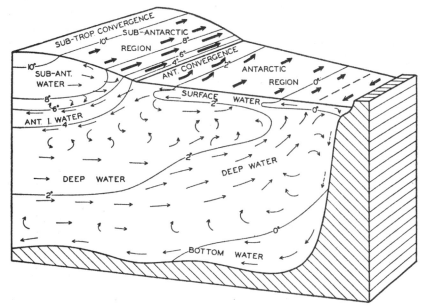

FIG. 15. Schematic representation of the currents and water masses of the Antarctic regions and of the distribution of temperature. (After Sverdrup et al., 1942, *The Oceans*, Fig. 164, p. 620, Prentice-Hall.)

the salinity, etc. In spite of these a stationary distribution of conditions characterizes the entire Antarctic Ocean. The action of the climatic factors is compensated by dynamic factors causing currents to replace the altered waters by new masses. These opposing influences must be in delicate balance.

Surface Currents. To study the surface currents a chart and not a section must be consulted because, by nature, these movements are restricted to the surface layer. Many atlases and oceanographical compilations contain charts representing the major surface currents. These are indicated by curved arrows, at a tangent to the direction (see Fig. 20). Transport lines of *pure* surface flows cannot intersect and have no beginning or ending because the currents must form closed systems. Where they start as diverging lines on the chart, upwelling of water must take place, and where they converge and end a sinking component is indicated. In areas where the lines approach each other the velocity should in general increase, and vice versa. The topographical irregularities of the bottom in shallow water

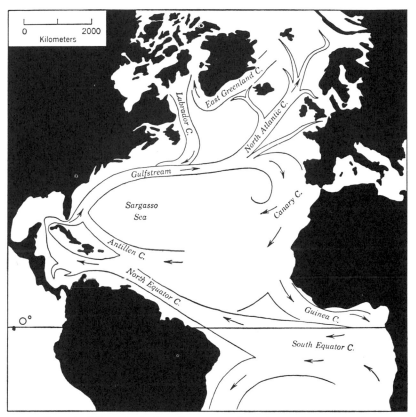

FIG. 16. The principal surface currents of the northern Atlantic.

and the coasts cause divergences of the direction of flow to considerable distances. Thus vertical undulations of isotherms over submerged ridges have been observed to attain amplitudes of more than 100 m. This can be shown by ascertaining the shape of boundary planes between masses of water with different properties.

Some systems of drift currents alternate with the seasons, under the influence of summer and winter conditions, which may show marked differences in the prevailing winds.

The largest of all current systems on the earth is generally designated by the term "Gulf Stream" (Fig. 16). Actually, however, there is a major circulatory system in the northern half of the Atlantic of which the Gulf Stream is merely a small portion. Not only drift currents but also flows caused by other motive forces play a part.

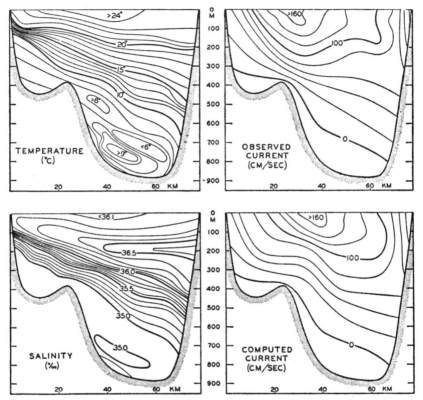

FIG. 17. *Left:* Observed temperatures and salinities in the Straits of Florida. *Right:* Velocities of the current through the Straits according to direct measurements and according to computations based on the distributions of temperature and salinity. (After Sverdrup et al., 1942, *The Oceans*, Fig. 184, p. 674, Prentice-Hall; according to Wüst.)

The South and North Equatorial Currents are the direct result of the trade winds. The northern current carries the water along the northern shores of the West Indies as the Antilles Current, but it also forces its way into the Caribbean Sea and thence into the Gulf of Mexico. The water is thus raised 19 cm in the Gulf. It flows out through the passage between the peninsula of Florida and the Bahamas back into the Atlantic as "jet" current. This current in the Straits of Florida shows an average surface velocity of no less than 6 km per hour (2 m per second) and sometimes attains a maximum of 10 km per hour (3 m per second). At a depth of 250 m a current of 4 km per hour has been measured. The transport of water is about 26 million cubic meters per second (Fig. 17).

Outside the Straits of Florida the current joins the Antilles Current to form the Florida Current that flows along the east coast of North America. The current reaches to

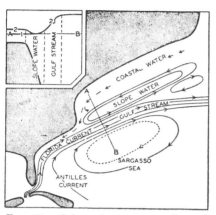

depths of no less than 600 to 800 m, whereas drift currents are only 100 to 200 m thick. This is probably due to the fact that the Florida Current is not a pure drift current but is also caused by differences in level. Locally velocities of 160 cm per second are reached at the surface, and the total transport is estimated at 40 $\times$ 10^6 m^3 per second.

Off Cape Hatteras the current diverges from the continental slope. Here the name Gulf Stream is used. Complicated giant gyrals appear to be developed especially on the left, landward side of the Gulf Stream (Fig. 18). To

FIG. 18. Schematic representation of the character of the Gulf Stream and accompanying eddies on slope. *Inset:* Profile of the sea surface along the line *A-B*. (After Sverdrup et al., 1942, *The Oceans*, Fig. 185, p. 680, Prentice-Hall.)

the southeast of Newfoundland the Gulf Stream meets the cold Labrador Current flowing south through the Torres Strait (Fig. 19). From thence onwards the current is driven across the Atlantic as the North Atlantic Current by the prevailing southwesterly winds. The average velocity to Ireland is ½ to 1 km per hour. A part is here diverted to the south to pass along the African coast as the Canary Current and thence to curve around the Sargasso Sea and merge imperceptibly with the North Equatorial Current. The other branch passes north, washes the coasts of Ireland, Scotland, and Norway, and loses itself in the Norwegian and North Polar Seas.

Although meteorological matters are not treated in this survey, we must recall here that the warm water of the North Atlantic Current influences the climate of northwestern Europe in a decided manner.

The January temperatures are 10° to more than 20° above the average for the latitudes concerned.

Viewing a world chart of surface currents (Fig. 20) one is struck by a double vortex in each of the oceans, similar to the one in the North Atlantic just discussed. To the north of the equator the waters

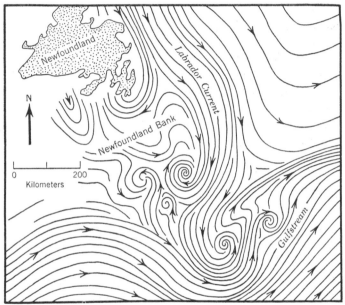

FIG. 19. Schematic representation of the mixing of the Labrador and Gulf Stream currents.

follow right-handed spirals and curves; to the south the movement runs in the opposite direction. This is due to the major systems of winds, the trade winds and the westerly winds, at middle latitudes.

TABLE 3. SURFACE CURRENTS AND THEIR MEAN TRANSPORT

Florida Current	Off Florida	40×10^6 m³/sec
Gulf Stream	Off North America	90×10^6 m³/sec
Kuroshio	Off Japan	20×10^6 m³/sec
North Pacific Current	Between Aleutians and Hawaii	40×10^6 m³/sec
Antarctic Circumpolar Current	Drake Strait	100×10^6 m³/sec
Amazon River	At mouth	$\frac{1}{10} \times 10^6$ m³/sec

The surface current causing the largest water displacement on the earth runs between Cape Horn and the South Shetland Islands, the so-called Antarctic Circumpolar Current. In Table 3 are listed a number of currents and the mean amount of water they transport (10^6 m³ per second equals $3\frac{1}{2}$ km³ per hour).

Basins with a Shallow Entrance. On page 9 several types of circulation occurring in basins were mentioned and the development of stagnant conditions was discussed. The present paragraph will deal in more detail with examples of uninterrupted exchange of water with the oceans (Figs. 2 and 3).

Currents arising in more or less completely closed basins form a separate subject. A simple and clear example is presented by the Mediterranean. This basin is surrounded by warm, dry countries, and few important rivers carry fresh water down to the coasts. Consequently evaporation predominates over precipitation and runoff by nearly 3000 km³ per year. The result is twofold. In the first place water must enter through the Strait of Gibraltar from the Atlantic to replenish the loss. The surface of the inland sea lies 10 to 30 cm lower than that of the ocean, and as a result of the sloping surface the water is driven through the Strait as a powerful current at 4 km per hour (Fig. 21).

In the second place the density of the water increases until the water sinks from the surface to fill the entire basin with uniform water that is relatively warm (13° C) and saline (38‰). But this concentration of dissolved matter cannot continue without a compensatory loss. The influx carries along a large quantity of dissolved salts. These are evidently returned to the ocean in some manner, because the salinity of the Mediterranean is not increasing. The return is effected by an outflowing current over the sill in the Strait of Gibraltar below the incoming current. Both components must carry the same amount of salts, but the lower has a smaller volume transport and a higher concentration. The difference in water transport must balance the evaporation surplus. The capacities of the two currents can therefore be calculated from the amount of evaporation and the salinities, or the evaporation can be calculated from the salinity and the capacities. The actual currents are complicated by tidal components.

The water that flows out at 300-m depth is considerably denser than the Atlantic water at the same level in spite of the higher temperature. Turbulence causes some mixing with the inflow in the straits. The salinity is thereby reduced from 38‰ to 37‰, but the temperature is also lowered from 13° to 11°. The resulting water is still relatively heavy and sinks along the bottom slope into the Atlantic. Finally at 1000 m it reaches a level at which the deep Atlantic water is of the same density. Here the Mediterranean water leaves the bottom and spreads out north, west, and south, forming a layer that can be recognized by the combination of high temperature and high

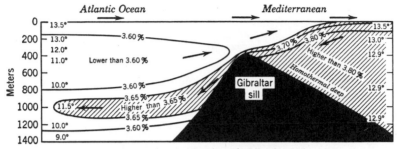

Fig. 21. Section over the sill in the Straits of Gibraltar, showing temperatures. (Mainly according to Schott, 1942.)

salinity. It has been traced beyond the equator in the south, the Azores in the west, and Ireland in the north by oceanographical serial measurements (Fig. 22).

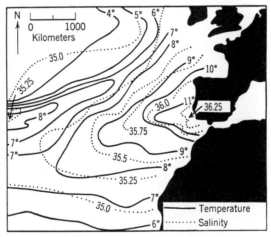

Fig. 22. Chart showing the outward spread of Mediterranean waters at 1000-m depth in the Atlantic (temperatures and salinities). (Mainly according to Schott, 1942.)

The transport through the Strait of Gibraltar is sufficient to ventilate the entire basin of the Mediterranean in about 75 years. The budget shown in Table 4 can be made for this inland sea.

TABLE 4. WATER BUDGET OF THE MEDITERRANEAN SEA

Gains	km³/year	Losses	km³/year
Inflow from the Atlantic	54,000	Outflow to the Atlantic	52,000
Inflow from the Black Sea	400	Outflow to the Black Sea	200
Precipitation	1,000	Evaporation	
Rivers	200	(145 cm/year)	3,400
	55,600		55,600

This discussion brings out an important difference between the Mediterranean and the Gulf of Mexico. Whereas the Mediterranean exercises a great influence on the deep water of the North Atlantic, the Gulf of Mexico is of no importance to the deep-water circulation. On the other hand, the influence of the upper layers on currents is profound only in the Gulf of Mexico. This basin acts as a transition receptacle for the major currents of the tropical Atlantic and directs the flow across the northern part of this ocean.

The conditions in the Bosporus and Dardanelles are entirely different. On the one hand, precipitation and runoff greatly predominate over evaporation in the Black Sea. On the other hand, the communication with the Mediterranean is much more restricted. Here the outflow must occur along the surface and must have the greater capacity (Fig. 23). The deeper water in the basin is not ventilated, for the surface waters of low salinity do not attain sufficient density even in winter to replace the saline water in the deep. The yearly convection due to the alternation of summer and winter conditions therefore does not reach deeper than 100 to 150 m. The manner in which the stagnating water has become depleted of oxygen has already been discussed.

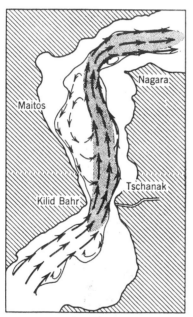

FIG. 23. Chart of the Dardanelles showing inflowing bottom current at 50-m depth with eddy and region of coarse bottom deposit. (After Defant, 1929, Fig. 17, p. 54.)

The currents in the Bosporus are shown in Fig. 24. The bottom velocity is so great that fine material is carried away and in the center a strip of gravel covers the bottom. The inflow at depth with a salinity of 38‰ attains a velocity of 4 km per hour and may be swifter locally than the outflow with its salinity of 18‰. In the narrowest portion of the straits the surface current runs 8 km per hour. In wider portions countercurrents are developed, forming gyrals.

An example of a basin with greatly predominating evaporation is provided by the Kara Bougas Gulf, a very extensive but shallow

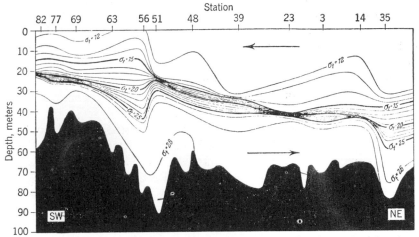

FIG. 24. Section along the Bosporus showing densities for September-October, 1917. (After Defant, 1929, Fig. 16, p. 52.)

lagoon situated on the eastern coast of the Caspian in a steppe climate. A bar cuts off the basin from the open water, and the only communication is through a narrow, shallow channel, which allows a continuous flow of water to enter, but there is no room for an outflow to pass over the sill. The waters of the lagoon, therefore, are continually becoming more saline. This situation is in sharp contrast to the stable basins previously described, in which a dynamical equilibrium prevails. At present the deep water of the Kara Bougas contains 160‰ salt as compared to only 13‰ in the Caspian. Gypsum ($CaSO_4 \cdot 2H_2O$) and Glauber salt ($Na_2SO_4 \cdot 10H_2O$) are precipitated. The name Adshidarja, synonymous with Kara Bougas, means bitter lake. The influx carries a daily quota of 350,000 tons of salt into the basin. The countless numbers of organisms swept along into the Kara Bougas perish in the concentrated brine of the lagoon.

The Caspian receives considerable quantities of salt through the Volga and other rivers. Moreover, the fauna indicates that formerly this inland lake formed part of the open ocean and that it was cut off at a not very distant period. As the surface stands at a lower level than that of the oceans in consequence of evaporation, one would expect to find a higher salinity than in the sea. But actually it has been found that the salinity is only one-third of normal. The explanation of this apparent contradiction is that the Caspian may be likened to a salt lake that is being gradually washed through. The rivers bring in fresh water, and salt is continuously lost into the Kara Bougas.

It is a legitimate prediction that eventually an enormous deposit of salt will be formed if the process described is continued indefinitely. As long ago as 1877 Ochsenius chose the Kara Bougas as an illustration of his theory on the formation of salt deposits from lagoons. The situation is not unique, for during the construction of the Suez Canal a subrecent salt deposit was cut through that may be considered to represent an evaporated extension of the Red Sea.

Basins with a Deep Entrance. A very different state of affairs develops when the entrance to a basin is much deeper. Many diversified examples occur in the Moluccas. Most of these basins have depths of several thousands of meters, that of the Weber Deep even attaining more than 7000 m. The entrances are many, but they seldom exceed a few hundred meters in depth. However, except for the Sulu Sea in the northwest between Borneo and Mindanao, they all possess at least one entrance that is more than 1000 m deep.

As the contents of the oceans are in stable equilibrium the deeper water is always the heavier. From this it follows that the deepest passage gives entrance to the water of greatest density. Consequently a flow comes in over the sill and fills the entire depths of the basin with water of uniformly high potential density. These deeps are termed homothermal, because the potential temperature is constant to within 0.1° C (Fig. 25).

The warmer, lighter water nearer the surface communicates freely with the open oceans, entirely independently of what takes place below. The water budget of the upper few hundred meters contains items of evaporation and precipitation with runoff, and also incoming and outgoing currents, but it is not linked with the circulation at sill depths.

Up to the present little has been published from the results of the *Snellius* expedition on the upper strata. Current measurements have shown (Lek, 1938) that velocities are of the order of a few dozen centimeters per second and of one to a few dozen centimeters between 300 and 1000 m. Concerning the circulation below sill depths very few data on velocity have been obtained by measurement, but the currents appear to be still slower. The tidal components have not been considered here but will be dealt with presently.

The ventilating currents that enter the basins over the deepest sills have been investigated by van Riel (1934, 1943). Figure 26 summarizes his results. It was found that the Sulu Basin receives its deep water through a long, narrow trench from the north with its deepest

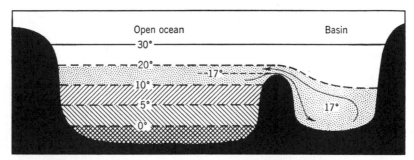

FIG. 25. Schematic representation of the filling of a basin with homothermal waters from the open ocean. The surface of the homothermal waters is depressed below sill level.

entrance at 400 m. It follows that the temperature of the deepest parts is relatively high, roughly 10° C. As in all Moluccan basins the homothermal deep begins a considerable distance below the level of the sill, here at more than 1200 m. The great length and the small capacity of the trench linking the Sulu Sea with the ocean retard the flow and have a detrimental influence on the ventilation of the deep water. Consequently the oxygen content is low and the solution of lime is much less effective than in the Celebes Sea.

The Celebes Sea has a deep inlet off the southern tip of Mindanao through which it receives Pacific water of 3.5° C at 1400-m depth (Fig. 27). The homothermal layer begins below 2500 m. The deeps in the Moluccan Passage between Celebes and Halmahera form a series linked one to another. The Gorontalo Basin receives its deep water from the Mangole Basin, the latter from the Batjan Basin; then follow the Ternate Trough and the Morotai Basin, which finally communicates with the Pacific (Fig. 28). Each time the water passes from one basin to the next some mixing takes place with overlying strata so that the temperature is slightly raised. Moreover, there occurs a kind of downward grade in the heavy incoming water, for, as already pointed out, the homothermal water does not reach to sill depth in the down-

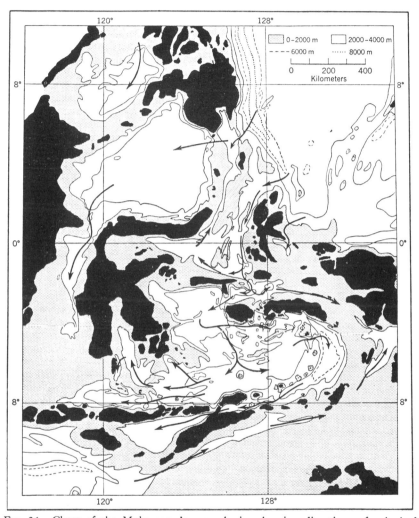

Fig. 26. Chart of the Moluccan deep-sea basins showing directions of principal ventilating bottom currents. (According to van Riel, 1934, Plate IV.)

current basin. This grade provides the force to drive the flow through the narrow entrance. Thus a slightly higher temperature is encountered in each successive basin even though the sill may lie deeper in some cases than that of the preceding trough (Fig. 29).

The Halmahera Basin has its own system of ventilation directly from the Pacific.

The flow towards the central and southerly basins of the Moluccan region is found to be highly unexpected. Only the Timor and Aroe

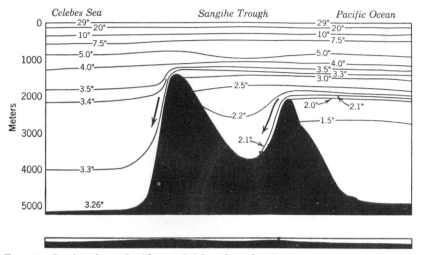

Fig. 27. Section from Pacific to Celebes Sea, showing temperature distribution and ventilating currents. Below true scale section. (Redrawn from van Riel, 1934, Fig. 8, p. 24.)

Troughs receive their deep water from the Indian Ocean over a sill of 1940-m depth to the south of Roti. But the Buru Basin, Ceram Sea, and Banda Basins all communicate with the Moluccan Passage over a sill at 1880 m between Obi and the Sula Islands while the deeps to

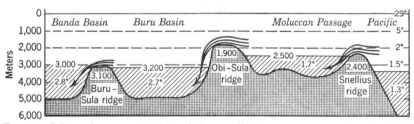

Fig. 28. Schematic representation of the ventilating currents entering the Banda Basin from the Pacific.

the south of Buru and between this island and Ceram are fed from the Banda Basin. The most surprising feature, however, is that not only the Weber Deep between the Inner and Outer Banda Arcs

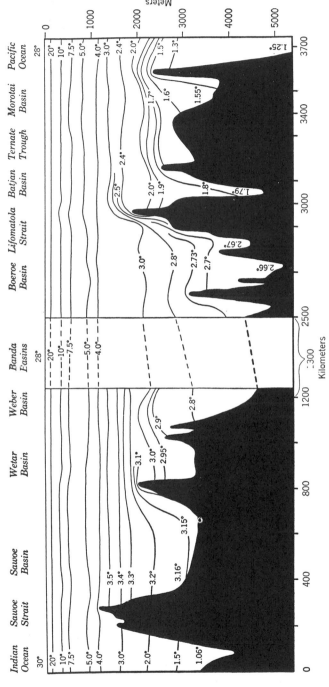

FIG. 29.   Section from the Pacific through the Banda Basins to the Sawu Basin and Indian Ocean, showing temperatures.

receives Pacific water but that even the Savu Sea is supplied from this source via the Weber Deep. The Flores and Salajar Troughs and even the Bali Basin to the north of Bali are all fed from the Pacific. The deeps of all these basins are cut off from the neighboring Indian Ocean by shallow sills that shut out all deep water effectively, in spite of the short distance across the submarine ridge connecting the Lesser Sunda Islands. The 3000-km path from the Pacific is followed because the greater depth allows colder and heavier water to pass this way.

This system of currents was deduced from the charts showing where the deepest entrances exist and from the distribution of temperature and salinity that demonstrates how water masses are connected. Excellent confirmation is found in the oxygen content of the bottom water. It was pointed out above that the deep-sea waters are replenished with oxygen in the polar regions ("the lungs of the ocean"), where the saturated surface waters sink and start their long wanderings through the deeps of the oceans. If the picture obtained for the ventilation of the basins in the Moluccas through the Moluccan Passage is correct, the waters richest in oxygen should be encountered in the entering oceanic currents. On the passage of the current through the Moluccan troughs and basins the oxygen would be gradually consumed and the percentage should decrease along the lengthy route followed through the successive deeps. This is actually found to be what happens.

In the south a tongue of water rich in oxygen leaks into the Timor Trough. The oxygen content gradually diminishes from 3.4 cm³ per liter to 2.2 cm³ per liter in the Aru Basin. The flow southward through the Moluccan Passage can be recognized by an oxygen content of 3.0 cm³ per liter. A branch turns off to the west and finally runs up north along the coast of Celebes. It is also clearly seen how a gradually impoverished flow with a content of 2.5 cm³ per liter passes into the northern Banda Basin. The offshoots in the Gulf of Boni in southern Celebes and the Flores Sea contain only 2.3 cm³ per liter, and in the Bali Sea the oxygen has sunk to 2.0 cm³ per liter. Finally in the Savu Basin a central mass is found where the oxygen has been depleted to 1.7 cm³ per liter.

It is curious to note that the water flowing into the Celebes Sea immediately attains the low oxygen content of only 2.3 cm³ per liter. In a wide sweep it circles along the northern and western margins of this large basin and passes southward into the Makassar Straits. It finally abuts against the shallow banks in the south with a content of

1.7 cm³ per liter. A remarkable, poorly ventilated area is encountered in the south of the Celebes Sea, where the content is below 1.7 cm³ per liter.

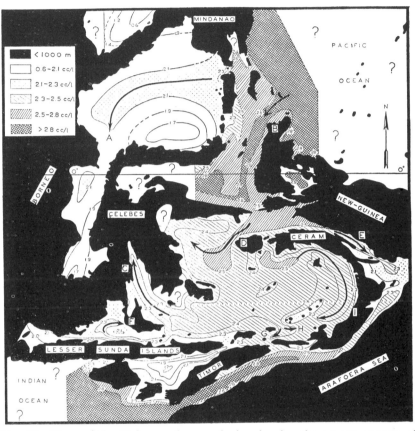

Fig. 30. Chart of the Moluccan deep-sea basins showing the oxygen content of the bottom water in cc/l (according to van Riel). Note the influence of the rotation of the earth combined with the centrifugal force as denoted by the arrows giving the main direction of the ventilating currents: right-hand curve north of equator, left-hand south of equator. (After Kuenen, 1948, Fig. 1.) See also Fig. 31.

Finally the poor communication of the Sulu Basin with the South China Sea is demonstrated by the extremely low oxygen content, which in the southern deep is less than 1.5 cm³ per liter and locally sinks even below 0.6 cm³ per liter. Here a stagnant condition is approached in which the development of hydrogen sulfide begins.

Kuenen has traced the apparent influence of the Coriolis force in the distribution of oxygen (Figs. 30 and 31). The right-hand curve in the flow through the Celebes Sea to the north of the equator is striking, and the current passing from the Pacific into the Moluccan Passage rises high up against the Snellius Ridge north of Halmahera on its right-hand side. Thrusting towards the left in the southern hemisphere is marked in the Gulf of Boni, Weber Deep, Sanana Strait northwest of Buru, and especially in the Flores Trough where a loop

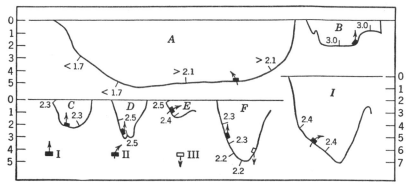

FIG. 31. Sections through the troughs of Fig. 30, showing the position of maximum oxygen content deflected to the right north of equator and to the left south of equator by the force of Coriolis and the centrifugal force. Sections seen in direction of the current (I, II) directed away from observer, (II) additional centrifugal force, (III) towards observer, (*A*, *B*) north of equator, (*C–I*) south of equator. (After Kuenen, 1948, Fig. 2.)

is formed. There even appears a marked tendency in the Ceram Trough to follow the left-hand side. It should be possible to calculate the velocity of these currents from the combined action of the Coriolis force, the pressure gradient, and the centrifugal force. Needless to say, this would prove of vital importance in understanding the biological and sedimentary processes going on in the basins.

Up to the present, very little is known concerning the velocity of these currents. Rough estimates can be made on the strength of a few current measurements. Only the flow over one sill can be evaluated with any degree of accuracy, however, namely, the entrance from the Moluccan Passage to the Buru and Ceram Seas, forming the inlet to the Banda Basins with all its ramifications (Kuenen, 1943). The oceanographical section across the sill shows that an incoming current about 400 m thick (at a depth between 1400 and 1800 m) passes southward. From the chart the cross section of this current can be estimated at 6 km². `

Lek (1938), who studied the current measurements of the *Snellius* in this strait, concluded that at 1500-m depth a current of 5 cm per second is directed towards the Buru Basin (Fig. 32). More measurements would be needed for a reliable value, however, because the average velocity for the entire section is required. It has been pointed

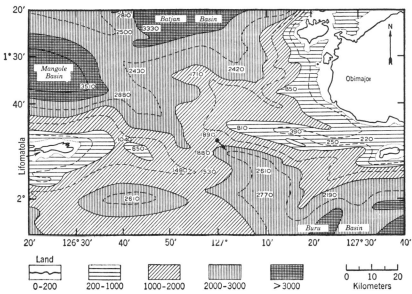

Fig. 32. The sill of Lifomatola Strait, north of Buru, showing position and direction of bottom current ventilating the Banda Basin. Depths in meters.

out above that current measurements made from an anchored ship have inherent errors due to yawing. For a preliminary estimate of the average velocity more than the measured value must be assumed, because the velocity was obtained near the upper limit of the current, and the pressure gradient increases downward. Assuming double the measured value, a velocity of 9 km per 24 hours is found, resulting in a flow of 54 km³ of water daily.

This flow must ventilate basins having a combined volume of 1,800,-000 km³, the estimated size below sill depths. A complete replenishment would take roughly 100 years. For the wider portions of the basins the velocity of the currents would be of the order of a few dozen meters per day.

It may prove possible to estimate the current velocities through the other narrow entrances of the archipelago from the slope of the current, which is indicated by the distribution of the densities of the water at opposite sides of the sill. A considerable amount of data is available, thanks to the soundings and oceanographical stations of the *Snellius* expedition. A very rough estimate for the flow through Lifomatola Strait just discussed is 30 cm per second southward. Although this is more than the 10 cm deduced from current measurements, the order of magnitude appears to be correct.

Finally the question arises as to what the cause of the currents may be (Kuenen, 1948). It is obvious that, if a sill were to be suddenly lowered in consequence of diastrophic activity, an invasion of colder water would enter the basin through the deepened inlet. But some cause must operate to keep the current flowing after the entire deep has been filled.

Since salinity cannot be altered in the deep, a gradual rise in temperature must be assumed. This would reduce the density and allow new cold water to enter over the sill. Of course the process is continuous, and dynamical equilibrium prevails. It is not found possible to trace the mechanism of this convection from the distribution of temperature in the deep. In the oceans the sinking currents are far more pronounced than the gradual return to the surface, and likewise in the Indonesian basins there are no well-marked upward flows. Evidently the movement is diffuse and takes place by some type of mixing.

Several factors may be considered to take part in heating the deep water: the flow of internal heat of the earth and turbulent mixing with higher strata, frictional heat, and the consumption of oxygen. The last two sources are probably considerably smaller than the others and will be left out of account.

We will assume that the flow of heat through the ocean floor is equal to that in continental areas, a postulate that still has to be proved. On this assumption, however, 50 gram calories are conducted annually upward through each square centimeter of the bottom. There are reasons for assuming that about an equal amount is carried downwards into the deeps by turbulent mixing. This turbulence is caused by the tidal currents that affect all parts of the basins, also at greater depths. The measurements of the *Snellius* show a slight rise in potential temperature going upwards in the homothermal deeps. In the Celebes Sea it amounts to 0.1° C. If it is assumed on this evidence that the homothermal waters of about 2000-m thickness are heated during their sojourn in the deep by the combined factors to an amount of 0.1° C, a period of 200 years would be required. These speculations thus lead to a similar though greater length of time for a complete change of water. But it is not improbable that turbulence plays a more active part, in which event the period of heating would be correspondingly reduced.

It will be obvious that only the order of magnitude can be estimated by the various methods given above. All that can be said is that the period is probably less than 300 years and more than 25 years.

TIDAL MOVEMENTS

Tidal Forces. It was shown by Newton that the tidal force is due to the attraction of the moon and in lesser degree to that of the sun. Since then many investigators have contributed to the development of the tidal theory.[1]

If the earth did not rotate, it would still move around the mutual center of gravity of earth and moon, a point situated within the earth. The movement would be comparable to that given to a cup of coffee to dissolve the sugar. Thumb and fingers describe similar circles situated beside each other. In the same way all points on and in the earth describe identical circles in the course of one month. The mutual center of gravity is displaced with respect to the earth and also describes a circle in one month.

As all points of the earth move in equal circles at the same rate they are subject to equal and parallel centrifugal forces. These forces are also parallel to the line connecting the center of gravity of the earth with that of the moon but are directed away from the moon (Fig. 33).

In addition each particle of the earth is attracted by the moon, but the strength of the attraction varies with the distance to the satellite. In a section through both centers of gravity the attraction on the side of the moon must for obvious reasons be greater than the average and that on the opposite side smaller than the average. At the surface of the earth the attraction of the moon amounts to only 1/300,000th of the gravitational force of the earth. Further, the total attraction of the moon must be equal and opposite to the centrifugal force, for if the attraction were greater the two bodies would approach, and if it were smaller they would move apart.

On the front side of the earth the larger attraction of the moon must predominate over the constant centrifugal force, and at the

[1] See Thorade, 1941; Defant, 1929; Schott, 1935, 1942; Sverdrup et al., 1942.

opposite side the reverse must hold. Hence on the front each particle undergoes an accelerating force towards the moon, and on the back one directed away. In both cases an observer would notice a force directed upwards.

At points outside the line connecting the two centers of gravity the attraction and centrifugal force are, moreover, not parallel. The parallelogram of forces shows that the resultant is directed obliquely with regard to the surface of the earth, except at the ends of the perpendic-

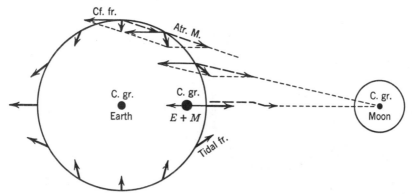

FIG. 33. The tidal force in a section through the line connecting centers of earth and moon. $E + M$ = center of gravity of earth plus moon. *Atr. M.* = attraction of moon. *Cf. fr.* = centrifugal force.

ular to the direction of the moon through the center of the earth. As all sections through the connecting line are equal, a circle may be drawn on the earth where the tidal force is directed vertically downwards. It is surrounded by a band with tidal forces pointing obliquely downwards, while in front and behind are areas where the force is directed obliquely upwards.

The tidal forces are extremely small. The centrifugal force is only 3.38 mg per kilogram; the attraction of the moon varies between 3.49 and 3.27 mg per kilogram. The tidal force is at the maximum in front and behind, where it attains 0.11 mg per kilogram or 1/9,000,000th of the force of gravity. For the sake of clarity the arrows in our figure are drawn comparatively large. On the same scale the force of gravity would be several dozens of kilometers long.

As the tides are related to the moon they run round the earth in a month (27.3 days). But the earth also rotates, and it revolves, as it were, under the system of tidal forces. Twice daily each point on earth passes through a region of upward-directed tidal force and twice through one with a downward force. But as the moon moves in her path each point on earth has to revolve slightly more than a complete rotation to arrive at a point in the same position with relation to the moon. For this reason the tides have a period of ½ × (1 day + 50 minutes). Consequently there occur during a month two highwaters less than double the number of days.

A further complication is due to the moon's not moving in the plane of the equator. This causes a daily inequality of the tide. A

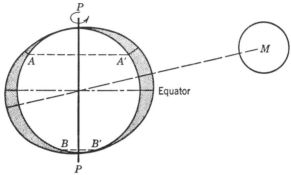

Fig. 34. Diagram showing cause of daily inequality of tides. The outer circumference denotes shape of ocean level. *A* and *A'*, *B* and *B'*, successive positions of two points on the earth's surface at half daily intervals.

point on the surface revolves alternately at a greater and smaller distance past the two points of maximum tidal force (Fig. 34). The influence of this daily inequality can be reduced to zero by chance local conditions, but it may also be so much exaggerated that only one highwater occurs daily.

Finally it should be borne in mind that the sun also causes a tidal force. When sun and moon lie on a straight line with the earth, that is at full or new moon, the tidal forces of both work together. At first and last quarter the band with downward-directed force due to the sun crosses the areas of upward-directed moon tide, and vice versa; in this manner the influences of the two celestial bodies are opposed. The tidal force decreases with the third power of the distance. Hence, owing to the enormous distance of the sun, the tidal force is only 46.6% of that caused by the moon, in spite of the greater gravitational force of the sun. At full and new moon the tidal force of the moon is enlarged 1½ times, and at first and last quarter it is reduced to ½.

These considerations explain the half-monthly inequality of the tides, finding expression in the alternation of spring tide and neap tide.

Schaffernicht succeeded in demonstrating that a bifilar horizontal pendulum shows a deviation under the influence of the tidal force, and with a different mechanism he also showed the action of the vertical component. As the solid crust of the earth also reacts to the tidal force, however, the deviation of the instruments remains below the theoretical value. It has not yet been shown whether the crust moves only under the direct influence of the forces or also in consequence of the piling up of tidal water along the coasts. At any rate the movements of the solid crust are larger than would be expected. At Marburg a displacement of nearly half a meter occurs twice a day.

The geological significance of tides is twofold: (1) the diurnal flooding and exposing of the beach has a profound influence on the biology and geology of the shore; (2) the tidal waves develop currents wherever shallow areas or narrows are passed. Tidal currents are the most powerful currents occurring in the sea and may attain velocities of many meters per second. Owing to their importance to navigation tidal currents have been accurately studied in many of the more-frequented coastal regions and are described in detail in pilot guides.

Tides in Lakes. On the strength of the known tidal forces the extent of tidal movements can be computed. This is relatively simple for a closed basin, such as a lake. It is especially the horizontal component of the tidal force that plays a part. The greater the east-to-west extension of a basin is, the greater the tidal range will be. Calculations have been made for many lakes and inland seas, but the measured range is often found to diverge considerably from the calculated magnitude. The explanation lies in the occurrence of resonance between the period of the tidal force and the period of free oscillation of the waters in the basin. These oscillations can be compared to the wobbling of water in a tub when one side has been abruptly lifted, or to the swinging motion given to a tray of developer in the dark room. In lakes these oscillations are caused by sudden changes in the wind or in atmospheric pressure. In Lake Geneva, they may attain amplitudes of 1½ m. The inhabitants give the name *Seiches* to these mysterious pendulations. Forel was the first to study them, in the second half of the last century. He showed that these standing waves occur both lengthwise with a period of 74 minutes and crosswise with a period of 10 minutes.

These seiches can be calculated also. For Lake Geneva, Doodson found a theoretical period of 74.45 minutes, in close accordance with the measured value of 74 minutes. The period is found to be directly proportional to the length of the basin and to increase with decreasing depth. For a basin 100 km long the period should be 336 minutes for a depth of 10 m, 106 minutes for a depth of 100 m, and 34 minutes for a depth of 1000 m.

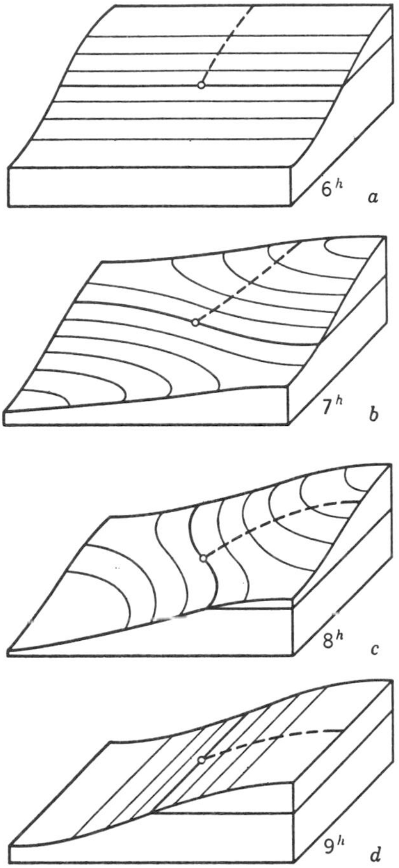

It is obvious that if the tidal force acts on a basin of which the period of free oscillation is similar to the rhythm of the tides the range will be markedly increased. For instance, the Plattensee and Lake Geneva are of similar length, but the former is much shallower and therefore has an oscillation period of 10 hours. This is not far from the tidal period of slightly over 12 hours, and resonance occurs. Consequently the tides of the Plattensee are 1 cm, those of Lake Geneva only 2 mm. Lake Erie, with an oscillation period of 14 hours, has tides of 8 cm, whereas Lake Baikal with a period of 4.6 hours has tides of only 1½ cm, in spite of greater length.

In the Baltic the tidal range is in general less than 2 cm, and in the Mediterranean the maximum is about 30 cm. In more or less circular basins like the Black Sea a circulating wave is formed, in this case with an amplitude of 8 cm (Fig. 35).

FIG. 35. Circulating tidal wave in a square basin from hour to hour with contours of sea level. (After Thorade, 1941, Fig. 47, p. 75.)

Tides in Inland Seas. Matters are more complicated if the basin has a connection with the open sea, so that a tidal wave can enter, as for instance into the Red Sea. Such a wave passes down the basin and is reflected at the opposite end. The primary and reflected waves will interfere and will be superimposed on the oscillations that are caused in the basin itself by the moon. The length of the Red Sea being large as compared with the length of the waves, a node is formed in the center off Port Sudan. There the tides cause only horizontal movements while the height of sea level remains constant (Fig. 36).

In shallow channels the friction with bottom and walls exerts a strong influence and puts a brake on the tidal waves. A pure standing wave then cannot develop, because the reflected wave is too weak to compensate the primary wave. A transitional form between a standing and a progressive wave is then developed.

In funnel-shaped estuaries the incoming tidal wave is forced into a gradually narrowing channel. This results in increased height, and

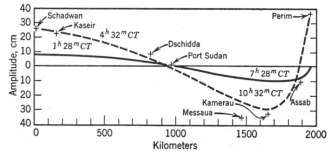

Fig. 36. Diagram showing tidal range in Red Sea. Crosses show observed amplitudes, the full line the local tide, dotted line the wave entering from the Indian Ocean. (After Thorade, 1941, Fig. 33, p. 55.)

the tidal range may be still further enlarged when the period of free oscillation in the estuary approaches the tidal period. The tidal range in estuaries may exceed 10 m (Bristol Channel in southern England, and St. Malo, Normandy, 12.5 m; Bay of Fundy on the Canadian Atlantic coast, 15 m). High tidal ranges tend to be accompanied by powerful tidal currents.

In river mouths the tidal wave cannot be reflected because there is no abrupt upstream ending to the channel. At the mouth an ingoing and outgoing current will be observed in conjunction with the tides at sea. The farther one proceeds up the river, the weaker the tidal currents will be and the later they will set in.

Moreover, the farther upstream one goes, the greater is the influence of the current of the river itself; the ebb current lasts longer and is more powerful. Finally a point is reached where the current no longer alternates in direction. The flow of the river there continues day and night towards the sea. But at certain times the velocity will decrease and at others increase in accordance with the tidal currents farther downstream. This rhythm in the flow also will abate upstream until finally a region is attained where the waters continue their seaward flow uninterrupted by any tidal influence.

In some river mouths the tidal wave is directly deformed on shallow banks. The front is steepened until it resembles a breaker on the beach and is followed by a few powerful oscillatory waves. These may start to curl over and break, and a foaming wall of water then proceeds up current. This rush of water strongly resembles the swash on the beach that will be discussed later.

This wall of water is followed by several normal waves. For reasons to be dealt with later the steepness of the front is maintained, and an observer, instead of witnessing a calm turning of the tides and gradual rise of the surface, sees a wild, roaring breaker rushing up the river at great speed. On a small scale this phenomenon is developed in the Severn and Trent in southern England and is there called the "bore." In the Seine and Gironde the term "mascaret" was applied to the bore, when it attained noteworthy dimensions. Since the shoals in the entrances to these French rivers have been dredged away, the mascaret has almost disappeared. The Amazon and the Tsientan in southern China show the bore on an enormous scale. With indescribable force a thundering wall of water several meters high dashes up the river, attaining velocities of 6 to 7 m per second. The roar can be heard at a distance of a few dozen kilometers, and this type of wave can be very dangerous to shipping. The greatest height observed in the Amazon is 5 m, and in the Tsientan even this figure is surpassed.

Bores on a miniature scale are sometimes developed by waves entering elongate pools on the beach from one end.

The direct tidal force develops only a very small range in the North Sea (Fig. 37), but strong tidal waves enter from the Atlantic. In consequence of the shallowness and complicated shape of the basin the tidal waves are strongly deformed and forced up to great heights locally. The wave entering through the Straits of Dover is of little importance, but through the broad entrance in the north a powerful wave passes into the North Sea. Along the Norwegian coast the range in height is small, locally not more than 25 cm; the amplitude along the British coast, however, is 4 m, and at certain points, as in the Wash, it reaches 6 m. Along the Dutch coast the height is 2 m in the north, 1 m in the center, and greater again in the south, with a maximum of 4 m.

These great vertical movements are coupled with strong horizontal currents. Over extensive areas currents attain as much as 2 m per second. In the Bristol Channel spring tides give rise to a current of 4½ m per second, and between the Channel Islands velocities of 4 m per second are reached with dangerous whirlpools. These are velocities hardly exceeded on navigable rivers. Although the velocity along

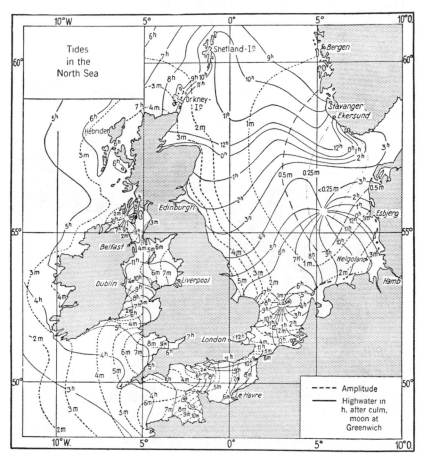

FIG. 37. Tides in the North Sea. (After Schott, 1942, Fig. 62, p. 218.)

the bottom is naturally less, values of ½ m per second have been observed a few meters above the sea floor in open water.

Very accurate data have been obtained by an investigation in the Straits of Dover by van Veen, who set out to study the shifting of sand through the straits. He found that under normal conditions the current velocity at the surface is 1 m per second and at 15 cm from the bottom ½ m per second. At spring tide the values are 1½ times as large; at neap tide, ½. The incoming tide carries 19 km³ of water into the North Sea, and the ebb current takes 17 km³ back again. Per tide, the net transfer is thus found to be 2 km³ into the North Sea. This is equivalent to an average flow of 4 cm per second.

Tides of the Dutch Tidal Flats and Indonesia. The tides in the region of tidal flats and the former Zuider Zee in Holland have been minutely

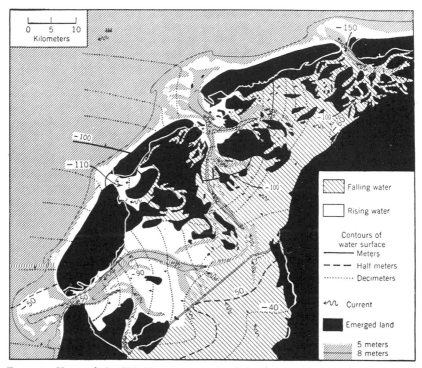

Fig. 38. Chart of the Wadden Zee, north of the former Zuider Zee in Holland, showing tidal currents and contoured sea level on May 31, 1919, 2 hours after culmination of moon. (Redrawn after Lorentz and Thijsse, 1926.)

studied by a committee under the great physicist Lorentz, ably assisted by Thijsse. Their findings comprise a thick volume, the main purpose having been to ascertain the minimum height required for the dyke that has since been constructed across the Zuider Zee.

A series of charts accompanies the report, showing the tidal phenomena. One of these is our Fig. 38. These charts indicate conditions hour by hour on May 31, 1919. They show accurately which areas were dry, where the water was rising and where falling, surface contours of 10 cm, and finally the direction and speed of the currents in the larger gullies over the entire area. The velocities are seen to lie generally between ½ and 1 m per second, locally surpassing 1 m per second. This date was chosen as being windless, and several current measurements had been carried out on that day. The conditions of the tides could have been computed with the same precision for any other date.

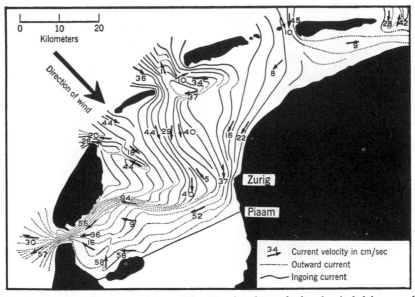

Fig. 39. Chart of same region as Fig. 38, showing calculated wind-driven and tidal currents for the storm of December 22–23, 1894, at 3 o'clock in the morning if the dyke had then existed. Velocities in centimeters per second. Outgoing currents dotted. (Redrawn after Lorentz and Thijsse, 1926.)

Many interesting details could be mentioned, but a few general remarks must suffice. The Coriolis force is found to raise the waters in some places 20 to 30 cm. The line dividing rising from falling water does not coincide with the line separating inflow and outflow, and the line between the areas with an inward and an outward slope is still different.

In this connection the influence of the wind will also be discussed, because this subject is covered by the same report. By way of example the storm of 1894 may be chosen, because in the report a map is reproduced, showing the calculated wind-driven currents for that event. Over wide areas velocities of ½ m per second must have been reached, in some places exceeding 1 m per second (Fig. 39). The total flow through the narrowest part forming the inlet into the basin of the Zuider Zee attained 210,000 m³ per second, or double the maximum flow of the Mississippi. Thus the wind-driven currents are found to equal the tidal currents in velocity.

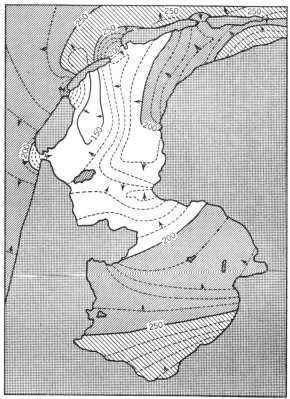

FIG. 40. Chart of the former Zuider Zee with contoured sea level during the storm of November 6–7, 1921. Heights in centimeters above normal sea level. (According to Lorentz and Thijsse, 1926.)

Formerly, storms used to raise the water level considerably against the dykes surrounding the Zuider Zee; heights of 3 to 4 m occurred along considerable portions of the circumference (Fig. 40). The result of cutting off a large portion of the Zuider Zee by a huge dyke has been to increase the range of the tide outside, and the report quoted contains calculations of what was to be expected. The predicted increase has since been confirmed within a few percent by actual measurements. The outcome of this extremely successful piece of hydrographical investigation was that the height of the dyke itself and of the dykes along the adjoining stretches of the mainland should be 1 to 1½ m higher than necessary under the conditions prior to the construction, varying according to the situation.

A map of the Indonesian Archipelago shows that many of the inland seas are connected with the open ocean by more than one passage. The tides that come in from the Pacific and Indian oceans meet a number of obstacles, and the tidal waves beyond the festoons of islands show all manner of interference. Hence the tides are highly complicated, and moreover exceedingly strong currents are developed. Especially between the Lesser Sunda Islands and the Sula Islands powerful tidal currents sweep in and out, attaining velocities of no less than 8 m per second (30 km per hour).

The tidal currents in Indonesia, as elsewhere, are by no means restricted to the surface. They were measured by the *Snellius* expedition at a number of anchor stations at all depths. Thus at 3000 m in the Weber Trough a current of 10 cm per second (⅓ km per hour) was found (Fig. 41). The most powerful flows were encountered over the sills between basins. They run so strong even along the bottom, at 1000 or 2000 m depth, that no loose deposits are laid down on the sills, only pebbles or hard bottom being found by soundings. These reversing movements are accompanied by strong eddies, causing mixing of the waters. It has already been shown that the ventilation of the basins can be maintained largely owing to the thermal energy carried downward by turbulence in the basins.

Comparatively little is known about the tides in the oceanic basins. Tide gauges along the surrounding coasts give us many details on local tidal range and period, but the shallow areas surrounding the land alter the tidal waves entirely. Besides, the number of stations is still quite small. Tide gauges on steep oceanic islands indicate that the range is of the order of ½ to 1 m. They give no indication, however, of the strength or direction of the currents.

The data collected by the *Meteor* expedition in the southern Atlantic at anchor stations are an important addition to our knowledge, but they are much too scarce to furnish a complete picture. It is not probable that oceanic tides are of any direct importance to geological processes, except on elevations of the sea floor, on which they are one of the factors preventing the accumulations of fine deposits.

In conclusion to this short summary of tidal phenomena it may be mentioned that the area alternately covered and laid dry along the

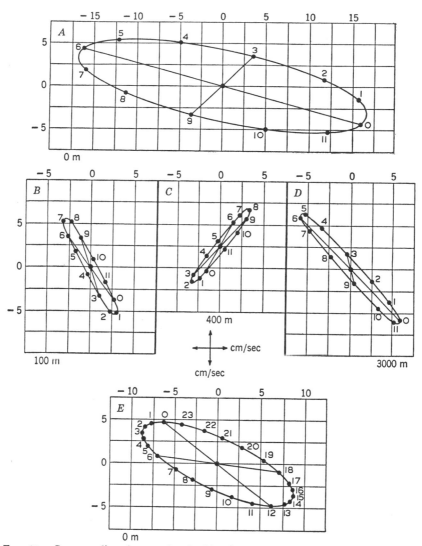

FIG. 41. Current directions and velocities in centimeters per second for half-daily and daily tides at various levels in meters, deduced from measurements by the *Snellius* expedition, anchor station 364, Weber Trough, southeast of Ceram. (Redrawn after Lek, 1938, Fig. 66, p. 135.)

coast is called the beach. The beach is covered by normal high tides, the dry beach only by storm waves. The beach can be quite narrow and disappear completely on steep rocky cliffs. Sandy beaches are generally not steep, slopes between 1° and 3° being normal. The width is closely related to the tidal range, exposure to waves, depth of the waters off the shore, etc.; it varies from a few to many dozens of meters, as a rule. In tidal mud flat areas the relief is very slight between the creeks, so that wide expanses fall dry at low tide. Between the Dutch coast and the islands to the north there are many sand flats of 6- to 10-km extent that are dry at each low tide. In the region of 10 by 10 km between the islands of Terschelling and Ameland and the Frisian coast only a few tidal creeks remain under water at low tide.

Along some rocky coasts extensive areas may fall within the tidal range. In consequence of the very slight slope and the great tidal range between Normandy and Brittany on the French coast the drying flats around Mont Saint Michel are some 20 km wide. Thus it follows that the discovery of fossil beach formations several kilometers wide does not necessarily prove a gradual transgression of the sea.

WAVES [1]

Oscillatory Waves. Waves form the third and last type of movement to be treated.

A wave is described by its length, i.e., the horizontal distance from crest to crest, and by its height, i.e., the vertical distance from trough to crest. A wave is furthermore characterized by its period, i.e., the time interval between the appearance or development of two consecutive crests at a given position.

The simplest form of wave is found in deep water, after the wind has died down. Then the waves are symmetrical with relation to a vertical plane through the crest, and according to the theory of Gerstner the particles revolve in circles (Fig. 42). The size of these circles decreases with depth; at about one-ninth of the wavelength the diameter has decreased to half, at two-ninths it is a quarter, at one-third it is an eighth, and so on. Evidently a level is soon reached at which .no perceptible motion occurs. It follows that a short wave dies out downward sooner than a long one, even if the amplitude is greater.

[1] Extensive bibliography of older observations in Johnson (1919). See also Thorade in: Defant (1940), Sverdrup et al. (1942), Hydrographic Office (1944), Bigelow and Edmondson (1947).

By measurement in a submerged submarine Vening Meinesz actually proved that the short waves disappear at smaller depths than the longer ones. Theoretically, a swell with an amplitude of 6 m and a length of 180 m should have an amplitude of 1½ m at 40 m below the surface and of only 0.6 cm at 200 m.

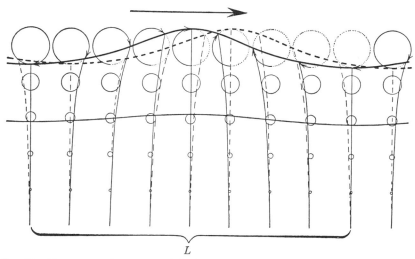

FIG. 42. Movement of water particles in a deep-water wave of small height. The circles show the paths in which the particles move. The size of the orbits below the surface is shown to scale, and the lower wave line shows the amount of vertical movement at that level. The dashed wave profile and dashed nearly vertical lines show the position one-eighth of a period later than the equivalent full-drawn curves. L = wavelength.

When a vertical column of water is viewed (Fig. 43) it is found to sway back and forth like corn in the wind. But it also stretches and contracts in length. At the moment a wave crest passes, the column is tall and thin; it then inclines in the direction of propagation and returns to vertical as the wave trough reaches the spot. At that moment the column is at its shortest and thickest, whereafter it stretches and bends in the opposite direction.

The surface shape of the wave is not a sine curve but a trochoid, which is the line described by a point on the spoke of a wheel that rolls along the under side of a plane surface. For waves of very small height, in which the ratio of length to height is 100:1 or more, the profile approaches a sine curve. The crest of a trochoidal wave is narrow and steep; the trough is broad. Still water level is therefore closer to the level of the troughs than to that of the crests. In shallow water, about three-fourths of the wave height, varying with the circumstances, is above still water level. According to theory the height may attain one-seventh of the wave length, but in nature the crest has often become unstable and has started to topple over before this degree of steepness is attained (for an explanation see p. 82). Seldom is a wave higher than one-twelfth of the length, and the ratio of 1:20 or 1:30 is frequent. But if two sets of waves bisect, pyramidal waves develop that are steeper than 1:12.

The relation between wavelength L, velocity V, and period T is $V = L/T$. With V in meters per second, L in meters, and T in seconds we have, for *deep* water (depth $> \frac{1}{2}L$),

$$V = 1.56T; \quad L = 1.56T^2; \quad V^2 = 1.56L$$

A characteristic of great importance to the movement of suspended particles is that a certain small mass transport of water takes place in the direction of propagation. A water particle moves in the direction of progress when it is above its mean depth, and in the opposite direction when it is below its mean depth. Owing to the decrease in velocity with depth, however, it moves somewhat faster in the direction of progress than in the opposite direction. After having completed one revolution in its orbit, the particle is advanced somewhat. This means that even in the absence of wind an actual mass transport of water takes place in the direction of propagation (Fig. 44).

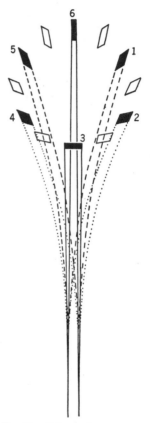

Fig. 43. Schematic representation of successive shapes of a column of water in a deep-water wave. (Mainly according to Thorade, in Defant et al., 1940, Fig. 51, p. 121.)

The velocity of mass transport is appreciable for high, steep waves but is very small for low waves of long period.

Where a wave approaches shallow water and the movement reaches to the bottom, the particles must follow elliptical courses. Downwards the ellipses will be flatter, finally becoming straight lines along the bottom, where a movement to and fro remains (Fig. 45).

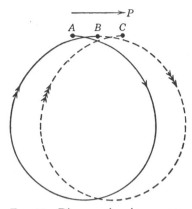

FIG. 44. Diagram showing successive orbits followed by a particle while two complete trochoidal waves pass in the direction P. The distances of transport are A to B and B to C.

It can be shown that the wind affects wave movement by three distinct processes working together. In the first place the wind presses against the rear and pulls at the front of the wave speeding forwards, pushes it along, and forces the water downwards. On the lee side of the wave a counter eddy with a horizontal axis is developed in consequence of the wind's not being able to follow the sharp form of the wave crest. The wind slides over the eddy and impinges on the back of the next wave (Fig. 46).

For obvious reasons this energy transfer by push and pull depends upon the difference between wind velocity and wave velocity. If the waves travel faster than the wind they meet an air resistance, and this must cause loss of energy.

This action of the wind, termed "push," probably begins at low velocities, but according to Jeffreys the first undulations do not become visible until the wavelength has reached 9 cm and the wind has attained 1.15 m per second.

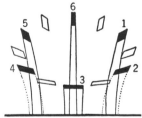

FIG. 45. The equivalent of Fig. 43 for a wave in shallow water. (Mainly according to Thorade, in Defant et al., 1940, Fig. 54, p. 123.)

Under certain conditions much shorter ripples ("cat's paws") have been observed, however. Ripples are so small that surface tension increases the speed of propagation. The surface tension reacts against the deformation as if it were a stretched elastic film. The increase of velocity is comparable to raising the tone of a string on a musical instrument. The influence of capillarity follows from the values in Table 5, for sea water at 15° C.

TABLE 5. VELOCITY OF PROPAGATION OF WAVES IN SEA WATER AT 15° C

Wavelength in cm	10	5	2	1.7	1.5	1	0.2	0.1
Velocity in cm/sec	40.1	29.6	23.3	23.1	23.3	24.8	48.3	68.0

With larger waves, the surface tension no longer has a noticeable influence and the velocity is regulated entirely by gravity. Thus a period of 10 seconds corresponds to a wavelength of 156 cm and a velocity of 15.6 m per second.

A second influence of the wind is caused by the friction, by which the water is carried forward in the wave crest and is set in motion like the string on a fiddle by the bow.

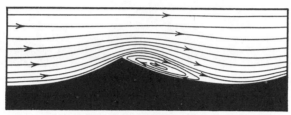

FIG. 46. Schematic representation of stream lines in wind passing over sharp-crested trochoidal wave and forming an eddy.

The surface layer of the water moves forward in the crest, and energy is transferred from the wind to the wave. In the trough the surface layer moves backward, against the wind, and energy is lost. If these movements were equal the two effects would compensate each other. But, as pointed out above, there is a slight advance of the surface particles. Hence the transfer of energy from the wind to the wave predominates. This is termed the pull or drag of the wind. Even when the *wave form* moves faster than the wind and the push has become negative, the drag can continue to transfer energy to the waves because the *water particles* advance very much more slowly than the wind. If this were not so no satisfactory explanation could be given of the fact that waves sometimes have a higher velocity than the wind producing them. According to computations by Jeffreys this influence does not start until the wind has attained 4.8 m per second.

Finally the wind acts on the water by suction and compression, as was shown by Helmholtz and by Lord Kelvin. Over the crest the wind is compressed and its velocity increased; hence the pressure must be lowered. Conversely, an extra pressure must develop in the wave trough (Fig. 47). This influence also is restricted to wind velocities of more than 6.5–7 m per second. In connection with the eddy mentioned above, this influence is displaced slightly in the direction of propagation (Fig. 48). However, this effect is mainly active in forming whitecaps on existing waves. The influence on the formation of larger waves is negligible.

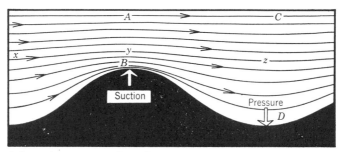

FIG. 47. Schematic representation of stream lines over a wave showing the suction and pressure exerted on the water.

For a given strength of wind there is a maximum size of wave. This maximum can be generated only in water of such depth that the bottom cannot hinder the development of the undulations. For the largest waves depths of more than one to two hundred meters are required, that is, true oceanic depths outside the continental shelf.

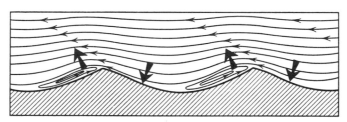

FIG. 48. Schematic representation of the displacement of suction and pressure on a wave due to the eddies behind sharp crests.

However, the maximum size is not attained immediately, but only after the wind has blown for a considerable time and over a considerable distance. The stronger the wind, the longer it takes to produce the greatest possible waves. Whereas slight ripples can attain their maximum size in a few minutes, a hurricane requires very many hours and seldom lasts long enough in a given area to develop the maximum size of wave theoretically possible. Meanwhile not only the size but also the shape is gradually altered. The velocity of the waves increases rapidly with time and may finally attain almost 1½ times the velocity of the generating wind. Concomitantly the steepness decreases.

The distance over which the wind can catch the water is called "the length of fetch." During the time while the wind is acting to raise the wave, the wave is propagated forward. Hence a wind of given force is not able to raise waves of maximum size directly by the lee shore but only over a certain length of fetch. For a given wind velocity there is a minimum length of fetch to form the maximum wave size possible. The stronger the wind, the greater this fetch must be. Conversely, for each fetch there is a maximum size of wave that can be raised by the strongest wind. In a minor reentrant of the sea the length of fetch is of course small, and for this reason really huge waves are encountered only in wide ocean basins. Table 6 shows the maximum size of waves for different lengths of fetch with a wind of 60 km per hour.

TABLE 6. LENGTH OF FETCH AND CORRESPONDING MAXIMUM HEIGHT OF WAVES, WITH A WIND VELOCITY 60 KM/HOUR

Length of fetch	Maximum height	Length of fetch	Maximum height
5 km	0.9 m	50 km	3.1 m
10 km	1.4 m	100 km	4.2 m
20 km	2.0 m	500 km	6.2 m

In order to form the very largest waves observed in nature a length of fetch of at least 1000 km is required. It is further necessary that the full force of a tempest blowing at 100 km per hour strike the waves over the whole of this length for a sufficient length of time.

It is no simple matter to determine the greatest size that waves can attain at sea, as the measurement of the vertical distance between crest and trough during a severe storm is no light task. The greatest height so far ascertained by stereoscopic photography is 16 m. A different and less accurate method is to seek a point at such a level above the water line that one sees the crests on the horizon at the moment the ship is at the bottom of a trough. The height of the eye above the water line should then correspond to the size of the waves. By this method almost inconceivable heights have been ascertained, reaching 20 to 25 m or the equivalent of a five- to six-storied building. Single pyramidal giants formed by interference of two sets of waves may rise to greater heights, and individual waves well over 30 m have been reported. The wavelength of enormous storm billows must be several hundreds of meters. In the Mediterranean, where the length of fetch is restricted, the highest waves reported are 4 to 5 m. A height of more than 15 m, even in the wide oceans, is certainly exceptional, and the average size is probably always less. The length of waves measuring 15 m in height is generally of the order of 300 m.

Attempts have been made to find a formula for calculating the wave height from the force of the wind, assuming that depth, length of fetch, and time are sufficient to allow of maximum development. One empirical formula given is $h = \frac{1}{3}W$, in which h is the height in meters and W is the velocity of the wind in meters per second. Other formulas are given but none of them appears to have a general application.

During the second world war the staff of Scripps Institution of Oceanography, La Jolla, studied the problems of wave formation. Their highly important results were published in reports by the Scripps Institution and by the Hydrographic Office of the U. S. Navy Department (see also Munk and Traylor, 1947). They arrived at the conclusion that there is no evidence of wave energy being dissipated by viscosity. In deep water, push (or air resistance) and drag of the wind on the sea surface are the chief processes altering the height or velocity of the waves. Formulas were obtained for calculating the size of waves from the strength and duration of the wind and the length of fetch that closely accord with observational data. It would lead us too far to record the results in any detail, but a few examples may prove of interest. A wind of 50 km per hour blowing for 5 hours has generated the largest waves attainable for the given length of fetch up to a distance of 45 km from the coast, where the waves are 3 m high. After 25 hours the maximum size has been reached at 400 km from the coast, where the waves are 4.5 m high. A wind of 105 km per hour needs a length of fetch of 1500 km to effect a wave height of 20 m and must continue for 50 hours in order to do so.

From observations the empirical relation shown in Table 7 has been deduced, to which is added the corresponding size given by the tables of the Scripps reports.

TABLE 7. EMPIRICAL AND CALCULATED RELATION BETWEEN VELOCITY OF WIND AND HEIGHT OF WAVES FOR GREAT LENGTH OF FETCH

Velocity of wind	Empirical	Calculated	Velocity of wind	Empirical	Calculated
5 m/sec	1 m	0.7 m	15 m/sec	7 m	7 m
10 m/sec	4 m	3.5 m	20 m/sec	10 m	12 m

It has been stated repeatedly that the greatest height of waves does not develop until the wind has started to slacken. Not only does the wind blow the top off the waves, but also the gusts of wind impede the billows in developing regularly and in combining. No sooner does the force of the wind begin to abate than these hindrances to the development are removed, and the waves grow in height before finally beginning to subside.

Wind waves are defined as waves that are growing in height under the influence of the wind, and *swell* as wind-generated waves that are decreasing in height through lack of sufficient wind. The swell, in typical form, constitutes a regular heaving motion of the sea caused by far-off storm centers. In practice no sharp distinction between wind waves and swell can be drawn. Therefore no maximum height can be given for the swell. But values of several meters are observed in a windless sea showing no breaking crests, and such waves should therefore be reckoned as swell. The length may be enormous.

FIG. 49. Sailing vessel on ground swell viewed from life boat (after photograph).

Thus in the neighborhood of Australia a swell with a wavelength of 400 m has been observed, and one with a wavelength of 580 m off the Cape of Good Hope, while 824 m has been reported from the Atlantic. From a period of 21 seconds measured on the coast of Morocco a length of 660 m follows. Even longer periods up to 30 seconds are said to occur.

By the energy of the waves is understood the average energy over one wavelength per unit breadth at right angles to movement. Half the energy in surface waves is potential, associated with the displacement of the water particles above and below the level of still water, and half is kinetic, associated with the motion of the particles. The energy per unit area is proportional only to the square of the wave height. The total energy per unit breadth between two crests is obtained by multiplying the energy per unit area by the wavelength.

The waves at sea are in general highly irregular. Thorade compared the surface of the sea to crêpe paper rather than to corrugated iron. Not only does the wind blow in gusts that vary in strength and direction, but when irregularities in the waves have once developed they deflect the wind and thus increase the irregularities in the motion of the air. Moreover, the wind almost always finds a surface on which a system of waves is already present, but a system that does not conform either to the strength or to the direction of the wind. In this manner two or more systems of waves are superimposed one on another.

When the waves have grown to a larger size the wind continues to generate smaller ones. But these continually pass into the shade of the larger ones and are also flattened out by the spray driven off the crests of the bigger waves. Hence, they receive insufficient energy to grow, and they die away again. This is the reason why in a general way the larger waves predominate, instead of all sizes down to the smallest being represented.

The modern method of investigating wave shapes is by stereoscopic photography, using two cameras with a base several meters long. The two photographs can be combined to give a chart with surface contours of the area covered by both. Among others the *Meteor* expedition brought home some exposures that have been worked out with later additions in an atlas showing contoured charts (Fig. 50). These maps show striking irregularity of the sea surface. In many it is with great difficulty that any definite system of wave ridges can be traced. It is also apparent that a systematic distortion of the rear part of the photographs is introduced by this method. Vertical stereoscopic exposures taken from a plane would therefore present great advantages over these obliques.

The shorter the wavelength and the steeper the crests, the sooner a set of waves must lose its energy during propagation or be deflected and suppressed by gusts and eddies of the wind. Moreover, the waves always tend to lengthen during propagation. Hence the longest waves developed in a stormy area must be propagated farthest beyond the region of generation, while shorter and possibly higher waves die out much sooner or are changed to longer ones. Such couriers of far-off storms are known to us in the shape of the ocean swell, already referred to.

When deep water waves spread out into a region of calm, only half the energy of the wave advances with wave velocity. As a result the energy of a train of waves advances with a distinct "front" moving at half the velocity of wave propagation. Waves are continuously running out in advance of the front but die out in a very short time. Behind the front the waves retain the original amount of energy, because loss by viscosity is small. However, the velocity (and therefore also the period) gradually increases with advance while the height decreases, because it has been found, as pointed out above, that this alteration is a general characteristic of wave propagation, whether wind waves or swell, and mainly as a result of the suppression of the shorter waves by eddy viscosity.

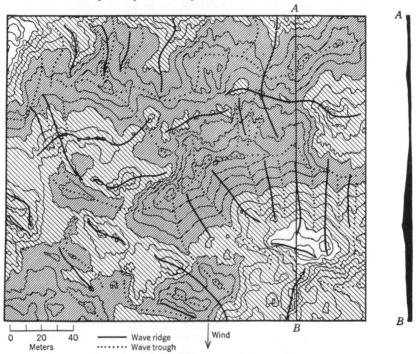

Fig. 50. Contoured chart and section of sea surface, showing two main trains of waves. The crest lines of one train are almost parallel to the wind. (According to data given by Schumacher, 1939.)

Tsunamic Waves. Tsunamic or "catastrophic" waves, often misnamed "tidal" waves, are generated by landslides and the calving of glaciers, by submarine slumping or faulting, and by submarine volcanic eruptions. Submarine earthquakes seldom develop visible waves at the surface, but rather a vibration that is propagated with great velocity. These seaquakes can be felt on board ships, but the amplitude is too small to be observed with the eye. Only when a submarine earthquake causes a slide, or when a fault scarp is developed suddenly on the sea floor, can a visible wave be generated by seismic action.

Tsunamis are related to the type of undulation induced by throwing a stone into the water. The amplitude may be very great. The waves generated during the eruption of the volcanic island Paloeweh north of Flores in the Lesser Sunda Islands in 1928, for instance, rose 5 to 10 m on the coasts of the island itself and on the opposite shores of Flores. Even much larger waves arose during the eruption of Krakatau in 1883 between Java and Sumatra. According to computations of Verbeek they must have attained 30 to 40 m in height.

In general the phenomena accompanying tsunamis are as follows. First the sea withdraws, leaving dry many kilometers on gently shelving coasts. Sometimes the water returns as gradually, but mostly a high wave comes rolling in. The time interval can be several minutes to one or two hours. More than once the tsunamis on the Japanese and Chilian coasts have reached heights of 30 to 40 m, causing vast destruction. On October 6, 1737, a wave estimated to be 70 m high threw itself on the coast of Cape Lopatka at the tip of Kamchatka.

The wavelength of these tsunamic waves is of the order of 100 km. The velocity depends on the average depth, the relation being $V = \sqrt{gD}$, when $L \gg D$. For the Pacific the velocity as found from calculation should be about 200 m per second, but considerable divergence is encountered when the distances covered are divided by the time of propagation. This should be attributed partly to the impossibility of ascertaining accurately the moment of arrival. Detailed studies of tsunamis were made in connection with the great seaquake of 1933 on the Japanese coast and the tsunamic wave of April 1, 1946, in the Hawaiian Islands (Macdonald et al., 1947).

The term "tidal wave" is also applied to inundations of low coastal areas by water driven onto the land by exceptionally severe storms. The level of the ocean may rise as much as 5 to 6 m against the coast, and great damage may result.

Some apparent transgressions of short duration which are occasionally met with between fossil terrestrial sediments may be due to such ephemeral covering by the sea as tsunamic or tidal waves, according to Grabau.

Waves in Shallow Water and Surf. When a wave meets a vertical or steep surface at the coast it is reflected and interferes with the incoming oscillations, producing high wave crests. Small divergences from the vertical or minor irregularities may cause the wave to break and to be thrown upwards. A considerable portion of the energy is given off in the small tip of the wave crest, that is shot up high into the air sometimes to 100 m or more. The wave may also be reflected from a notch cut in a steep rocky coast. The air contained in the hollow is compressed, and the water spouts back with great force.

Most coasts, however, are fronted by a sandy or stony platform that shelves gradually seaward, starting from some distance above high-water mark. Reflection of the waves is then largely suppressed.

When a train of waves comes in from offshore towards a gently shelving coast, one of the first things to happen is the disappearance of short-crested waves at a distance from the shore. Two other deformations are also brought about.

As soon as a depth is reached at which the movement reaches the bottom the velocity of propagation is reduced and the crests are crowded closer together.

Roughly, a wave is influenced by the bottom when the depth becomes less than half the wavelength. This change in wavelength and consequent steepening of the waves is not due to friction but to the restricting effect of the bottom on the wave motion. Because of the steepening the wave appears to grow higher, but actually the increase of *short*-period waves is slight. Very *long*-period waves, however, may attain almost three times their deep-water height before breaking.

If the crest runs obliquely to the depth contours the retardation sets in first at the end nearest the beach. In consequence the wave swerves around and gradually comes to advance more and more nearly at right angles to the beach (crest parallel to the beach). This phenomenon is termed wave refraction (Munk and Traylor, 1947). By the time the beach is reached the rollers are often practically parallel to the water line, irrespective of the original direction. On an irregular coast also the wave fronts conform to the shape for the same reason and meet the beach in flowing curves. In a bay they spread out fanwise, and around a cape they concentrate and advance from both sides (Figs. 51 and 52). This characteristic may also be observed by noting that on an island the surf likewise breaks on the lee shore, advancing in a direction opposed to the generating wind.

As there is hardly any transfer of energy parallel to the wave crest, one of the results of refraction is that more wave energy is concentrated on forelands than in bays; another is that the sideways transport of material is reduced.

On the Californian coast observation has shown that the refraction is strongly influenced by the submarine topography of the foreshore. Breakers on the coast inside submarine ridges extending normal to the shore, where convergence takes place, are often 10 times as high as at the heads of valleys approaching close to the shore, where the waves spread out. Hence these valleys form natural points for safe anchoring or landing.

Surf is strongly related to the phenomenon of deep-water waves breaking. Deep-water waves become unstable and break when the

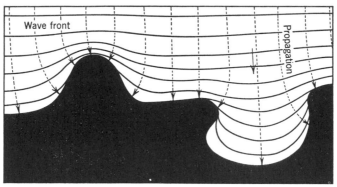

FIG. 51. Schematic representation of refraction of waves running on an irregular coast. Note concentration of energy on foreland and protection of beach in reentrant.

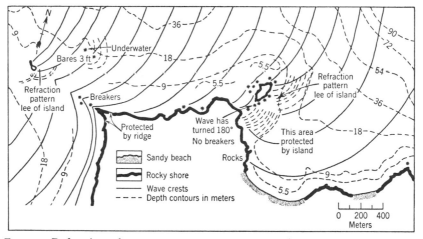

FIG. 52. Refraction of waves around northern coast of San Clemente Island off California as deduced from aerial photographs taken on June 20, 1944. (Redrawn from Scripps Institution Report, Hydrographic Office, U. S. Navy Dept., Pub. 234, 1944.)

orbital velocity of the water particles at the top of the crest exceeds the velocity of the wave. The particles move forward faster than the wave and topple over onto the front slope. Theoretically this must take place when the steepness increases to $\frac{1}{7}$; the top angle is then 120°. The wind drag hastens the breaking of the wave. Hence this phenomenon occurs before the theoretical maximum steepness has been attained.

The development of surf along a coast is a second consequence of a shelving sea bottom. It is most characteristically shown when a long ocean swell advances over a gently sloping and smooth bottom (Fig. 53).

The lessening depth detracts from the velocity, causing the waves to crowd together, and therefore to become steeper. In the crest of the wave the velocity of the water particles in their orbital movement approaches and finally exceeds the velocity of the wave. At this

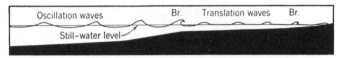

Oscillation waves   Br.   Translation waves   Br.

Still-water level

Fig. 53. Schematic representation of development of surf on a shelving beach. *Br.* = breakers.

moment the wave "curls" and the crest shoots forward in a circular course, without there being sufficient material to fill the central concavity. The crest is then no longer supported and crashes forward in a foaming line of surf, sending a swirling mass of water, called the "swash," up the beach. When the upward movement has ceased, the water runs back again as the "backwash." This is roughly the way the surf is generated, but a complete understanding of the phenomena has not yet been reached (Fig. 54).

It has already been pointed out that the bore is of a similar nature, but the gradual narrowing of the estuary aids in increasing the height of the wave.

The depth at which a wave breaks varies according to its height and steepness. Steep waves break like deep-water waves. White water appears on the crest, and the wave top gradually rolls over. The breaking continues for a considerable distance and does not take place with a crash. The term "spilling breakers" is applied to this type. Irregularity of the waves or the bottom, and gentle slope of the bottom, tend to cause spilling. Not-so-steep waves in deep water do not start to break when approaching the beach until the greater part of the energy becomes concentrated in the crest. The description of surf given above applies to this type, and the term "plunging breakers" is used. Steepness and regularity of the bottom, and the absence of other waves and of wind, are factors favorable to the plunging of waves.

It is often found that a wave topples over where the depth below still water becomes less than 1.3 times the height of the roller. But sometimes the surf develops in much deeper water, even 2½ times the value according to the above rule. Besides, waves may break over the edge of submarine declivities in fairly deep water. Airy observed breakers in the Channel at a spot where the depth is 200 m, and Tizard reported them from the Shetland Islands in depths of 300 to 500 m. Probably several factors are involved, such as smoothness of the bot-

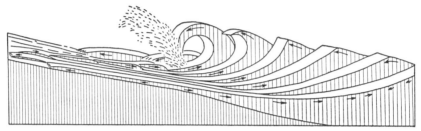

FIG. 54. Block diagram of a breaking wave. (After Davis, 1912, Fig. 185, p. 472.)

tom, steepness of the beach, and force of the wind. Off the Dutch coast several rows of sandbanks are found, and each may cause a separate line of surf. The heavier the waves, the farther out the first row of whitecaps is observed. Over the following banks additional lines of surf are formed, so that three or four white strips may be seen in front of the beach.

Heavy surf may be caused in two different ways, either by an onshore storm or by ocean swell. In a storm the rhythm is comparatively swift, because the wavelength is not very great. Obviously the size of the rollers increases with length of fetch and with degree of exposure of the coast to waves from deep water. When the surf is due to ocean swell the period is much longer.

Certain stretches of coast are ill-famed for their heavy surf; French Morocco is among these. As the height increases with lessening of depths a swell of a few meters' amplitude may result in breakers 9 to 10 m high at the moment they curl over. The length of the crests is so great that sometimes a white line is formed almost simultaneously as far as the eye can reach. Communication by boat between ships in the offing and the coast is excluded under these circumstances. The treacherous nature of this phenomenon lies in the fact that it may set in suddenly without warning because the source is far out in midocean.

Thanks to the results of wartime work, mainly by Scripps Institution, mentioned earlier, surf can now be predicted with considerable accuracy from weather charts.

Solitary Waves. Besides the oscillatory waves dealt with so far another type may also occur in shallow water, namely, solitary or translation waves. The particles of water in these waves do not revolve in circular or elliptical orbits but undergo a single displacement in the

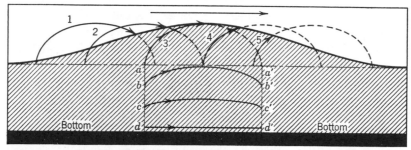

FIG. 55. Schematic representation of the movement of water particles in a pure solitary wave. Full-drawn curves 1 to 5 show tracks of particles already followed; *aa'* to *dd'*, full tracks at various levels when the wave has passed.

direction in which the solitary wave is propagated. They do not return to the point of origin. Hence the water is shifted suddenly forwards, while in front of or behind the wave the water remains at rest. A typical property of this type of wave is that, whereas oscillation waves can occur only in trains, each solitary wave is independent and forms a separate entity. The name translation wave, now obsolete, referred to the permanent displacement of the water particles.

Solitary waves were discovered in the middle of the nineteenth century by Scott-Russell. They can be generated by moving a vertical board horizontally through the water in a shallow channel or by the sudden addition of a large body of water. A single wave is then propagated through the channel as a moving ridge without an adjoining hollow shape. A necessary condition is that the propagation be swifter than $\sqrt{gd}$ (g = acceleration of gravity, d = depth).

Analysis of the solitary wave has brought out that the particles move in a sort of parabolic orbit (Fig. 55). All particles are brought forward an equal amount, but the ellipse is flatter nearer the bottom, and along the bottom the water is moved forward in straight lines.

The volume per unit of breadth of the wave above still water must equal the space between the positions of a set of particles in a vertical section before and after the wave has passed.

At sea, solitary waves are developed gradually from oscillation waves on nearing the coast, or suddenly after breaking of the surf. In the first case the depth gradually decreases; in the second, the surf suddenly throws a large volume of water over the shallow strip fronting the beach.

As noted above, the regular waves running on a beach during calm weather are formed from oceanic swell and have undergone important modifications while approaching the coast. Instead of showing crests and troughs, practically flat expanses are seen between widely spaced, regular welts on the surface of the sea. Even when coming in groups, as is usual, the distance from crest to crest is much greater than corresponds with the steep slopes of the waves, and it varies within wide limits for the same height of crest. Such forms constitute almost pure solitary waves.

The maximum height of a solitary wave above still water equals 1.3 times the depth; otherwise the wave starts to break. Very few observations have been made in nature of magnitudes of solitary waves before breaking, because observers have generally not distinguished between oscillatory and solitary waves. The irregularity of the shapes in nature and the occurrence of transitional forms complicate matters and render the making of quantitative observations exceedingly difficult.

Large volumes of water are piled up against the beach by the action of breakers. The water returns to the open sea by so-called rip currents or by undertow, dealt with in a later chapter. Longshore currents are set up within the breaker zone where the wave crests advance obliquely towards the shore. From the formulas given in the *Hydrographic Office Report* (1944) on this subject it follows that appreciable velocities may be expected (1 to 2 m per second under favorable conditions).

Bibliography

ALLEN, J. *Scale Models in Hydraulic Engineering,* 407 pp., Longmans, Green, London, 1947.

AMERICAN GEOPHYSICAL UNION. Symposium on the Geophysical Exploration of the Ocean Bottom, *Proc. Am. Philos. Soc.,* Vol. 79, pp. 1–44, 1938.

BIGELOW, H. B. *Oceanography,* 263 pp., Houghton Mifflin, Boston, 1931.

BIGELOW, H. B., and W. T. EDMONDSON. *Wind Waves at Sea, Breakers and Surf,* 177 pp., Hydrographic Office, U. S. Navy, Publ. 602, Washington, D. C., 1947.

BOURCART, J. *Géographie du fond des mers, Étude du relief des Océans,* 307 pp., Payot, Paris, 1949.

CHUN, C. *Aus den Tiefen des Weltmeeres,* 592 pp., Fischer, Jena, 1903.

CLARKE, F. W. The Data of Geochemistry, *U. S. Geol. Surv., Bull.* 770, 841 pp., 1924.

COKER, R. E. *This Great and Wide Sea,* 325 pp., Chapel Hill, N. C., 1947.

CORNISH, V. *Ocean Waves and Kindred Geophysical Phenomena,* 164 pp., Cambridge University Press, 1934.

CORRENS, C. W., et al. *Tiefseebuch,* 144 pp., Mittler und Sohn, Berlin, 1934.

DAVIS, W. M. *Die erklärende Beschreibung der Landformen,* 565 pp., Teubner, Leipzig, 1912.

DEFANT, A. *Dynamische Ozeanographie,* 222 pp., Julius Springer, Berlin, 1929.

DEFANT, A., et al. *Wind, Wetter und Wellen auf dem Weltmeere,* 150 pp., Mittler und Sohn, Berlin, 1940.

EARTHQUAKE RESEARCH INST. TOKYO IMP. UNIV., *Bull. Supp.,* Vol. 1, Papers and Reports on the Tsunami of 1933 on Sanriku Coast, Japan.

EMERY, K. O., and A. R. CHAMPION. The Underway Bottom Sampler, *Int. Hydr. Rev.,* Vol. 25, pp. 61–62, 1948.

EWING, W. M., A. C. VINE, and J. L. WORZEL. Photography of the Ocean Bottom, *J. Optical Soc. Am.,* Vol. 36, pp. 307–321, 1946.

FLEMING, R. H., and R. REVELLE. Physical Processes in the Ocean, in TRASK et al., pp. 48–141, 1939.

HENTSCHEL, E. *Das Leben des Weltmeeres,* 153 pp., Springer, Berlin, 1929.

HYDROGRAPHIC OFFICE, U. S. NAVY DEPT. *Breakers and Surf, Principles in Forecasting,* 52 pp., 1944; *Supplement,* 19 pp., 1945.
Wind Waves and Swell, Principles in Forecasting, 61 pp., no date.
Forecasting Longshore Currents, 6 pp., 1945.
Ice Atlas, 107 pp., Publ. 550, Washington, D. C., 1946.

JOHNSON, D. W. *Shore Processes and Shoreline Development,* 584 pp., John Wiley & Sons, New York, 1919.

KNUDSEN, M. *Hydrographische Tabellen,* 63 pp., Gad, Copenhagen, 1901.

KON. NED. AARDR. GEN. *De Zeeën van Nederlandsch Oost Indië,* 506 pp., Brill, Leyden, 1922.

KRÜMMEL, O. *Handbuch der Ozeanographie,* Bd. 1, Die räumlichen, chemischen und physikalischen Verhältnisse des Meeres, 526 pp., 1907; Bd. 2, Die Bewegungsformen des Meeres, 728 pp., 1911.

KUENEN, PH. H. Influence of the Earth's Rotation on Ventilation Currents of the Moluccan Deep-Sea Basins, *Proc. Kon. Ned. Akad. Wet.,* Vol. 51, pp. 417–426, 1948.
De Kringloop van het Water, 408 pp., Leopold, The Hague, 1948.

KUENEN, PH. H., and G. A. NEEB. Bottom Samples, *The Snellius Expedition,* Vol. 5, part 3, 268 pp., Brill, Leyden, 1943.

KULLENBERG, B. The Piston Core Sampler, *Svenska Hydro-Biol. Komm. Skrifter,* S. 3, Bd. 1, Hf. 2, 46 pp., 1947.

LEK, L. Die Ergebnisse der Strom- und Serienmessungen, *The Snellius Expedition,* Vol. 2, part 3, 169 pp., Brill, Leyden, 1938.

LORENTZ, H. A., and J. TH. THIJSSE, *see Verslag Staatscommissie.*

MacDonald, G. A., F. P. Shepard, and D. C. Cox. The Tsunami of April 1, 1946, in the Hawaiian Islands, *Pacific Science*, Vol. 1, pp. 21–37, 1947. (Shepard, F. P., G. A. MacDonald, and D. C. Cox, The Tsunami of April 1, 1946, in preparation.)

MacEwen, G. F. Modern Dynamical Oceanography, *Proc. Am. Phil. Soc.*, Vol. 79, pp. 145–166, 1938.

Munk, W. H., and M. A. Traylor. Refraction of Ocean Waves, a Process Linking Underwater Topography to Beach Erosion, *J. Geol.*, Vol. 55, pp. 1–26, 1947.

Murray, J., and J. Hjort. *The Depths of the Ocean*, 821 pp., Macmillan, London, 1912.

National Research Council. *Bulletin 85*, Oceanography, Physics of the Earth, Vol. 5, 581 pp., 1932.

Riel, P. M. van. The Bottom Configuration in Relation to the Flow of the Bottom Water, *The Snellius Expedition*, Vol. 2, part 2, Chapter 2, 63 pp., Brill, Leyden, 1934.

The Bottom Water, Introductory Remarks and Oxygen Content, *The Snellius Expedition*, Vol. 2, part 5, Chapter 1, 77 pp., Brill, Leyden, 1943.

Riel, P. M. van, et al. Voyage, *The Snellius Expedition*, 177 pp., Brill, Leyden, 1937.

Rouch, J. *La mer*, 252 pp., Flammarion, Paris, 1939.

Météorologie et physique du globe, tome 2, Physique des mers, Soc. d'Éditions, Paris, 222 pp., 1941.

Traité d'océanographie physique, I *Sondages*, 256 pp., 1943, II *L'eau de mer*, 349 pp., 1946, III *Les mouvements de la mer*, 413 pp., Payot, Paris, 1948.

Russell, F. S., and C. M. Yonge. *The Seas*, 379 pp., F. Warne, London, 1944.

Schott, G. *Geographie des Indischen und Stillen Ozeans*, 413 pp., Boysen, Hamburg, 1935.

Geographie des Atlantischen Ozeans, 438 pp., Boysen, Hamburg, 1942.

Schumacher, A. Stereophotogrammetrische Wellenaufnahmen, *Deutsche Atlant. Exp. Meteor, Wiss. Erg.*, Bd. 7, H. 2, L. 1, 156 pp. and Atlas, 1939.

Seiwell, H. R. Results of Research on Surface Waves of the Western North Atlantic, *Pap. Phys. Ocean. Met.*, Mass. Inst. Tech., Woods Hole Ocean. Inst., Vol. 10, 4, 56 pp., 1948.

Shepard, F. P. *Submarine Geology*, 348 pp., Harper, New York, 1948.

Stetson, H. C. *Oceanography*, Geol. Soc. Am., 50th Anniv. Vol., pp. 45–69, 1941.

Strøm, K. M. Land-Locked Waters and the Deposition of Black Muds, in Trask et al., pp. 356–372, 1939.

Sverdrup, H. U. *Oceanography for Meteorologists*, 246 pp., Prentice-Hall, New York, 1942.

Sverdrup, H. U., M. W. Johnson, and R. H. Fleming. *The Oceans, Their Physics, Chemistry, and General Biology*, 1060 pp., Prentice-Hall, New York, 1942.

Sverdrup, H. U., and W. H. Munk. Theoretical and Empirical Relations in Forecasting Breakers and Surf, *Trans. Am. Geophys. Union*, Vol. 27, pp. 828–836, 1946.

Thorade, H. *Ebbe und Flut*, 115 pp., Julius Springer, 1941.

Trask, P. D., et al. *Recent Marine Sediments, A Symposium*, 736 pp., Am. Assoc. Petr. Geol., 1939.

VAUGHAN, T. W. *International Aspects of Oceanography*, 225 pp., Nat. Acad. Sci., Washington, D. C., 1937.

VEEN, J. VAN. *Onderzoekingen in de Hoofden*, 252 pp., Landsdrukkerij, The Hague, 1936.

Verslag Staatscommissie Zuiderzee 1918–1926, 345 pp., Landsdrukkerij, The Hague, 1926.

WORZEL, J. L. Ocean Bottom Sampler for Ships under Way, *Geophysics*, Vol. 13, pp. 452–456, 1948.

The Sea Basins

THE SHAPES OF SEA BASINS

SOUNDINGS AND CONSTRUCTION OF CHARTS

The taking of soundings and the establishment of submarine topography are generally considered to belong to the domain of hydrography. However, as contoured charts of the sea floor are of prime importance to marine geology a short summary on the techniques of sounding and the construction of charts will be given before the geological aspects of submarine topography are considered. For a more comprehensive treatment the reader is referred to Rouch (1943), Shepard (1948), and Bourcart (1949).

Originally soundings were always performed with a rope, even in deep waters. The relatively small strength of rope as compared to its weight, and the considerable friction with the sea water, made it difficult to ascertain the moment at which bottom was touched. Thus in 1858 a depth was recorded in the Banda Sea of 7200 m, at a position where the actual depth was later proved to be only 4400 m.

Sir William Thomson was the first to introduce a wire sounding line, and since then this technique has been universally adopted. Nowadays deep-sea soundings are generally carried out with a wire of about 1-mm diameter, of which the tensile strength is between 150 and 200 kg. At the greatest known depths of over 10,000 m such a wire has sufficient strength, in spite of its weight, to extract a sampler from the bottom and to bring it up together with a water bottle and thermometers.

The greatest drawback to deep-sea sounding by wire is the amount of time consumed, 1 to 2 hours being required for each determination in oceanic depths. Taking into account the cost of running a deep-sea expedition, each sounding works out roughly at fifty dollars.

Although depth determinations by sonic methods (Fig. 56) do not produce a bottom sample, nevertheless, from the topographic point of view they are much to be preferred. The ship does not need to stop, because soundings can be taken on the run. This presents three marked advantages. (1) The saving of much valuable time, so that as many soundings as desired can be taken along the route followed. Most instruments are now capable of giving a continuous record, at least in shallower waters. (2) The absolute position of each sounding is known with greater accuracy when the vessel sails at a constant speed than when it is left to drift for a couple of hours during each sounding, when wind and currents may carry it for an appreciable distance unnoticed. (3) The relative position of two succeeding wire soundings taken out of view of land cannot be ascertained with greater accuracy than 1 km. Even when a difference in depth of 1000 m is recorded, the existence of a slope steeper than 45° cannot be proved. But in echo soundings the intervening distance is known with an error less than a few per cent, even during night or fog. This has rendered possible the detection of almost vertical cliffs, many hundreds of meters high, in oceanic depths far from any coast.

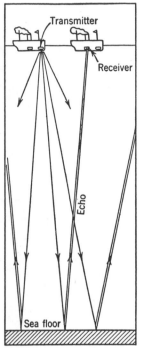

Fig. 56. Diagram showing the principle of echo sounding.

A disadvantage of the sonic method is that the echo is not necessarily returned from a point vertically below the ship. When cruising over a slope the sound rays are reflected from points some distance upslope, where the perpendicular from the ship meets the bottom. The depth found is then too small (Fig. 57). The error can be reduced by drawing circles, taking the successive positions of the ship at the moments of sounding as centers and the depth as radii. The tangent to the circles thus constructed then gives the bottom profile (Fig. 58). Correct values are found only where the sounding line runs directly up or down the slope; otherwise the error is merely reduced, not eliminated, by this graphic method.

Where the bottom is very irregular, or where very steep to vertical drops occur, the echo may be indistinct, or it may fail to return from the deepest point within reach. Hence, narrow gorges, steep scarps, etc., will frequently remain undetected or will show up poorly. Possibly the technical difficulties in using directed high-frequency sound waves will be overcome. The main disadvantages of echo sounding will then have been eliminated.

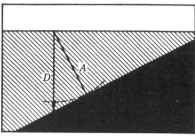

FIG. 57. Diagram showing decrease of apparent depth by echo sounding on sloping floor. *A*, apparent depth; *D*, true depth.

Up to the present the accuracy with which the depth can be ascertained is similar for wire and echo soundings. With wire soundings the wire may be curved below the surface, the measuring wheel may be inaccurate, etc. With echo soundings the time interval cannot be measured with absolute accuracy, and an error of a tenth of a second corresponds to a difference in depth of 75 m. Lack of knowledge about the velocity of propagation of the sound waves at depths is a second source of errors. When no especially adverse conditions, such as rough weather or irregular bottom, prevail, the errors can be reckoned not to exceed some 1 to 2%. Doubtless the sonic method is capable of further improvement, and the errors will probably be reduced to 0.5% or even less.

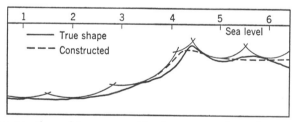

FIG. 58. Construction of bottom profile from successive echo soundings. 1–6 location of soundings.

So far the most accurate method of ascertaining great depths is probably by reversing two deep-sea thermometers at a known distance above the bottom. If one is protected from hydrostatic pressure and the other is not, the difference in temperature readings is a measure of the water pressure. It is said that by this method the errors should not exceed some 10 m, but the technique is much too delicate ever to become of general use.

The foregoing remarks show that not only the units, but even the tens, of the depth figures on a chart, beyond the continental shelves have no real meaning. The reason for not rounding off all deep-sea

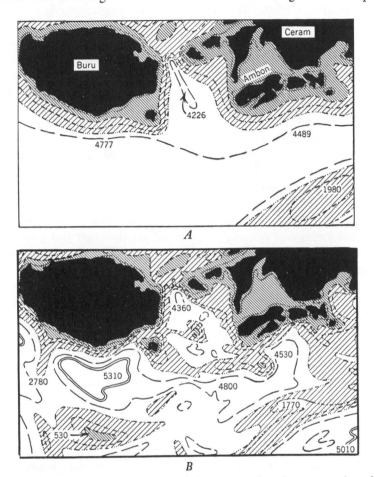

Fig. 59. Example of increase in knowledge concerning the topography of the sea floor by echo sounding between Buru and Ceram. *A*, chart prior to *Snellius* expedition, based on a few deep-sea soundings. *B*, chart based on several hundred echo soundings of the *Snellius* expedition. (After Kuenen, 1941, Fig. 36, p. 155.)

soundings to 50 or 100 m is merely the practical consideration that the finding of a certain sounding on the chart is facilitated by the characteristic last two figures. The deceptive appearance of accuracy must be taken into consideration.

However, the depth is but one aspect of the accuracy of a sounding; the position is almost as important. With a slope of 10°, certainly no abnormal declivity on the sea floor, the depth changes 175 m with a displacement of 1 km. Beyond view of the coast, that is with practically all deep-sea soundings, it is reckoned that an astronomically determined position is accurate only to within 1 km under favorable conditions. As most soundings are taken between two astronomical determinations of position and are then located by dead reckoning, errors of the order of at least 3 km are to be expected, and much larger mistakes are certainly not exceptional. Even with a bottom slope of 1° mistakes of 50 to 100 m and more can result. Over strongly diversified topography discrepancies of 1000 m and more must occur frequently merely in consequence of errors in position.

Naturally methods have been sought to increase the accuracy of position finding at sea. Where bearings or sextant readings on fixed points along the coast can be taken, that is at distances of 10 to 20 km from land, sufficient accuracy is guaranteed. Improvements were therefore required especially farther out on the shelf and beyond the 200-m line. Between the world wars the U. S. Coast and Geodetic Survey worked out an entirely new method, called acoustic range finding, by which it was found possible to obtain fair accuracy to a couple of hundred kilometers from the coast. More recently the electronic methods known as Shoran and Loran have been perfected to a high degree, and gradually they are replacing the former acoustic method.

The use of sonic depth finders has been combined extensively with these modern determinations of position over broad belts along the coasts of the United States. By these means a wealth of data has been procured that stands out as a monumental achievement and has rendered possible the compilation of surprisingly accurate and detailed charts. Only by the great number and unprecedented accuracy of the soundings has it proved feasible to ascertain the shapes of the countless submarine canyons that furrow the continental slopes off North America.

Although only the older methods of reckoning were employed during the *Snellius* expedition in the Moluccan region (1929-1930), the charts constructed by the Dutch Hydrographic Survey for the reports of that expedition rank among the finest deep-sea charts hitherto pro-produced, according to Vaughan (1937).

A geologist has little use for a chart containing merely the recorded depths. Depth curves must be constructed, and the different depth zones should be indicated in color to enhance the legibility. The construction of depth curves cannot be carried out entirely automatically because generally the number of soundings is not sufficient. Bottom

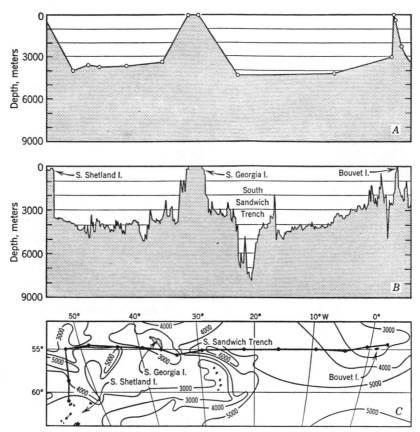

FIG. 60. Bottom topography in the South Atlantic Ocean. *A,* Profile of the bottom between the South Shetland Islands and Bouvet Island based on 13 wire soundings. *B,* Profile over the same course constructed from over 1300 sonic soundings (*Meteor*). *C,* Bottom configuration and the track of the *Meteor.* Vertical exaggeration in *A* and *B* about 200:1. (After Sverdrup et al., 1942, *The Oceans,* Fig. 1, p. 18, Prentice-Hall.)

contours can be given angular or more rounded shapes. Where similar irregularities are encountered in neighboring sounding lines they may be connected to form a single structure more or less at right angles to the direction of these lines. Or one may prefer to draw an isolated knoll or hollow on each line, by which method a hummocky topography is introduced. Thus the sounding sections of the *Meteor* expedition in the southern Atlantic were situated some 700 km apart (Fig. 60). It is obvious that the elevated areas encountered in the central part of each section should be connected to form the Mid-Atlantic Rise. But how far should one go in attempting to connect the separate

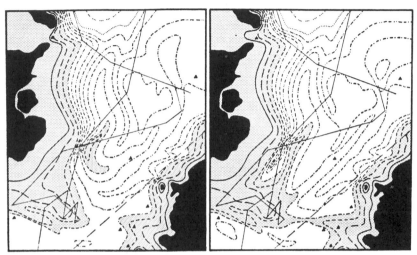

Fig. 61. Alternative construction of depth contours, northern end of Makassar Strait. Thin lines denote echo sounding lines, triangles wire soundings. Contour interval 500 m. Scale approximately 1:3,000,000. (After Kuenen, 1935, Plate I.)

heights and depressions into which this swell is divided along each of the sections? In other words: is the Mid-Atlantic Rise diversified by separate peaks or by lengthwise ridges? A few sections run close together might help to solve this question, but without a complete survey individual features will always remain open to more than one interpretation. Kuenen (1935), by an example from the Moluccas, has shown how two very different interpretations of the topography can be based on the same set of comparatively closely spaced sounding runs (Fig. 61). Veatch and Smith (1939) give similar examples from the eastern continental slope of the United States. Later we will point out how their interpretation of the bathymetrical character in that area is apparently open to serious criticism because they overemphasized the valley pattern when drawing the·depth contours. van Riel showed (1934) how in special cases the temperature recordings in basins may be called upon to show the sill depths and thus to aid in drawing the contours at the entrances of deep-sea depressions.

SUBMARINE TOPOGRAPHY

Various systems for the classification of the oceans and seas have been proposed. Some, as for instance those of Suess, Krümmel, and Andrée, are founded partly on hypotheses concerning the genesis. For a geologist a purely morphological arrangement would be of little value. On the other hand the introduction of hypothetical elements into a classification should be avoided as far as possible. In the following a compromise has been struck. It is unavoidable that all manner of transitions will be found between the various elements of our classification, for nature does not work according to a taxonomic plan. (A discussion of the nomenclature of submarine forms may be found in Publ. Scient. No. 8, Association d'Océanographie Physique, 1940.)

First to be distinguished are the *oceans*—the Pacific, Atlantic, and Indian oceans. The true oceanic basins (that is, in a geological sense) are situated beyond the continental shelves, starting from the 100- or 200-m line. The continental slopes lead down to the deep-sea floor. Certain parts of the major oceans are frequently considered separate units, such as the North Polar Basin, the Antarctic Ocean, and the Norwegian Sea.

Besides the oceans the *adjacent seas* can be distinguished. The water circulating in these smaller units is less uniform in consequence of the influence exerted by the surrounding land masses.

The seas can be divided into *marginal seas* and *inland seas*. The marginal seas are widely open to the oceans. The *shallow marginal seas* or *shelf seas* are situated on the continental shelf and therefore rarely exceed 200 m in depth, except off formerly glaciated coasts. They form thin flanges to the oceanic basins. Examples are the North Sea, Bering Strait, etc. The *deep marginal seas* are separated from the true oceans by submarine ridges with or without islands. Examples are the eastern Asiatic marginal seas.

The inland seas are largely surrounded by land or shallow waters, so that the communication with the open waters is restricted to one or a few straits. Inland seas also show great variations in depth. *Shallow inland seas* or *epeiric seas* with less than 250-m depth as the Baltic, Hudson Bay, Sunda and Sahul shelves (the latter two forming transitions to shelf seas) may be looked upon as flooded continental areas, although it is also possible that sedimentation has filled up deeper depressions.

By far the greater number of fossil sedimentation basins belong to the groups of shallow adjacent and inland seas, for in few cases did geosynclines and basins obtain greater depths and both were formed on continental areas. The temporary deepening of some geosynclines, as for instance the Alpine Trough, clearly shows that this parallel and the classification in general have only a relative value. We will return to these matters in the next chapter.

The *deep inland seas, mediterranean seas*, or *deep-sea basins* show depths from 200 m and more to depths exceeding those of the ocean floor. Generally the floor is from 2000 to 5000 m below sea level. As examples may be cited the Mediterranean, the East and West Indian basins, the Red Sea, and the Black Sea.

All shallow seas, that is all seas covering part of the continental blocks, may be classed together as *epicontinental seas*.

The *deep-sea troughs* or *deep-sea trenches* comprise all deep, oblong depressions either of the ocean floor or between continental areas. A not very sharp distinction can be made between *deep-sea troughs* or *deep-sea trenches* with a V-shaped cross section (in the Moluccan Passage, the East Asiatic deep-sea troughs) and the *deep-sea troughs* or *deep-sea trenches* with a U-shaped cross section (Bartlett Trough south of Cuba, Weber Trough in the Moluccas). Whether the Red Sea should also be classed in this group is doubtful. Some writers distinguish between troughs, showing gentle slopes, and trenches, showing relatively steep ones. *Basins* are larger depressions with a more or less circular or oval form. Small depressions may be termed *pits*, as for instance in Strait Manipa between Buru and Ceram (Fig. 59), and the Romanche Pit in the Mid-Atlantic Rise. The name trench or trough is given to long and narrow, steep-walled depressions without marked lengthwise slope, while *submarine canyons* are valleylike trenches on continental or insular slopes.

The positive forms of the sea floor are classed as *ridges* that are long and narrow, *rises* that are long and broad, and *swells* that are of small relative height. Some are decorated by lesser ridges and hummocks (Mid-Atlantic Rise, Whale Ridge, the ridge south of Java, Carlsberg Ridge, etc.). There are also *plateaus* (Seychelles Plateau, Azores Plateau, Albatros Plateau) and *seamounts* of lesser horizontal extension, the latter generally submarine volcanoes or drowned atolls; *banks* are elevations covered by less than 200 m of water; *shoals* approach the surface and constitute dangers to shipping. *Guyots* are flat-topped, deep-lying seamounts of more or less conical shape.

Mention should also be made of *straits*. The geographical term is used for all narrow passages, but geologists would do better to restrict the term to interruptions in isthmian links or chains of islands. In this restricted sense the passages between the Lesser Sunda Islands or the Japanese Islands, Strait Bab-el-Mandeb, the Straits of Gibraltar, the Dardanelles, and the Bosporus fall under the term of strait. One might also include the Straits of Dover and the openings between the Danish Islands. On the other hand Makassar Strait between Borneo and Celebes is a basin and not a strait in the geological sense.

Other terms frequently met with are *fiord, estuary, bay, lagoon, watt* (*tidal flat*). They need not be discussed here.

The study and description of coasts and shorelines requires a system of classification. Johnson (1919) formerly proposed a system based on the emergence or submergence of the area in question, but Shepard (1948) found that the recent eustatic movements of sea level during the Pleistocene have obscured the features due to emergence or drowning. He therefore proposed an entirely different classification of a double nature. One system is meant to care for the smaller subdivisions of the coasts and shorelines; the other pertains to the larger subdivisions of the coastal region as a whole. The main elements of the first system are as follows:

I. Primary or youthful coasts and shorelines, configuration due primarily to nonmarine agencies.
   A. Shaped by terrestrial erosion and drowned by deglaciation or down-warping. (Drowned river valley coasts; drowned glacial erosion coasts.)
   B. Shaped by terrestrial depositional agencies. (River deposition coasts; glacial deposition coasts; wind deposition coasts; vegetation extending the coast.)
   C. Shaped by volcanic activity. (Coasts with recent lava flows; shorelines due to volcanic collapse or explosions.)
   D. Shaped by diastrophism. (Fault scarp coasts; coasts due to folding.)
II. Secondary or mature coasts and shorelines, configuration primarily the result of marine agencies.
   A. Shorelines shaped by marine erosion. (Sea cliffs straightened by wave erosion; sea cliffs made irregular by wave erosion.)
   B. Coasts and shorelines shaped by marine deposition (straightened by bars, prograded, longshore spits, coral reefs).

The classification of major subdivisions runs thus:

1. Coasts with young mountains.
2. Coasts with old mountains.
3. Coasts with broad coastal plains.
4. Glaciated coasts.

The geomorphology of the coast forms a subject by itself that will not be treated in this volume, but in Chapters 4 and 5 the processes active on the shore will be referred to. Figure 121 shows the terminology of the beach.

Following this classification a few additional remarks may be made on submarine topography.

The areas of greatest depths in the oceans are almost as small in extent as the areas of greatest heights on land. Most of these deeps present elongate troughlike forms of a synclinal nature. The breadth is of the order of 100 to 200 km, and the length may be one to several thousand kilometers. They are not situated centrally in the oceans but are encountered along the borders of the continental masses, generally along the convex side of island arcs.

One of the most typical and best-explored deep-sea troughs is the Aleutian Trench (Murray, 1945) (Figs. 66, 67, and 68). It extends from Yakutat Bay in the Gulf of Alaska westward to Attu Island at the end of the Aleutian Islands. This remarkable trench is over 3500 km long and has a maximum depth of more than 7500 m. The floor lies 400 to 3000 m below the ocean floor to the south. The Aleutian Islands form an almost perfect arc of a circle having a radius of about 1200 km; the length of the arc is about 2300 km. The Trench is less perfectly curved, with an almost straight part in the center. The islands and part of the peninsulas just north of the trough are volcanic. Bowers Bank forms a broad, arcuate mountain range looping off the northern side of the island arc. Evidence as to whether the top of the outer, oceanward face of the trench terminates in a longitudinal ridge is not clear, but there are some topographic highs. In the Gulf of Alaska a number of seamounts occur in rows trending northwestward across the gulf transverse to the arc and trough. The continental and insular slopes average 3–4° but locally exceed 30°. The average outer slope of the south face of the trough is 1–2°, locally ranging to more than 12°.

The area between Japan and New Guinea is now much better known, thanks to a paper by Hess (1948). Figure 62 reveals great diversity in ground plan and size of the trenches, their meeting at right angles in two cases, the presence of single or double ridges on the concave side with or without volcanoes, and the occurrence of swells and ridges not related to troughs.

Whereas the great majority of deep-sea troughs are curved in ground plan, the Kermadec-Tonga Troughs form long, straight furrows to the east of New Zealand and the Fiji Group. Some of the deep-sea troughs are found between island festoons or even outside the true oceanic basins, as for instance in the Moluccas. The Porto Rico Deep is relatively short and broad. The Flores Trough skirts the inner side of the Inner Banda Arc. The great Japan Trench

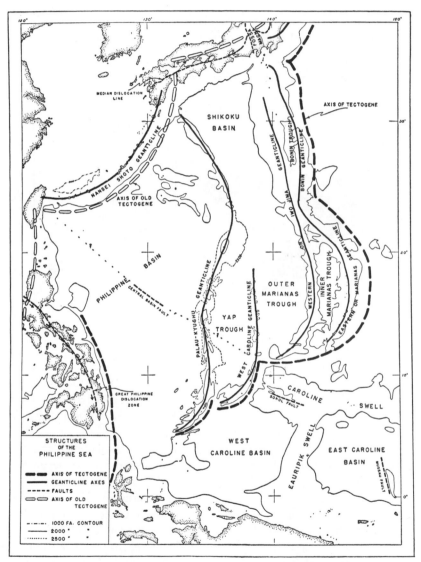

Fig. 62. Morphology of the Pacific between Japan and New Guinea. (After Hess, 1948, *Bull. Geol. Soc. Am.*, Vol. 59, Plate 1.)

forms a concave curve from the Bonin Islands along the northern Japanese Islands as far as the Kurile Islands. The position of the Bougainville Trough is unusual (Fig. 63). It follows the convex side of New Britain, whence it takes a sharp turn from a northeasterly to a southeasterly direction skirting the Salomon Archipelago but not continuing so far.

Kuenen (1935) attempted to classify the deep-sea depressions of the Indonesian Archipelago, principally on the shape of the cross

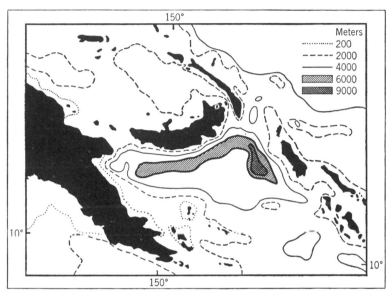

FIG. 63. Sketch map of the Solomon Basin with Bougainville-New Britain Trough.

section and the degree of elongation. The groups established were later found by Umbgrove (1947) to coincide to a remarkable degree with his own subdivision of diastrophic basins on the continents. We will return to this problem in Chapter 3.

Besides the elongate deep-sea troughs, other, broader depressions, more of the nature of basins, are also encountered on the ocean floor. But while the troughs frequently exceed 8000 m in depth, the depressions scarcely exceed 6000 m. In part these basins are found between islands or continental masses; as for instance the Celebes Sea, the Banda Sea, the Gulf of Mexico, the Mediterranean, and the Black Sea. They vary from basins 6000 m deep to insignificant depressions like the Baltic.

It is a remarkable fact that, while many oceanic islands and banks rise steeply from deep waters and show no great extensions in any direction, no corresponding deep hollows appear to occur in the ocean floors. Pits that extend a few thousand meters below the general level of open ocean floors but are restricted in horizontal extension are not known. The possibility that such forms may yet be detected cannot be denied, but the probability is small.

The elevations along the ocean floor generally take the form of oblong ridges. Eminences (seamounts), either of volcanic or of diastrophic nature, may crown these ridges and sometimes appear above the waters as oceanic islands. Most submarine ridges are compara-

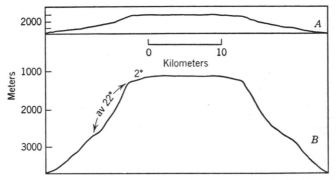

Fig. 64. Typical section of a guyot (8° 51′ N; 163° 10′ E) from fathometer record (adjusted for slope). *A*, natural scale; *B*, vertical scale 5 × horizontal scale. (Redrawn after Hess, 1946, *Am. J. Sci.*, Vol. 244, Fig. 2B, p. 777.)

tively narrow, but the Mid-Atlantic Rise is more than 1000 km broad.

Besides ridges, more plateaulike elevations also occur. These are nearly all situated as eminences on the crest of ridges, from which they rise more or less abruptly. Some of them have complicated shapes, such as the Azores Plateau; others have a rounded outline, as for instance the Seychelles "Bank," Fiji Plateau, and the Toekang Besi Plateau to the southeast of Celebes. A number of plateaus are to be considered extensions of the continental masses, as the Birdwood Bank off Cape Horn, the Bahama Plateau, and the Sokotra Bank. But elevated areas, some of great extent, are also found independently of ridges, as that of Wake Island or the Albatros Plateau to the west of Central America.

Hess has drawn attention to the occurrence of many more or less conical seamounts in the northwestern parts of the Pacific that have a flat horizontal top at depths of 1000 to 2000 m. He calls them *guyots* (Figs. 64 and 65). They have since been encountered also in the northeastern and southwestern Pacific. Perhaps some of the isolated elevations crossed by the *Snellius* expedition in the northwestern Indian Ocean are also guyots (Kuenen, 1935).

As the Antarctic Ocean and extensive areas in the Pacific have so far been very sparingly sounded, important topographic features may still be brought to light there. But Wüst has shown that the bottom temperatures in the Pacific between 50° N and 50° S vary only be-

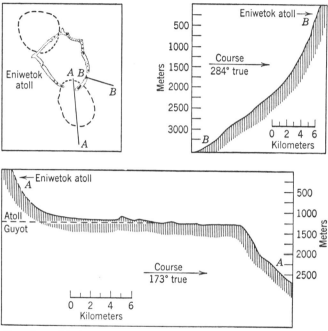

FIG. 65. Situation of Eniwetok atoll on two guyots. (Redrawn after Hess, 1946, *Am. J. Science*, Vol. 244, Figs. 4, 5, and 6, p. 780.)

tween 0.6° and 1.2°, indicating the absence of obstructions to circulation. In this respect the Atlantic Ocean is quite different. In the Brazilian Basin alone the variations amount to 1.6°. Evidently the morphology of the Pacific is simpler.

In marked contrast with the deep sea the margins of the continents and the coastal waters of islands have been intensively sounded for the benefit of navigation. While many oceanic islands and coral reefs plunge steeply into deep water, the larger islands and the continental blocks are skirted by narrow or broad belts of shallow water. These belts are termed the *continental or insular shelves* or *terraces*. Farther out a steeper slope commences, reaching down to the deep-sea floor, called the *continental (insular) slope*. The break in slope at the edge of the shelf generally lies at a depth of about 130 m, but in some places it is less, and it also frequently approaches 200 m. Only exceptionally are depths of a few hundred meters encountered at the edge of the shelf.

The most extensive shelf on earth is that connecting Java, Sumatra, Malacca, and Borneo. It has an area of 2 million km². Other wide shelves are found south of the Bering Strait, north of Siberia, between Australia and New Guinea, to the east of the Argentine, off Korea, and in the North Sea, all of about 1 million km². Apart from coral reefs, drowned river valleys, and glacial troughs the surface of the shelves is generally considered to be a featureless plain. But Shepard has shown that minor irregularities abound. In some cases indications of faults are met with, possibly scalloped by Pleistocene glacial action (Holtedahl, 1940).

The breadth of the shelf varies from less than 1 to more than 1000 km, averaging 70 km. The total length the world over is about 100,000 km. The slope is roughly 1 in 540 (= 7'). In general the shelf is narrow where young mountain chains border the coast, as along the western borders of North and South America (5–15 km off California). The eastern borders of these continental blocks are of more ancient development, and their shelves are broad (for further details see p. 154).

The continental slopes, although better explored than the deep sea, have not been sounded in sufficient detail to permit the construction of accurate charts. How scanty our knowledge of the continental slopes still is was brought out by the detailed surveys off the American coasts mentioned above. Formerly only a few examples of deep, winding gorges cutting down the slope to considerable depths had been detected, for instance off the mouth of the Hudson and the Congo, and off Cape Breton in southern France. No sooner was the random exploration of the continental slopes replaced by a systematic survey than several dozens of these so-called submarine canyons were found both on the east and west coasts. Smaller tributaries join the major incisions, and in some areas the entire slope appears to be furrowed by a system of subparallel trenches. In Chapter 7 the submarine canyons will be discussed in detail.

Off the coast of southern California there exists a region with a complicated submarine structure with several basins and ranges at intermediate depths. The term *continental borderland* has been applied to this type of submarine topography. The adjacent land shows a similar relief.

The average declivity of the continental slope off mountainous coasts exceeds 6% ($= 3\frac{1}{2}°$); off broad lowlands it attains only 3.5% ($= 2°$).

Regional descriptions of the submarine topography may be found in several oceanographical treatises, for instance in Rouch (1943), in *National Research Council Bulletin* 85 (1932), Schott (1935, 1942), Shepard (1948), Bourcart (1949). A survey of the distribution of soundings was given by Vaughan in 1937. See also Mecking (1940).

Some general information concerning the submarine and continental forms of the earth is given in Table 8.

TABLE 8. GENERAL FEATURES OF TERRESTRIAL TOPOGRAPHY

Area of the earth $= 510 \times 10^6$ km²	Average height of land	$= 875$ m
Area of land $= 149 \times 10^6$ km²	Average depth of oceans	$= 3800$ m
Area of oceans $= 361 \times 10^6$ km²	Average level of crust	$= -2430$ m
$\dfrac{\text{Land area}}{\text{Oceanic area}} = \dfrac{1}{2.43}$	Cubic content of oceans	$= 1370 \times 10^6$ km³
	Cubic content of ice	$= 22 \times 10^6$ km³
Highest mountain $= 8800$ m	Cubic content of lakes + rivers	$= 0.13 \times 10^6$ km³

Continental terrace		
Total length of terrace $= \pm 100,000$ km	Average breadth of continental slope	$= 75$ km
Average breadth to break in slope $=$ 70 km	Average slope of continental slope	$= 1:15$
Average depth at break in slope $=$ 130 km	Total length of coastline	$= \pm 400,000$ km
Average slope to break in slope $= 1:540$		

From Tables 8–10 it is seen that the seas cover about three-fourths of the surface of the earth and that the cubic content is equal to a layer $2\frac{1}{2}$ km thick covering the entire earth. Although the average height of the land is $\frac{3}{4}$ km above sea level, the frequency of each successive zone decreases upwards. The lowlands below 200 m, for instance, cover twice the area occupied by land lying between 1000 and 2000 m, although the latter zone is 5 times as high. The area of the sea floor between the coastline and the 200-m depth contour is only half that of the land less than 200 m high. Then follows the continental slope, that is in general much steeper, for the zone from 200 to

TABLE 9. AREA OF LEVELS OF THE SURFACE OF THE CRUST

Land			Sea		
km	10^6 km^2	%	km	10^6 km^2	%
Over 5	0.5	0.1	0–0.2	28.3	5.5
4–5	2.2	0.4	0.2–1	15.4	3.0
3–4	5.8	1.1	1–2	15.2	3.0
2–3	11.2	2.2	2–3	24.4	4.8
1–2	22.6	4.5	3–4	70.8	13.9
0.5–1	28.9	5.7	4–5	119.1	23.3
0.2–0.5	39.9	7.8	5–6	83.7	16.4
0–0.2	37.0	7.3	Below 6	5.0	1.0
Over 0	148.1	29.1	Below 0	361.9	70.9

TABLE 10. AREA AND DEPTH OF THE OCEANS

EXCLUDING ADJACENT SEAS

	Pacific Ocean		Atlantic Ocean		Indian Ocean	
	N of Equator	S of Equator	N of Equator	S of Equator	N of Equator	S of Equator
Area in 10^6 km^2	71	94	37	46	11	63
Average depth	4,750 ↓	3,930	3,790 ↓	4,040	3,310 ↓	4,080
	4,280		3,930		3,960	

INCLUDING ADJACENT SEAS

	Pacific Ocean	Atlantic Ocean	Indian Ocean
Area in 10^6 km^2	180	107	75
Average depth	4,030	3,330	3,900
Greatest depth	10,550	8,750	7,450

1000 m, though having 4 times the range in depth, shows only half the area of the shelf. The depth zone from 3500 m to 5500 m is again more extensive. It is doubtful, however, whether this area is also exceptionally flat, for undulations of the ocean floor between the given margins, if they occur, would not affect the frequency percentage.

A problem worthy of closer examination is whether there exist fundamental differences between the continental and the oceanic topography. Formerly, when insufficient data were available, the deepsea floor was thought to consist of a featureless, slightly undulating expanse. Use of sonic depth finders has shown how far this conception is from actual conditions. It is true that the floors of many wide basins are uniform and level, or slightly depressed towards the center, but numerous ridges and depressions are being discovered as reconnaissance proceeds. The broader rises are generally found to show undulations both lengthwise and in cross section and are in some cases almost as irregular as mountain chains on land. Obviously the sea floor is far from being a monotonous, level plain.

On the other hand there can be no doubt that the blanketing effect of sedimentation and the absence of erosion must tend to retard or even to exclude the development of the finer sculpture characterizing elevated regions of the continental surface. However, processes are at work, or have recently been active, to carve out the huge submarine canyons on the continental slopes, and this system of gorges is unparalleled on dry land.

In another respect conditions under water may possibly tend to encourage the development of forms that are destroyed on land. The absence of weathering and to a large degree of the creep of surface layers on the sea floor should allow bold forms to persist almost indefinitely that would soon crumble away under the influence of atmospheric attack. Anticlinal ridges, fault scarps, and fault blocks may perhaps grow to their full potential height on the sea floor, as denudation does not attack them during gradual development. Our knowledge of the submarine topography is too scanty as yet for asserting to what extent such forms are actually present. But Kuenen (1935), Shepard and Emery (1941), and Dietz (1948) have given instances of possible fault scarps of 1000 m or more. Future investigation will have to show whether all the recorded scarps are real or due to errors in sounding. Parallel ridges and troughs in the Gulf of Aden are interpreted by Cloos (1942) as topographic expressions of a system of fault blocks. In Chapter 7 we will return to the subject of submarine fault scarps, and it will be shown that the continental terrace, at least,

appears to consist of deposits that would be unable to withstand the
stress of gravitational pull on steep slopes of larger dimensions.

It is possible that deep-sea troughs find no counterpart in continental forms. Probably, however, continental geosynclines differ only

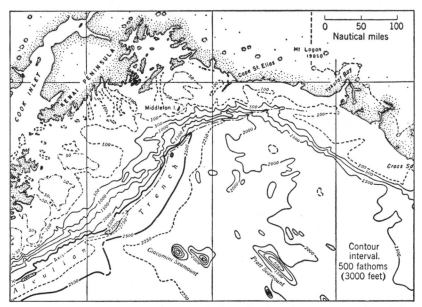

Fig. 66.   Chart of the eastern end of the Aleutian deep-sea trough.   (After
Murray, 1945, *Bull. Geol. Soc. Am.*, Vol. 56, Plate 3.)

in having been kept brimful with sedimentary deposits during the
gradual basining process, whereas the deep-sea troughs received insufficient sediments to compensate for their sinking movement. The

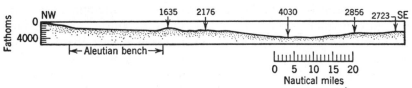

Fig. 67.   Natural scale section of the Aleutian Trough.   (After Murray, 1945,
Bull. Geol. Soc. Am., Vol. 56, Fig. 11, p. 777.)

difference between the two forms would then be due merely to external conditions. This view is substantiated by the relations of the
Aleutian Trough. The accompanying island arc continues uninter-

rupted in the North American Continent, and the trench itself passes upwards at its eastern end onto the shelf towards the mouth of Yakutat Bay (see Figs. 66, 67, and 68).

As far as present knowledge goes, therefore, the continental and deep-sea surfaces show no structural differences of a fundamental nature. All actual divergences may be attributed to differences in

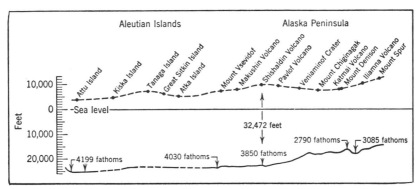

Fig. 68. Generalized lengthwise profile of the Aleutian Trough and the adjacent mountain arc. (After Murray, 1945, *Bull. Geol. Soc. Am.*, Vol. 56, Fig. 12, p. 777.)

external influences, such as weathering, transport, erosion, and sedimentation, while some apparent contrasts may be due to insufficient knowledge of the submarine morphology.

THE EVOLUTION OF SEA BASINS

CHARTING OF THE ROCKY SEA FLOOR

Theoretically the evolution of a sea basin could be elucidated by examining the geological structure of the rocky substratum. This line of approach is barred, however, because few attempts have been made to construct geological maps of the rock formations cropping out in regions of non-deposition. One reason is that there are not many areas of any extent where the solid rock is not overlain by recent sediments. The main reason, however, lies in the difficulty of obtaining samples. Two notable exceptions may be cited. Dangeard (1929) succeeded in constructing a map of the British Channel, where Cretaceous rocks are extensively exposed. Recently King (1948) has improved on this first effort, by drawing in boundary lines and by showing the presence of Triassic to the south of the Isle of Wight (see also Tesch and Reinhold, 1946). The sea floor of the continental borderland off southern California has been sampled by dredging and the results have been described by Emery and Shepard (1945). They found that the rocky substratum is exposed on the banks and canyon walls and consists of the same types of rock as are found on the islands and mainland. Besides metamorphic and igneous rocks, doubtful Triassic-Jurassic and Cretaceous, Eocene, Miocene, and Pliocene sediments were encountered. Many samples were evidently derived from actual outcrops, and most of the others cannot have been transported from far off. The features suggesting sampling at or near rock outcrops are fresh fractures, large size, abundant rocks of similar lithology, angularity, fragile rock, and catching of the dredge.

ALTERATIONS IN THE SHAPE AND SIZE OF SEA BASINS

The sea basins situated on continental blocks may be newly formed or extended by rising of sea level, by sinking of the crust, or by the erosive action of waves and currents on the coast. The last process is termed "marine erosion" (or "abrasion" by some authors). In the first case the depths will never exceed 100 or 200 m, because that appears to be about the limit of eustatic swings of sea level (see Chapter 8). For example, sea level is generally believed to have sunk about 140 m below the preglacial stand (that is 100 m below the present position) during the maximum extension of the Pleistocene land ice masses. When the formation of land ice did not intervene, eustatic movements of a slower type were going on almost continuously. But the range appears to have been restricted to a few dozen meters, so that only shallow seas can have been formed in consequence of such movements.

When, on the other hand, the cause is to be sought in sinking of the continental surface, greater depths can have been developed. As far as has been ascertained all geosynclines have been formed on continental blocks and must therefore be ascribed to depression of the bottom. The majority of these basins were continuously filled by sediments nearly up to sea level, as is evidenced by the frequent occurrence of shallow-water organisms, false bedding, ripple marks formed by waves, sun cracks, etc. Consequently the depths of water seldom exceeded a few to several dozens of meters. But in a few basins the subsidence appears to have prevailed for a length of time over the sedimentation. This may be demonstrated either by the presence of large-scale slumps (the Lower Paleozoic geosyncline of Wales) or by the intercallation of bathyal sediments (200- to 1000-m depth) between the earlier and subsequent neritic deposits (less than 200-m depth). A typical example is furnished by the Alpine geosyncline in Mesozoic times. It is doubtful, however, whether true abyssal sediments (more than 1000-m depth) have been formed as maintained by Haug, Steinmann, and others. It should be borne in mind that proof is extremely difficult that a sediment, deposited at great distances from the coast, has also been laid down in water of depths surpassing several hundreds of meters. Before the advent of planktonic Foraminifera in the Cretaceous, practically all deposits forming far from the coast in depths exceeding 200 m were probably poor in lime. Hence a low percentage of calcium carbonate is no argument in favor of abyssal depths of pre-Cretaceous deposits (see Chapters 3 and 5).

Theoretically a study of the regional stratigraphy should show whether there had been an episode of deep water. If, for example, the sea remained shallow, bottom sediments would be distributed across the whole basin (as they were certainly throughout the history of the Appalachian geosyncline). On the contrary, if deep water had existed, terrigenous sediments would come to rest near shore and deposits would be built out from the coast (as they are now into the Gulf of Mexico). The deep part would then form a barrier to the spread of detrital sediments. Such barriers appear to have been rare in geosynclines, a strong indication of small depths throughout their history.

For less elongate or more irregularly shaped basins that have been formed by transgression and that have not subsequently undergone intensive orogenic activity, the rule that they remained filled to near or even above sea level by sedimentation applies in even stronger measure.

Erosion of the coast by waves and currents may also cause the extension of a sea basin over former land areas. In general the displacement of the coasts by this mechanism remains relatively unimportant if a rise of sea level does not come to the aid of the erosive force of the waves. The farther erosion cuts into the land and broadens the shallow area fronting the shore, the more the energy of the waves is wasted before reaching the land. Hence, the waves can exert less power in destroying the coast and the products have to be transported further away to deeper water before coming to rest. Before major paleogeographical alterations have been brought about by this means, eustatic or orogenic influences will have interfered and outweighed the action of marine erosion. Yet during the entire geological past the seas have gnawed at almost all coasts and the sum total of this activity must have been enormous.

We can attempt to estimate the minimum land area eroded by the seas in the geological past. The total length of all receding coasts may be taken as 200,000 km [1] and the average rate of coastal erosion at 1 m per 1000 years (an arbitrary but conservative figure). The yearly amount of erosion then works out at $\frac{1}{5}$ km^2 per year. During the total length of the geological past this very low estimate would attain no less than 3 times the present area of all land above sea level. The true amount, however, is probably several times as much. Although this shows that erosion is an important geological factor, the extent of physiographic alteration due to other processes is vastly greater. Denudation, for instance, is estimated to result in the transport of at least 10 times as much material to the coast as is cut away by marine erosion (see p. 234).

The disappearance of epicontinental seas can again be caused by eustatic movements or by deformations of the crust and by the deposition of sediment.

Epirogenic doming and eustatic sinking of sea level frequently result in impressive alterations in shape of large shallow seas or even lead to their entire extinction without the intervention of important sedimentation. This follows from cases in which depth has varied much more than the thickness of the sedimentary deposits. For example, the Cretaceous sea covering southeastern Holland varied in depths from a few hundred meters to zero during the deposition of a few dozen meters of sediment. Also, swift, worldwide regressions can be accounted for only by eustatic movements that result in the retraction of epicontinental seas which formerly covered large portions of the continents.

It might be thought that sedimentation must be the most active cause in the obliteration of basins because deposition is going on over most of the sea floor, especially of inland seas. However, stratigraphy has brought to light comparatively few examples in which sedimentation appears to have reclaimed extensive epicontinental non-geosynclinal seas without the aid of earth movements. The thickness of the sediments should then exceed the depth of the basin in which they were laid down, and the marine deposits should grade upwards into terrestrial deposits.

[1] Total length of coasts according to Kossina, about 400,000 km.

To understand why sedimentation has not often succeeded in filling shallow basins, it should not be overlooked that waves and currents tend to scatter the incoming sedimentary matter and to carry it to deeper depressions and especially to the wide ocean basins. This loss of material to the oceans must strongly counteract the infilling of basins by sediment. Barrell pointed out that the closer the bottom approaches to sea level the stronger this dissipation of sediment will generally be, and the more slowly will shoaling proceed.

One could object that waves are reduced by shoaling of the bottom and hence that the shallower a basin becomes the less sediment will be carried away. However, a bottom lying beyond the reach of wave turbulence will collect practically all sediment. Shoaling will eventually allow waves to churn up particles. These are partly carried away even by slow currents, and loss will increase with further elevation. Whether a maximum is finally reached and still further shoaling will result in a new increase in sedimentation the present writer is not able to say. Local conditions as to exposure, tidal influence, etc., will doubtless be of importance. In any event there must have been many instances in which the supply of sedimentary matter was insufficient to reduce depth beyond optimum conditions for transport and loss. Deposition would then finally cease until subsidence was renewed. This applies more especially to shallow marginal seas, much less to inland seas.

But instances are by no means lacking in which sedimentation has indeed succeeded in converting sea into land. Examples are met with in which the destructive forces appear to have been outweighed by the supply of sedimentary material. Extensive fossil delta deposits are known, and it follows that, here, sedimentation has led to natural reclaiming of marine areas.

There even occur cases in which continued subsidence has been outweighed by sedimentation. In many geosynclines the juxtaposition of rising land close to the subsiding area has resulted in a vast supply of detritus. Thus foredeeps of major geosynclines, such as the Alpine or Himalayan troughs, finally ended by being entirely changed to dry land owing to the dumping of huge quantities of coarse sediment eroded from the rising mountain chain itself. The troughs now containing coal fields were maintained above sea level by sedimentation, except for short marine ingressions while the floor gradually subsided. The Cretaceous sea of the Rocky Mountain geosyncline apparently disappeared largely by silting up, for hundreds of meters of non-marine formations accumulated over a large area after the sea was gone.

It need hardly be emphasized, in conclusion, that sedimentation influences the ultimate size of a basin even if no dry land is formed at the time, for, if shoaling by sedimentation has gone before, this must lead to more extensive regressions when elevation or eustatic sinking takes place later than if no deposition had preceded.

CONSTITUTION OF THE CONTINENTS AND OCEAN FLOORS

The formation of the ocean basins is a subject on which practically no direct evidence is obtainable and speculation finds little sure ground to go on.

This problem concerns the major features in the earth's morphology, and one can hardly expect a satisfactory answer in view of the scantiness of our present knowledge of geophysical phenomena. One need but refer to the processes of orogenesis on which a far greater number of data have already been obtained, and to note the absolute lack of unity in views not only on the ultimate causes but even on the mechanics of rock deformation, to realize how far we must still be removed from a satisfactory explanation of the development of oceans and continents. The gravity field of the oceanic basins forms a basic set of data, but as yet only a few widely scattered preliminary determinations have been carried out along a small number of sections crossing the oceans. The experimental investigation of the properties of rock under high pressure at elevated temperatures is still in its infancy. The occurrence of deep-focus earthquakes has become known only recently. Data on these phenomena are indispensable foundations on which to build a theory explaining the development of the major features of the earth's crust. Must not many additional keystones be added to our knowledge before construction can be started in earnest? In the meantime only rough working hypotheses can be formulated and no definite results can be expected.

It is not the place here to give a detailed exposition of all hypotheses on the formation of the oceanic basins that have already been brought forward. Almost the entire field of geology and geophysics would be involved. A short review of a few more important aspects, which will show how far we are still removed from a definite solution, must suffice. The reader is referred to Gutenberg (1930 and 1939), Umbgrove (1947), Bucher (1933), and Daly (1942) for fuller treatments of the views held on the formation of continents and oceanic basins.

Geologists and geophysicists have long pondered the question why the surface of the earth is divided into low-lying ocean floors and high-standing continental masses. Direct observation on the latter is limited to small depths, and the substratum of the deep-sea floor below the covering of recent sediment cannot be sampled at all, except on bare seamounts, which may be quite foreign to their surroundings. Hence inferences on the composition must be drawn from indirect

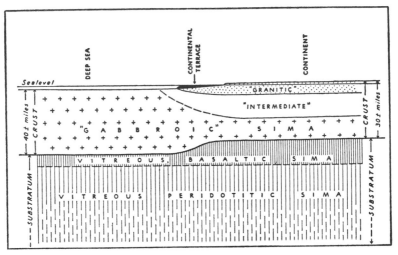

Fig. 69. Diagrammatic section illustrating inferred character of the earth's outer shells according to Daly, 1942, *The Floor of the Ocean,* University of North Carolina Press, Fig. 30, p. 59.

sources of evidence. Luckily there are several geological and geophysical methods of investigation that give valuable indications in this problem. These have led to several working hypotheses. One that has found widespread favor is shown diagrammatically in Fig. 69.

There is a world-encircling layer of basaltic material called *sima*. The lower part of this layer is too hot to crystallize, and according to Daly it is in a glassy state with a density of 2.8 on account of the high hydrostatic pressure. Below, the sima passes into more basic materials believed to consist of peridotitic glass. Together these plastic layers are termed the substratum. The solid *crust* is roughly 40-50 km thick. In oceanic sections it consists throughout of basalt (density 3.0), but in continental areas there is a passage upwards to lighter rocks, called *sial*. The sialic rocks are of the nature of granite (density 2.7) and granodiorite (density 2.8) above an intermediate layer of "diorite" (density 2.9). The elevated position of the continents is ascribed to the buoyancy of the sial.

This model of the outer shells of the earth is founded chiefly on petrographic, gravimetric, and seismic evidence.

Petrographic investigations in deeply denuded regions of the continents have shown the dominant rocks underlying the thin veneer of sediments to consist of granitic material (granite and granodiorite). These are the lighter types of igneous rock. Volcanoes on land have extruded mainly basalt, though more acid types, such as andesite and rhyolite have also been emitted in large volume. The volcanic islands in the Pacific, on the other hand, have delivered only basalt and minute quantities of special types of acid rock such as trachyte.

These findings can be explained by assuming a continuous layer of basaltic magma (the substratum) which is available to force its way to the surface as soon as opportunity presents itself. While passing upwards through the basaltic ocean floor it undergoes no alterations, but in the continental areas contamination with granitic materials may take place and acid lavas will result. The complex question of the nature of this contamination and differentiation need not concern us here.

Not all oceanic volcanoes belong to the basaltic Pacific type. A line may be drawn in the Pacific (Fig. 70) that divides the truly basaltic central area from peripheral regions with more acid rocks. It runs from Alaska via Japan, the Marianas, Palau Islands, Bismarck Archipelago, and the Fiji and Tonga Groups to the east of New Zealand and Chathem Island. Some doubt exists about the position of the line along the eastern side of the ocean, but probably it should be drawn along the coasts of North and South America. In the south it has not yet been traced. It is generally referred to as the "andesite line," because landward of this boundary more acid lavas, especially andesites, are among the main extrusives. Even rhyolite and granitic inclusions are common among lavas of this area. Granitic and other continental rocks are encountered on some islands (Hobbs, 1944; Hess, 1948). The same holds for the islands on the Mid-Atlantic Rise (Ascension, etc.) and on the ridges in the western part of the Indian Ocean (Kerguelen Islands, Seychelles, etc.). Hess (1948) suggested drawing the andesite line on the outer, convex side of the arcuate trenches, because this permits it to be a valid structural as well as petrographic boundary.

Some authors prefer a "sial line" drawn slightly on the oceanic side to include some non-volcanic islands with sialic igneous rocks.

It is further found that while the Pacific type of volcano appears to rise directly from the ocean floor or from narrow, straight ridges, the andesitic type is founded on arcuate ridges assumed to be of non-volcanic nature on account of their structure and their great size. This leads to the conclusion that masses of continental rock underlie the andesitic type of volcano.

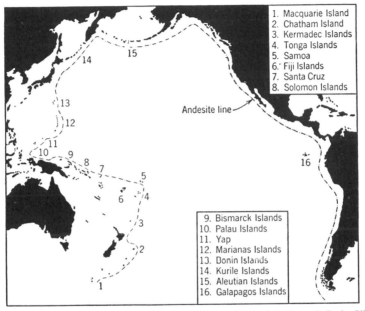

1. Macquarie Island
2. Chatham Island
3. Kermadec Islands
4. Tonga Islands
5. Samoa
6. Fiji Islands
7. Santa Cruz
8. Solomon Islands

Andesite line

9. Bismarck Islands
10. Palau Islands
11. Yap
12. Marianas Islands
13. Donin Islands
14. Kurile Islands
15. Aleutian Islands
16. Galapagos Islands

FIG. 70. The andesite line, mainly according to Hess (1948) and Smit Sibinga (1943).

The gravimetric evidence shows the crust to be roughly in isostatic balance. This means that columns of equal area down through the crust to the plastic substratum at about 30- to 50-km depth are of equal weight. The ocean waters represent a deficiency in mass, as compared to the continents above the level of the sea floor, which must be compensated at depths by greater density of the ocean bed. As the continents consist of the lighter types of rock and as voids are excluded at depths of a few kilometers, the isostatic equilibrium of the crust requires a considerable thickness of granitic sial in the continents and a rock of greater density in the oceanic sections. This requirement is met by the assumed basaltic sima of the ocean floor.

Matters are complicated by the fact that the floor of the oceans is not a horizontal surface. Inspection of a chart showing the depths discloses a number of major basins with comparatively uniform floors, all lying at depths of 5000 to 6000 m. These are separated from each other by ridges and island festoons and submarine plateaus that are isostatically in equilibrium. Hence these elevations must constitute narrow strips of lighter rock, and on the evidence of the emergent volcanoes and islands it may be assumed that they consist of normal sial somewhat thinner than that of the continents. By far the largest of these true oceanic basins is the great North Pacific Ocean. The eastern and western Indian Ocean, the center of the southern Pacific, the basins at both sides of the Mid-Atlantic Rise, the Antarctic Basins, and the center of the North Polar Basin all belong in this category. The somewhat shallower basins west of the andesite line, the Pacific east of the 120th western meridian, the Atlantic north of 45°, and other areas of less than 4000-m depth require a lower density of their floors. A thin cover of sial would meet this requirement. An exception must be made for the Philippine Basin. Although of great extent and situated well on the continental side of the andesite line, the floor has a greater average depth than any other large basin on earth. Some difficulty arises over the great swell in the southeastern Pacific, for although it is a broad rise and should have a sialic foundation the few crowning islands show the Pacific type of lava in almost pure form (Smit Sibinga, 1943). Other minor misfits occur, where the andesite line should be drawn on the landward side of areas that require a thin cover of sialic masses on account of small depths.

Many authors have postulated absence of sial in the Pacific seawards of the andesite line and a thin stratum over the remainder of the ocean floors (cf. Umbgrove, 1947). They generally base this conclusion partly on the greater average depths of the Pacific. This reasoning is not sound. It would hold only if the floor of the areas compared were flat. But the smaller average depth of the "shallower" oceans is due to the scarcity of deep-sea troughs and the presence of ridges and gently sloping continental margins (Figs. 71 and 72). The basins, however, are of roughly the same depth in all oceans as far as the contouring at 1000-m intervals can show. They all dip below the 6000-m line in restricted areas. *When only the topographic forms are used* the logical conclusion is that all the deeper basins are floored by sima, while the oceans with smaller average depth are also simatic but are surrounded and divided by areas with a sial cover of variable thickness. Umbgrove presents other reasons besides average depths for assuming sial below the deep Atlantic basins. These will be dealt with presently.

The gravity profiles across the continental margins led Vening Meinesz to assume a fairly abrupt ending of the sial layer. He is inclined to favor a continuation of the intermediate layer across all oceans. The isostatic balance of oceanic ridges in areas where absence of sial is assumed might be explained by a greater thickness of the intermediate layer along the ridges. An alternative is that the substratum shows a greater density than the sima crust, and that the latter thickens below the simatic ridges.

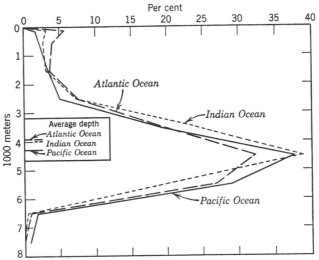

FIG. 71. Percentage of area of depth zones (in thousands of meters) in the three oceans, excluding adjacent seas. *Inset:* average depth of the three oceans. Note that the greater average depth of the Pacific is due mainly to low percentage of small depths and high percentage of abnormal depths.

Turning to the seismological evidence, it is found that the main features of the suggested working model are again confirmed. The velocity of propagation of an earthquake wave increases with the density of the propagating medium. Generally speaking, travel times across oceans are found to be shorter than across equal distances of the continents. Hence the greater density of the ocean floor is confirmed.

On theoretical grounds it has been shown (e.g., by Gutenberg and Richter, 1935) that an earthquake wave of the longitudinal type coming from below and reflected against the surface of the earth must lose a greater percentage of its energy when the reflection takes place in an area with a homogeneous layer (Pacific type) than when a continental layer with lower velocity of propagation (continental type) overlies the substratum.   Refraction in the latter case causes the direction of propagation to approach nearer to the vertical.   On reflection at the surface less energy is then dissipated in other wave types.

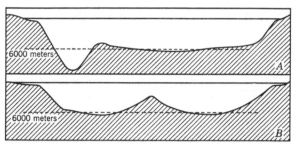

FIG. 72.   Diagrammatic sections of oceans.   A, Northern Pacific with great average depths; B, Atlantic with lesser average depth.

By comparison of the energy displayed in recordings from a single earthquake at different stations it can be shown in which cases reflection between hypocenter and station must have taken place in an area with a sial layer and in which a Pacific type of crust was met (Fig. 73).

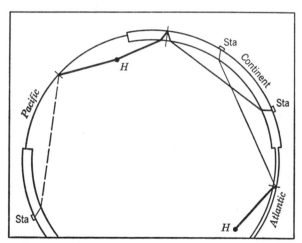

FIG. 73.   Loss of energy of longitudinal earthquake waves on reflection in various parts of the earth's crust.   H = hypocenter.

In applying this principle it was found by the authors mentioned that the Pacific type of reflection is restricted to the Pacific Ocean within the andesite line and to the Arctic basin.   Over the entire remainder of the earth, they conclude, a sial layer at least 10 km thick must exist. It is curious that the Arctic Basin is found to be decidedly of Pacific character, because, except for a small eccentric deep, it is one of the shallower major basins.

According to others (Wilson, 1940), the evidence does not necessitate the assumption of a granitic layer below the deeper basins of the Atlantic and Indian oceans.

The surface waves (Love and Raleigh waves) can also give evidence concerning the nature of crustal layers (Hiller, Byerly, e.g.). The greater the wavelength, the deeper in the crust the disturbance by waves must reach. The velocity of propagation is in accordance with the average rate for the whole layer disturbed. A short wave must therefore show the velocity belonging to the superficial layers, a long wave the average of a much thicker stratum. The observed periods vary between 10 and 50 seconds with velocities of 3 to 4½ km per second. In the Pacific area and probably also the Arctic Basin the velocity is found to increase but slightly with lengthening period of the waves, which is in close accordance with the moderate increase in density downwards in a homogeneous layer of sima. The continents, on the other hand, show much lower values for short-period waves (only the sial is disturbed). As granite shows lower rates of propagation than basalt the seismological evidence favors the picture of granitic continents versus basaltic ocean floors. The velocity increases with the period (when the underlying sima of the continents is also involved in the disturbance), finally approaching the Pacific values (Fig. 74). The remaining oceans hold an intermediate place, but velocities are closer to those of the Pacific. Here again we meet with several misfits. The deep Philippine Basin shows continental structure, and the same applies to the rather deep area east of Easter Island Plateau. On the other hand, Pacific structure is encountered in the comparatively shallow basin west of the Galapagos Islands.

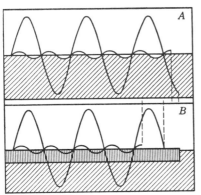

FIG. 74. Propagation of surface earthquake waves in Pacific (A) and continental (B) areas.

These findings might be explained by a uniform thin layer of sial in the Atlantic and Indian oceans, but a discontinuous layer of somewhat greater average thickness would also account for the travel times of surface waves. Some seismologists, however, favor yet another arrangement, already mentioned, in which the intermediate layer of the continents is continued below these oceans.

Conclusions by different seismologists as to the thickness of continental layers on the evidence of seismic data diverge strongly. Evidently the magnitude varies from place to place. But the disagreement is principally due to inaccuracies of recording and differences in the interpretation of seismograms. It has been pointed out above that geologists are no less divided in their opinion on the layers of the crust. The granitic layer is generally held to be 10 to 20 km thick, and the intermediate layer also to be 10 to 20 km. As stated earlier, only the upper part of the basaltic layer is supposed to be crystalline and to belong to the solid crust. At a depth of 50 to 60 km indications are found of a slight decrease in the velocity of propagation of seismic waves. This probably represents the passage from crystalline to amorphous material.

At the junction between Pacific and continental areas a strong absorption of short surface waves takes place, which is evidently due to the alteration of material as the wave passes from the sima of the ocean floor to the sial of the continent. Longer waves reach down below this boundary and are scarcely affected. From this Gutenberg deduced that the sial boundary reaches to a depth of 40 to 50 km but no deeper. At the boundaries of the Atlantic and Indian oceans no absorption is detected. Hence no indication is found of a change in materials. This again confirms the assumption that there is a layer of sial along the edges of these shallower oceans ending more gradually towards the deeper basins than on the steep Pacific margins.

Our model of the earth's outer shells has stood the various tests applied reasonably well. But there is still ample room for divergence of opinion as to details, and we may even be on an entirely wrong track. It cannot be overemphasized that when inferring the nature of subsurface layers from petrological investigation of volcanic products, and when expressing the results of gravimetric and seismic methods in terms of sial and sima, and when applying the principle of isostasy to the topography of the crust, we are dealing merely with deductions. Actual proof is still far beyond our grasp.

THE PROBLEM OF PERMANENCY

The problem of permanency poses the question whether the ocean basins and continental blocks have always shown the same dimensions and shapes as nowadays. Strongly divergent notions on these matters have been expounded by a number of authors.

An extreme opinion was expressed by Walther, who argued that the absence of ancient forms of life among the inhabitants of the deep sea shows that this environment was not developed until after the close of the Paleozoic era. He refrained from commenting on the nature of the processes by which the deep sea was formed so late in

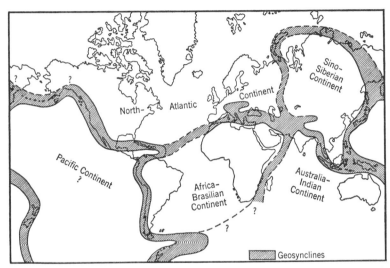

FIG. 75. Continents (partly flooded by shallow seas) and geosynclines of the Mesozoic according to Haug, Armand Colin, 1907, Fig. 37, p. 162.

geological history. Apart from the uncertainty of the postulate, there are several possible explanations for the supposed youth of the deep-sea fauna. For instance, it might be suggested that during periods of equable climate over the entire earth the deep-sea circulation was insufficient to ventilate the deep waters, normal life thus being excluded (Kuenen, 1937). After the establishment of climatic contrasts circulation set in again and the deep sea was then invaded by an entirely new population of recent forms. Another explanation is that in this exceptional environment of the deep sea conservative organisms could not survive and were superseded by new, more highly organized forms.

Along entirely different lines a number of paleogeographers as Suess and Haug (Fig. 75) arrived at practically the same conclusion as Walther. These authors postulated enormous continental masses in almost all oceanic areas up to comparatively recent times. It is true that some basins are allowed for between the reconstructed continents, but on the other hand part of the subsidence was supposed to have taken place even later than the early Mesozoic. Thus in some respects these authors are more, in others less, extreme in their views than Walther.

A more moderate conception is held by those who assign a youthful development only to the Atlantic and Indian oceans, but who consider the Pacific to represent an ancient and permanent feature of the earth's crust (Daly, 1939; Gutenberg and Richter, 1935; Fourmarier, 1940; Stille, 1944; Fairbridge, 1948; and many others). The chief evidence on which this view is founded is of a biogeographic and paleogeographic nature and tends to show that the "younger" oceans were formerly occupied by continental masses allowing of plant and animal migration. The Gondwana Continent included South America, Africa, India, Australia, and Antarctica, but more than half of its former extent is now changed to deep-sea floors. The Atlantic Continent linked North America with Greenland and Europe. In this scheme the so-called sialic oceans are supposed to be of post-Paleozoic age.

A step further in the direction of permanency is the position taken by those who assume that the disappeared connections were not of a continental nature, but "isthmian links" and island festoons. Only relatively small and probably temporary elevations need then be assumed to have sunk away to oceanic depths (Schuchert, 1932; Willis, 1932; Umbgrove, 1947).

Taylor, Wegener, Du Toit, and other exponents of the theory of continental drift are adherents to a certain form of permanency because they leave the area and cubic content of the oceans unaltered, but the shapes and positions are thought to have changed drastically during the sliding of continental blocks.

The most extreme opinion regarding permanency is to consider the oceanic basins as primitive features of the earth's crust, dating from the early pre-Cambrian, since when they have changed neither in place nor extent; the existence of land bridges across the deep sea is also denied under this hypothesis. Paleobiographical similarities are explained by parallel evolution and by migration over long distances. This view is held by some geophysicists, who deny the possibility of the conversion of sialic blocks to simatic ocean floor.

Arguments have been brought forward to throw light on this highly controversial problem. In the first place it has been frequently emphasized that no fossil deep-sea deposits have ever been found on true continental blocks. Only a few small exposures have been discovered on islands in the West and East Indies, and even of these the true deep-sea nature has been questioned. (For references concerning Barbados see Senn, 1947; for the East Indies see the next chapter.)

It is stated that, if oceanic floors are never elevated to form part of the continental masses, the opposite process, the subsidence of sialic areas to oceanic depths, cannot then be reasonably assumed. One important argument can be opposed to permanence, namely, the strong evidence for subsidence of marginal belts bordering many continental masses. In constructing paleogeographic maps the necessity is frequently encountered of assuming former regions of denudation outside the present limits of the continental blocks. This applies to certain geosynclines that run parallel and close to the border of the present continental area. On examination of the distribution of thicknesses in these troughs and the arrangement of grain sizes in each stratum it is found that the origin of detrital matter is to be sought on the oceanic side. Some examples are Scandia (pre-Caledonian) to the west of Scotland and Spitzbergen, Appalachia (pre-Variscan) east of the United States, and Cascadia (pre-Mesozoic) to the west. Here one is confronted with pertinent evidence of the former existence of high land where oceanic depths now prevail. The theory of Wegener would have it that the former denudation areas are to be sought either at the opposite side of the present oceans, before these were opened by drifting, or in the drawn-out masses now forming the continental slopes and midoceanic rises. But this argument fails entirely in respect to Cascadia, as this mass was situated in the Pacific, an ocean that is also permanent in the view of Wegener.

So far, therefore, no alternative explanation can be offered to the subsidence of large borderlands along many Pacific and Atlantic coasts during different phases of crustal evolution.

It is not the place here to treat the almost endless series of arguments that have been brought forward in the controversy around continental drift. Only the aspects that stand in close relation to our general subject can be reviewed.

An important argument that has not been formulated before, as far as the writer is aware, is as follows. Orogenesis, and the development of mountain chains, takes place, according to Wegener, where two continents float against each other or along the broad front of a drifting block. But if there is one well-established rule in geology, it is that an orogenic revolution is preceded by a much more prolonged period of gradual geosynclinal subsidence. Why, one may ask, should a very long-lived downwarping of the crust take place in a belt that is predestined to be compressed in a few quick convulsions when the continental sliding finally sets in? Must alternate stretching be assumed, in the manner Bucher (1933) formerly suggested and that is implied by the geosynclinal stages of the pre-Carboniferous intercontinental orogenic belts of the Pangea continent? Or do long periods of slight movement cause geosynclines, while more energetic sliding in the same direction brings matters to a head, causing compression and elevation? Neither of these possibilities appears to conform with the postulates of the Taylor-Wegener conceptions.

Turning to another aspect, it can be pointed out that the gravity investigation of oceanic volcanic islands shows how these heavy masses are not compensated by light roots. The crust appears to bend elastically beneath the superimposed weight but does not react plastically (Vening Meinesz, 1941). The velocity of propagation of seismic waves across the Pacific floor further shows the great rigidity down to several dozens of kilometers in the suboceanic crust. Both observations strongly militate against Wegener's conception of the plastic nature of the sima along the Pacific floor.

If America were plowing through the sima westwards, as Wegener supposed, one would expect a raising of the sima in front of the continent, or at least that the thick cover of deep-sea sediment on top of the sima had been crowded together like scum floating in front of a blunt-nosed ship (see p. 399). Instead we find a trough along the South American coast and normal depths fronting North America. Bucher (1933, p. 72) further points to an illogical postulate of Wegener: "The less plastic mass of the continent is pictured as thrown into folds by the 'resistance' of the more plastic substratum [plasticity as postulated by Wegener, Ph.H.K]. We shall be willing to entertain such seemingly illogical ideas only if the theory of drift as a whole proves to be a real key to the understanding of the continental structure as a whole."

A lower temperature and a higher melting point for sima than for sial are unavoidable conclusions from the data we possess on the nature of the sea floor and continental masses. Granite crystallizes at lower temperatures than basalt, and it is more strongly radioactive. At the same level as the ocean floor a temperature of nearly 200° C must prevail in the continental masses. Hence, if forces exist tending to shift the continents with respect to the ocean bed the consequence should be that they give way and buckle while the ocean floor remains fixed and undisturbed. The assertion by Wegener that sima of the ocean floor reacts to stress in the manner of sealing wax and will flow under moderate pressure is refuted by the crystalline nature of the basaltic materials. It constitutes an entirely unwarranted postulate.

The foregoing points form insurmountable obstacles to the mechanism of drift as proposed by Wegener.

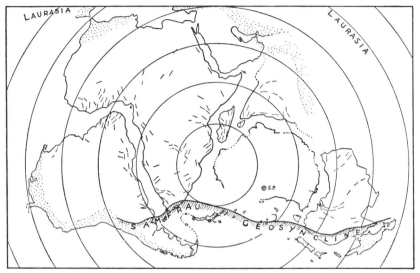

FIG. 76. The comparatively large distance between the African and South American continental blocks prior to drifting according to Du Toit's reconstruction (1937, Oliver & Boyd, Fig. 7, p. 64).

Continued investigation after Wegener first published his theory, especially the work of Du Toit (1937), has shown that a broad belt along the former joining line of the continents bordering the present Atlantic must be assumed to have disappeared by stretching or subsidence. In that case, however, several attractive points in favor of the theory must be discarded. The distance that fossil faunas must have migrated is increased by more than 500 km, and the fitting together of shelf edges and tectonic chains is that much less striking (Fig. 76).

The orogenic history of the continents in no way confirms Wegener's contention that the drifting did not begin to attain appreciable velocities until the Cretaceous period. Neither in intensity or regional distribution, nor in duration or in time interval, can a fundamental change in the orogenic rhythm of the earth's crust be traced between the ages before the Mesozoic and since the beginning of the Alpine cycle.

For the special case of Indonesia the present writer showed how the geological and bathymetrical data cannot be reconciled with Wegener's synthesis (1935). The only possibility appears to be to accept Du Toit's reconstruction and to suppose that the Moluccas remained in contact with New Guinea from first to last, thus wheeling round during the drift of Australia. Further details are mentioned in the next chapter.

No doubt there are also arguments in favor of the theory of drift, but they lie principally in the field of regional geology, biogeography, and paleoclimatology, and therefore fall outside the scope of the present volume. Many specialists on these subjects have also raised grave objections.

If the conclusions of adherents to drift in some form or other, such as Du Toit, Wegmann, Gutenberg, and Kirsch, are confronted with the opinion of opponents, for instance Bucher, Umbgrove, Stille, and Cloos, it becomes obvious that neither of the two camps can claim a decisive victory. But the evidence favorable to drift often proves illusive, or at least open to serious doubt, on closer inspection. For the time being most geologists appear to have lost faith in continental drift as a sound working hypothesis.

On seismological grounds Rothé suggests that the Atlantic east of the Mid-Atlantic Rise is of continental nature, while to the west it is of the same type as the Pacific. The latter part is supposed to have been created by westward drift of the Americas in the sense of Wegener. But the depths and the morphological structure of the two halves of the Atlantic are practically identical and do not warrant postulating an entirely different origin.

Returning to the problem of permanency, an important argument must be emphasized. It is concerned with the cubic content of the oceanic basins. The present time is certainly not poor in volcanic activity, yet the yearly production of extrusive materials is not more than about 1 km^3, according to Sapper. The intrusive magmas average roughly the same amount as far as can be ascertained. The highest estimate that can be admitted for the loss of juvenile water by all this material is 5%. Hence, the yearly production of juvenile water since the beginning of the Paleozoic can hardly have exceeded $\frac{1}{10}$ km^3; possibly it was considerably less. If this highest figure is assumed, the amount of water in the oceans has increased but 50×10^6 km^3 since the beginning of the Cambrian. As the present volume is

1370×10^6 km³, the amount of water at the close of the pre-Cambrian must have been of the order of 1300×10^6 km³ at the very least (Fig. 77).

There is further no paleontological indication that marine waters have become less saline through marked dilution in post-Algonkian times. But this is what would have occurred if the salts had been delivered gradually to the oceans through weathering, while the water was produced principally during the last quarter of terrestrial history. It is thus found to be a reasonable postulate that the total amount of

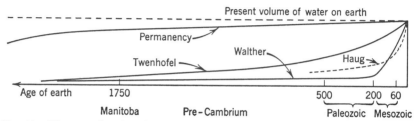

FIG. 77. Diagram showing the volume of oceanic waters as deduced from various views on permanency.

sea water has not been augmented by more than a fraction since the beginning of the Paleozoic (for further details see Chapter 5). This water must have found room in the oceans, and the theory that the deep-sea basins are of relatively recent formation is thus found to encounter serious obstacles.

As the volume of the Pacific is but half that of all oceans put together, the other oceans must also have existed since early times; otherwise there would have been no space to contain all the waters at the surface of the earth. The alternative, that the Pacific showed double the present depth and that all continents were connected by dry land, where the Atlantic and Indian oceans now lie, is too unlikely to be assumed.

It is of importance to note that, since as far back as the Cambrian, at least, the upper surface of the continents has been close to sea level, just as it is at present, being sometimes partly flooded, sometimes laid almost completely dry. As the amount of water was almost equal to that of the present seas, the cubic content of the ocean basins must also have closely approached the conditions that now prevail.

The same reasoning can be applied to pre-Cambrian times, but the farther back we go in geological history the less certain our conclusions can be. The presence of conglomerates among the oldest rocks known proves that land emerged above sea level, and that running water, clouds, etc., were present from the earliest pre-Cambrian onwards. But concerning the salinity of the seas and the rate at which juvenile water was given off by the crust of the young and active earth only a guess can be offered. Still, it is justifiable to assume that the volume of the oceans as well as the area and depth of the oceanic basins were of the same order of magnitude as they are at present.

Knothe (1933) also came to the conclusion that the volume of the primitive oceans must have been considerable, even if a strong contraction of the earth has occurred since then. Schuchert likewise expressed the opinion that the volume of the oceans has not increased very drastically during geological history. He estimated the increase at 25%, without, however, presenting concrete arguments. But even if we assume this comparatively high figure the enlargement since the end of the Paleozoic would amount to only 2½%. The opinion held by the present author is expressed in one of the curves of Fig. 77.

In the writings of Plato a myth is recorded relating to Atlantis, a large island, with a highly developed culture, that must have existed outside the Straits of Gibraltar, and that was engulfed in the ocean in prehistoric times. On the strength of this legend many writers representing several branches of science have occupied themselves with the problem of a foundered continent in the Atlantic Ocean. A literature of more than 2000 papers has appeared on this subject (Högbom, 1941). On geological grounds the possibility can hardly be entertained, for, although some geologists who do not believe in the permanency of the oceans have brought forward arguments in favor of land bridges across the Atlantic from Europe to America, these connections would be so ancient that there could be no question of historic tradition. The mutual resemblance of the faunas and floras on the Atlantic oceanic islands and the bordering continents is so slight that no connection can have existed after about the middle of the Tertiary. Many millions of years before the first appearance of primitive man the Atlantic Ocean must already have been in full existence. The occurrence of globigerina ooze dating from the last interglacial period on the ocean bed where parts of Atlantis are reconstructed is not only proof against a very recent subsidence but also evidence of a great depth during at least the last 100,000 years.

Whatever point of view is taken by a geologist on these matters, the most zealous opponent to the theory of permanency will readily concede that there is no possibility of extensive areas having subsided from above sea level to normal oceanic depths since late prehistoric times.

VARIOUS FURTHER VIEWS ON THE ORIGIN OF CONTINENTS AND OCEANS

In the foregoing paragraph some hypotheses have been treated that are concerned not only with the age but also with the mechanism by which oceanic basins may have been formed. We will now consider more especially the problem of how the contrast between continents and ocean basins may have evolved. The present survey must also be far from complete, and only those aspects will be discussed that appear to the present writer to be representative and of special importance.

Some General Hypotheses. The suggestion has been made that the Pacific is the mark left by a second satellite dropping on the earth. However, no one appears to maintain this view nowadays.

The idea was propounded by G. Darwin and Fisher (1882–1889) that the Pacific represents the scar where the moon was produced from the body of the earth. Pickering, Bowie (1935), and Mohorovičić (1925) expressed similar views, and Escher (1939) has worked out details. Escher showed that the volume and specific gravity of the moon correspond with the size and composition of the missing portion of sial if it is assumed that originally sial formed an uninterrupted layer around the entire earth of the same thickness as the present continents. According to Fisher the remaining crust, after the disappearance of the moon, split apart to form the present Atlantic and Indian oceans. He thus gave the first version of the drift theories.

This hypothesis has many attractive features, although not all astronomers agree that the moon was born from the earth in the manner described. But Umbgrove (1947) has pointed out a weakness in it. The astronomical theory requires the moon to have been thrown off at a very early stage of terrestrial history. The perfect spherical shape of the moon, in spite of the small force of gravity upon it, is in accordance with this requirement, for, had the sial already consolidated and crystallized, a far less regular shape would have been assumed by the torn-off fragments. The question that must be faced is how the sial remnants on earth could have remained in separate, steep-sided blocks of uniform thickness. The continents are intact in spite of the unconsolidated state at the time of rupture. The enormous tidal forces when the moon was still close to the earth must have set up fantastic stresses and caused great deformations on the remaining body of the earth. The growing distance of the moon gradually reduced the tidal influence to its present small values. Should not the stronger force of gravity on the earth have succeeded more completely in erasing all differences in height, than on the small celestial body of the moon, by causing the plastic sial to spread out in a uniform stratum covering the entire earth?

In former years, when geophysical arguments had not yet been brought into the field, investigators such as Suess and Haug postulated great continents not only in the Atlantic and Indian oceans but even in the Pacific. Many paleogeographers have followed this lead. Even a few years ago Dreher (1942) advocated a Pacific land that he supposed to have persisted in the Mesozoic, possibly even in the Tertiary. Umbgrove has rightly shown (1947) that the arguments in favor of the absence of sial on the floor of the Pacific must have escaped Dreher's attention (seismological arguments, the absence of sialic material as inclusion or differentiate in Pacific volcanics).

Kober (1942) adheres strictly to the contraction theory. The oceanic basins, even the Pacific, are held to be formations like the continents, composed of normal rocks, ancient orogenic belts, etc. To account for the present isostatic equilibrium he assumes a greater amount of simatic material below the ocean floor but that otherwise the oceanic basins formerly differed in no respect from the continental blocks but simply subsided by contraction of the earth. His chief arguments are the subsidence of borderlands and the possibility of tracing the main features of continental structure right into the oceanic basins. Although it is admitted that his reconstructions (for instance, his Figs. 182, 191, and 193 and his Table II) are highly suggestive, they are founded, as far as the oceanic structures are concerned, merely on a few topographic data and a fertile imagination. No proof is given that the oceanic basins actually possess a structure similar to that of the continents. Kober's diagrams show only one of many possible structural pictures, even if the postulate of normal structures in the oceans is granted.

Nölke (1939) also believes in the theory of thermal contraction and suggests that gradually increasing stresses in the crust tend to raise bridge continents connecting the main continental masses. Biomigration is thereby rendered possible. On the setting in of orogenic deformations the stress is reduced and the links are allowed to sink back below sea level. But unwarrantably great strength must be assigned to the crust in order to allow the doming up of the sea floor to amounts of several thousands of meters without isostic compensation. The postglacial history of Scandinavia, where negative anomalies of but a few dozen milligals are enough to induce swift updoming, clearly demonstrates the extreme weakness of the crust as soon as stress is applied over wider areas. A submarine ridge with several hundreds of milligals positive anomaly, held in place by the strength of the crust, is certainly not a legitimate supposition.

Trabert and Geszti have essayed to explain the difference in level between continents and ocean floor by the difference in temperature and consequent greater density of the crust below the deep sea. However, Gutenberg (1930) was able to show that under reasonable assumptions as to physical constants and other numerical values the possible extent of develeling is far too small.

As an addition to his theory of continental drift Wegener suggested that originally the sial layer may have covered the whole earth. In consequence of folding, this cover was split open and crowded together at the opposite side of the earth. The process is compared to the closing up of a round Chinese lantern. By this process the thickness increased and the difference in level between sial and sima was enlarged. In this manner his Pangea, the single original continent, is supposed to have been formed in pre-Cambrian times and to have risen above sea level. The hypsographic curve of the earth's surface thus became gradually steeper (see his Fig. 56). Later Daly (1938) arrived at the same explanation for the development of continents and ocean floors by the folding of a primeval world-encircling layer of sial. Daly, however, does not follow Wegener in his theories on drifting.

Wegener also suggested the possibility that thinning of the sialic layer may have taken place through tensile stress in fault zones. He assumed that the extent of transgressions has gradually lessened in consequence of the thickening of the continents. When drifting started there was not much stretching of the sial in the zones of rupture, but a certain amount of sial was introduced into the widening gaps from the lower surface of the sliding blocks.

Later Umbgrove followed much the same lines of thought (1947). He also assumes a uniform stratum of sial to have covered the entire earth (possibly after the moon had been cast off) formed as acid differentiate of the original silicate mantle of the earth. Owing to internal forces in the hot, mobile earth the sial layer was crowded together and thickened, part of the underlying sima being thereby laid bare to form the original Pacific basin. The primeval continental masses were asymmetrically distributed: They drifted apart to attain a more balanced position, and so the present antipodal distribution of continents against ocean basins was attained. In this process some parts of the continental masses were stretched and eventually formed thin sialic layers below the Indian and Atlantic oceans. The loss of

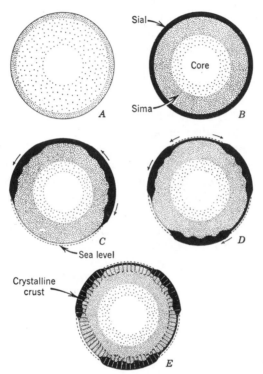

Fig. 78. Schematic representation of the origin of continents and oceanic basins in the early pre-Cambrian by a process of buckling and drifting of an originally siallic layer enveloping the whole earth. (After Umbgrove, 1947, Fig. 3, p. 175.)

heat continued, and a rigid crust gradually formed around the earth. After that, great tangential displacements were excluded (Fig. 78).

It is obvious that all orogenic cycles determined by field observations—also the most ancient such as the Marealbian, Svecofennian, etc.—are supposed by Umbgrove to have followed the consolidation of the earth's rigid crust. No vestiges remain of the disturbances by which the primeval sial layer was crumpled into a thicker stratum. This evolution took place entirely in pregeologic times. This would imply that the formation of the continents and oceanic basins must remain a hypothetical deduction not amenable to direct field investigation.

Umbgrove contends, however, that the structural pattern of basins and swells, which characterizes the sialic regions, both continental and oceanic, was developed during those early revolutions when the rigid crust was forming. His main argument is that, for the case of the African continent, this pattern has been shown to date from at least early pre-Cambrian times and has been merely rejuvenated in later orogenic cycles. It is logical, according to Umbgrove, to make the same assumption for the oceanic sialic regions and to place the original development at the very beginning of crustal evolution.

In these matters Umbgrove joins issue with Krenkel, who came to the conclusion (1925) that both rock materials and orogenic forces of the Atlantic and Indian ocean floors correspond with those of the African continent. The deep-sea topography with its basins and swells is thought by Krenkel to be identical with the rigid basins and mobile intervening belts that he had traced in the geology of Africa and that he considered to form primeval features of that continent. He even went so far as to trace several elements of the structure directly off the continent onto submarine ridges. The same ideas will be encountered presently when dealing with the views of Cloos.

Umbgrove assumes that originally the Atlantic was of uniform depth at the present level of the ridges. The basins then sank to the position now occupied in the same manner that the floors of the continental basins have shown great subsidence in the course of geological history. The present writer would like to point out that the African ridges have been greatly elevated and have kept the intervening basins full by shedding large amounts of denudation products. It is therefore not logical to deny elevation of the submarine ridges. The original level of the Atlantic before the basins were formed should be assumed at about the average depth of this ocean, if Umbgrove's theory as to the history is followed. But there is as much to be said for the view that the basins are of the same structure as the northern Pacific without a sial layer and that the ridges represent strips of sial thinner than the continental sial blocks (Fig. 79).

The above exposition shows that Umbgrove employs the same main elements as Wegener had proposed: a uniform layer of sial that is first pushed together to form continental blocks. It is then ruptured and drifts apart to form the Atlantic and Indian oceans with a thin cover of sial. The only main point of difference is that, whereas Wegener believed the drifting to have started towards the end of the

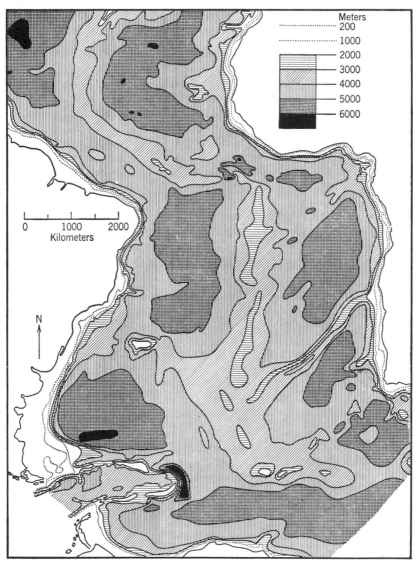

Fig. 79. Bathymetric chart of the southern Atlantic Ocean. (Redrawn from Schott, 1942, Plate V.)

Paleozoic, Umbgrove crowds the entire process into an early stage of terrestrial development, before the earth had obtained a rigid crust. Formulated thus the difference between the two conceptions may appear only slight, but actually entirely opposed pictures of the geological development of our planet result from the difference in time assigned to the process of drifting.

In this connection an interesting hypothesis evolved by Vening Meinesz should be mentioned. On theoretical grounds this author

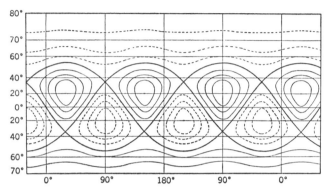

FIG. 80. Distribution of primeval convection currents in the surface layers of the earth (Mercator projection). Full-drawn lines = rising currents, dotted = descending currents, each for 0, ¼, ½, and ¾ of the maximal intensity. (After Vening Meinesz, 1944, p. 157.)

finds that convection currents reaching down to depths of 2900 km, during early stages of a cooling earth, should acquire a size and shape corresponding to four rising and four descending systems. These should present an antipodal arrangement remarkably similar to that of the present continents and oceans (Fig. 80).

Vening Meinesz suggests two ways in which this system of currents could have generated the continents. The rising currents may have segregated acid differentiates at the surface and these may have congealed to form the sial blocks. The continents would thus form above rising currents. Their radioactive heat would have helped to energize the hot current rising below them. The other suggestion is that the movements took place below a thin cover of sial already present and tended to crowd this floating layer together above the sinking currents. The convection would thus act as the motive force in Umbgrove's hypothesis. With this picture one must suppose that the radioactive heat of the sial blocks was insufficient to influence the convection, because it would act in an opposite sense by heating the cold downward current.

Hills (1947) also invokes convection currents at an early stage of cooling, the currents rising at the equator and sinking at the poles, owing to the lower surface temperatures and greater cooling at high latitudes. A continent was formed at each pole out of feldspar crystals with entrapped magma. Later the currents ceased, and the continents drifted towards the equator. Originally the freeboard was 1½ km, but later the continents were gradually domed up to their present height by radioactive heating of the substratum down to 700 km. The basaltic layer is plastic only under the continents. It tends to break out at the margins of the continents, where weak zones have gradually been created by the deposition of great masses of sediment. There it has welled out and flowed in sheets over the Pacific sea floor, carrying parts of the continent with it and opening the Atlantic Ocean as a rift.

Space does not permit to give more than this bare outline of Hills' hypothesis. Several objections can be raised against this picture of crustal evolution. Although his treatment contains many interesting suggestions, several points appear speculative or even highly improbable.

The growing continents should have counteracted the cooling effect of polar climate by insulation and radioactive heating, thus upsetting the convection system. The mechanism would tend to form thin sheets of crystal rafts, not continents 15 km thick over their entire surface. The oldest rocks known are conglomerates (Manitoba) and prove that the continents emerged above sea level at an early stage, long before the date set by Hills at 700 million years before the Cambrian. There is no evidence of a gradual increase in the freeboard of the continents, because transgressions and regressions have alternated throughout geological history. The gravity field does not conform with the suggestion that the high level of the continental blocks is mainly due to expansion of rocks down to a level of 700 km by radioactive heating. The isostatic balance of the sea floor indicates that the rock underneath the crust is plastic and not strong, as Hills believes.

Daly, as we saw, also postulates a world-encircling layer of sial as the first stage in crustal evolution (1938, p. 176). But his conception of continental development differs from that of Umbgrove in that the normal orogenic cycles of historical geology are considered to represent the agents that crumpled the sial into thick masses, in the same manner as Wegener suggested. Continental thickening is thus supposed to be a gradual process that is still acting vigorously. As one cannot well picture an orogenic cycle without local thickening of the sial, and as the repeated cycles appear to have acted now here now there over practically the entire expanse of the continental blocks, the proposed picture of gradual thickening has a strong appeal. It should not be forgotten, however, that denudation is continuously active to cut down the continental blocks and to spread their materials out again over wider surfaces. Later on we will return to these opposed actions of orogenesis and denudation (p. 163).

H. Cloos (1937, 1939) emphasizes the flexurelike character of some continental borders (Southeast Africa, Greenland) that testify to the ocean floor of the Atlantic and Indian oceans having been formed by crustal subsidence from a normal level. Following Krenkel (1925) and Bucher (1933) he considers the earth's crust to be divided, also in the oceanic sectors, into rigid masses that form basins, with intervening mobile belts that present themselves as swells. Cloos further arrives at the same conclusion as Krenkel that the structural plan of the sea floor is similar to that of the continents, so much so that no fundamental contrasts can be assumed. Possibly the sialic crust of the ocean bed may be thinner, however. He asserts that the submarine swells around Africa agree entirely with the labile borders of the African basins in magmatic, seismic, morphologic, and gravimetric respects (exceedingly little is known of these qualities for the case of submarine ridges), and he points to the connection of Madagascar with the mainland of Africa by a submarine ridge bearing the crystalline island of Juan de Nova as a link. Further, the basins on land and below the sea show marked similarities in size and shape. As, moreover, the structure of Africa dates back from the early pre-Cambrian, the major features and subdivision in separate basins of the submarine area should also represent a primeval feature of the earth's crust.

Cloos does not appear to have questioned whether the relatively recent, Mesozoic flexuring of coastal areas, cited by himself, does not indicate that the Atlantic and Indian oceans were developed after the Paleozoic by subsidence. This conclusion, however, does not appear to fit in with his general picture of crustal development. Cloos reasons somewhat in a circle, first arguing that the submarine swells cannot represent fault blocks because that type of formation is not encountered on land, and then going on to emphasize the essential similarity between land and sea floor on the strength of the close parallel that can be drawn between submarine and continental swells.

If Cloos is right in supposing that ocean floors consist of the identical materials found on continental blocks, but occurring in a thinner layer, one would expect the structures to resemble each other in their general forms but to exhibit a considerable difference in size. Hence, the identity in dimensions of the continental and oceanic structural elements, far from constituting an argument in favor of his contentions, is rather an obstacle in following him.

Rittmann (1938) attempted to explain the development of the continents as follows. The original crust was alkali-basaltic. Weathering produced siliceous sediments that were washed into deep depressions, together with a concentrate of radioactive elements which combined with the blanketing effect of the sedimentary cover to heat and finally to melt the underlying crust. The sediments were then granitized. Finally isostatic equilibrium was established by the elevation of these light parts of the crust to form the present continents. This hypothesis is apparently almost identical with the opinions published by Lawson in 1932.

Closer inspection shows this hypothesis to be untenable. Thus Umbgrove (1947) pointed out that the original relief, necessary to allow weathering on the topographic heights and sedimentation in the depressions, is not explained by Rittmann. Under his postulates it can even be shown that no considerable develeling was possible. The original crust is supposed to have been homogeneous. Yet there must have existed sufficient difference in height between the primeval continents and ocean basins to allow the accumulation of several thousands of meters in the basins, for the mass of the present sial is supposed to have been sedimented as siliceous deposits in the ancient depressions. In Rittmann's speculations the total volume of water was already present at this early stage. The differences in level in the supposed homogeneous material must therefore have amounted to some 10 to 15 km. This implies isostatic anomalies of over 1000 milligals in a youthful and mobile earth! After a considerable mass had been added to these sediments during granitization and the anomalies had sunk to 500 milligals, isostatic equilibrium was suddenly restored and the continents rose to their present level.

Another deduction can be made, which proves to be fatal. The primeval continents continued for a long time to deliver sediment, whence it follows that no eluvium was left on their surface. Such a residual covering would have effectually cloaked the surface and would soon have brought weathering to a standstill. But if all weathering products were washed into the seas, how could the average composition differ from that of the original crust? Where were all the aluminum, magnesium, calcium, and iron stored when siliceous sediments were formed from the alkali basalt? Only a small amount could have gone into solution in the sea water.

Other objections need not be entered into, as the primary postulates are found to be untenable.

Wiseman and Sewell (1937) consider the ridges in the Arabian Sea to be normal orogens (Fig. 81). Thus the set of ridges discovered some 100 km off the Persian coast is "almost certainly a part of the Lagros System of Persia" and the Murray Ridge "appears to be a continuation of the Khirthar Range of Sind." On the other hand they point out that the trough between the two parallel ridges crowning the Murray Ridge and the other double ridges of this region form the mirror image of the African Rift Valley system. This comparison would imply that faulting, not folding, was the chief type of tectonic deformation. It is therefore not quite clear what type of orogenic structure they have in mind when drawing a parallel between continental and suboceanic forms. This point remains somewhat obscure when they first deduce a subsidence along a fault system on account of the breaking off of the coastal strata and then formulate their final conclusion as follows: "it seems highly probable that the floor of the northwest part of the Indian Ocean, as we know it today, assumed its present form as a result of compression in the Tertiary times, probably contemporaneously with the upheaval of the Alpine-Himalayan mountain system and the arcs of the Malay Archipelago and the formation of the Rift Valley. Subsequently in the Pliocene or Post-Pliocene times the area of land that once filled the triangle now bounded by ··· [Africa and Persia and India] became separated off by a series of faults and was submerged to its present depth." So much is clear, however, that they do not assume a fundamental difference between the portions of the crust forming continental areas and those forming oceanic basins. The great difficulty of explaining the conversion of high standing blocks to deep-lying areas has not been discussed by them.

Formerly Bucher (1933) considered the deep-sea troughs to have been caused by tensional stress in the crust. Later (1941–42) he discarded this view but retained the conviction that deep-sea troughs and geosynclines are identical formations. He emphasizes the essential similarity of oceanic and continental structures.

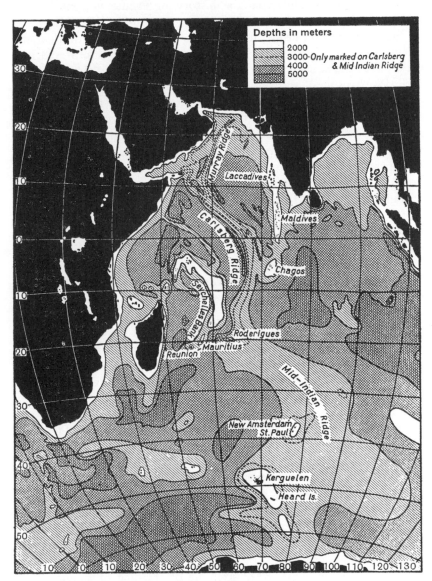

Fig. 81. Bathymetric chart of the Indian Ocean. (After Wiseman and Sewell, 1937, Fig. 1, p. 221.)

Stearns (1945) summarized the history of Pacific volcanic islands and emphasized the widespread evidence of considerable subsidence. In the discussion on atolls in Chapter 6 the importance of this subsidence will be pointed out. Stearns and others have interpreted it as proof of a general deepening of the Pacific Ocean floor. He attributes it to the extrusion of the lava forming the islands. It is evident, however, that the volume of lava when spread out over the ocean floor represents but a very thin stratum. Hess invoked the gradual relative rise of sea level due to deep-sea sedimentation. This process, however, is very slow—probably of the order of 1 to 2 m in a million years. We must assume a swifter subsidence that carries the volcanic cones downwards in early stages in order to explain the observed drowning of valleys. Vening Meinesz has shown that the gravity field denotes regional compensation of oceanic islands. This means that a wide area is slightly depressed by the weight imposed on the crust by the volcanic cones. Probably the depression keeps pace with the gradual erection of the cone and cannot explain the physiographic drowning. It is conceivable, however, that eventually the crust gradually gives way and allows the cone to subside, while the surrounding depression returns to its original position. Compaction and squeezing aside of the oceanic deposits on the ocean floor below the cone is another possibility pointed out by Kuenen.

Are the Continents Extending? A very important problem is whether continents can be extended by the incorporation of new geosynclinal belts along the margins. Much has been written on this subject, but confusion as to the meaning of the terms continents, consolidated areas of the crust, etc., has tended to obscure the points at issue. The word continent will here be taken as meaning regions of the crust close to or above sea level and so extensive that the weight of their mass protruding above the level of the deep-sea floor cannot be borne by the strength of the crust. A thick layer of light sial must therefore be postulated to maintain isostatic equilibrium. There is a widely accepted view that the continents consist of old nuclei onto which new orogenic zones are successively welded. By this process the ancient shields are gradually extended to form the so-called *kratogenic areas*. A comparatively recent example of this line of thought is to be found in writings of Born (1933). This picture of continental development, however, does not meet the facts. It is true that a geosyncline often migrates during the successive phases of an orogenic cycle. But this movement frequently happens in a direction towards the ancient nucleus. An example is the Molasse Trough along the northern margin of the Alpine geosyncline on the side where this chain borders on ancient Hercynian Europe. The simple picture of a gradual spread of the nucleus from the Scandinavian shield to the south is thus not confirmed. Admittedly it may hold a certain measure of truth.

But when the spread of geosynclinal activity is interpreted as indicating a gradual growth of the continental mass, more serious objections can be raised. The basement of all geosynclines is found to be a continental area. The folding of a geosyncline therefore does not imply an extension of the continent, but only an addition to the ancient nucleus of intensely crumpled rocks. In fact, it means the opposite to expansion, for an orogenic cycle results in thickening and narrowing of a belt that already belonged to the continent.

This reasoning is borne out by the important fact that nowhere has true oceanic sea floor been incorporated in the continents, because no extensive pelagic deep-sea deposits are found in geosynclinal or other sedimentary prisms. We do not know what agents cause the labile conditions in a geosyncline, but in any event these troughs develop from continental areas underlain by a thick sialic crust. The writer has had occasion to emphasize this significant point (1935) and to show that Schuchert's type of mesogeosyncline appears to have been founded on a misinterpretation of European geology. His prototype was formed by the Alpine Geosyncline. According to Schuchert it originated between two continents, the African and European. But the word "between" should not be taken literally, for the Alpine Trough was formed by the subsidence of a denuded land area. Everywhere Permian and Triassic are found to transgress over more ancient denuded rock surfaces. Not until the Jurassic and Cretaceous were greater depths developed through subsidence.

Neither is it true that a new geosyncline is always developed in a region in which orogenic quiescence had reigned before. In the center of the Alps ancient massifs have been laid bare that show strong Hercynian orogenic structures. Wherever the pre-Cambrian is exposed, intensive tectonic disturbance prevails, yet these formations appear to underlie all post-Cambrian mountain belts. Although it must be admitted that generally a great length of time elapses before an orogenic belt is again invaded by a geosynclinal cycle, the repetition of compression in one and the same area thus appears to be the rule. In spite of this the idea that a folded region remains exempt from orogenic activity is prevalent.

The above considerations show that orogenesis does not lead to the extension of continents but, conversely, to a certain measure of contraction and thickening. A development in structure has been mistaken for a growth in size by writers who advocate continental expansion by orogenic cycles.

It now remains to be investigated whether growth is possible by some other process. Born mentioned the extension of continents by the dumping of sediment in geosynclines, but as we saw this means only a local thickening of the sial. In the times following the pre-Cambrian, growth of the continents has taken place only through deposition on the continental slopes, and it is highly probable that the same picture applies to earlier sections of terrestrial history. It is not probable, however, that the prism of sediments building the continental terrace outwards has ever been folded and incorporated in the kratogenic nuclei of the continents. Not only is it doubtful that geosynclines ever originated right on the margin of continental blocks, but also the true oceanic floor has never been carried upwards above the level of the sea. Bucher, at any rate, denies that marginal geosynclines were developed at the very edge of a continent, for on the side fronting the ocean there was always a denuding belt, now sometimes lost by subsidence (Appalachia, etc.). Umbgrove (1947) came to the same conclusion, that the continental blocks do not expand by incorporation of orogenic belts.

In his undation theory, van Bemmelen (1939) postulates a primary salsima layer formerly enveloping the whole earth and now forming the floor of the oceans. Differentiation has generated the sial of the continents and a heavy sima layer underneath. This process is continuing in the salsima bordering on the continents. van Bemmelen shows how this differentiation into a lighter upper part and a heavier lower stratum must upset hydrostatic equilibrium. Consequently sideways injection of salsima between the sial and sima of the continental sections must follow, resulting in elevation of the continents and depression of the sea floor along the continental border. This process causes a slope at the surface on which unconsolidated sediments slide downwards, being thereby folded to tectonic structures.

van Bemmelen's line of speculation cannot be followed in detail here. The reader is referred to the original publications. All that need concern us is that it leads to the conclusion that the continents expand by the incorporation of ocean floor into the margins of the sial blocks. If van Bemmelen were right the lower strata of a geosynclinal prism should be formed of pelagic oceanic sediments. Neither the growth of the continents nor the incorporation of deep-sea floor into these blocks appears to have taken place, as shown above. When dealing with the continental terrace presently it will be shown that there is strong evidence for the opposite to continental growth. It is difficult to avoid the conclusion that marginal areas have subsided to form part of the present deep-sea floor.

Patterns in the Earth's Crust. More than a century ago Dana and Darwin remarked on the alignment of the Hawaii and Galapagos Volcanoes in rows with constant interspaces. Since then many others have traced certain regularities in the arrangement of volcanic cones (Green; Friedländer, 1918; Kuenen, 1945). It is now obvious that we are not dealing with a peculiarity of the sea floor but with a general property of the crust. Evidently the suboceanic and continental sections of the earth's crust react in a similar manner to stresses producing volcanic fissures.

Mecking (1940) draws attention to a number of similarities in the surface relief of the earth. In the southern hemisphere a north-to-south direction prevails not only in the forms of the continents but also in the mountain systems and the great midoceanic rises. He further concludes: "The less oceanic regions are hedged in, the more extensive and less marked the subdivision in basins is found to be. The narrower they are, the smaller and the more intensive and marked the subdivision becomes." [1] But one has to admit that there are many exceptions to these rules where intensive relief occurs in portions of wide oceans or where simple, poorly marked forms are situated in narrow offshoots of the main oceans. The present writer believes that many such homologies are to be expected from merely chance distribution of forms and that no great value can be placed on a repetition once or twice of any special feature when seeking for a satisfactory geophysical picture of crustal development.

Some authors have gone much further and have attempted to trace certain rules in the morphology of the crust: preferred directions, constant intervals, etc. Thus Sonder (1939) advocated what he terms *Lineamenttektonik*. He assumes that the ocean floor is rigid and unable to react to tangential stress by normal orogenic processes. Faulting is believed to form the main type of deformation, and volcanic eminences to play a major part in the surface relief. Swells produced in this manner are said to intersect at fixed angles and at

[1] Je freier die ozeanischen Räume, desto groszzügiger und schwächer die Felderung, je beengter die Räume, desto kleinzügiger, intensiver und ausgeprägter die Felderung.

fixed distances, the value of 1500–2000 km recurring again and again. Although his maps are highly suggestive (Fig. 82), the lines shown could also be drawn quite differently on the basis of available data. Thus there is no basis for connecting the South Antillean Arc to the Mid-Atlantic Rise by an east-to-west line and to assign the same direc-

tion to the equatorial section of that rise in spite of the obvious west-northwest trend in that region. It can hardly be doubted that when Sonder connected the Antillean Arc with Brazil and Newfoundland by straight lines he was prompted by the wish to trace a preconceived system. The occurrence of certain preferred directions and straight faultlines is a characteristic both of the ocean floor and of the continents, and merits our full attention. But critical examination of facts is a requisite to the finding of such rules.

Vening Meinesz (1947) was also struck by certain regularities and preferred directions in terrestrial morphology. He offered an entirely different explanation from Sonder's, suggesting that early in the earth's history a displacement of the axis of rotation caused stresses in the crust. In

FIG. 82. Map by Sonder showing inferred linear tectonics of the Atlantic region. (Sonder, 1939, Fig. 1, p. 36.)

a network of lines covering the surface he gave the direction of principal stresses for an assumed direction and amount of displacement of the poles (Fig. 83). These stresses led to rupture and breaking up of the crust in a system of more or less diamond-shaped blocks. Later volcanic and orogenic forces would tend to avail themselves of these ancient zones of weakness and rejuvenate the pattern. Hence, the present morphology still shows a number of features derived from the ancient pre-Cambrian cracks in the crust. Vening Meinesz showed that many major topographic forms, such as ridges in the northern Pacific and Atlantic, the structure of the Canadian Shield as revealed by aerial

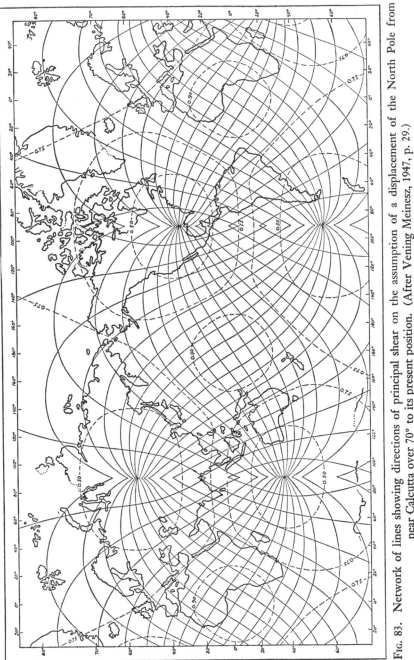

FIG. 83. Network of lines showing directions of principal shear on the assumption of a displacement of the North Pole from near Calcutta over 70° to its present position. (After Vening Meinesz, 1947, p. 29.)

photographs, and the boundaries of continental blocks, fit his scheme to a remarkable degree. However, there is always the danger of selecting the favorable evidence and overlooking misfits. An evaluation of this hypothesis must await a detailed and statistical survey of the direction of the main morphological and structural features of the crust.

Whatever the result, a second system of preferred directions in the earth's crust is of equal importance, a north-south east-west system. According to Umbgrove (1947) this system requires a second cause, and, being related only to the present and not to the supposed former axis of rotation, it would necessarily be of later origin. Vening Meinesz suggests that any stress tending to rupture the crust nearly along the shear pattern will make use of these old lines of weakness, but if diverging strongly new lines of disturbance will be formed. This should automatically cause a second system of preferred directions bisecting the angles of the shear pattern and running roughly north to south and east to west.

We must leave the problem of linear patterns in this early stage of reconnaissance.

The Evidence from Earthquakes. Some authors have attempted to fathom the structural nature of the oceanic basins by considering the regional distribution of earthquakes. Clements and Emery (1947) state that the seismic activity and the submarine topography in the borderland off southern California are related. They believe that the major topographic features are of tectonic origin and that the forces which brought them about are still active. Their map, however, indicates that the great majority of shocks show no connection with surface features. Probably they occur too deep in the crust to be accompanied by movements at the surface.

More far-reaching conclusions on oceanic structure were drawn by Rehm (1936) on the basis of seismic data. Gutenberg and Richter (1941, 1945) have since shown, however, that older maps giving the location of epicenters contain a large number of errors, so that little value can be attached to earlier reviews. Moreover, Rehm makes the mistake of ascribing all shocks to fault tectonics. Even when only a few epicenters are recorded in a region he excludes the possibility of other tectonic happenings. The possibility that transverse horizontal shifts, overthrusts, or faulting may cause earthquakes as minor accompaniments or aftermaths of folding is left out of consideration.

The fact that the great majority of earthquakes originate at several dozens of kilometers below the surface (not to speak of deep-focus earthquakes) is sufficient reason for doubting that they can teach us anything directly concerning the tectonic structure of the accessible crust. For the time being the opposite procedure, as followed by Gutenberg and Richter, is more promising, namely, to locate epicenters and observe whether a correlation can be established with certain features of the crust. Not until such correlations have been firmly established and a far greater volume of data has been collected can a tentative determination of crustal structure be founded on seismic data.

The careful sifting of data by the authors mentioned led to the remarkable result that seismicity is concentrated in narrow belts to a much greater degree than was hitherto suspected and that there are large stable areas practically free of activity. This clarifies the picture and renders the correlations of certain types of seismicity with gravity, volcanism, submarine rises, island arcs, and deep-sea troughs far more pronounced than was formerly supposed. Thus the andesite line is closely linked with a belt of excessive activity, and moderately seismic belts follow the Mid-Atlantic and Easter Island rises and the rise in the western Indian Ocean. But up to the present it is not possible to deduce the structural nature of the oceanic basins or submarine ridges and troughs from the distribution of epicenters. Thus seismologists find the same absence of shocks in the Pacific as in the Canadian and other continental shields, while the Tertiary orogenic belt of Central Asia much resembles the Mid-Atlantic Rise and is not very different from the East African Rift Valley.

It is not the writer's intention to detract from the value of regional seismic studies, but again the conclusion must be that the time is not yet ripe for far-reaching and well-substantiated conclusions.

Positive Forms of the Sea Floor. Thus far we have been mainly concerned with the major depressions of the earth's crust, although minor negative forms have also been mentioned. Turning now to the positive forms of the sea floor we find that again little is known with certainty and that each author makes his own guess as to the nature of submarine ridges and plateaus. As, moreover, these problems are even more closely related to those of structural and regional geology, fields of investigation we have avoided as far as possible, the topic cannot be discussed in detail. A few aspects, however, should be treated briefly.

Many positive forms are doubtless due partly or entirely to volcanic activity. Countless oceanic islands are known to be built up exclusively of eruptive rocks, and a volcanic origin of many isolated seamounts, with or without a crown of coral reefs, is highly probable. Shepard and Emery (1941) offered an interesting interpretation of morphological data on the San Juan and Davidson's seamounts and other isolated, steep rises off southern California. These seamounts form oblong ridges with separate small mounts on top. They lie oblique to the structural trend of the region. Several of the small rises show a pit in the summit, probably a crater, and a large "caldera" is also present. Basalt has been dredged from the surface.

In the same region many scarps and angular forms are encountered on the strongly diversified ridges and banks. The rocks and general structure (apart from the "volcanic" seamounts) closely resemble those of the adjacent coast of California, and the trend lines are the same. The interpretation, by the authors cited, as a faulted orogenic region is thus well founded.

The Indonesian ridges and island arcs of the western Pacific are of orogenic origin, partly built up further by volcanic activity. They will be referred to again in the next chapter.

Although the higher eminences of the Mid-Atlantic Rise are all of volcanic nature the main bulk of the mass is generally held to be a product of orogenic processes. Whether faulting or compression has played the main part is uncertain. Several writers believe that this swell is a strip of sial and has little to do with tectonics of the crust. It may contain tectonic structures, but the elevation is due to the buoyancy of the sialic materials. The present writer is inclined to favor this view on account of the observed isostatic equilibrium. If the high position of the sea floor were due to faulting or updoming of a simatic crust, strong positive anomalies should prevail. Seismic data point to a certain amount of sial in the Atlantic, and placing it below the ridges and continental slopes, to explain their relatively elevated position, appears reasonable.

The Hawaiian volcanic islands rise abruptly from a slight swell of the Pacific floor. This swell is too broad and represents too great a weight to be the result of lateral pressure. Gravity observations also show approach to isostatic equilibrium of the swell (not of the volcanoes), which means that not stress but buoyancy carries the load represented by the elevated position. Slight depressions are encountered at both sides of the swell. Betz and Hess (1942) tentatively suggested that the ridge represents vesicular volcanic material with a density 0.4 less than that of the crust. A gentle elastic downbowing of the crust beneath the broad, flat lens of the volcanics would account for the longitudinal depressions along the margins of the swell

(Fig. 84). This presupposes that the basining of the crust extends over an area 100–200 km broader than the load. This view leads to unexpected thicknesses of the volcanics, approaching 7000 m along the axis of the ridge. If one follows Kuenen in assuming a thick layer of deep-sea sediment, which becomes compacted below oceanic volcanoes, the amount of volcanics required is augmented by a few thousand meters. Elastic bending of the crust had already been assumed by Vening Meinesz, for this and other cases. This author evolved the theory of "regional compensation" on the evidence of the gravity anomalies at sea.

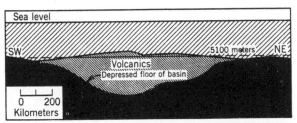

Fig. 84. Average profile of the Hawaiian Swell, showing body of volcanics as suggested by Betz and Hess (1942). Vertical scale about 40 × horizontal scale.

Another possibility is that chambers of magma with low specific gravity play a part in the buoyancy of the swell. Further exploration by gravity measurements and echo sounding must be awaited before a choice can be made between these and other possible explanations of ridges below volcanic islands of the deep oceans.

A typical proof may be cited, showing that considerations concerning the submarine morphology must remain highly speculative, especially since the exact morphology is as yet poorly established. Sonder and Cloos offer the following interpretations for the formation of submarine swells. Sonder writes (p. 28): "Die ozeanische Tektonik ist eine Bruchschollentektonik mit der festländischen entgegengesetzten Verwerfungstendenz (Grabenbruchtendenz-Langhorsttendenz)." (Faultblocks, down-faulted on land, and up-faulted on the sea floor.) Cloos on the other hand denies the faulted character of submarine swells and interprets them as plastic welts between rigid basins.

THE CONTINENTAL TERRACE

Available Data. Our treatment of the oceanic basins may be rounded off by considering the regions bordering the continents. Many prob-

lems are involved in treating the origin and evolution of the continental slope and shelf and the adjoining coastal area. Some aspects,
such as the formation of submarine canyons, erosion, and deposition,
will be dealt with in greater detail elsewhere in this volume, and brief
reference to the boundary between oceanic basins and continents has
been made in the preceding paragraphs. In this section a summary
will be given of the views held by geologists on the nature of the
continental terrace.

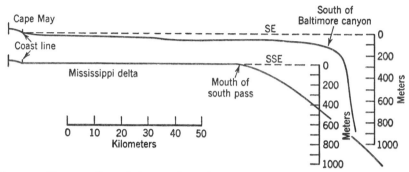

FIG. 85. Two profiles of the continental terrace. *Upper:* On the east coast of
the United States from Cape May to a ridge south of Baltimore Canyon. *Lower:*
Off the mouth of the Mississippi. The approximate position is indicated of the
coastline from Barataria Bay to Chandeleur Sound at base of present delta.

Umbgrove (1947) has reviewed the theoretical aspects and shown
how far we still are from a complete picture and general agreement.
Shepard (1948) has summarized the data collected by sounding and
sampling.

Shepard (1948) arrived at the following general conclusions concerning the morphology of the shelf. The average width is 70 km;
the depth at the edge averages 130 m but may attain 500 m. Hills of
20 m or more occur on 60% of the profiles, hollows of 20 m or more
on 35%. The average slope is somewhat steeper in its inner half than
in the outer half. In restricted bay entrances deeper channels are the
rule, and a shallow sill exists farther out, probably a sand bar. Off
formerly glaciated coasts the shelf is wide and deep with a very
irregular surface, due to glacial troughs and morainic deposits. Off
large rivers the shelves are shallow and broad, except where covered
by a protruding delta. In areas of active coral growth the shelves
are shallow and strewn with irregular shoals and banks. Off young
mountain ranges shelves tend to be narrow and deep (20 m deeper

than the average), or they are even entirely lacking. Where powerful oceanic currents impinge along the coast the shelves are narrow or missing. Thus Florida, a low flat area, has a broad shelf on the west but virtually no shelf on the south and southeast where the Gulf Stream sweeps close along the shore, commonly attaining 1 to 2 m per second. At greater depths of nearly 1000 m, however, the slope is again gentle and terminates outward with an escarpment which is in line with the edge of the continental shelf beyond the reach of the current.

Shepard finds no simple relation between marginal depths and width, or between depths and degree of exposure to storm waves.

The same writer further emphasizes that sand is the dominant sediment of the shelves. Mud is common off larger rivers and downcurrent from them. It is also found in embayments and depressions of the shelf. Pebbles, cobbles, and rock bottom are common on most shelves, especially towards the outer margins.

Shepard (1948) also gives a regional description of the continental slopes and arrives at the following conclusions. The average slope is $4\frac{1}{4}°$ for the first 2000 m. Off large deltas the slopes are gentle and smooth, averaging $1\frac{1}{3}°$ to 2000 m, but with numerous irregularities (due to slumping and pressing out of soft strata?). Off fault coasts the average slope is $5\frac{2}{3}°$. Along the Pacific coasts the slopes are steeper than the average, but the presence of deep-sea troughs close along the coast does not coincide with exceptionally steep continental slopes. Mud covers no less than 60% of the slopes, 25% are covered by sand, 5% by shells and ooze, and 10% are occupied by rock.

Veatch and Smith showed the existence of an ancient "Franklin Shore" at 70 to 110 m depth on the Atlantic shelf of North America. Bourcart found two or even three terraces below one another along the eastern Atlantic border. He assumes that the deepest at 500 to 1000 m is of Mio-Pliocene age (Pontien), one at 200–500 m is supposed to be Upper Pliocene (Villefranchienne), while the terrace at 0–200 m is of composite age from Mid-Paleolithic to Recent. On the other hand elevated marine terraces occur along many coasts up to heights of 100 m, perhaps even more. The lower of these may be attributed to eustatic rises in consequence of the interglacial melting of all ice on the continents. But this does not apply to the higher ones, because a rise of only 40 to 50 m could be accounted for by that mechanism. Further morphological evidence of recent updoming of the continental border comes from many localities. Hence, one cannot avoid the conclusion that the continental margin is unstable and is marked by periodic warping, the seaward part subsiding, the land rising, or vice versa. In part this is due to ice-loading during the Pleistocene. But far beyond the reach of isostatic reaction to land ice, and in periods of mild climate, vertical movements of considerable and uniform amount have taken place over wide areas. Umbgrove suggested the possibility that these warpings may be due to sub-crustal convection currents. However, these warpings cannot explain the shape or the formation of the shelf as a whole.

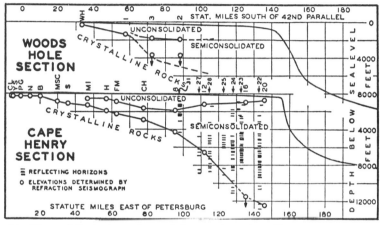

FIG. 86. Two of Ewing's sections of the continental shelf, eastern United States. (Note exaggeration of vertical scale.) (After Daly, 1942, *The Floor of the Ocean,* University of North Carolina Press, Fig. 59, p. 109.)

Highly valuable evidence on the internal structure of the continental terrace has been discovered by seismic prospecting under water, by drilling, and by sampling. Ewing and his collaborators (1937) succeeded in demonstrating the presence of unconsolidated sediments forming the terrace on the east coast of the United States and overlying a wedge of semiconsolidated deposits thickening seawards. Below this wedge hard crystalline rocks were detected. This "basement complex" lies close to the surface 100 km inland; at the coast it is 1500 m deep; and 100 km out, where the depth of water is still less than 200 m, it attains 4000 m below the surface (Fig. 86). The boundary surface appears to be an ancient peneplane. These observations were later duplicated by Bullard and Gaskell for the English Channel and by Ewing et al. (1946) and Worzel and Ewing (1948) for some other sections off the American Atlantic coast. About 30 km off the mouth of the Orinoco in depths of 40 m the basement was located at a depth of 7500 m.

These findings have been confirmed by deep wells drilled off North Carolina. The one put down at Cape Hatteras encountered Tertiary and Cretaceous down to 3200 m resting on weathered granite (Swain, 1947). In the Upper Cretaceous some non-marine sediments interfinger with the marine deposits (Fig. 87).

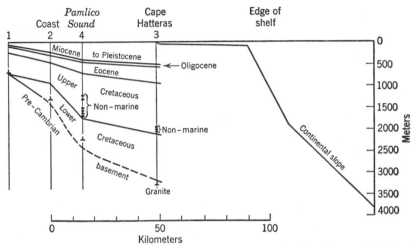

FIG. 87. Structure of the continental terrace as revealed by deep wells, North Carolina. Position arranged according to distance from coastline; drilling data according to Swain, 1947.

Sampling in submarine canyons and on the shelf has been carried out by Stetson, Shepard, and others. They repeatedly encountered hard rock cropping out on the canyon walls, or even on the continental slope itself. Again the evidence shows that Mesozoic and Tertiary sediments resembling those found on adjacent land build up much of the terrace. Off California, granite and other crystalline rocks are not uncommon.

Origin of the Continental Terrace. Various views are held on the origin of the shelf (see Kuenen, in press). One, championed by Novák and Shepard, is that the terrace is largely the result of marine and subaerial erosion of the continental mass, while the continental slope is a major fault zone where the downfaulted sea floor and the raised continental masses meet. Another hypothesis, advocated by Cloos, ascribes the continental slope to a major flexure of the crust (see p. 140). Bourcart maintains that subaerial denudation is the principal agent, followed by drowning, because he denies the possibility of effective marine erosion.

Some authors have ascribed the terrace to outbuilding from the continents by sediment in the manner of a delta front. Upbuilding on a subsiding foundation might also be imagined. Finally the view is held that the terrace has been built up on a subsiding foundation but has at the same time grown out towards the deep-sea floor (Daly, 1942; Umbgrove, 1947). Concomitant erosion of the coast may have cooperated with any of these major processes, or uplift of the coast may have occurred.

Shepard gained much experience by sampling off the Californian coast (1948). He founds his conclusion about the faulted nature of the shelf edge mainly on the following arguments: (1) the shelf shows a surprisingly high percentage of rocky exposures, especially towards the outer margin; even on the slopes, rock ledges crop out in many places; (2) the edge is on the whole straight, resembling major fault zones on land; (3) frequent earthquakes indicate the fault nature of the slopes; (4) Deep trenches occur along approximately half of the ocean-basin margins—obviously there must have been either downwarping or downfaulting to account for these marginal deeps; (5) narrow shelves cut transversely across trends of formations on the coast. As one might expect the slopes to be much steeper if formed by a fault scarp, he assumes a certain amount of scree building and deposition, especially out along the lower end of the slope. Off large rivers deposition has been more important.

Holtedahl (1940) is also of the opinion that the continental slope represents a major fault zone of the earth's crust. The depression in the shelf found parallel to the coast along most of the Atlantic border of Norway is believed by him to have been formed by erosion along a comparatively recent fault zone. The land mass is supposed to have been elevated along this line. Transverse faults, that may in part be much older, have been scoured out by rivers and glaciers. These now show up as submerged, fiordlike depressions in the shelf. They form the drowned glacial troughs referred to in Chapter 7.

Some arguments can be presented against the view that the shelf is mainly due to cutting by marine erosion and not to sedimentation; they apply especially to the east coast terrace of North America.

(1) The information gradually gained on the terrace structure along the east coast of North America gives no indication of faults, but only of a gradual outward slope of the basement. (2) Neither

does wave cutting appear to have been important, because the surface of the shelf is underlain by young deposits. (3) The absence of a broad shelf in regions where a powerful oceanic current impinges along the coast indicates that no sediment could accumulate and build out the shelf. There is no foundation for the opposite contention that marine erosion of the continental mass should have been less under these conditions. Although the deeper-lying plateau off Florida could be explained by downwarping of a normal shelf there is more satis- faction in assuming not a mere coincidence but a causal relation, namely, non-deposition due to the Gulf Stream. Shepard is inclined to follow Prouty in his suggestion that a shelf formerly existed here and has since been eroded. The velocity of the current where it reaches the sea floor is hardly strong enough to confirm this possi- bility. (4) The great breadth and slight slope of the shelf off major rivers are evidently due to outbuilding, because there is no reason for greater erosion of the coast in such localities. It is reasonable to assume that smaller but considerable amounts of sediment are added in similar manner to other parts of the shelf elsewhere. (5) The slow rate at which marine erosion cuts into hard rock is opposed to the view that terraces 100 km or more wide could have been formed by this agent alone. (6) The almost total absence of earthquakes along the edge of many shelves is not in favor of assuming a fault along the continental margin.

It is true that faults appear to play a part in the structure of some coasts and that the absence of a shelf in a few limited areas might be explained by faulting. But such cases are exceptional, and the above arguments apply to the great majority of continental margins.

The simplest process by which the shelf on the east coast could have been formed is by outbuilding as represented in Fig. 88, B. This picture can be definitely ruled out, because wells drilled in the terrace near the coast do not pass straight into older formations as they should do in the event of gradual seaward growth of the terrace. Evidently subsidence has occurred. When the enormous volume of the terrace is taken into account, the reason becomes evident. The crust of the earth is not strong enough to carry the weight, and subsidence must necessarily accompany the building of the terrace.

The next interpretation of the terrace is represented by Fig. 88, C. The terrace is gradually formed by upbuilding while the substratum subsides. Instead of building out towards the deep-sea floor, each formation reaches a shorter distance than its predecessor. It is diffi-

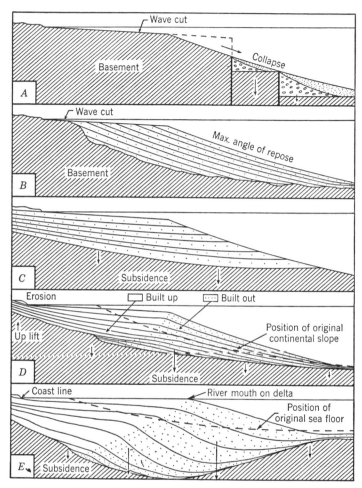

Fig. 88. Diagrams illustrating various views on the constitution of the continental terrace. *A*. Due mainly to marine erosion of faulted structure with collapse and some deposition. *B*. Due mainly to outbuilding and moderate marine erosion. *C*. Due to upbuilding on subsiding substratum. *D*. Due to combined upbuilding and moderate outbuilding on subsiding substratum. *E*. Similar to *D* but with greater outbuilding by a large river. The vertical scale, and hence also the amount of outbuilding, is exaggerated.

cult to explain the steeper front represented by the continental slope, but otherwise this picture can account for the data so far obtained.

In the view represented by Fig. 88, *D*, the terrace is formed by up-building on a substratum which subsides under the weight of the accumulating deposits while outbuilding also takes place. This outbuilding is due to sediment transported from the coast to the edge of the shelf and deposited on the slope in the undisturbed water below wave base. The isostatic depression it causes cannot be entirely local, according to the theory of regional isostatic compensation. The strength of the crust, although insufficient to carry large masses without bending, is enough to cause depression over an area several dozen kilometers (probably 50 to 150 km) broader than the burden imposed on the crust. Hence the shelf surface is depressed together with the continental slope. The space thus provided by deepening allows accumulation to proceed not only on the slope but also on the top. A distinction can therefore be made between the material deposited on the shelf and that laid down on the slope. These grade into each other at the break in slope at the edge of the shelf. The point of transition is gradually moved seaward as the terrace builds outwards. Owing to the slight slopes and great breadth of the area involved, the resulting deposits approach horizontal strata and the relative amount of outbuilding is much less than in the diagram of Fig. 88, *D*.

Supposing the outbuilding to be double the amount of upbuilding, the total advance towards the ocean need only amount to some 10 km. The whole structure from coast to deep-sea floor, however, is of the order of 100 to 200 km. If the outbuilding is five times as much as the upbuilding it would have totaled some 25 km. If the sinking is due only to isostasy the present surface must lie on the average somewhat above the original surface, because the new deposits are less dense than the substratum on which the crust is supposed to float. It may be estimated that three-quarters of the volume of the terrace sediments lies below the original slope surface.

Off the mouth of a large river the delta will advance further than normal into deep water. The load of sediment on the crust is then greater, and an equivalent increase in the amount of depression must result. The original surface can then be carried far below the level of the deep-sea floor (Fig. 88, *E*).

The geology of the coastal land area can be explained by assuming that the depression of the shelf formerly reached some distance inland from the present coastline. Later the depressed area rose at the inland side, causing emergence. This might be due in part to gradual shifting of the main zone of accumulation towards the ocean as outbuilding proceeded. The main cause, however, might be sought in a slow, plastic bending of the crust, whereby the regionally depressed area recoils to its original position, while the loaded area sinks farther.

The deep wells cannot show which of the two views on terrace structure represented in Fig. 88, C and D, is nearer the truth. The seismic results (Ewing et al., 1937) show that more consolidated strata approach the surface near the edge of the shelf, a finding that has been interpreted as indicating basining of the terrace during Tertiary times and rise of the Cretaceous deposits towards the edge. But this interpretation is in need of confirmation. Sampling in the Georges Bank submarine canyons demonstrated the outcropping of Upper Cretaceous rocks at depths of 550 m. But the position is 10 km in from the 550-m depth contour on the slope beside the canyon. Hence, the terrace may have been built out several kilometers during the Tertiary by fore-set beds which lie in the blank area seaward of the samples procured.

In the view put forward by Umbgrove (1947) the cause of subsidence lies, not in external forces, but in reaction to internal processes. As the observed subsidence can be accounted for by isostasy alone, the present author prefers to assume purely local tectonic deformations.

Conclusive evidence as to the structure of the east-coast terrace is thus found to be lacking, but the combination of upbuilding with moderate advance towards the deep Atlantic is the most logical working hypothesis.

There is doubt what agent has caused the greater depth of the shelf off glaciated regions. The trenches remaining in these terraces are evidently due to glacial scour. But even if piedmont glaciers developed on the shelf it is not clear how a general abrasion could result together with great deepening of the trenches. Another explanation is that the depressed position is due to loading of the crust by the Pleistocene land ice and that isostatic recoil will ultimately bring the shelf back to normal depth.

Special mention should be made of the conclusion to which Emery and Shepard came concerning the development of the continental borderland off southern California, on the strength of sampling described above: "The widespread distribution on the sea floor of rocks similar to those found on land precludes the possibility that the continental borderland off southern California is a wave-built terrace dislocated by faults" (p. 448). They believe that post-Miocene pre-Pleistocene diastrophism must have broken up the borderland into blocks and

basins. The submarine fault scarps are attributed to even later movement in order to explain the absence of submarine canyons where the
scarps are found.

It would not be right, of course, to transfer these conclusions to
all shelves and continental margins, for the borderland off California
is evidently an exceptional feature.

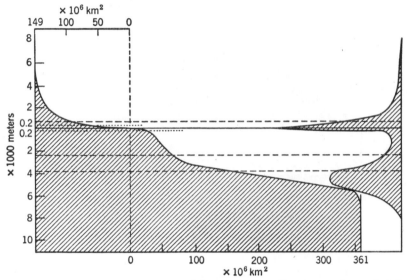

FIG. 89. Frequency curves of terrestrial topography. Levels are shown in kilometers. In the left part, a cumulative frequency curve; areas occupied by each
level are given in millions of square kilometers. The same data are shown on the
right in a simple frequency curve.

Frequency Curve of Crustal Elevation. The problem of the coastal terrace can also be studied by means of the frequency curves of crustal
elevation (Fig. 89). More than half a century ago O. Fischer drew
attention to the occurrence of two dominant levels in the earth's crust,
and in 1892 Gilbert followed suit. It might be maintained that this
is proof of the existence of two types of crustal material, each of more
or less uniform composition, the sial and the sima. Wegener attempted
to prove this view, but he failed to consider the part played by isostasy. Thus he imagined the possibility of a crust of uniform density
that should have a frequency curve with one maximum (Fig. 90, *A*).
He rejected this earth model on account of the double frequency
curve of terrestrial topography. A sounder objection is to be found

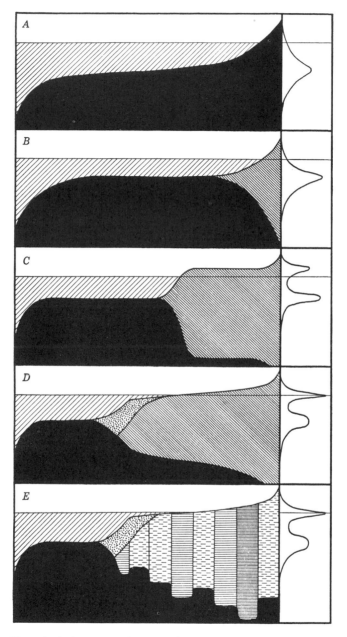

Fig. 90. Hypothetical models of the earth's crust with deduced frequency curves of elevation.

(*Continued on facing page.*)

in the isostatic equilibrium of the crust that calls for differences in density.

If the crust consisted of a large number of units of differing densities and thicknesses one could reason that the frequency curve should resemble a Gausz curve with one maximum at minus 2450 m, the average level of the crust. For, according to the laws of probability, the greatest deviations from the average should occur with least frequency. Now that two maxima occur, is that not sufficient reason for postulating uniform sial floating in uniform sima?

This, however, is only one out of two possibilities. The explanation may be sought in the existence of two main types of crustal material (Fig. 90, C). But the lighter type should then also show uniform thickness; otherwise there need still not be a second maximum frequency (Fig. 90, B). There is the other possibility, pointed out by Bucher, that denudation and deposition have caused the second maximum. If these factors had worked on uniform sial of variable thickness or on sial of variable density and thickness, the result would in both cases have been to bevel off the parts emerging above sea level. Isostatic rise to counteract denudation would have continued until each section of the continent was in isostatic equilibrium, with its surface slightly above sea level. The denudation products should form deltalike screes around the margins with a flat top at wave base and a gradual slope towards the floor of the deep sea.

Naturally, with uniform sial, uniform thickness of the continents would eventually prevail, while with sial of variable density the lower surface should conform to the amount of hydrostatic support required for maintaining the surface of the section in question at sea level (Fig. 90, D or E).

Which of the three suggestions (C, D, E, Fig. 90) resulting in a double frequency maximum is the most probable? The view expressed in C cannot account either for the shape or for the position of

---

A. Crust of uniform density, a possibility imagined by Wegener, but excluded on account of isostatic equilibrium.

B. Uniform sial of variable thickness. No external forces. Deeps due to lack of isostatic balance and to local heavy masses.

C. Uniform sial of uniform thickness outside mountain ranges. No external forces. Postulated by Wegener.

D. Uniform sial of variable thickness, cut down by denudation. Terrace built by deposition.

E. Sial of variable density and thickness, cut down by denudation. Terrace built by deposition.

the upper maximum. It should lie at about 800 m above sea level at the average height of the continental blocks. It should further be of similar shape to the maximum formed by the lower level, the surface of the sima. The more variable the thickness of the sial is supposed to be, the less pronounced the upper maximum would be.

The facts that the upper maximum is more pronounced than the lower and especially that it is situated at sea level can be accounted for only by attributing it to external forces. These are regulated by the position of sea level. For denudation leads to an equilibrium curve above erosion base (= sea level) and deposition to a deltalike terrace at wave base (= slightly below sea level).

A choice between possibilities D and E must be based partly on the evidence of earthquakes. This tends to favor case D, as the lower surface of the crust is comparatively flat outside regions of topographic elevation. But data are still rather scarce to justify an opinion. Geological evidence as to the degree of uniformity of the sial is also vague, but a certain variation is certainly probable. The true situation, it would appear, is to be sought between the two extremes.

Our analysis of the frequency curve of terrestrial topography thus leads to the following conclusion. The lower, rounded maximum is caused by the uncovered surface of sima pools, with depressions resulting from crustal deformation (isostatically uncompensated) and local differences in specific gravity (compensated). The upper, more pronounced maximum is due to external forces working during the length of geological time on a stratum of sial of variable thickness and specific gravity. Denudation tends to eliminate all topographic elevations above sea level and has greatly reduced the results of former orogenic cycles. This entails concomitant reduction of irregularities at the base of the sial layer. But owing to differences in specific gravity smaller variations in thickness will persist indefinitely. Had external forces been absent the continents would have been much higher, smaller, and more irregular. In short, the thickness is regulated by the position of sea level. The waste products are partly spread out on the deep-sea floor, but a considerable proportion of the coarser material has been used in building the continental terrace. Erosion has had a much smaller influence on the formation of the terrace.

It is worth while estimating whether the amount of denudation required to account for the terrace by deposition (either outbuilding or upbuilding) is a probable quantity. It is pointed out elsewhere in this volume (pp. 113 and 234) that denudation is a far more active agent than marine erosion. This is favorable to the view that the terrace is mainly due to deposition and not to marine planation. But sedimentation does not necessarily occur mainly along the border of the continents; it might take place principally on the deep-sea floor. We must therefore go into this matter somewhat further.

The main difficulty is found to lie with the uncertainty as to the original shapes from which terrace building started. On this the volume of the terrace largely depends. The largest volume is represented

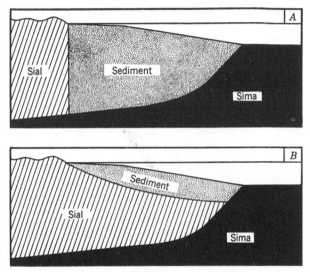

FIG. 91. Volume of the continental terrace: *A*, assuming no substratum of sial; *B*, with a subsided substratum of sial, a more probable assumption.

by the assumption that there is no primary sial underlying the terrace. Taking the specific gravity of the terrace as 2.5, of water as 1, and of sima as 3, the volume above the deep-sea floor should be one-quarter of the total volume. The area of the cross section of this prism of sediment is roughly 2000 km², and the total length on earth 100,000 km. The volume then works out at 200×10^6 km³.

The hypothesis of no sial below the terrace is doubtless too extreme. The geophysical results obtained by seismic methods mentioned above are certainly in favor of assuming a substratum of continental rock below the more recent sediment. The true situation is probably more like Fig. 91, *B*. As a first approximation a volume of sediment of 50×10^6 km³ will be assumed.

The next difficulty is to select the length of time required to build the terrace.

The structure in localities where geophysical investigations and drilling have been carried out is best explained by assuming growth since the Triassic. But even if it is supposed that the construction did not start until the beginning of the Cretaceous, 100 million years ago, the annual growth works out at no more than ½ km³. This value is certainly admissible. The annual delivery of detritus to the sea by rivers is estimated to attain 12 km³ at the present. Even if present denudation is ten times the average for the past, less than half that average would suffice to have built the terrace. (For other aspects of the problem of sediment volume, see Chapter 5.)

The present author is far from claiming that the above estimates even approach the truth. They are given only to show that the hypothesis of terrace building by sedimentation does not call upon values for denudation and deposition that exceed legitimate assumptions.

Pratt (1947) reasons that the continental terrace contains an enormous volume of sediment with a large proportion of younger deposits. The deposits were formed in the transitional area between erosion and deposition. The mobility of the continental margins is great, and conditions of deposition must repeatedly alternate with mild erosion or winnowing of all mud leaving coarse sands. Hence fine deposits acting as source beds and interfingering with coarser lenses acting as reservoirs should both occur. Organic matter is plentiful, and in depressions it will have been preserved in the fine deposits accumulating there. His final conclusion is that all general requirements for the accumulation of oil pools are provided. The chances of finding great reserves of petroleum in the continental terraces are highly favorable. Shepard (1948) indicates which methods could be applied to the mapping of oil structures on the continental platform.

Before leaving the subject of the structure of the continental terrace attention must be focused on a baffling problem. As all observations so far tend to show that the present continental terraces are comparatively young, Mesozoic or Tertiary, one may well ask where are the accumulations of sediment and the masses planed off by marine erosion that must have developed during preceding geological ages. The period of which the terrace-forming activity appears to have left no record is at least ten times longer than the time during which the present continental shelves were developed. Have all the ancient terraces foundered?

The inner parts of some ancient terraces may have been incorporated in coastal orogenic structures. This does not solve the problem, and for the majority of continental borders this partial solution cannot apply.

The difficulty becomes even more formidable when the strong evidence in favor of the subsidence of ancient borderlands along many coasts is taken into account. There should have been terraces even beyond these borderlands, right out in the present deep-sea areas.

The question to be solved is how the old borderland and the vast accumulations of terrace sediments of pre-Mesozoic age were transformed to normal oceanic areas. Should one assume that in some mysterious manner the sialic foundation was chemically altered to sima? Did vast invasions of ultrabasic igneous rock radically change the specific gravity? Was the sial stretched out to a thin stratum by continental drift or by gravitational pull? The view was advanced on former pages that the present east-coast terrace was built out on an old land surface downwarped in pre-Mesozoic times by some unknown revolution, which resulted in a gradual continental slope of consolidated basement rocks. The gradual subsidence which followed is probably of an entirely different nature, because it is due to maintenance of isostatic equilibrium during accumulation of sediment. It is well to realize that the explanation offered must remain unsatisfactory as long as it has to start from conditions that cannot be accounted for.

To the mind of the present author the problem of the subsided ancient borderlands and the disappearance of former terraces is one of the most weighty and urgent questions in the field of geology and geophysics. Until it has been solved we can never understand the fundamental features of the earth's crust. It is closely bound up with the origin of oceans and continents, with the formation of the continental shelf and slope, with isostasy and geosynclinal evolution. In the meantime the sweeping statement that continents cannot possibly have sunk away to form ocean beds should be avoided.

It is obvious that the problem of the shelf is still far from being definitely solved. The tentative conclusion reached is that the terrace on the Atlantic coast of America is due mainly to upbuilding, with some outbuilding, while erosion has operated in varying but small degree. In the Californian continental borderland faulting is of more importance. What happened to pre-Mesozoic terraces and ancient borderlands, and what the margins of the continents were like when the present cycle of terrace building started, must be left open questions. The surface has been largely modified and swept clean during glacial times of low sea level. A covering of coarse material has been left by this action.

During the exposure minor topographic irregularities were evolved and channels were cut by rivers (see Chapter 7). Sea level is still 30 m or more below its preglacial position. Hence the shelf may originally have been built at a relatively deeper level than it at present occupies. At any rate, the continental terrace cannot have been built under the present conditions, as Shepard has emphasized.

The possible reasons for widespread absence of postglacial sedimentation on the outer shelf will be dealt with later.

Bibliography

ASSOCIATION D'OCÉANOGRAPHIE PHYSIQUE. *Report on the Criteria and Nomenclature of the Major Divisions of the Ocean Bottom*, 124 pp., University of Liverpool, 1940.

BARRELL, J. Rhythms and the Measurement of Geologic Time, *Bull. Geol. Soc. Am.*, Vol. 28, pp. 776–785, 1917.

BEMMELEN, R. W. VAN. Das Permanenzproblem nach der Undationstheorie, *Geol. Rundschau*, Bd. 30, pp. 10–20, 1939.

BETZ, F., and H. H. HESS. The Floor of the North Pacific Ocean, *Geographical Review*, pp. 99–116, 1942.

BORN, A. Die Entstehung der Ozeane, *Meereskunde*, Bd. 18, 3, Ht. 199, 31 pp., 1932.

    Über Werden und Zerfall von Kontinentalschollen, *Fortschr. Geol. u. Pal.*, Bd. 10, Ht. 32, pp. 345–422, 1933.

BOURCART, J. *Géographie du fond des mers, Étude du relief des océans*, 307 pp., Payot, Paris, 1949.

BOWIE, W. The Origin of Continents and Oceans, *Sci. Monthly*, Vol. 41, pp. 444–449, 1935.

BUCHER, W. H. The Deformation of the Earth's Crust, 518 pp., 1933.

    Mechanics of Crustal Deformation, *Digest*, Vol. 10, *Tulsa Geol. Soc.*, pp. 50–61, 1941/42.

CLEMENTS, T., and K. O. EMERY. Seismic Activity and Topography of the Sea Floor off Southern California, *Bull. Seism. Soc. Am.*, Vol. 37, pp. 307–313, 1947.

CLOOS, H. Zur Grosztektonik Hochafrikas und seiner Umgebung, *Geol. Rundschau*, Bd. 28, pp. 333–348, 1937. .

    Hebung-Spaltung-Vulkanismus, *Geol. Rundschau*, Bd. 30, pp. 403–527, 1939.

    Tektonische Bemerkungen über den Boden des Golfes von Aden, *Geol. Rundschau*, Vol. 33, pp. 354–363, 1942.

DALY, R. A. *Architecture of the Earth*, 211 pp., Appleton-Century, New York, 1938.

    For: Relevant facts and inferences from field geology, *see* Gutenberg, 1939.

    The Floor of the Ocean, 177 pp., University of North Carolina Press, 1942.

DANGEARD, L. *Observations de géologie sous-marine et d'océanographie relatives à la Manche*, 295 pp., Thèse, Paris, 1929.

DIETZ, R. S. Some Oceanographic Observations on Operation Highjump, *U. S. Navy Electr. Lab.*, Rept. 55, 97 pp., 1948.

DREHER, O. Besteht der Boden des pazifischen Ozeans aus Sima oder aus Sial? *Geol. en Mijnb.*, pp. 39–48, 1942.

DU TOIT, A. L. *Our Wandering Continents*, 366 pp., Oliver & Boyd, Edinburgh, 1937.

EMERY, K. O., and F. P. SHEPARD. Lithology of the Sea Floor off Southern California, *Bull. Geol. Soc. Am.*, Vol. 56, pp. 431–478, 1945.

ESCHER, B. G. Moon and Earth, *Proc. Kon. Akad. v. Wetensch. Amsterdam*, Vol. 42, pp. 127–138, 1939.

EWING, M., A. P. CRARY, H. M. RUTHERFORD, and B. L. MILLER. Geophysical Investigations in the Emerged and Submerged Atlantic Coastal Plain, *Bull. Geol. Soc. Am.*, Vol. 48, pp. 753–812, 1937.

EWING, M., G. P. WOOLLARD, A. C. VINE, and J. L. WORZEL. Recent Results in Submarine Geophysics, *Bull. Geol. Soc. Am.*, Vol. 57, pp. 909–934, 1946.

FAIRBRIDGE, R. W. The Juvenility of the Indian Ocean, *Scope, J. Sci. Un. Un. W. Austr.*, Vol. 1, 3, pp. 29–35, 1948.

FOURMARIER, P. Que faut-il penser de la notion de la permanence des océans, *Bull. soc. belge, d'étud. géogr.*, T. 10, pp. 26–48, 1940.

FRIEDLÄNDER, I. Regelmässigkeit der Abstände vulkanischer Eruptionszentren, *Zeitschr. f. Vulkanologie*, Bd. 4, pp. 15–32, 1918.

GEYER, R. A. Annotated Bibliography of Marine Geophysical and Geological Surveys, *Bull. Geol. Soc. Am.*, Vol. 59, pp. 671–696, 1948.

GLAESSNER, M. F., and C. TEICHERT. Geosynclines: A Fundamental Concept in Geology, *Am. J. Sci.*, Vol. 245, pp. 465–482, 571–591, 1947.

GUTENBERG, B. Geotektonische Hypothesen, *Handb. d. Geophysik*, Bd. 3, Lf. 1, pp. 442–547, 1930.

GUTENBERG, B., et al. Internal Constitution of the Earth, *Physics of the Earth*, Vol. 7, 413 pp., McGraw-Hill, New York, 1939.

GUTENBERG, B., and C. F. RICHTER. On Seismic Waves (second paper), *Gerlands Beitr. Geoph.*, Bd. 45, pp. 280–360, 1935.

GUTENBERG, B., and C. F. RICHTER. Seismicity of the Earth, *Geol. Soc. Am.*, Spec. Paper 34, 131 pp., 1941, and *Bull.*, Vol. 56, pp. 603–668, 1945.

HAUG, É. *Traité de géologie*, T. 1, 546 pp., Armand Colin, Paris, 1907.

HESS, H. H. Drowned Ancient Islands of the Pacific Basin, *Am. J. Sci.*, Vol. 244, pp. 772–791, 1946.

Major Structural Features of the Western North Pacific, *Bull. Geol. Soc. Am.*, Vol. 59, pp. 417–446, 1948.

HILLS, G. F. S. *The Formation of the Continents by Convection* 102 pp., Arnold, London, 1947.

HOBBS, W. H. Mountain Growth, a Study of the Southwestern Pacific Region, *Proc. Am. Philos. Soc.*, Vol. 88, pp. 221–268, 1944.

HÖGBOM, A. G. Die Atlantislitteratur unserer Zeit, *Bull. Geol. Inst. Upsala*, Vol. 28, pp, 17–78, 1941.

HOLTEDAHL, O. *The Submarine Relief off the Norwegian Coast*, Norske Vidensk, Akad. Oslo, 43 pp., 1940.

JOHNSON, D. W. *Shore Processes and Shoreline Development*, 584 pp., John Wiley & Sons, New York, 1919.

KING, W. B. R. The Geology of the Eastern Part of the English Channel, *Quart. J. Geol. Soc. London*, Vol. 104, pp. 327–338, 1948.

KNOTHE, H. Die Entstehung der Ozeane und der Wasserhaushalt des Weltmeeres, *Peterm. Mitt.*, Bd. 79, pp. 126–129, 1933.

KOBER, L. *Tektonische Geologie*, 492 pp., Bornträger, Berlin, 1942.

KOSSINA, E. Die Erdoberfläche, *Handb. d. Geophysik*, Bd. 2, pp. 869–954, 1933.

KRENKEL, E. *Geologie Afrikas*, I, 461 pp., Bornträger, Berlin, 1925.

KUENEN, PH. H. Geological Interpretation of the Bathymetrical Results, *The Snellius Expedition*, Vol. 5, part 1, 124 pp., Brill, Leyden, 1935.
Quantitative Estimations Relating to Eustatic Movements, *Geol. en Mijnb.*, pp. 194–201, 1939.
Kruistochten over de indische Diepzeebekkens, 220 pp., Leopold, The Hague, 1941.
Volcanic Fissures with Examples from the East Indies, *Geol. en Mijnb.*, 7, pp. 17–23, 1945.
The Formation of the Continental Terrace, *British Assoc. Adv. Sci.* (in press).

LAWSON, A. C. Insular Arcs, Foredeeps and Geosynclinal Seas of the Asiatic Coast, *Bull. Geol. Soc. Am.*, Vol. 43, pp. 353–381, 1932.

LEET, L. D. *Practical Seismology and Seismic Prospecting*, 430 pp., Appleton-Century, New York, 1938.

MECKING, L. Ozeanische Bodenformen und ihre Beziehungen zum Bau der Erde, *Peterm. Mitt.*, Bd. 86, pp. 1–10, 1940.

MOHOROVIČIĆ, S. Das Erdinnere, *Zeitschr. f. angew. Geophysik*, Bd. 1, pp. 330–383, 1925.

MURRAY, H. W. Profiles of the Aleutian Trench, *Bull. Geol. Soc. Am.*, Vol. 56, pp. 757–782, 1945.
Topography of the Gulf of Maine, *Bull. Geol. Soc. Am.*, Vol. 58, pp. 153–196, 1947.

NATIONAL RESEARCH COUNCIL. *Bull.* 85, Physics of the Earth, 5, Oceanography, 581 pp., 1932.

NÖLKE, F. Zur Tektonik des atlantischen Beckens, *Geol. Rundschau*, Bd. 30, pp. 21–27, 1939.

NOVÁK, V. J. On the Origin of the Continental Shelf, *Mém. soc. roy. lettres et sci. de Bohême*, Cl. sci., Vol. 18, pp. 1–27, 1937.

PRATT, W. E. Petroleum on the Continental Shelves, *Econ. Geol.*, Vol. 42, pp. 83–85, 1947.

REHM, H. Die Erdbebentätigkeit der Weltmeere sowie ihre Beziehungen zur Tektonik, *Veröff. Reichsan. f. Erdbebenfor. Jena*, Ht. 27, 24 pp., 1936.

RIEL, P. M. VAN. The Bottom Configuration in Relation to the Flow of the Bottom Water, *The Snellius Expedition*, Vol. 2, part 2, Chapter 2, 63 pp. + charts, Brill, Leyden, 1934.

RITTMANN, A. Über die Herkunft der vulkanischen Energie und die Entstehung des Sials, *Geol. Rundschau*, Bd. 30, pp. 52–60, 1938.

ROTHÉ, J. P. Hypothèse sur la formation de l'océan atlantique, *Compt. rend. acad. sci.*, T. 224, pp. 1295–1297, 1947.

ROUCH, J. *Traité d'océanographie physique, Sondages*, 256 pp., Payot, Paris, 1943.

SAPPER, K. *Vulkankunde*, 424 pp., Engelhorn, Stuttgart, 1927.

SCHOTT, G. *Geographie des indischen und stillen Ozeans*, 413 pp., Boysen, Hamburg, 1935.
Geographie des atlantischen Ozeans, 438 pp., Boysen, Hamburg, 1942.

Schuchert, C. Gondwana Land Bridges, *Bull. Geol. Soc. Am.*, Vol. 43, pp. 875–916, 1932.

Senn, A. Die Geologie der Insel Barbados B. W. I. (Kleine Antillen) und die Morphogenese der umliegenden marinen Grossformen, *Ecl. Geol. Helv.*, Vol. 40, pp. 199–222, 1947.

Shepard, F. P. *Submarine Geology*, 348 pp., Harper, New York, 1948.

Shepard, F. P., and K. O. Emery. Submarine Topography off the California Coast, *Geol. Soc. Am.*, *Spec. Paper* 31, 171 pp., 1941.

Smit Sibinga, G. L. On the Petrological and Structural Character of the Pacific, *Verh. Geol. Mijnb. Gen.*, *Geol. Serie*, Vol. 13, pp. 335–354, 1943.

Sonder, R. A. Zur Tektonik des atlantischen Ozeans, *Geol. Rundschau*, Bd. 30, pp. 28–51, 1939.

Staub, R. *Der Bewegungsmechanismus der Erde*, 270 pp., Bornträger, Berlin, 1928.

Stearns, H. T. Late Geologic History of the Pacific Basin, *Am. J. Sci.*, Vol. 243, pp. 614–626, 1945.

Stetson, H. C. Geology and Paleontology of the Georges Bank Canyons, *Bull. Geol. Soc. Am.*, Vol. 47, pp. 339–366, 1936.

Stille, H. Geotektonische Probleme des pazifischen Erdraumes, *Abh. Preusz. Akad. Wiss.*, *Math.-naturw. Kl.*, Nr. 11, 77 pp., 1944.

Sverdrup, H. U., M. W. Johnson, and R. H. Fleming. *The Oceans*, 1087 pp., Prentice-Hall, New York, 1942.

Swain, F. M. Two Recent Wells in Coastal Plain of North Carolina, *Bull. Am. Assoc. Petr. Geol.*, Vol. 31, pp. 2054–2060, 1947.

Tesch, P., and Th. Reinhold. De Bodem van het Zuidelijk Uiteinde der Noordzee, *Tijdschr. Kon. Ned. Aard. Gen.*, Vol. 63, 1, pp. 72–84, 1946.

Umbgrove, J. H. F. On the Origin of Continents and Ocean Floors, *J. Geol.*, Vol. 54, pp. 169–178, 1946.

The Pulse of the Earth, 358 pp., Nijhoff, The Hague, 1947.

Veatch, A. C., and P. A. Smith. Atlantic Submarine Valleys of the United States and the Congo Submarine Valley, *Geol. Soc. Am.*, *Spec. Paper* 7, 101 pp. + 12 charts, 1939.

Vening Meinesz, F. A. Gravity over the Hawaiian Archipelago and over the Madeira Area. Conclusions about the Earth's Crust, *Proc. Kon. Akad. v. Wetensch. Amsterdam*, Vol. 44, pp. 2–12, 1941.

Topography and Gravity in the North Atlantic Ocean, *Proc. Kon. Akad. v. Wetensch. Amsterdam*, Vol. 45, pp. 120–125, 1942.

De Verdeling van Continenten en Oceanen over het Aardoppervlak, *Versl. Kon. Akad. v. Wetensch. Amsterdam*, *Afd. Nat.*, Vol. 53, pp. 151–159, 1944.

Shear Patterns of the Earth's Crust, *Trans. Am. Geophys. Union*, Vol. 28, pp. 1–61, 1947.

Vening Meinesz, F. A., J. H. F. Umbgrove, and Ph. H. Kuenen. *Gravity Expeditions at Sea, 1923–1932*, Vol. 2, 208 pp., Waltman, Delft, 1934.

Walther, J. Die Methoden der Geologie als historischer und biologischer Wissenschaft, *Handb. Biol. Arbeitsmeth.*, Abt. 10, 599 pp., Urban und Schwarzenberg, Berlin, 1926.

Wayland Vaughan, T. *International Aspects of Oceanography*, 225 pp., Nat. Acad. Sci., Washington, 1937.

WEGENER, A. *Die Entstehung der Kontinente und Ozeane,* 242 pp., Vieweg, Braunschweig, 1941.

WILLIS, B. Isthmian Links, *Bull. Geol. Soc. Am.,* Vol. 43, pp. 917–952, 1932.

WILSON, J. T. The Love Waves of the South Atlantic Earthquake of August 28, 1933, *Bull. Seism. Soc. Am.,* Vol. 30, pp. 273–301, 1940.

WISEMAN, J. D. H., and R. B. S. SEWELL. The Floor of the Arabian Sea, *Geol. Mag.,* Vol. 74, pp. 219–230, 1937.

WORZEL, J. L., and M. EWING. Explosion Sounds in Shallow Water, *Mem. Geol. Soc. Am.,* Vol. 27, pp. 1–53, 1948.

The Indonesian
Deep-Sea Depressions

THE ORIGIN OF THE INDONESIAN DEEP-SEA DEPRESSIONS

The deep depressions between and surrounding the Moluccan islands merit separate discussion. Not only is the region the most diversified area of the earth's crust, but for no similar part are so many topographical, geological, and geophysical data available. The *Snellius* expedition sounded the Moluccan seas in considerable detail; geological reconnaissance has been carried out on all the major islands; the seismological stations on Ambon and Java have been active during many years; and, finally, the gravimetric survey by Vening Meinesz stands out as a remarkable scientific achievement.

A detailed geological and morphological description of Indonesia would require too much space, but the main features are as follows. On the western side the Asiatic continental block extends by the shallow Sunda Shelf to include the islands Borneo, Sumatra, and Java. In the east the Australian block comprises New Guinea and the shallow Arafura Shelf. The intervening belt of the Moluccas forms a mobile area with young mountains, deep depressions, and island arcs. It continues northward into the Philippines and westward in a narrow belt along the southern margin of the stable Asiatic block by way of southern Java and western Sumatra with the adjoining islands and deep-sea troughs towards Malacca and Burma.

The main element of the Moluccas (see Plate A) is a double island arc: first, the non-volcanic Outer Banda Arc, starting at Buru, and running via Ceram, Kei, Timor, and the submarine ridge south of Java to the islands west of Sumatra; second, the volcanic Inner Banda Arc from Banda south of Ceram via the Lesser Sunda Islands to the row of volcanoes on Java and Sumatra. The remainder of the Moluccas is less simple in structure. Celebes shows a double arc, convex to the west, with connecting links in the southwest towards Java and the Lesser Sunda Islands, a link eastwards to New Guinea, and northwards to Mindanao. Halmahera is joined to New Guinea and Mindanao by island festoons, while Borneo and the Philippines are connected by three rows of islands crowning submarine ridges. Volcanoes are met with from Celebes northwards and on Halmahera. The shape of the depressions in between will be described separately later.

The Moluccan islands are composed mainly of Paleozoic, Mesozoic, and Tertiary sediments and igneous rocks, showing moderate to intensive orogenic disturbances. During Upper Tertiary times overthrust sheets were developed on the Outer Banda Arc and in eastern Celebes. A covering of young volcanic products characterizes not only the volcanic areas but also large tracts of Celebes. Recently elevated reef limestones are encountered on most of the islands, locally up to heights of 1000 m.

The gravity survey by Vening Meinesz revealed the occurrence of large divergences from isostatic equilibrium. Along a narrow belt there exists a great deficiency of gravity in which some of the most extreme anomalies known on earth were measured. This belt of negative anomalies follows all along the Outer Banda Arc and is continued northwards between Celebes and Halmahera in the direction of the Philippines. An offshoot appears to follow the eastern arms of Celebes. The positive anomalies are either arranged in belts following the negative strip on both sides, or they form separate broader fields.

Indonesia forms a strongly seismic area. Although devastating shocks are rare, the number of recorded epicenters is surprising. Shallow-focus earthquakes are clustered along the Outer Banda Arc; deep-focus earthquakes are situated mainly on the Asiatic side of this strip.

An excellent summary of geological knowledge, especially from the stratigraphical point of view, has been given by Umbgrove (1938). Critical discussions of various theories on the structure and geophysics may be found in Vening Meinesz, Umbgrove, Kuenen (1934), and Kuenen (1935). A recent survey is provided by Umbgrove (1947).

A few dozen hypotheses concerning the geological origin of Indonesia have been propounded during the last half century, but since new data have come to hand most of them no longer hold and need not be considered here. Thus many writers have postulated long faultlines demarkating the island margins (Elbert, Voltz) (Fig. 92). The new bathymetrical chart, however, brings unequivocal proof that the morphology does not confirm the lines drawn by those authors. Neither are indications revealed of any such faults continuing for hundreds of kilometers.

Furthermore, the conception that all deep depressions are due to vertical faults, by which continental areas were dropped to great depths, certainly does not merit general application. Yet the sugges-

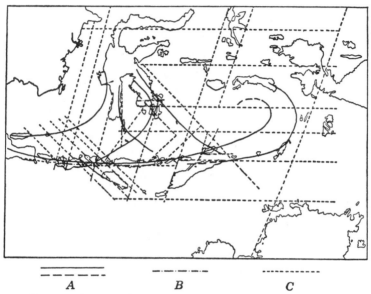

Fig. 92. Geotectonic map of the Moluccas according to Elbert. *A.* Mountain arcs. *B.* Faults deduced from structure. *C.* Faults deduced from morphology. (After Rutten, 1927, Fig. 155, p. 525.)

tion made by Verbeek (1908), that Australia and Asia were formerly connected via a continental Indonesian block finds support in several observations. It will be shown later that the Moluccan region was formerly partly covered by epicontinental seas, in which depressions were later developed by subsidence.

The picture first painted by Wegener (1941) and later developed by Smit Sibinga of the evolution of the Moluccan Archipelago (1927, 1933) is entirely different (Fig. 93). They suppose that insular arcs were formerly suspended from the Asiatic continent, with uncovered pools of sima in between forming deep depressions. The mass of Australia with New Guinea is thought to have drifted up against these festoons, and to have warped and distorted them into their present shapes.

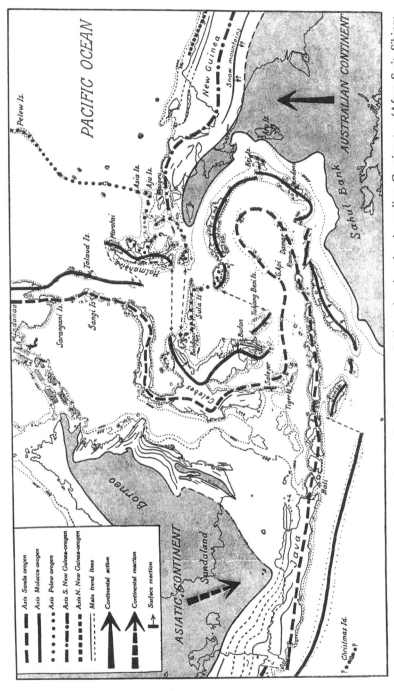

Fig. 93. The triple orogen of the Moluccas after the supposed disruption by the Australian Continent. (After Smit Sibinga, 1933.)

Serious objections can be raised to this conception (Kuenen, 1935), the more important of which are as follows (Plate A). 1. Australia and Asia are connected by shallow submarine ridges (New Guinea-Obi-Sula islands; New Guinea-Halmahera-Snellius Ridge). This absence of a seam in the form of a continuous trough between the parts welded together is not in accordance with the expected result of sialbergs drifting up against each other. If the latter were true the morphological structure should be directed parallel, not at right angles, to the joining line. Biogeography requires former dry-land connections between the Australian continent and the Moluccas. But there is no apparent manner in which the line along which welding took place could become bridged by land connections.

2. The trough from Ceram to Timor continues uninterrupted into the Java Trough. Obviously they form one genetic unit, although the depth varies considerably. From the first objection it followed that no continuous seam marks the blocks supposed to have been joined. The present argument clearly shows that the trough supposed by Wegener to mark the line of junction can be traced far beyond the region of contact, so that it cannot represent a junction (Fig. 94).

3. Several ridges discovered since Smit Sibinga traced three disrupted insular arcs cannot be fitted into the picture of former festoons. Examples are the Snellius Ridge north of Morotai, the Luymes Ridges south of Buru, the submarine ridge east of the Kei Islands, the ridge upon which is situated Kisar, etc. But if not all submarine ridges are parts of former arcs, the entire reconstruction loses its foundations. For then the morphology must be younger than the time of junction, in which event former festoons could not be deduced from the present forms.

4. Some Mesozoic rock series are identical in fauna and facies on New Guinea with Misool on the one hand (Australian block) and the Moluccas (Asiatic) on the other, forming in fact connecting strips between the two continents. This demonstrates that a close connection existed at a time when Wegener supposed several thousands of kilometers of deep sea to have separated the two regions. The drifting would then have brought these identical portions of the two blocks directly opposite each other—an improbable coincidence.

5. The stratigraphy of the Moluccas proves the former existence of denuding land areas adjoining the present islands. Moreover, the present coastlines cut off the tectonic and stratigraphic structures obliquely. Both facts testify to the subsidence of land directly along-

side the present island arcs. According to the theory of drift, however, the islands have been bordered by sima pools since a comparatively remote past.

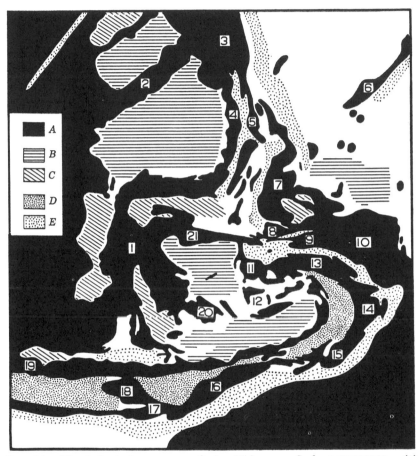

FIG. 94. Morphological structure of the Moluccas. Scale 1:20,000,000. (1)
Celebes, (2) Sibutu-Basilan Ridge, (3) Mindanao, (4) Sangihe Ridge, (5) Talaud
Ridge, (6) Palau Ridge, (7) Halmahera, (8) Obi, (9) Misool, (10) New Guinea,
(11) Buru, (12) Luymes and Siboga Ridges, (13) Ceram, (14) Kei, (15) Jamdena,
(16) Timor, (17) Savu, (18) Sumba, (19) Bali, (20) Tukangbesi Islands. (Redrawn after Kuenen, 1935, Fig. 47, p. 114.)

6. The last point shows that the deep-sea troughs did not develop
until intensive folding of the Outer Banda Arc had taken place in
Miocene times. Two explanations might be offered for this fact under
the theory of drift. (*a*) The meeting of Australia with Asia occurred

after the orogenic period mentioned. But this would mean that the folding of the rocks on the Outer Banda Arc had taken place by being pressed up against the surrounding sima. This is not in harmony with the postulated ductile nature of sima. Moreover, Wegener explains the formation of the island arcs by the rupture of Asia drifting away westwards from the ancient oceanic section of the Pacific, while the island structures testify to compression. (*b*) The other suggestion would be that the deep-sea relief of Indonesia dates from after the joining of Australia to the Moluccas. In this event the orogenic compression could be attributed to the pressure exerted by the Australian block. But, as pointed out above, this would imply that the present structure and morphology cannot serve as a key to the geological history prior to the advent of Australia. The island arcs would not represent Wegener's floating strips of sial, but secondary structural elements. Obviously both suggestions lead to deductions that cannot be fitted into the theory of continental drift.

7. The supposed intensive buckling of island arcs, without their having toppled over or even capsized, is hard to maintain and would at any rate need a highly mobile and unresistant sima in between. Under such conditions the pools of sima should show perfect hydrostatic equilibrium. Yet some, like the Weber Deep, are 2½ km lower than the normal level of sima.

8. If the island arcs are such narrow strips of sial, how could the batholiths with sialic magma underlying the volcanic Inner Banda Arc have been maintained? The volcanoes would almost resemble bottles full of magma bobbing around in a sea of sima!

9. The gravity field is entirely discordant with the system of arcs as traced by Smit Sibinga. Thus there is but one belt of negative anomalies as against three postulated arcs. The belt disappears more or less where Smit Sibinga connects Buru to the Tukangbesi Islands, but is present, on the other hand, from the Banggai Archipelago northward up the Moluccan Passage, where he infers no connections. Halmahera is part of his arc but is not characterized by negative anomalies. From these and other misfits it follows that the strip of negative anomalies must have come into being after the buckling of Smit Sibinga's island arcs. Enormous displacements of mass must have occurred to bring about the negative anomalies. No less than 1000 to 1500 km³ of sima must have been replaced by sial per kilometer length of the belt, or several times the volume of the island arc above the level of the deep sea. It is improbable in the extreme that such drastic structural revolutions could have taken place partly in perfect

coincidence with the present shape of the arcs (Buru to Timor), partly entirely independent of them (north of Buru). And this must be supposed to have occurred without influencing the surface structures, because they are taken as a trustworthy key to the buckling and displacements of former simple arcs.

All these and several other arguments are opposed mainly to the local details of Wegener's theory as applied to the Moluccan region. They cannot carry much weight in our judgment of the theory as a whole.

Although the application of continental drift to the Indonesian region, as suggested by Wegener and others, appears to lead to contradictions, an attempt can be made to apply the general principle in a modified form. The present writer proposed (1935) a tentative alternative to Wegener's reconstruction for southeastern Asia that now appears to fit Du Toit's maps of the southern hemisphere fairly well (Fig. 76). Australia is supposed to have remained in contact with Asia via the Moluccas from the start, but to have swung around when it came apart from Gondwana and Antarctica. During this drift Indonesia must have been bent and crumpled. The deep-sea depressions would have been formed by folding and subsidence in and around the isthmus connecting Australia to Asia.

It was emphasized in the foregoing chapter that many geologists and geophysicists are strongly opposed to the theory of drift (see especially Umbgrove, 1947) and that the present writer is also skeptical of its merits. The survey just given shows that Indonesia, far from giving eloquent testimony in favor of Wegener's views, as some authors have held, presents many features strongly opposed to the theory of drift. Only by assuming the admittedly farfetched reconstruction outlined above can a flat contradiction be avoided.

A somewhat different conception of the structural development of the Moluccan arcs was suggested by Brouwer. He believes that the Banda Arcs were originally much farther away from the margin of the Australian continent and simpler in outline. By strong horizontal movements during the thrusting of the overthrust sheets the arcs approached the border of the continent and adapted themselves to the outline of the resisting block. The basins and troughs are thus not considered to be new developments, but they have altered in shape, breadth, and position (Fig. 95).

Some of Brouwer's arguments have been refuted by Stille, and Kuenen attempted to show from the new charts of the *Snellius* expedition that other objections can be raised. The distortion of the Outer

Banda Arc appeared to follow convincingly from the former charts. Two explanations could be offered: either the arc had gradually adapted itself to the shape of the continental border, as supposed by Brouwer—it was, so to speak, pressed into a mold; or the arc was formed primarily parallel to the border, about in its present position.

The new chart confirms the second suggestion (Fig. 96). The advanced position of the Tanimbar Islands was explained by Brouwer from the indenture in the continent directly opposite. Now, however, this embayment has disappeared on the new chart, bringing the advanced part of the arc closer to the opposite wall than elsewhere. In Brouwer's conception this would imply that the arc had bent forward in spite of a smooth wall opposite. The new chart shows, moreover, that there is no question of an outward bend of this part of the arc, but that an *en échelon* arrangement of two interchanging swells causes the sudden advance of the Tanimbar Group. This cannot represent a gradual adaptation but must of necessity be a primary structure. Thus two arguments are found against the mechanism of pressure molding.

Opposite the advanced portion of the Kei Islands there does actually exist an indenture in the continental border, the Aru Basin. But instead of swinging outwards as assumed by Brouwer, the main mass of the arc passes by in a smooth curve as may be seen by noting the steep slope into the adjoining Weber Deep in the rear. Instead a second (Groot Kei) and third (submarine) ridge have developed along the outer side of the arc. Again all signs are missing that the arc has advanced against the continent, and primary irregularities are strongly suggested.

Kisar, according to Brouwer, formed a part of the Outer Banda Arc, but, in consequence of the sharp angle in the Australian block just opposite, it was severed from the main mass and left behind. Not only has the corner of the continent disappeared from the new chart, but a separate ridge is found of which Kisar forms the culmination. It further becomes obvious that the depression in Manipa Strait between Buru and Ceram (Fig. 59) can no longer be interpreted as the surface expression of a transverse fault with horizontal displacement (Brouwer's contention). A small broad basin, closed to the south by a ridge, is now found on the chart.

The almost perfect symmetry of the Timor Trough does not accord with the conception that one slope represents an ancient continental border and the other the front of an advancing thrust (orogenic) swell.

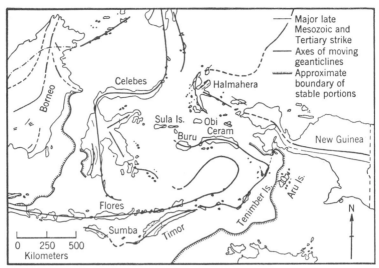

FIG. 95. The major tectonic axes of the Moluccas postulated by Brouwer. Redrawn after Brouwer, 1925, *The Geology of the Netherlands East Indies,* Fig. 1, p. 58, University of Michigan Press.)

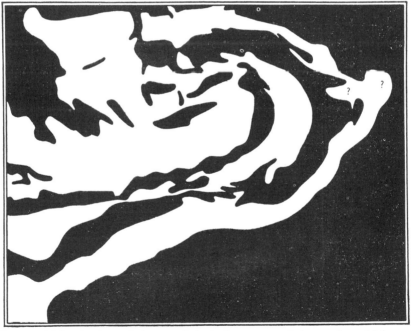

FIG. 96. Main elements of the morphological structure of the southern Moluccas based on the charts of the *Snellius* expedition. (After Kuenen, 1935, Fig. 101, p. 86.)

Finally it may be recalled that the Outer Banda Arc and the accompanying trough pass westwards beyond the Australian continent. Here, if anywhere, Brouwer's moving geanticlines should have found the minimum of resistance and could have swung southward unopposed. The chart shows, however, that there is no outward bulging where the continental "resistance" is lacking.

The outcome of this review is thus found to be strongly opposed to Brouwer's contentions.

A few words must be said concerning the comparison between the Indonesian island arcs and waves entering a coastal embayment. Argand was the first to draw this comparison, but merely in order to describe the general shape. Staub, however, attempted to explain the structure by this mechanism. To the writer this is inadmissible. In the case of waves an undulation is propagated but the medium remains in position. But, under Staub's contention that geanticlines have adapted themselves to an indenture in the foreland, the rock itself is pushed forwards, while the undulations remain fixed with respect to this propagating medium. The physical laws governing wave mechanics may on no account be applied to a moving geanticline. The fan-shaped spread of waves in a bay is therefore no explanation for the similar outward appearance of orogenic features of the earth's crust.

It was pointed out above that strong arguments are at hand to show that the adaptation of the geanticlines to the continental border is a primary feature. What is termed the border of the continent appears to be merely the edge of the undisturbed part of a formerly more extended block. If that is granted, theorizing on the cause of present parallelism of arcs and continental border is as futile as questioning why a canal is parallel to its banks.

Molengraaff was the first to state clearly that the Moluccas may be considered a folded mountain chain *in statu nascendi*. This investigator called attention (1913, 1922) to the occurrence of overthrust sheets of Miocene age and a block-faulted structure of Pliocene age on the Outer Banda Arc in the Moluccas, especially on Timor and surroundings. He suggested that during the Pliocene, and possibly also recently, the overthrusting may have continued at depth, while the orogenic processes at the surface remained restricted to fault tectonics. This younger thrusting is not exposed because erosion has not yet cut deep enough into the crust. Wanner, Weber, and Argand expressed similar ideas about exposed structures. Most later writers followed Molengraaff, each postulating more or less original tectonic lines, guided by the morphology of the region as far as known through the older soundings, but giving free rein to his imagination for the areas where the deep-sea charts provided insufficient guidance. Since publication of the *Snellius* charts, with their wealth of detail, these tectonic diagrams may be looked upon as antiquated and their exact forms will have to be revised. Hence, at present we only need to inquire into the principles involved in the various structural hypotheses, but not into their details.

Even the map (Fig. 97) given by Hobbs (1944), although based on the new depth chart, shows a number of "anticlinal arcs" that run obliquely across submarine ridges (connection between Borneo and North Celebes, between the two southern arms of Celebes, and between Sumba and the ridge south of Java), while several major topographic elements are ignored (Halmahera with the Snellius Ridge to the northwest, Buru with Sanana to the north, the ridges between Halmahera and North Celebes), and the postulated ridge on the edge of the Sahul Shelf does not occur on the deep-sea chart, although there are a few reefs.

All new data indicate that a generalization for the whole region is not warranted. From the bathymetrical charts, the distribution of earthquakes, field work, and gravimetrical surveys it becomes ever more apparent that an active belt runs through the archipelago, along Sumatra, Java, the Outer Banda Arc (possibly also the eastern arms of Celebes), and the Moluccan Passage west of Halmahera. For this strip the comparison may hold, drawn by Argand in his classical treatments of the Alps in 1916, between the present conditions in the Moluccan Arcs and the Mesozoic Alpine geosyncline. In both cases a double island arc is encountered where the frontal margins of the thrusting sheets come to the surface. To grasp the full measure of similarity the map of the Alps must be held upside down (Figs. 98 and 99).

Later Kuenen (1935) viewed in more detail the points of agreement (the similar arrangement of two major geanticlines with a smaller element [Kisar-Monte Rosa] in between, crowned by denuding islands and accompanied by deep troughs; the development of overthrust sheets) and the points of difference (larger dimensions of the Indonesian orogen, partly surrounded by oceanic basins; far greater intensity of volcanic activity; absence of recent sediments comparable to synorogenic Flysh deposits; longer duration and more leisurely development in this region).

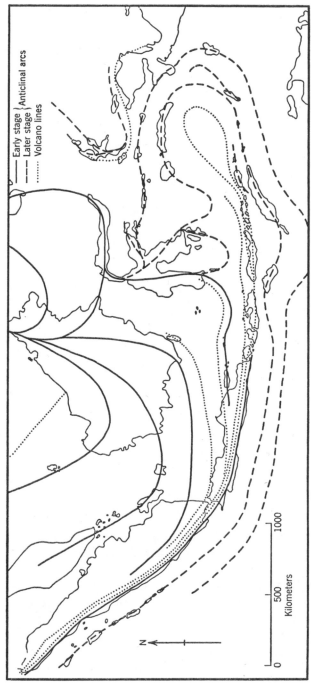

Fig. 97. The principal arcs of the Sunda-Banda system according to Hobbs. Full lines show the anticlinal arcs of an early stage, dashed lines those added in a later stage. (Based on Hobbs, 1944, maps 26 and 27.)

The remaining parts of the Moluccas farther from the active belt resemble the "Innensenken" or nuclear basins, or basins in the rear, such as the Pannonian Basin of Hungary and the Po Basin of northern Italy.

Umbgrove (1947) is also convinced that the Indonesian belt of island arcs and troughs is of the same nature as the orogenic belts of

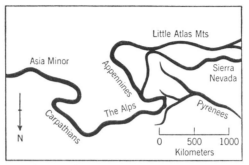

Fig. 98. The structural plan of the Alpine system of Europe (inverted) according to Staub. (Redrawn after Staub, 1928, Fig. 18, p. 33, and Fig. 24, p. 90.)

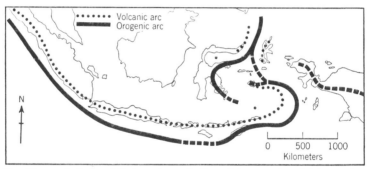

Fig. 99. Orogenic belt of Indonesia as indicated by gravity field, on the same scale as Fig. 98.

the continents. The great depth of the troughs is not due to abnormal characteristics but merely to lack of sufficient detritus during their subsidence.

Stille (1943) holds that the Moluccan orogenic area has passed through the active period of compression and that the recent vertical movements represent the final stages of development. Strong compressive movements leading to the formation of Alpine structures are not going on, nor will they take place in a later stage. Hence, this region should not be compared to the Mesozoic stage of development of the Alpine orogen, in spite of outward similarity. While the Mesozoic Alps were an early tectonic stage of development, the Moluccas are in a final stage. Stille's arguments are not convincing, and he fails to take into account the excessive isostatic anomalies of Indonesia which are in marked contrast to the slight deviations from normal gravity in the Alps. They indicate that powerful crustal deformations are still going on or have taken place comparatively recently in the Moluccan region.

According to Hobbs (1944), the arcs in Indonesia first developed in the west on Sumatra, Java, Borneo, and part of Celebes (Fig. 97). In a later stage the arcs of the Moluccas were added. This view finds no confirmation in field evidence, however. The orogenic history (summarized by Umbgrove, 1947) clearly demonstrates the synchronous development of geosynclines and of tectonic structures in the eastern and western parts of the archipelago.

It was shown by Kuenen that the festoons of elongate troughs, with an axial depression running slowly up and down, are all situated along the active belt. Most of these have a V-shaped synclinal section; those with a U-shaped, boxlike section are found between the two arcs. The roundish or slightly oblong basins, each with a nearly constant depth, are situated farther away. We will return to these depressions in the next paragraph.

The islands, on which a very intensive thrust structure has been detected, in all cases restricted to the Upper Miocene (Tertiary f 2), are all situated above the strip with negative anomalies of gravity (Umbgrove, in Vening Meinesz, 1934). The earthquakes with normal focus depths are crowded together along the same narrow strip, while those with a deep focus are restricted to the Asiatic side (Vening Meinesz, 1934). The volcanoes lie in a row at some distance from the negative anomalies on the concave side of the arc.

The correlation among the various groups of phenomena may not be strict, but the difference in depth at which they originate within the crust is sufficient reason for explaining minor divergences.

It may be recalled that Vening Meinesz attributes the belt of negative anomalies to a downward buckling of the sial crust to form a deep root in the heavier substratum of sima (Fig. 100). The anatomical dissection of folded mountain chains clearly exposes a shortening of the earth's crust. Nevertheless only the upper, sedimentary cover of the crust has been squeezed upwards. The much thicker substratum of the geosynclinal pile of sediments must be supposed to have undergone the same measure of shortening. Yet nowhere is this crust found to have bulged upwards during the compression, for erosion products do not become plentiful in the surroundings until after the main compressive phase. Consequently the conclusion cannot be avoided that the main part of the earth's sialic crust is forced downward during orogenic compression.

On several grounds it is generally inferred that in continental areas the crust consists mainly of light rocks like granite, the sial, with

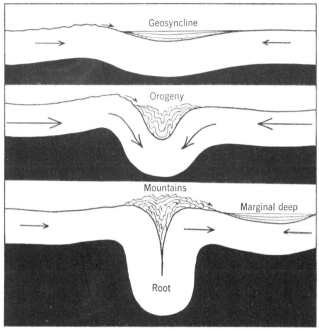

FIG. 100.   Three stages in the development of a geosyncline according to the theory of Vening Meinesz.

heavier rocks farther down, while the plastic substratum is formed by a heavy non-crystalline mass of basaltic composition, the sima (Chapter 2). Vening Meinesz thus arrives at his theory of crustal buckling.

In consequence of horizontal compressive stress the floating crust is first laid in slight undulations. Erosion of the crests and deposition in the depressions leads to the geosynclinal stage of development. As the stress increases, the weakest downward wave gives way and buckles downward. The contents of the geosyncline are folded and thrust upward. Owing to the small specific gravity of the downward bulge of the granitic crust, the "mountain root," that forces aside the heavy sima, a local deficit of mass is produced. This deficit causes the low values of gravity measured at the surface along the strip of negative anomalies. When the orogenic compression relaxes, the negative anomaly causes the crust to rise. By this process, the post orogenic elevation of mountain chains is explained, as exemplified by the elevated reefs on Moluccan islands. The root, besides rising, gradually melts and spreads out below the crust, while the folded rocks of the geosyncline are invaded from below by batholiths resulting from the concentration of radioactive heat in the swelled granitic layer.

This theory has the merit of explaining, in a simple and logical manner, first the geosynclinal stage preceding the orogenic stage, then the sudden compression without the appearance at the surface of the main mass of the shortened crust, while it accounts for the strip of negative anomalies found in Indonesia and elsewhere. This last point is highly important. On the one hand the deficit is so large that it amounts to the equivalent of a volume of rock of many hundreds of cubic kilometers per kilometer length of the strip. And, as huge voids cannot exist in the crust, the reduction in mass must be due to the replacement of heavy by light materials. Assuming a difference in specific gravity of 0.5, a volume of no less than 1000 to 1500 km^3 per km length of the strip is required. On the other hand, the locus of the deficit must lie at a depth not greater than 50 km because otherwise a small anomaly would be found over a wide area instead of a large anomaly over a narrow belt.

Since Vening Meinesz first propounded his theory highly significant confirmation has been obtained. Umbgrove showed that all islands situated in the belt of negative anomalies are characterized by exceptionally intensive orogenic compression during the Upper Tertiary (Tertiary f 2) and that nowhere have thrust nappes of the same orogenic cycle developed outside this belt. This shows that Vening Meinesz was right in postulating a close relation between the negative anomalies and compression in the crust (Plate B).

Experimenting with a crust of paraffin floating on water, Kuenen was able to demonstrate that a plastic crust with little strength is first laid in weak undulations by a compressive force (geosynclinal stage) and then suddenly buckles downwards along one of the synclines to form a deep root. More mobile "sedimentary" layers deposited in thin sheets in the "geosyncline" were crumpled, overthrust, and pinched out towards the surface while the downward buckle of the main crust developed. Although these results naturally prove nothing with respect to the processes in nature, they nevertheless suggest that the main elements of Vening Meinesz' conception are correct if the mechanical properties assigned by him to crust and substratum are real. Moreover, the reason why the crustal buckle turns downward, in spite of the greater freedom of movement upward, became evident. If it were to buckle upward the same volume of air would be replaced by sial, as of sima in the case of a downward movement. The difference in specific gravity between air and sial being about five times greater than between sial and sima, it follows that an upward movement would require a much greater application of energy. In other words, the buckling takes place with the closest approach to isostatic equilibrium possible.

The question now arises what deductions can be made concerning the formation of the Indonesian deep-sea depressions. It has already been emphasized above that all geosynclines examined have been formed on a substratum that belonged to the continent beforehand. Nowhere has a portion of the ocean floor been incorporated in an orogenic belt and thus welded onto the continental mass. The Mesozoic red clay and other "deep-sea" sediments of Timor (Molengraaff, 1920) are not oceanic deep-sea deposits but geosynclinal sediments formed under exceptional pelagic conditions and resting on shallow-water deposits. It is also known that even in the Alpine Geosyncline shallow Permian and Triassic seas transgressed over an ancient peneplaned land surface before the subsidence of the Jurassic led to abnormal depths. It is not improbable that the ocean floor is subjected to similar orogenic convulsions, but, in the absence of sufficient light sediments and ultimate elevation, no structural details can be studied, and this speculation remains unconfirmed by evidence.

For Indonesia the conclusion from the above reasoning must be that from Timor to the Philippines a continental area formerly existed in which the depressions were later formed by subsidence during and following the orogenic phase of compression in the Outer Banda Arc. Geological evidence confirms this conclusion in a satisfactory manner, as Wanner and Molengraaff have demonstrated in a slightly different connection. These facts are as follows.

The tectonic structures are cut obliquely by the present coastlines, and the strata themselves also break off abruptly at the edges of the troughs. Hence the present course of the coastlines and adjacent deep troughs is of more recent development than the sedimentation troughs and Upper Tertiary tectonic structures. In this connection attention may be drawn to many Upper Pliocene and Pleistocene faults on the islands that may be related to the development of the troughs. The facies of the Tertiary sediments denotes the former existence of extensive regions of denudation where depths of a few thousand meters are now found. Otherwise no source would have existed for the detritus contained in the sediments. Among the extensive and diversified Tertiary sediments no single deposit of great depths appears to be present. Moreover, as far as known all Tertiary

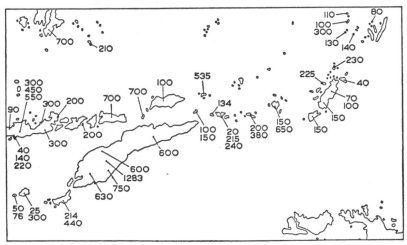

Fig. 101. Highest elevated "Pliocene-Pleistocene" reef limestones and fluviatile terraces in the southern Moluccas, in meters. (After Umbgrove, 1947, Fig. 125, p. 188.)

deposits of the Moluccas lie unconformably on denuded pre-Tertiary rocks. After that transgression practically the whole of the area now occupied by the islands was flooded by shallow seas, that is to say during the Tertiary. Then followed one or more orogenic phases, and finally the islands emerged above sea level. The elevated Pliocene-Pleistocene reef-covering of most islands proves how recently they rose to their present heights, sometimes exceeding 1000 m (Fig. 101), while on Ceram marine Pliocene has been found at elevations of 3000 m above sea level.

As the islands of the Outer Banda Arc and the Timor-Ceram Trough together form one major unit of anticlinorium and synclinorium—the two arms of a pair of scales, as it were—the conclusion of Molengraaff is unavoidable that elevation of the land and subsidence of the troughs went hand in hand. The possibility is not excluded that deep depressions existed in an earlier stage, but they must have been much smaller and must have lain entirely within the present depressions. But the uniformity of each of the present basins or troughs, with their evenly modulated profiles, renders this supposition highly improbable. Hence the conclusion is warranted that the deep-sea morphology of the Moluccas is entirely of Upper and post-Tertiary development.

The formation of an elongate trough with a synclinal cross section can be readily explained by moderate lateral compression of a floating crust. The development in close connection with the accompanying belt of negative anomalies and the strong overthrust structures also point to lateral compression. On the other hand it is probable that these two phenomena were caused long before the troughs came into being. A state of compression causing the older phenomena need no longer prevail at the present time.

Another explanation is that before the elevation of the arc, when the sial root had just been created, the adjacent crust was held by its strength above its natural level on account of the negative anomaly (Kuenen, 1936). This condition might be compared to a block of ice locally buoying up a sheet of ice. During the gradual elevation of the island arc in Pliocene-Pleistocene times in consequence of the upward pressure of the root, the superelevation of the neighboring portions of the crust should have been allowed to decrease, because the buoyant root was gradually diminishing in depth. In other words a subsidence would occur at both sides of the rising island arc.

This brings us to the moot question whether the present strong negative anomalies are the gradually decreasing remains of an even greater Upper Miocene disturbance of isostasy, or whether the compensation occurred long ago but a renewed compression rejuvenated the negative anomalies. However, to enter into this and similar matters would lead us into the maze of geotectonic problems and farther and farther away from ascertained facts and direct deductions therefrom. The discussions between Vening Meinesz, Bijlaard, Escher, van Bemmelen, Kuenen, Hobbs, Umbgrove, and others will not be gone into here.

It will only be pointed out in conclusion to this review that the remaining deep-sea basins, beyond the region of negative anomalies, present a U-shaped section and are probably due to purely vertical forces. They are characterized by positive anomalies of gravity, especially the Celebes Sea and Banda Sea, less marked in Makassar Strait and the Gulfs of Boni and Tomini around Celebes. This anomaly should cause a further downward movement and is thus in accordance with the view that these basins were recently developed by subsidence.

For the West Indies similar conclusions can be drawn as to recent formation of the deep-sea depressions and a young orogenically active area (Rutten, 1934; Hess, 1938).

COMPARISON BETWEEN THE INDONESIAN DEEP-SEA DEPRESSIONS AND FOSSIL SEDIMENTATION BASINS

A century ago Hall discovered that certain areas of the earth's crust showed long-continued subsidence and received a thick cover of sediments. These areas were later folded, and they now form the tectonic belts of the crust. Dana introduced the term geosyncline to denote these areas. Hall pointed out that all the sediments in geosynclines were deposited in shallow water, and, although their aggregate thickness may attain thousands of meters and greatly exceeds that of the equivalent sediments of neighboring "continental" areas, the geosyncline can never have formed more than a slight topographic depression at the surface. Later authors, especially Haug, have maintained that in many instances the surface depression temporarily attained larger amounts, reaching values of 1000 m, and perhaps even assuming oceanic depths. For the majority of geosynclines, however, this is certainly not true. The problem to be considered here is whether deep-sea troughs are recent examples of geosynclines.

At the outset we are faced with a difficulty because much depends on how a geosyncline is defined. Some authors, like Stille (1940), use the term to cover all sinking areas of the crust. This definition is too wide to be of much use. Naturally all deep-sea depressions would fall under it, without our having ascertained anything concerning their true nature. Stille's definition would also comprise basins, such as the Mesozoic-Tertiary basins of Paris and London, that are of an entirely different nature from the crustal elements that have generally been termed "geosynclines." In the following we will first consider elongate areas that have undergone long-continued, important subsidence and subsequently have been intensely compressed by tectonic forces. According to general use, these are typical geosynclines. The definition can be extended to cover also those units of the crust that have experienced the first stages of development of ·normal folded geosynclines but that have not yet shown the orogenic phases. This is also the normal custom, for it is usual to speak of the sedimentation in a geosyncline, a stage in which the tectonic phase is still to come. Instances in which a time of such length has elapsed since the subsidence that future tectonic activity appears improbable also occur, according to Stille, but in any event they are highly exceptional.

A geosyncline, thus defined, has gone through a stage in which it was not yet folded and then a stage in which the folding had begun but was not yet completed, and finally the tectonic history came to a close with the elevation of the entire area to form a geographic mountain range. Later we will inquire into whether deep-sea depressions (either troughs or basins) appear to be modern equivalents of normal or abnormal geosynclines in the initial stages, before folding began or was completed. If that is found to be so we could apply the term geosyncline to them and predict with a large measure of probability that they will also undergo compression in the future.

To make our point of view clear a comparison can be made with the insect world. Caterpillar and chrysalis are not denoted by the term butterfly, although they do receive the same species name. Biology lacks a term to cover the entire development. In the present problem one might follow the same procedure and speak of the trough, the orogen, and the geosyncline of, for instance, the Pyrenees. But geologists have preferred to denote all stages by the one general term of geosyncline and to describe the various phases of development by separate descriptive terms. A recent deep-sea trough is not the equivalent of the "butterfly," but we want to ascertain whether it is a "caterpillar" or "chrysalis." This question is of importance because the field geologist cannot observe directly what his "caterpillars" or "chrysalises" were like. If we can find some examples for him to study in this youthful stage, much more could be learned about the entire development. Even if our "caterpillars" are representatives of an abnormal type of "butterfly" (and this we will find to be so), and although we cannot ascertain what type will emerge in the distant future after the final metamorphoses, still the knowledge gained by examination of them will form an important contribution to the problem of tectonic evolution and will throw light on many questions about the former stages of fully developed geosynclines.

The terminology of geosynclines is growing in complexity as knowledge of these crustal features increases (see Glaessner and Teichert, 1947; Kay, 1947). Various types and separate parts of complex forms or stages of development have received different names, generally prefixes attached to the word geosyncline, as idiogeosyncline, miogeosyncline, etc. The same term has been used to denote different elements by some writers. While some lay emphasis on the shapes in their definitions, others have looked mainly to stages of development, size, magmatic evolution, etc. Hence the definitions overlap, and the terms are sometimes almost synonyms without, however, fitting precisely. Although we will attempt to avoid getting entangled in these controversial details, it is impossible to discuss our subject without making use of a few of these special terms and concepts.

Many authors have considered the problem whether geosynclines and deep-sea troughs are similar formations (Grabau, 1924; Leuchs, 1927; Stille, 1919; etc.). Haug (1900) was the great advocate of the view that these two elements are identical, and he considered the Java Trough to be a typical recent geosyncline. Bucher (1933) also denied a fundamental difference between the filled-up "furrows" of continental areas and the open troughs of the deep sea. Molengraaff similarly held that the Indonesian deep-sea basins are geosynclines (1913, 1922). Daly (1939) believes the deep-sea troughs to represent "open" geosyncline and explains both forms as "fault warps," that is, warpings of the crust in consequence of compression where great faults, passing right through the crust, have developed weak places. The curved shape on maps and the symmetry in section, at least of many deep-sea troughs, are considered by the present writer to militate against this hypothesis, and such faults have seldom been proved in the basement of old geosynclines. Of latter years Kuenen (1935) and Umbgrove (1947) have dealt at length with this problem. It appears from these studies that the problem cannot be stated quite so simply as it was formerly, because there are several types of fossil sedimentation depressions and also recent deep-sea depressions.

Umbgrove divided the fossil sedimentation depressions into two classes: the eugeosynclines, comprising primary depressions and major geosynclinal belts, like that of the Alpine chain, as against all other basins and troughs, which, in turn, are divided into two groups each with two types as follows: [1]

Group 1. Troughs.
  Type I. Marginal deep.
  Type II. Intramontane trough.

Group 2. Basins.
  Type III. Nuclear basin.
    (a) With an isochronous frame.
    (b) With an anisochronous frame.
  Type IV. Discordant basin.

[1] Several other classifications of geosynclines have been proposed, but they are less suitable to our purpose and will be left out of account (cf. Kay, 1947).

Eugeosynclines, a term coined by Stille, are either single geosynclines as they first develop by subsidence in a continental area, or complicated major depressions divided up into secondary troughs by geanticlinal ridges. The geosyncline of the Alps is a classical example of the latter type. It probably consisted of separate synclinal basins from the very start, but many new troughs were formed later and these fall into group 1 of Umbgrove's classification given above.

The marginal deeps are markedly elongate depressions situated along the border of the already folded and elevated orogen. They correspond to Stille's "Saumtiefen" and the "foredeeps" and "hinterdeeps" of other authors. The type example is the Miocene Molasse depression along the northern margin of the Oligocene Alps. Other examples are the Upper Carboniferous, paralic coal-bearing basins strung out from Ireland to Westphalia and Silesia, or the Carboniferous-Permian marginal deep along the western border of the Acadian Appalachians. Umbgrove in his table gives his term marginal deep as synonymous with Schuchert's "monogeosynclines." However, Schuchert's term is somewhat broader as it does not require an earlier orogenic period in the adjoining strip of the crust.

Umbgrove's intramontane troughs form in the core of an orogen as elongate depressions. Transitional forms lead over to the marginal deeps. Examples are: Saar and Saale Troughs in the European Variscides, Lake Caledonia in the Scottish Caledonides, California Valley in North America, and the Miocene "idiogeosyncline" that Umbgrove had earlier distinguished in the western part of Indonesia.

The nuclear basins, "Innensenken" of Stille, "parageosynclines" *pro parte* of Schuchert, are situated as rigid masses within the virgations of an orogen. In contrast with the types of group 1 these show no folding subsequent to the strong depression which they are found to undergo. Examples of type IIIa are: the Pannonian Basin of Hungary as Alpine formation; the Tarim Basin between the Kwenlun and Tianshan as post-Variscian formation. In the case of the Salt Basin of Texas the frame is partly older than the basin so that it belongs to type IIIb.

The discordant basins show no connection with an orogen. They develop as more or less equidimensional depressions, partly of enormous extent, and they cut right across older structures of the continent. The following examples can be given: the Basin of Paris of Mesozoic-Tertiary age; the Amazon Basin of Caledonian age; the Congo Basin, Moscow Basin, Gobi Basin, etc. This type corresponds to von Bubnoff's "labile shelf" and to Schuchert's parageosynclines *pro parte*. In this type of basin folding is likewise restricted to slight disturbance.

Fig. 102. Classification of the Moluccan deep-sea depressions based on the morphology. Scale 1:23,000,000. For explanation see text and Table 11. (Redrawn after Kuenen, 1935, Fig. 17, p. 38.) I Java, II Timor, III Aru, IV Ceram, V Buru, VI and VII Molucca, VIII Mindanao, IX Flores V-troughs. 1 Weber, 2 Sawu, 3 Sunda U-troughs. *a* Makassar, *b* Bone, *c* Tomini basins (shallower). *A* Sulu, *B* Celebes, *C* North Banda, *D* South Banda basins (deeper).

The foregoing exposition shows that the term geosyncline comprises the eugeosynclines and Umbgrove's group 1 of troughs. The basins, however, should not be included among geosynclines. Some geologists might consider small nuclear basins as forming part of a major geosynclinal belt, but it appears better not to include them in the term geosyncline.

It is interesting that the earlier subdivision of the Indonesian deep-sea depressions given by the present author, based on purely morphological grounds, was found by Umbgrove to fit his classification of fossil sedimentation depressions. The morphological classification of the Moluccan deeps is given in Fig. 102, and Table 11 shows the correlation with the fossil depressions.

TABLE 11. TYPES OF DEPRESSION IN THE EARTH'S CRUST

Recent deep-sea depressions	Fossil sedimentation depressions
A. Banda Arcs with troughs.	A. Eugeosynclines.
B. Separate deep-sea depressions.	B. Separate depressions.
Group 1. Troughs.	Group 1. Troughs.
Type I = I–IX (Timor Trough).	Type I. Marginal deep.
Type II = 1–3 (Weber Trough).	Type II. Intramontane trough.
Group 2. Basins.	Group 2. Basins.
Type III = A–D (Celebes Sea).	Type III. Nuclear basin.
Type IV = a–c (Gulf of Boni).	Type IV. Discordant basin.

The deep-sea V-troughs (I–IX) (Fig. 103), according to Umbgrove, correspond to his marginal deeps, on account of their shape and position adjacent to a markedly orogenic belt and almost directly over the belt of gravity deficiency discovered by Vening Meinesz. This opinion conforms with the view earlier expressed by Argand, Stille, and others.

The deep-sea U-troughs 1–3, to which may be added the troughs between Sumatra and Java on the north, and the submarine ridge and row of islands on the south, are situated between the orogenic zone of the Inner Banda Arc and Sunda Islands on the one hand and on the other the belt of negative anomalies along the Outer Banda Arc and its submarine continuation to the west as far as the Mentawi Islands. According to Umbgrove they correspond to his intramontane deeps.

The basins A–D form a parallel with Umbgrove's nuclear basins, for they are elongate, show a flat floor, and are situated between the virgating arms of island arcs.

The basins a–c were classed by Umbgrove with his discordant basins. In the opinion of the present writer this is the only doubtful point in the correlation.

In Kuenen's classification the close relationship between the first two types (the troughs) and between the second two (the basins) had been recognized and expressed by grouping under two separate headings. This forms a further confirmation of the remarkable correspondence between the morphological and geological classifications.

There remain a few smaller depressions, the pits (α–δ) that were not classified by Kuenen, while a small number of transitional examples were noted (especially III, V, and IX).

Most of the external Pacific deep-sea troughs belong to the deep-sea V-troughs of Umbgrove's type I, marginal deeps. Of the West Indian examples the Bartlett Trough cuts off the geological structures of the region (Bucher, 1933, p. 350) and has a U-shaped cross section.

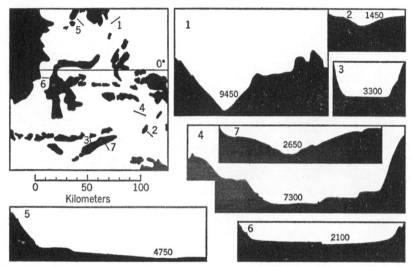

Fig. 103. Profiles of some Moluccan deep-sea depressions based on echo soundings of the *Snellius* expedition. Vertical scale 10 × horizontal. 1, 2, 7, V-troughs; 3, 4, U-troughs; 6, shallower basin; 5, deeper basin.

It might therefore be correlated with Umbgrove's type IV of discordant basins. But with a view to the position between the orogenic belts together with an elongate shape, there is more to be said for classification as Umbgrove's type II of intramontane troughs.

In spite of the clear correlation between fossil and recent depressions of the earth's crust (see also Fig. 104) there is one important point in which they differ fundamentally so that doubt may be felt whether they are actually identical. The bulk of the fossil sediments were deposited in water not exceeding a few hundred meters in depth, whereas continental facies dominates the paralic series. The ancient basins and geosynclines now forming part of the land thus seldom or never presented greater depths at their surface, and during the subsidence sufficient sediment was always brought in to fill them almost to the brim. In this respect the Indonesian depressions, with their depths of many thousands of meters, form a sharp contrast with the normal conditions in fossil troughs, and they cannot be looked upon as *typical* recent geosynclines. It is possible that some shallow seas, as for instance parts of the Sunda Shelf and Strait Madura at the northeastern end of Java, as also the Gulf Coast of southern United States and the upper end of the Gulf of California, are recent examples of geosynclines of typical development.

The difficult question must now be faced whether fossil sedimentation troughs ever developed abyssal depths. Only if this is found to

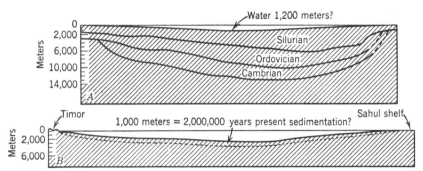

FIG. 104. Comparison between a geosyncline and a V-trough. Horizontal scale 1:1,200,000, vertical scale 1:600,000. *A*. The Welsh Geosyncline, assuming depth of 1200 m water at close of Silurian. Data from O. T. Jones, 1938, Plate B. *B*. The Timor Trough, assuming that the present rate of sedimentation has obtained for 2,000,000 years.

have occurred can the correlation given above obtain a deeper significance. On theoretical grounds there is no evident reason for denying that a geosyncline could ever have attained great depth. It has been suggested by Hall, Russell, and others that the primary cause of subsidence is the accumulation of a heavy column of sediments. The following arguments have been brought forward against this view (Grabau, Umbgrove, etc.). (1) Only part of the original area over which sedimentation begins develops into the final geosyncline. (2) The elongate, regular shape denotes an internal diastrophic cause and not a chance exogenous cause. (3) The section is synclinal with the largest depths and therefore the greatest subsidence at a distance from the margin. As the detritus is normally brought in from one side, weighting alone would result in a wedge-shaped cross section. (4) The juxtaposition in the immediate neighborhood of a rising geanticline indicates the operation of diastrophic forces in the area. (5) The specific gravity of the sediments is much smaller than that of the substratum that has to be displaced (even if the paramorphic principle of Du Toit is given due consideration). Obviously the weight of sediment deposited in the trough must encourage subsidence, but an endogenous cause must operate as well to bring about a wavelike deformation of the crust. According to the view of Vening Meinesz, Bucher, and others this cause is compressional stress. If this endogenous cause is admitted, it must also be conceded that the primary subsidence must lead to an unfilled depression if no sediment happens to be supplied.

A second theoretical consideration is that the determination of depths in which fossil sediments were deposited is a controversial problem, especially in the case of bathyal formations (200–1000 m deep). It is not improbable that some sediments, held to be bathyal, have been laid down at greater, abyssal depth, provided that the distance to the coast was limited. The pelagic character of the oceanic deep-sea deposits is taken far too lightly as indication of great depths, and it is overlooked that actually the great distance from land has caused the typical characteristics of the oozes. Thus radiolarian ooze, pteropod ooze, and red clay can be formed only far from land, and globigerina ooze is also very scarce nearer inshore. The recent oozes of the Indonesian deep-sea depressions forming at depths of 5000 to 10,000 m are identical with some deposits from 1000 m or even less. In fossilized state these would be readily classed as bathyal or even neritic (0–200 m deep) formations that had been deposited some distance from the land. The investigation of the *Snellius* samples has established that within the range of continental influence depth alone plays no appreciable part in sedimentation beyond the 200-m line. Ooze with a high percentage of lime was brought up from depths of 5000 m in the Sulu Sea, but in the better-ventilated Celebes Sea the deposits were found to contain but a trace of lime at similar depths. The normal blue mud of the Weber Trough from 7400 m was identical with that of the Timor Trough at 1000-m depth or less.

The present author knows of no property by which, in the absence of typical Foraminifera, it can be proved with certainty that a fossil hemipelagic sediment was formed in depths of 500 to 1000 m and not in depths of 5000 to 6000 m (see also Chapter 5). When full weight is given to this consideration it must be admitted that no proof is forthcoming that some of the bathyal sediments of the Alpine geosyncline were not laid down in depths exceeding 1000 m. There are no grounds for denying the possibility that this geosyncline developed depths several times as great as is generally assumed. The same holds for a few other geosynclines.

The third argument to show that fossil sedimentation basins may sometimes have grown to considerable depths is the occurrence of equivalents to recent eupelagic deep-sea deposits among the Mesozoic series of Timor and Roti in the Moluccas. This situation is the opposite to that cited above, and we are confronted with arguments in favor of actual deep-sea oozes formed at great distance from a coast and at abyssal depths. The series contains typical red clay with manganese nodules and Cretaceous sharks' teeth with the bony substance dissolved so that only the enamel remains (Molengraaff, 1920). In the recent seas this red clay is found only at abyssal depths, where lime is dissolved. There are also silicified Monotis limestones, fragments of which have been encrusted by iron-manganese oxides, and heaped-up cephalopods with crusts of iron-manganese oxides. The cephalopods represent a considerable portion of the Triassic although the thickness of the limestones is but a few meters. Finally there occur fine-grained pink limestones with manganese nodules. The combination of all these phenomena leaves no doubt as to the pelagic nature of the series. Considerable depth is also probable because organisms thriving on the bottom of shallow waters are absent and because recent equivalents are formed only in abyssal depths. Whether the alpine radiolarites also represent pelagic deep-sea deposits (Steinmann) has not yet been definitely established but appears to be rather doubtful.

The various arguments presented appear to show that fossil geosynclines may have formed temporarily into deep depressions of the sea floor under special conditions and by way of exception. Therefore the great depth of the Indonesian deep-sea troughs and basins cannot be urged as argument against the correlation with fossil sedimentation depressions.

The problem of how far the similarity goes between deep-sea depressions in general and fossil sedimentation depression is therefore worth examining in more detail. First the deep-sea V-troughs will be dealt with because they will be found to provide the clearest evidence. Kuenen extended the arguments already presented by Argand (1916) and Stille (1919) and showed how closely certain troughs of the Alpine geosyncline resemble certain of the Moluccan deep-sea troughs, and Umbgrove drew a parallel with his marginal deeps.

As with primary and marginal deeps, a rising belt runs parallel to these deep-sea troughs (Outer Banda Arc) and delivers detritus into the depressions. At the other margin of the deep-sea V-troughs a continental shelf or deep-sea floor is found. The ancient primary and marginal deeps were likewise generally bounded on the outer side by a shallow sea or an old continental shield. Both types show a more or less symmetrical V-shaped cross section (synclinal), and both are markedly elongate with varying depths along the axis. They similarly form festoons several thousands of kilometers long. Length, breadth, and depth are also of comparable magnitude (Fig. 104). The marginal deeps and Indonesian deep-sea V-troughs are similarly situated along the convex margin of a curved orogenic zone, and both were formed after the orogenic compression and after this belt began to rise. As far as known this also holds for deep-sea V-troughs outside the Indonesian area. It appears highly probable that they may also be formed in virgin areas, in which case they would then form a close parallel with the simple eugeosynclines.

Formerly the present writer was of the opinion that the entirely different character of the deposits in the Tertiary Molasse Trough of the Alps did not allow of a correlation with the synclinoral type of deep-sea depression. Umbgrove's exposition clearly demonstrates, however, that this parallelization is warranted. The coarser nature of the sediment in the Alpine Trough must be attributed to a higher average level of the crust with larger areas of denudation. Hence it is not of basic importance from our point of view. Possibly an even closer similarity obtains with the most northerly of the Penninic Deeps, the "geosynclinal dauphinois et valaison," or the Helvetian Deep, as Argand has pointed out.

The deep-sea troughs with U-shaped section also strongly resemble the corresponding type of sedimentation depressions, namely the intramontane deeps. Both are decidedly elongate and are intimately related to an orogenic belt. Thus the Indonesian deep-sea U-troughs are situated between the Inner and Outer Banda arcs with their continuations to the west. Again in both types long festoons are developed. The varying breadth and depth are likewise typical of both. It remains to be shown whether the U-shaped section of these recent troughs is also a characteristic of the fossil deeps.

Following Staub, Kuenen correlated his basins of the Celebes Sea type with "Innensenken," while Umbgrove drew a parallel with his corresponding type of nuclear basins. The more or less equidimensional shape and the framing by geanticlines, the steep walls, and the flat floor are joint characteristics. We already noted that the great depth of the Indonesian basins may form an objection to the correlation, but that the absence of trustworthy indications concerning the maximum depth of fossil sedimentation basins leaves us in some doubt.

The other basins (Gulf of Boni type) were correlated by Umbgrove with his discordant basins. The less regular shape, the abrupt truncation of older structures found on surrounding islands, and the absence of festoonal arrangement are points of resemblance.

Evidently there are fewer data on which to base a correlation of the deep-sea basins with the fossil basins, than for the correlation of deep-sea troughs with geosynclinal deeps.

The identity of the deep-sea troughs and geosynclinal deeps allows an important conclusion to be drawn. It follows clearly from the *Snellius* charts that the Timor deep-sea V-trough and the Java deep-sea V-trough form one genetic feature. The original question whether deep-sea troughs and geosynclines are identical should be answered in the affirmative, if it is admitted that the Timor Trough is a certain type of geosyncline. For if the shallower Timor Trough is a recent geosyncline its deep continuation, the Java Trough, must be one also.

Two reservations have to be made, however. In the first place the deep-sea basins are evidently ruled out from the correlation with geosynclines, and the case for the deep-sea U-troughs is more open to doubt than that for the deep-sea V-troughs. In the second place the great majority of fossil sedimentation depressions has certainly never exceeded neritic depths and has therefore never resembled deep-sea depressions in a morphological sense.

Two interesting aspects may be emphasized in this connection. The first is that judging by the results of gravity observations the ocean floor offers the same resistance to horizontal compressive stress as the continental blocks. The root developing in both cases is of the same magnitude. It is true that the anomaly of oceanic roots is not so strongly negative, for instance opposite Java and Sumatra, as in the continental area of the Banda Arcs. But relative to the surrounding area the deficiency of gravity is nearly as great because of the average positive anomaly of the sea floor. There is a close parallel in the morphology, for the accompanying V-troughs are as deeply depressed with relation to the adjoining ocean floor as is the Timor-Ceram Trough relative to the adjacent shelf. In this respect gravimetric and bathymetric results again bear each other out satisfactorily. We are led to confirm in a decided manner Bucher's opinion: "The origin of 'welts' and 'furrows' is independent of the elevation of the earth's crust; it is especially independent of the distinction of the two dominant levels, the ocean bottoms and the continental platforms" (1933, p. 14).

The second point is that for the Timor-Ceram V-troughs a future folding and elevation to a geographical mountain chain may be predicted with a large measure of probability. For the Java-Sumatra Trough, that of Mindanao, and the other major furrows of the ocean floor this evolution appears very improbable. In the first place we know of no single example of a geosyncline that has developed from the ocean bottom or even from the outer margin of a continent. For geosynclines that now border the continent there are generally indications in the sedimentary prism of the former existence on their outer sides of borderlands that have later sunk away.[1] A more probable prediction is that these oceanic synclinoria will indeed experience orogenesis, but no elevation will ensue to high altitudes; at most they will rise only to submarine ridges.

Hess has brought forward the following interesting view (1938) concerning deep-sea troughs and submarine ridges. He pointed out that in the West Indies a ridge follows the belt of negative anomalies in the south but that in the north the axis coincides with a furrow. This might find an explanation in the much stronger sedimentation close to the great South American continent. Consequently there was sufficient incompetent sedimentary material in the trough to be squeezed upward and to form a ridge when compression and buckling took place. In the north only slight oceanic sedimentation had occurred in the geosyncline when orogenesis set in. As a result almost the entire crust buckled downward to form the mountain root, while an unfilled furrow remained to show where the downward root had been formed.

Similar ideas were later developed by Umbgrove (1947), who maintains that the orogenic zones of the continent are continued into the ocean basins or right across to the opposite side. In the absence of a geanticline reaching above sea level and being denuded, the ocean section of the geosynclinal belt would remain an open depression. On compression and buckling a root would be formed in this section also, but there would be insufficient detrital contents in the trough to be squeezed out and form a ridge on its back. The orogenesis of the ocean bottoms would thus take place without producing a per-

---

[1] The Mississippi Delta sedimentation trough may be an exception to this if it should really be classed as a geosyncline.

manent morphological feature.   At most a slight depression or elevation would remain.   It should not be overlooked that the crust is supposed to consist of the same material as the substratum but for a thin
cover of sial so that the root would gradually melt away and no major
anomalies of specific gravity would remain in the crust itself.   In a
marginal deep-sea geosyncline, receiving sediment from the neighboring continent, there would probably be sufficient light fill to form a
permanent elevation.

Bibliography

ARGAND, É.   Sur l'arc des Alpes occidentales, *Eclog. Geol. Helv.*, Vol. 14, pp.
    145–191, 1916.

BROUWER, H. A.   On the Crustal Movements in the Region of the Curving Rows
    of Islands in the Eastern Part of the East Indian Archipelago, *Proc. Kon.
    Akad. v. Wetensch. Amsterdam*, Vol. 22, pp. 772–782, 1920.

    The Horizontal Movements of Geanticlines and the Fractures Near Their Sur-
    face, *J. Geol.*, Vol. 29, pp. 510–577, 1921.

    The Geology of the Netherlands East Indies, 160 pp., Macmillan, New York,
    1925.

BUCHER, W. H.   *The Deformation of the Earth's Crust*, 518 pp., Princeton Uni-
    versity Press, 1933.

DALY, R.   Relevant Facts and Inferences from Field Geology, pp. 40–69 in B.
    GUTENBERG et al., Internal Constitution of the Earth, *Physics of the Earth*,
    Vol. 7, 413 pp., 1939.

DU TOIT, A. L.   *Our Wandering Continents*, 366 pp., Oliver & Boyd, Edinburgh,
    1937.

GLAESSNER, M. F., and C. TEICHERT.   Geosynclines: A Fundamental Concept in
    Geology, *Am. J. Sci.*, Vol. 245, pp. 465–482, 571–591, 1947.

GRABAU, A. W.   Migration of Geosynclines, *Bull. Geol. Soc. China*, Vol. 3, pp.
    207–349, 1924.

HAUG, É.   Les géosynclinaux et les aires continentales, *Bull. soc. géol. France*,
    Vol. 28, pp. 617–711, 1900.

HESS, H. H.   Gravity Anomalies and Island Arc Structure with Particular Refer-
    ence to the West Indies, *Proc. Am. Phil. Soc.*, Vol. 79, pp. 71–96, 1938.

HOBBS, W. H.   Mountain Growth, a Study of the Southwestern Pacific Region,
    Proc. Am. Phil. Soc., Vol. 88, pp. 221–268, 1944.

KAY, M.   Geosynclinal Nomenclature and the Craton, *Bull. Am. Assoc. Petr.
    Geol.*, Vol. 31, pp. 1289–1293, 1947.

KUENEN, PH. H.   Geological Interpretation of the Bathymetrical Results, *The
    Snellius Expedition*, Vol. 5, part 1, 124 pp., Brill, Leyden, 1935.

    The Negative Isostatic Anomalies in the East Indies, with Experiments, *Leidsche
    Geol. Med.*, Vol. 8, pp. 169–214, 1936.

KUENEN, PH. H., and G. A. NEEB.   Bottom Samples, *The Snellius Expedition*,
    Vol. 5, part 3, 265 pp., Brill, Leyden, 1943.

LEUCHS, K.   Tiefseegräben und Geosynklinalen, *N. Jahrb. f. Min., etc.*, Beil. Bd.
    58, B, pp. 273–294, 1927.

MOLENGRAAFF, G. A. F.   Folded Mountain Chains, Overthrust Sheets and Block-faulted Mountains in the East Indian Archipelago, *Comp. rend. 12 congr. géol. intern.*, pp. 689–702, 1913.

Mangaanknollen in mesozoische Diepzeeafzettingen van Nederlandsch-Timor, Versl. Wis- en Nat. Afd., Kon. Akad. Wet. Amsterdam, D1.29, pp. 677–692, 1920.

De Geologie der Zeeën van de O. I. Archipel, in Kon. Ned. Aardr. Gen., *De Zeeën van Nederlandsch Oost-Indië*, pp. 272–357, 1922.

MURRAY, H. W. Profiles of the Aleutian Trench, *Bull. Geol. Soc. Am.*, Vol. 56, pp. 757–782, 1945.

RIEL, P. M. VAN. The Bottom Configuration in Relation to the Flow of the Bottom Water, *The Snellius Expedition*, Vol. 2, part 2, Chapter 2, 63 pp. with charts, Brill, Leyden, 1934

RUTTEN, L. M. R. *Voordrachten over de Geologie van Nederlandsch Oost Indië*, 839 pp., Wolters, Groningen, 1927

Oude Land- en Zeeverbindingen in Midden-Amerika en West Indië, *Tijdschr. Kon. Ned. Aardr. Gen.*, Vol. 51, pp. 551–600, 1934.

SCHUCHERT, C. Sites and Nature of the North American Geosynclines, *Bull. Geol. Soc. Am.*, Vol. 34, pp. 151–230, 1923.

Gondwana Land Bridges, *Bull. Geol. Soc. Am.*, Vol. 43, pp. 875–916, 1932.

SMIT SIBINGA, G. L. Wegener's Theorie en het Ontstaan van den Oostelijken O.-I. Archipel, *Tijdschr. Kon. Ned. Aardr. Gen.*, Vol. 44, pp. 581–598, 1927.

The Malay Double (Triple) Orogen, *Proc. Kon. Akad. v. Wetensch. Amsterdam*, Vol. 36, pp. 202–210, 323–330, 447–453, 1933.

STAUB, R. *Der Bewegungsmechanismus der Erde*, 270 pp., Bornträger, Berlin, 1928.

STILLE, H. Alte und junge Saumtiefen, *Nachr. Ges. Wiss. Göttingen, Mat.-Phys. Kl.*, pp. 337–372, 1919.

Die angebliche junge Vorwärtsbewegung im Timor-Ceram Bogen, *Nachr. Ges. Wiss. Göttingen, Mat.-Phys. Kl.*, pp. 174–180, 1920.

Grundfragen der vergleichenden Tektonik, 443 pp., Bornträger, Berlin, 1924.

Einführung in den Bau Amerikas, 717 pp., Bornträger, Berlin, 1940.

Malaiischer Archipel und Alpen, *Abh. Preusz. Akad. Wis. Math.-Nat. Kl.*, Nr. 1, pp. 1–16, 1943.

UMBGROVE, J. H. F. Geological History of the East Indies, *Bull. Am. Assoc. Petr. Geol.*, Vol. 22, pp. 1–70, 1938.

The Pulse of the Earth, 358 pp., Nijhoff, The Hague, 1947.

Structural History of the East Indies, 63 pp., Cambr. University Press, 1949.

VENING MEINESZ, F. A. The Earth's Crust Deformation in the East Indies, *Proc. Kon. Akad. v. Wetensch. Amsterdam*, Vol. 43, pp. 278–293, 1940.

Deep-Focus and Intermediate Earthquakes in the East Indies, *Proc. Kon. Akad. v. Wetensch. Amsterdam*, Vol. 49, pp. 855–865, 1946.

Convection Currents in the Earth, *Proc. Kon. Akad. v. Wetensch. Amsterdam*, Vol. 50, pp. 237–245, 1947.

VENING MEINESZ, F. A., J. H. F. UMBGROVE, and PH. H. KUENEN. *Gravity Expeditions at Sea, 1923–1932*, Vol. 2, 208 pp., Waltman, Delft, 1934.

VERBEEK, R. D. M. Molukkenverslag, *Jaarb. Mijnw. Ned. Oost-Indië, Wet. Ged.*, 826 pp., Landsdrukkerij, Batavia, 1908.

WEGENER, A. *Die Entstehung der Kontinente und Ozeane*, 242 pp., Vieweg, Braunschweig, 1941.

WILLIS, B. Isthmian Links, *Bull. Geol. Soc. Am.*, Vol. 43, pp. 917–952, 1932.

Sources and Transportation
of Marine Sediment

SOURCES DELIVERING SEDIMENT TO THE SEA

Marine sediments are derived from a great number of different sources (see Twenhofel, 1932, 1939; Trask, 1939). Viewing the earth as a whole, the main sources of sedimentary matter are the continental areas, the coasts, and marine life, while the atmosphere, rivers, icebergs, etc., are media of transport. But when emphasis is to be laid on the marine environment only, as in the present volume, the media can be looked upon as sources delivering sediment to the sea. This manner of treatment will help in restricting the scope of the present inquiry and in focusing attention on the sea.

The sources of marine sedimentary materials will be discussed under nine separate headings, but it should be realized that any grouping must be more or less arbitrary owing to the close interrelation of many geological processes. Moreover, no sharp boundary can be drawn between sources on the one hand and media of transport on the other. Thus nobody would wish to exclude planktonic Foraminifera as source of sedimentary matter, although their function is restricted to the concentration of constituents that are already present in the water to form calcareous tests. But is it also legitimate to speak of a source of sediment when referring to the activity of mud-feeding animals that merely coagulate fine mud to coprolitic pellets? A current becomes a source of sediment where it erodes the bottom, but what frequently takes place is merely the picking up of unconsolidated particles that had been deposited shortly before by the same current. Then there is simply intermittent transport. Still, the writer believes that the separate discussion of sources will prove enlightening, before turning to transportation and afterwards to the sediments themselves.

As frequent reference will be made to materials of various grain sizes, Table 12 shows the most used size classifications (grade scales).

TABLE 12. SIZE CLASSIFICATION OF SEDIMENTARY PARTICLES

Diameters in millimeters

Wentworth			Atterberg		
Boulder	Above 256		Block	2000–200	Gravel } Psephite
Cobble	256–64		Cobble	200–20	
Pebble	64–4		Pebble	20–2	
Granule	4–2				
Very coarse sand	2–1	2–1	Coarse sand	2–0.2	
Coarse sand	1–½	1–0.5			Psammite (arenaceous)
Medium sand	½–¼	0.5–0.25			
Fine sand	¼–⅛	0.25–0.125	Fine sand	0.2–0.02	
Very fine sand	⅛–¹⁄₁₆	0.125–0.0625			
Silt	¹⁄₁₆–¹⁄₂₅₆	0.0625–0.004	Silt	0.02–0.002	Pelite or lutite
Clay	Below ¹⁄₂₅₆	Below 0.004	Clay	Below 0.002	

The finest fractions of sediments are frequently called "clay." But as this word has a definite mineralogical implication the terms "pelite" or "lutite" or "lutum" are used by some authors to denote all particles smaller than the sand fraction, whether consisting of clay minerals, calcite, or any other mineral. The word "ooze" signifies a fine deposit composed principally of the shells and debris of pelagic organisms. By "mud" the marine geologist means all fine-grained deposits of a more or less plastic nature in moist condition.

For a more extensive review of this and other problems of sedimentary petrography the reader may consult Krumbein and Pettijohn (1938), Pettijohn (1949), or other manuals of petrography and also Twenhofel's books.

THE ATMOSPHERE

The particles dropping from the atmosphere are of three different kinds. *Meteoric dust* of extraterrestrial origin forms an interesting though small contribution to some sediments. The earth with its atmosphere moves continuously through interstellar space and collects a large number of dust particles, estimated at 10 to 20 million per day. Three-quarters of them must drop directly into the sea. Some are readily distinguished, namely minute spheres, that are formed from "falling stars." When a meteorite shoots through the atmosphere a superficial layer is melted by frictional heat, and this material is blown off to form small drops. The drops solidify to globules from $\frac{1}{10}$ to $\frac{1}{2}$ mm in diameter (Murray and Hjort, 1912). In most sediments these are sought in vain, but in some deep-sea lutites deposited at an extremely low rate they are relatively plentiful and may be sufficiently concentrated to be extracted. The deep-sea deposit called red clay contains locally from 20 to 30 such spherules per liter, but in most red clays and the other types of deep-sea sediment they are more scarce or even absent.

A large quantity of sedimentary material is thrown directly into the sea from *volcanoes*. During powerful eruptions, bombs, fragments of pumice, or blocks of older rocks may be flung into the surrounding waters. Porous material will frequently float and drift to great distances, even being transported across the entire ocean, before it becomes waterlogged and sinks to the bottom. After the eruption of Krakatoa in 1883 (Verbeek, 1885), extensive rafts of pumice drifted about in the Indonesian waters and farther afield. On many coral coasts evidence of that ancient catastrophe is found to the present day among the coral detritus washed up on the beach. It is even reported that Krakatoan pumice has been found among the flotsam and jetsam on the east coast of Africa. Naturally, however, by far the largest part has sunk to the bottom in Indonesian and Indian Ocean waters.

Volcanic ash is of even greater importance. The finer particles are frequently thrown to a great height during eruptions and are then spread out over a wide area by the prevailing winds. In consequence of their minute size the particles may float in the atmosphere for days on end and be carried hundreds of kilometers. The very finest fraction does not sink back to earth for many months, and in the meantime it is whirled many times round the earth.

Even when the ash is greatly diluted by other products it may still be detected far away from the volcano from which it came. Illustrative examples have become known through the *Snellius* expedition (Neeb, 1943). Thus the Tambora ash of 1815, coming from the Lesser Sunda Islands, is found in the bottom samples in Makassar Strait as far away as the latitude of Borneo's south coast, a distance of 400 km (Fig. 147, p. 343). The ash from Oena Oena, in the Gulf of Tomini, is traceable in the deposits across the northern arm of Celebes in Makassar Strait, also at 400-km distance. The ash derived from the volcanic islands of Minahassa-Sangi forms an important constituent of the muds covering more than half the Celebes Sea and as far as 500 km from the source. The Banda ash appears even as far off as Ambon, and many other examples could be cited (Fig. 146, between pp. 342 and 343).

Although some such material has been transported while settling in the water, wide scattering doubtless occurred partly in the atmosphere, as is definitely established by the Oena Oena ash found beyond the island of Celebes (Fig. 105).

The third source of sedimentary particles in the atmosphere is dust and sand raised by the *wind* on land and carried far out to sea. In dry

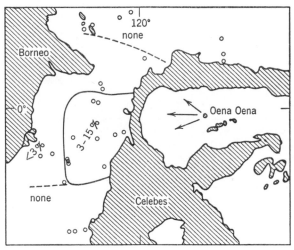

Fig. 105. Distribution of ash from the Oena Oena Volcano in bottom samples from the neighborhood (shown by circles) according to data by Neeb, 1943.

climates dense sand and dust storms are of frequent occurrence, and it is certain that particles may be carried in large quantities hundreds of kilometers from their source. The dropping of thick layers of dust on board ships far out at sea during pitch-dark dust storms bears evidence to repeated sedimentation of desert dust in the center of oceanic basins (Fig. 106).

In the *Meteor Reports* it was shown that fine Sahara sand, detectable by a film of iron oxide, occurs in noticeable amounts in the deep-sea deposits of the Gulf of Guiana and off the Cape Verde Islands (Barth, Correns, and Eskola, 1939). Close inshore it is strongly diluted by non-eolian material, but farther out it increases relatively. Not until a few thousand kilometers offshore does the Sahara sand diminish to imperceptible amounts, the grain size meanwhile gradually decreasing. In some fractions more than half the quartz grains were unmistakably of desert origin. Thus at 300 km from the coast 60% of the quartz was identified as of desert origin of which one-third was from 0.1 to 0.5 mm in diameter. Besides quartz, feldspar, and clay minerals, a high percentage of calcite occurs in this Sahara sand. As compared to the size of the equatorial Atlantic the area receiving larger amounts of desert sand is small, however.

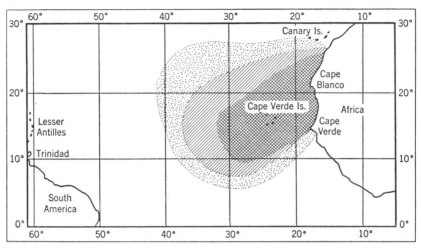

FIG. 106. Dust falls in the Atlantic as recorded by ships at sea. (Redrawn after Schott, 1942, Fig. 79, p. 259.)

In smaller basins surrounded on all sides by deserts a relatively much greater proportion of dust will occur and it may even predominate entirely over materials from other sources.

Sand that is subjected during prolonged periods to wind abrasion acquires a frosted surface. But in shallow water this surface is soon removed by solution and wear. In aquatic transportation along the bottom only the larger particles develop this characteristic frosted surface (see p. 280).

SKELETONS AND TESTS OF ORGANISMS

One of the most important sources of marine sediments is the skeletons and tests of plants and animals. Some of these, as corals, calcareous algae (lithothamnion), balanides, and oysters, live anchored to the bottom and may be incorporated directly in the sediment. Another unimportant source is formed by the skeletons of vertebrates. Although the largest animals that ever lived, the whales, are among these, the number of individuals was always relatively small and the span of life very great. Furthermore the materials building up the skeletons is not very resistant, especially those of fishes. Consequently vertebrate remains are seldom very much in evidence. But when insufficient ventilation of basin waters causes anaerobic conditions, scavengers and normal bacteria are excluded and then the skeletons or scales of fishes and other higher animals are excellently preserved. Incidental or periodic mass mortality on the shelf may have the same result. The most resistant parts, the teeth (sharks, rays, etc.), earbones of whales, finspines (sharks), or scales (ganoids), are sometimes found concentrated in fossil deposits, although it is difficult to ascertain the exact causes of this abundance. These most resistant parts are relatively frequent where the rate of sedimentation is abnormally low, as for instance in some Pacific areas covered by red clay.

In the deep sea, benthonic forms of life (bottom-living animals and plants) do not play a very important part, although many species of Foraminifera, deep-sea corals, holothurians, etc. flourish there. It is the plankton, the drifting population of surface waters, that contributes the bulk of material to sedimentation. Among the forms of life with a siliceous (hydrated silica) frustule or test the diatoms play the major role in high latitudes and the radiolarians in tropical waters. Siliceous spiculas of sponges are of frequent occurrence, on an average forming 2 to 3% of deep-sea deposits. The pelagic Foraminifera, especially the globigerinas, rank foremost among the suppliers of lime. In about half of the recent deep-sea deposits the tests of these unicellular animals predominate. The tests of pteropods and the loose plates (coccoliths) of a certain type of planktonic algae, the Coccolithophoridae, also have a wide distribution, although they hardly ever attain to half the total bulk of a deposit.

In shallow waters planktonic forms are generally less in evidence. Only under abnormal conditions, for instance in shelf regions where upwelling water causes exceptional abundance of plankton, do they become of greater importance. Examples from fossil deposits are radiolarians in the formation of radiolarites in shallow water and planktonic Foraminifera in the development of the chalk rocks along the coasts of the English Channel. On the shelf and in beach deposits benthonic forms of life predominate, such as gastropods, lamellibranchs, brachiopods, echinoderms, Foraminifera, sponges, and corals, each of which may take the upper hand in turn. Less frequently worms, crustaceans, cephalopods, Bryozoans, or calcareous algae occur en masse.

Not all the lime and siliceous tests delivered by dying organisms or by shedding of tests is incorporated in the sediment, because part is again dissolved. This topic will be treated in the next chapter (p. 277).

DECOMPOSABLE ORGANIC MATTER [1]

Besides skeletons and tests, the decomposable organic matter of plants and animals also plays an important part in sedimentary deposits of the sea floor. Again it is the group of unicellular organisms that contributes most, the enormous number of individuals compensating for their small size.

Determination of the production of organic matter and of its dissolution is far from simple. Hence quantitative data can be given only for certain restricted areas and even these should be looked upon as rough estimates only (Sverdrup et al., 1942). For the present the average production is estimated roughly at 1 kg per m^2 per year in coastal waters, but farther out it becomes less, and doubtless extreme variations occur.

The composition of sea water, that is to say the proportions of the principal dissolved elements, is constant except for some scarce nutrient salts used by plants in their metabolism. As nearly all elements necessary for plant life are present in excess of requirement, the available amounts of a few essential constituents determine the intensity of vegetable production. Generally phosphorus or nitrogen forms the bottleneck, and in regions where radiolarians and especially diatoms occur in great abundance, available silica may perhaps limit the production. In some regions, as the Antarctic Ocean, all nutrient salts are provided in sufficient amounts, in which case other factors limit plant growth, such as light or the consumption by herbivorous animals.

The distribution of plankton in the oceans clearly indicates that the fertility of the water is of much greater importance than temperature. Thus coastal waters that receive an ample supply of nutrient salts from the adjacent land or from upwelling water, and colder environments where a yearly overturn of the waters brings fertile water to the surface, produce greater quantities of plankton than regions far out in the oceans and tropical waters with stable stratification the year round.

This relation is brought out strikingly by comparing maps of the southern Atlantic showing the density of planktonic life and the percentage of phosphorus pentoxide (Fig. 6). Both indicate a rich zone along the western coast of Africa with two tongues extending far into the ocean at 10° north latitude and just south of the equator. On

[1] See especially Trask, 1939.

both maps a concentration is shown towards Antarctica and also an isolated area in midocean off Trinidad, 20° south latitude (see Wattenberg, in Correns, 1934).

Organic matter (possibly held by clay particles) is carried to the sea by rivers. It has not yet been ascertained whether this organic matter is incorporated in the sediments or how great a contribution it makes to the organic content of various types of marine deposits, but it appears probable that in certain localities this source is of considerable importance. In Arctic regions with extensive peat deposits, or in the tropics where plant life on land is so intensive, this source of organic matter in marine deposits should be reckoned with (Trask, 1939; Kuenen and Neeb, 1943).

But from initial production to final incorporation in bottom deposits there is a long way to go, and something like 98 to 99.98% is lost, according to Trask. Even after deposition a 10 to 20% reduction takes place. Some of the vegetable plankton is swallowed by animals, and a rich fauna feeds on animal and vegetable plankton. The portion that dies a natural death sinks to the bottom but is then devoured by benthonic mud-feeders and is further attacked by bacterial decomposition (rot). Only under anaerobic conditions, as described in Chapter 1, is most of the organic matter on the sea floor preserved (Strøm, in Trask, 1939; Brongersma-Sanders, 1948).

PRECIPITATES [1]

Several substances can be precipitated from sea water, in many cases by plants or animals, but concerning most of the chemical processes involved little has as yet been ascertained. Lime may be precipitated when the assimilation of plants extracts too much carbon dioxide from the water, by which process the solubility of lime is reduced. Probably the precipitation of lime from sea water is generally a consequence of bacteriological activity. It is supposed that these organisms produce ammonia, with the result that the more alkaline water will become oversaturated with lime. Apparently aragonite mud is produced in this manner in shallow waters of the Bahamas (Thorp, in Trask, 1939). It has not yet been discovered to what extent bacteria are also concerned in the formation of oölites. In a later paragraph (p. 219) further details on the precipitation of lime are given.

Although precipitated iron has been observed in recent sediments, at the present time no rich deposits of this element are being formed anywhere on the sea floor. Nevertheless, concentration of iron in

[1] See Correns, 1939.

marine environment must be possible, because several fossil marine deposits are known, such as the oölitic "minette" ores of Central Europe, that are composed of iron hydroxide and iron silicates, believed by most geologists to be of primary marine origin.

The manner of formation of glauconite, a green, blue, or brown hydrous silicate containing iron, magnesium, and aluminum, is still a debated question. It generally forms at moderate depths where sedimentation is very slow. Some investigators attribute glauconite to an alteration either of biotite or of clay, volcanic glass, or pyroxene; others, to a chemical reaction in (echinoderm) coprolitic pellets. But the frequent occurrence inside foraminiferal tests, in microscopic fissures in shells, etc., can hardly be thus accounted for.

Wherever the absence of oxygen causes anaerobic conditions, iron sulfide may form. Hydrogen sulfide is produced by the rotting of organic substance, and this forms iron sulfide with the available iron compounds. It is not requisite that oxygen be entirely absent from the water above the bottom as long as there is deficiency within the deposit. Thus the dark color of muds in tidal flats and of the "blue mud" of the continental slopes is due partly to organic matter but also to iron-sulfur compounds that are produced internally in the sediments in the manner described.

Although the activity of bacteria in the precipitation of manganese oxide is not excluded, it is generally assumed that gradual oxidation of the manganese in alkaline environment leads to deposition. We will return to this process in a later paragraph.

Furthermore, all coprolites, including those of mud-feeders such as worms, holothurians, etc., and the pellets produced by lamellibranchiates may be counted as secondary biological deposits. These coprolites may contain grains that have been attacked chemically in the intestines, or they may be cemented, or they may contain new—or have lost initial—organic matter; in short, they have been influenced to some extent by the animals (Moore, in Trask et al., 1939). Coprolites often play a part as kernels of oölites.

It has already been mentioned that in the case of manganese oxidation is principally responsible for the precipitation. Manganese, as hydrate and oxide, is encountered in three forms in marine sediments: (1) as a finely disseminated coloring; (2) as a coating on shells, bones, rock fragments, etc. (thus it is sometimes observed that if a cobble protrudes from the bottom deposit the exposed part is covered by a dark brown layer of "manganese," while the buried portion remains bright); (3) as nodules and concretions up to 15 cm in diameter. Such nodules are composed of a mixture of manganese dioxide (sometimes manganic oxide) and ferric oxide with other, minor constituents. They have been deposited in successive layers around fragments of pumice, sharks' teeth, etc. The geochemistry of manganese will be treated in the next chapter (p. 395).

Phosphate nodules ($Ca_3(PO_4)_2$) are also formed on the sea floor. Though rare in general, they are sometimes dredged in considerable numbers from non-depositional environments, such as the shallow waters on the Agulhas Bank, on escarpments, and on walls of submarine canyons (Dietz et al., 1942). It appears that they are generated under the same conditions as glauconite, that is, mainly in depths less than 1000 m and where sedimentation is slow or absent.

Various views have been expressed on the origin of phosphorite nodules and closely related fossil beds of marine phosphorite. The authors mentioned present strong evidence in favor of direct precipitation. Calculation indicates that ocean water is essentially saturated with tricalcium phosphate. Hence, slight changes in the physical-chemical environment should cause the direct precipitation of some form of phosphate. The nodules have evidently grown in situ. They are layered, sometimes with a coating of manganese oxide formed between periods of accretion. Although enclosed calcareous material is generally replaced by phosphate, this is not the process by which the nodules themselves are formed. As the nodules grow in exposed situations, there is no support for the former view that stagnant water and concentration of organic remains are essential to the deposition of phosphate.

Phillipsite is encountered as loose crystals in deposits of clay forming far from land. It is supposed to develop when volcanic material is decomposed.

Many other substances are met with sporadically as concretions in marine sediments, but they will not be treated here.

The tropical surface waters are saturated with calcium carbonate so that any factor causing the abstraction of carbon dioxide must bring about oversaturation and may thus lead to the precipitation of lime. Both increase of temperature and decrease of pressure may have this effect. It is true, however, that geological observation on tropical coasts shows that the surface layer of water strongly attacks limestone, as will be more fully dealt with in Chapter 6. But this action is restricted to the upper film of water and does not preclude oversaturation directly below.

Although several possible reasons thus appear to exist that may cause the formation of lime in sea water, a strong oversaturation is probably required before precipitation takes place.

The fine crystalline to amorphous groundmass of many fossiliferous limestones presents a separate problem. The following opinions as to its formation have been expressed. It is formed from minutely triturated tests and skeletons (Sorby); it has been precipitated by oversaturation (Heim) or by microorganisms (Bishof); it was formed from coccoliths (Voelzkow); it was precipitated by bacteria (Drew); the absence of scavengers in the pre-Cambrian caused rotting and the inorganic precipitation of lime on a wide scale (Daly); the finest fraction of triturated tests is unstable and has therefore recrystallized to a structureless mass, while at the same time the more coarsely grained fossils remained intact (Kaisin); the gradual rise in temperature of a saturated current has caused inorganic precipitation (Johnston and Williamson). As yet, a choice between these various suggestions cannot be made. We will return to this question when dealing with the total mass of sediments in the crust of the earth. However, an adequate treatment of this vital problem cannot be attempted in the present volume, and the reader is referred to treatises on sedimentary petrology.

An entirely different cause of precipitation in sea still has to be mentioned, namely, evaporation. In shallow waters surrounded by deserts, lime may be precipitated, and it has been suggested by Walther that oölites are formed in this manner in agitated waters by the rolling and spinning movement of the particles. Where strong evaporation takes place in nearly or entirely closed basins in a dry climate gypsum or anhydrite are deposited; afterwards rock salt is precipitated, and finally even potassium and magnesium salts. The Kara Bogaz Gulf was treated in Chapter 1.

Van't Hoff and his school made an elaborate investigation of the sequence of crystallization of salts from evaporating sea water. Besides simple salts of sodium, potassium, calcium, and magnesium, often double or even triple salts are formed. The temperature has a marked influence not only on the saturation points but also on the composition of the products deposited.

Although these studies have taught us much on the nature of the processes involved, it cannot be claimed that they lead directly to an explanation of the natural salt accumulations. In places where evaporation reached the stage in which the soluble compounds were precipitated, for instance at Stassfurt in Germany, the salts actually found conform neither in volume nor in composition to the theoretical sequence. Evidently the formation of these fossil salt deposits was marked by many complications not occurring when a well-stirred beaker of sea water is evaporated. Variations in temperature from place to place and with the seasons, differences in pressure according to the depths, with evaporation going on at the surface and the sinking of concentrated brine or even of separate crystals, the influx of new sea water, or the supply from peripheral deposits by rain wash— all these factors bring about complications in nature.

Moreover, the fossil deposits may have undergone important changes in consequence of diagenetic or even metamorphic influences, because salts will react more readily to altered conditions of temperature and pressure than normal sediments. The original structure and composition may have changed while the accompanying sediments are still unaltered. It is then no longer possible to deduce the geographical and climatic conditions at the time of deposition by studying the present composition. But from the sections of the Stassfurt salt deposits it is at least clear that invasions of the sea have repeatedly taken place during the evaporation, interrupting the regular deposition of the salts. Thus intercalations of clastic sediments are found that are followed by renewed deposition of the less soluble salts until finally the "Abraumsalze" (magnesium and potassium salts) were again precipitated. This testifies to the flooding of the evaporating reservoirs by new deluges of sea water.

The formation of dolomite is still a moot question, although it has been shown that limestones have frequently been altered to dolomite in warm, shallow waters. This is yet another interesting field of investigation for geochemistry.

COASTAL EROSION AND BOTTOM EROSION

Erosion of the coast and bottom are processes that contribute to the production of sedimentary matter (see especially Johnson, 1919, 1925). No sharp distinction can be made between erosion and intermittent transportation. For this reason a certain amount of overlap between the present section and that dealing with transport of sedimentary matter cannot be avoided.

Wave Erosion. In coastal erosion waves are by far the most active agents of destruction. Smaller waves during calm weather roll pebbles and sand continuously up and down the beach, thus causing surface abrasion and producing fine cuttings. We will return presently to this attrition of debris (p. 277).

The surf generated by strong swell is more powerful, although less constant in action. The most effective factor, however, is the action of storm waves.

Storm waves can exert an enormous pressure. By means of dynamometers, pressures have been measured on the Scottish coasts of 3 kg per cm² (or 30 tons per m²). Joints and bedding planes gaping only slightly are subjected to the impact of the water, and the contained air is suddenly put under excessive pressure. It is as if the wave drives a wedge into the crack, forcing the rock apart.

As the wave recedes the compressed air suddenly expands with explosive force, and large as well as small blocks thus become loosened and ultimately blown out by pressure from the back. Solution is also activated by the pressure, especially in the case of limestone. Finally deep chasms and often caves are produced and the loosened blocks are rolled away.

Wave action is even more effective on loose stones and boulders. The shifting, overturning, or even rolling aside of gigantic rocks has been observed during storms. Thus, at IJmuiden on the Dutch coast, a block of concrete weighing 20 tons and 4 m high was once thrown onto the pier above high-water mark, in spite of the fact that in the North Sea exceptionally large waves cannot be generated. In the harbor of Wick in Scotland a mass of concrete weighing 2600 tons was torn from the pier and thrown bodily into the entrance of the harbor during the storm of 1877. During the December storm of 1894 a boulder of 50 kg was hurled through the roof of the light-keeper's house at Tillamook Rock on the Oregon Coast at a height 30 m above sea level. The very thick panes of glass of the Dunnet Head lighthouse on the Scottish coast, situated 100 m above high-water mark, are sometimes broken by stones swept up the cliffs by waves. The pounding of blocks too heavy to be lifted by a man causes a dull rumbling during storms on rocky coasts. Boulders of tough rock types, weighing upwards of 50 kg, are frequently found with the entire surface covered by large conical cracks due to impact where they were hurled against their neighbors, and the places where large chips have been knocked off are clearly visible. The obvious rounding of originally polygonal fragments testifies to the powerful abrasive action even on huge boulders.

All the loose material is likewise employed by the waves in their attack on the solid country rock, to batter and plane it off. This action is found to cut into the cliffs quickest just above high-tide level and to form a deep notch in suitable types of rock. When the wave-cut notch becomes too deep the roof subsides, a slide often forming a reentrant in the cliffs above. But usually the rocks forming the coast are too incoherent or too strongly stratified or they weather too quickly to produce a notch. Instead, a protecting heap of boulders may be formed along the foot of the cliff. A balance is then struck between the rate at which subaerial weathering attacks the face of the cliff and that at which the waves attack its base. Lessening of wave attack will allow more time for decomposition, solution, and disintegration to weather back the cliff to a gentler slope. This, in turn, will allow more protective waste to accumulate on the face of the cliff and thus slow down the rate of weathering. Conversely, a slower rate of weathering will allow more time for the waves to break up the blocks accumulating at the base of the cliff and to carry away the smaller fragments. This will lead to steepening of the cliff face (Fig. 107).

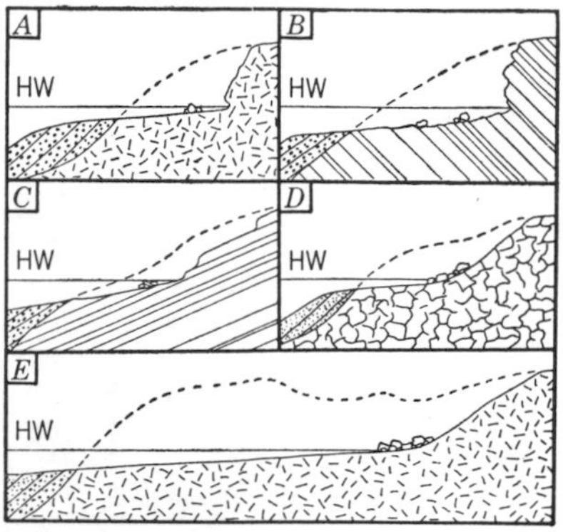

FIG. 107. Diagram illustrating marine erosion of various types of country rock on a steep coast. *A*, hard, unstratified; *E*, the same when a broad marine erosion platform has developed; *B*, strata dipping away from shore; *C*, strata dipping towards the shore; *D*, more swiftly weathering rock than *A*.

The direction of dip of bedding planes also influences the shape of the cliff. Where the dip is towards the land the steepness will be found to increase. But where the dip is towards the sea portions will tend to slide off the face of the cliff along the bedding planes, thereby reducing the declivity. Furthermore, greater height of a cliff will tend to lessen the slope, because more material has to be carried away by the waves for each meter of recession. Obviously this must have an adverse influence on the rate at which coastal erosion is accomplished and leave more time for the action of weathering.

It goes without saying that the shape of the coastline is largely determined by the height and durability of the rocks. The higher the land and the more resistant the country rock, the more slowly coastal erosion will advance. Capes will form where resistant rocks crop out, while bays will correspond to the more easily attacked formations. It is not merely the mass properties of the rock but to a

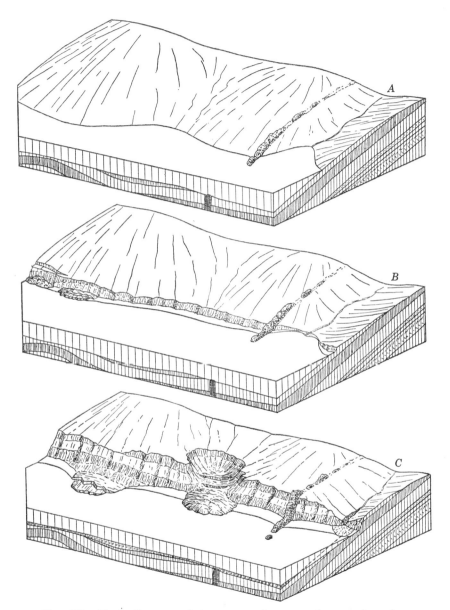

Fig. 108. Block diagrams of three successive stages in coastal erosion.

great extent also the degree of jointing and bedding that regulates the rate of destruction (Fig. 108).

Now and again a smaller mass withstands the onslaught longer than the surrounding rock. The erosion will by-pass it and isolate a column, connected to the mainland by a *natural bridge*. When the bridge collapses, or where the connection with the land had been severed in the first instance, an isolated pillar is left standing, often termed *outlier* or *stack* (Fig. 109).

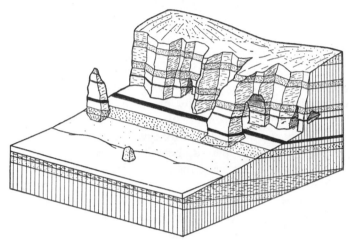

Fig. 109.   Block diagram of arch, stack, and sea caves on a surface of marine erosion.

But although coastal erosion works selectively and tends to cut out an intricate pattern along the coast, other factors are also involved that attempt to draw the coastline straight again. In Chapter 1 the tendency was mentioned of waves to curve around and concentrate their attack on protruding portions of the coastline, while on the other hand they fan out in a bay and spend their energy on a larger section of the shore. This must result in a stronger attack on headlands and a certain degree of protection in reentrants.

This explains why headlands often show steep cliffs or at any rate a bare, rocky, wave-cut platform, whereas bays are almost always characterized by a sand or shingle beach. As the jutting-out portions of a coastline are closer to deep water than reentrants, the submarine slope must be steeper. Naturally this greater steepness of the foreshore fronting headlands helps to increase the power and effect of wave onslaught and the dispersion of the waste products.

Where the irregularities of the coastline are not due to differences in resistance, but to the drowning of a diversified land surface (rias shoreline, fiord coast) the tendency to smoothing will be brought out more strongly. In this case capes will not always be formed of rocks with extra resistance to erosive action, and the bays need not correspond with material of lesser resistance.

The platform developed in front of a marine cliff is termed *marine erosion platform* or *coastal terrace*. The broader and shallower it is, the less effective will be the activity of the waves beating on the beach. But the coastal terrace is in itself also subject to wear and tear, because the waves shove and roll the loosened blocks over its surface. Boring organisms and solution, especially in limestone, strongly support the mechanical abrasion.

As the incoming waves possess the greatest energy at the outer edge of the platform and gradually dissipate their force while rolling inwards, a perfectly horizontal surface would be attacked most strongly at its seaward margin. Moreover, erosion has been able to act here for the longest period, because it gradually extends landwards during the process of planation. From these two causes the coastal terrace obtains a slight seaward slope, with the greatest depth where the waves come from. As, however, the oscillatory movement of the water quickly dies out below, as explained in Chapter 1, the greater depth at the edge provides a certain degree of protection from wave action. A balance is struck whereby at each distance from the beach the wear on the bottom is just sufficient to produce a certain slope. This slope is such that the amount of material coming from the shallow side added to that produced locally equals the amount delivered outwards to the neighboring area. Where the depth for a time becomes too great, a certain amount of detritus is deposited, while a too shallow portion is subjected to extra attack. In the case of too great a slope more protecting material is brought along from the coast, and, conversely, a flat area is open to more effective attack because less sediment is delivered from the landward side to protect it.

Hence, we find that, just as in a river, a *profile of equilibrium* tends to develop. In neither of these two cases is erosion stopped by attainment of this equilibrium, but from that time onward the shape of the bottom curve alters but insignificantly. Whereas in a river the position remains unaltered thereafter but the grade is gradually reduced, the profile of equilibrium in coastal erosion is slowly shifted landwards while approximately the same shape and level are retained.

A number of factors influence the steepness and shape of the curve. Local conditions as to climate, type and structure of the country rocks, the degree of exposure of the coast, current action, and fauna and flora all play a part in determining the shape of the profile of equilibrium. In the following chapter the profile of equilibrium will be dealt with in connection with sedimentation.

The attack on the rocks of the coast produces particles of all sizes and shapes. The finest chips of the silt and clay fractions are washed away, the coarsest fragments remaining where they were formed until sufficiently reduced in size to become transported. The material of middling sizes is gradually moved either sideways to build up shingle and sand beaches in embayments or seawards along the bottom. The deeper the water to which it is carried, the slighter wave turbulence at the bottom will be and hence the smaller the traction exerted. This results in sorting, and one generally encounters sand or gravel below low water line and sand or silt farther out from the coast. We will return to the sorting action later. On a bold coast under wave attack, for instance a volcano rising from the sea floor, the edge of the erosion platform must be reached some distance from the shore, where the original slope begins. The material transported across the platform rolls over the edge and builds up a talus or submarine scree. By this process the platform is extended gradually seaward by a wedge of dumped matter.

Normally the submarine slopes are slight and the area of erosion gradually merges with the area of deposition. Nothing comparable to a scree then develops, because only sand or silt is available. As a rule even the areas undergoing marine erosion are largely cloaked with sediment, at least during most of the year.

It may be asked to what depths mechanical erosion can reach, but the question is found extremely hard to answer.

Many authors (Bourcart, Shepard) hold that erosive action reaches only a few meters below sea level, because cobbles with delicate plant and animal growth attached are sometimes dredged close to the shore. According to Bagnold the depth to which shingle can be moved is very small—of the same order as the wave height, whereas for fine silt it is of the order of the wavelength, but this probably does not apply to waves with a long period that cause only slow oscillatory movements of the water. Otherwise ocean swell would disturb silt at depths of 500 or 600 m, which it almost certainly does not. From the limitation of fine silt to depths exceeding 60 to 70 m off the New

England coast, Stetson concluded that this is the limit to which waves can stir the bottom sediments.

Others are of the opinion that erosion is possible to many dozens of meters. In support of this contention it may be recalled that several observations possibly indicate appreciable wave action down to 100 or 200 m below sea level. Discoloring of the sea water during storms, the production of wave (?) ripple marks on the sea floor, the hurling of sand on board ships during storm in comparatively deep waters, and the absence of fine silt in central portions of the North Sea all point to wave turbulence reaching depths of many dozens of meters. One of the most striking instances is that off Land's End in Cornwall stones up to half a kilogram in weight are sometimes washed into lobster crawls at depths of over 60 m. In the English Channel shells are occasionally injured by the movement of gravel at depths of 70 m, and on the east coast, when ballast foreign to the region is dumped in 20 to 35 m of water, the shore after storms is strewn with these pebbles.

Even if waves are able to churn up unconsolidated debris at greater depths, there can hardly be active abrasion of consolidated rocks down to depths of 150 m. In any event, to carry erosion of firm rocks to greater depths than 100 m would require such an extremely long time that it is highly doubtful that the relative level of land and sea ever remained the same long enough to allow this depth to be attained.

It should not be inferred from the above that erosion is everywhere active or at least that no deposition can take place at lesser depths than 100 m. Over large areas of the shelf the bottom currents are extremely weak and, at most, are able to retain clay in suspension. Where wave turbulence is restricted by offshore winds, or in more or less enclosed basins, the currents and turbulence are generally unable to prevent deposition. Depressions in the terrace, in spite of being in themselves quite shallow, are generally sites of sedimentation, even of clay particles. Where currents are absent or move in a closed course even the most violent wave turbulence cannot stop sedimentation; it can only cause the deposition to be intermittent. In inland seas this is the rule. Most fossil sediments, it should be recalled, were laid down in shallow water. Here the combination of turbulence and throughgoing currents must have been absent. These aspects will be taken up again when dealing with sedimentation.

After what has been given above little need be said on the action of waves on uncemented rocks as sand, marl, clay, etc., where these are exposed on the coast. The washing away of compact clay is found to take place comparatively slowly, but once churned up this material is more readily transported than sand, although sand is eroded more easily.

In general the factors regulating transportation also determine the shape of sandy coasts and of the adjoining sea floor. In this case the waves and currents spend their energy in rolling about, picking up, and transporting the loose materials. On rocky coasts, on the other hand, the destruction of the solid country rock requires most of the available energy, and the forms are mainly determined by the relative resistance of the various stretches of coastal rock.

Current Erosion. The problem as to how far currents may directly erode the bottom must now be considered. Without doubt, the main geological activity of currents is merely the transportation of particles loosened and raised by wave action. Even in the North Sea, where powerful tidal currents prevail, these are by themselves insufficient to move large quantities of sand. It is true that current measurements along the eastern and western coasts of the United States by Stetson, Fleming, and Shepard proved the occurrence of irregular eddying currents with velocities up to nearly 40 cm per second close to the bottom. If one may apply Hjulstrøm's figures for stream transportation to marine environments these currents would be able to move sand particles but would not be sufficient to disturb compacted silt-clay aggregates or gravel. But we will learn later on that there are reasons for doubting the efficiency of these currents in eroding the bottom.

Again, the fact that at depths of 1000 to 2000 m on the sills between the Indonesian deep-sea basins coarse gravel, coral detritus, and in some cases even bare rock bottom were found may mean no more than that deposition was prevented. A reason for doubting active erosion is that precipitation of manganese coatings on the loose materials and the marly rock forming the bottom were generally encountered wherever the *Snellius* expedition took samples on these sills. The highest current velocities measured some distance above the bottom attained 0.5 m per second. This current in itself might suffice to erode the sills, but the absence of sufficient tools to cause abrasion should not be overlooked.

Matters are different in narrow passages between islands in shallow areas, as around Ushant, where tidal currents reach velocities of 3 to 4 m per second. In shallow passages connecting deeper basins, as between Java and Bali or the other Lesser Sunda Islands (Fig. 110), between Taliaboe and Mangoli in the Moluccas, between the Orkney and Shetland Islands, in the Seymour Narrows between Vancouver Island and the mainland of British Columbia, such high velocities as 6 to 7 m are reported for spring tides. These currents are comparable in velocity with those of mountain streams. Although the meas-

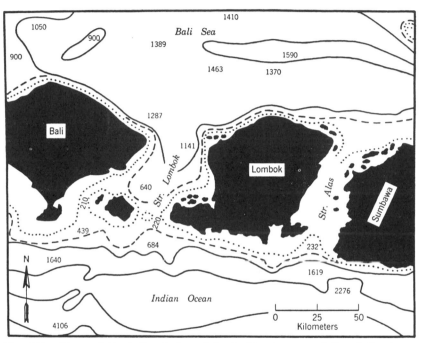

Fig. 110. Chart of Strait Lombok and Strait Alas between Bali and Sumbawa, Lesser Sunda Islands.

urements apply to the surface there can be no doubt that the velocities along the bottom are also sufficient to cause erosion. Even in these instances where deeper water is found at both ends of the passage and no tools in the form of detritus are brought along by the currents themselves, the walls will be attacked and deliver fragments to the bottom of the straits, while streams from the adjoining islands will also contribute material. It may be safely assumed that powerful erosion of the bottom and walls takes place. The wider the passage becomes, the weaker the currents will grow. The formation by erosion of very wide and deep straits between islands will therefore not be possible under these conditions.

In the Straits of Dover we have an example that has been studied in great detail by van Veen (1936). At the surface, velocities of 2 m are seldom if ever exceeded, while 15 cm above the bottom the maximum is 60 cm per second. Erosion of the bottom, that lies at about 40-m depth, does not take place, for not only are large areas covered

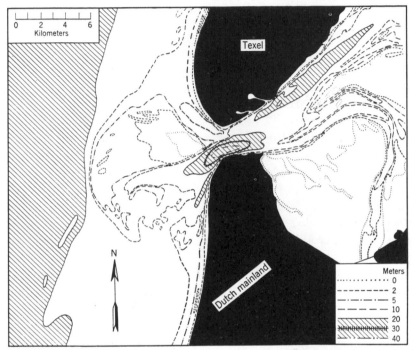

Fig. 111. Depth chart of the Marsdiep, a tidal passage between the island of Texel and the Dutch mainland, showing deep scour and tidal delta.

by seaweed but even loose sand is hardly shifted. The increase in breadth of the straits, that is roughly 1 m per century as far as can be ascertained, must be attributed entirely to wave action.

The chief agents in the development of deep passages through off-shore bars, like those between the islands to the northwest of Holland, are tidal currents. But in Chapter 1 it was recorded that wind-driven currents attain similar velocities during storms on the Dutch coast. In the Marsdiep both types may reach velocities of 1 m per second at the surface (Fig. 111). When the two kinds of current are working together the bottom velocity is sufficient to cause moderate erosion of unconsolidated Pleistocene sands and silts. In the south of Holland some tidal waters have scoured out gullies to depths of 50 and 60 m, cutting through Tertiary deposits. Tertiary fossils are regularly washed up on the shores of the Island of Walcheren.

When discussing submarine valleys on the shelf (Chapter 7) instances will be given of channels scoured out between islands of the shallow Sunda Shelf by tidal currents. These attain depths 30 m below the surrounding sea floor.

On some coasts wind-driven currents of 1½ to 2 m per second are reported during storms. When they are combined with a tidal component, surface velocities of well over 2 m may be expected. That is equal to the flow of the Rhine in the middle reaches when in spate. Similar velocities in consequence of wind action are observed in Yucatan Strait between the Caribbean Sea and the Gulf of Mexico, and in Florida Strait. Unhappily all these figures relate to surface velocities. Obviously this calls for extensive observations on bottom velocities, combined with measurements of sediment in the overlying waters.

As a general result it is found that erosion of consolidated rock by currents at sea is possible only in constricted passages of moderate depth. The eroded material can therefore be of only local significance. The erosion of unconsolidated deposits will be dealt with later on, in connection with transport (p. 260).

In conclusion it should be pointed out that not all sedimentary lime is directly delivered by organisms or precipitation. A certain amount derives from bottom and coastal erosion and from river transport. To this lime detritus should be credited only that portion that had its source in limestone. Deposits of tests that have been reworked and displaced should be counted as of biological origin.

RIVERS

Apart from marine erosion and the biosphere, rivers form the chief source of sedimentary material. Only very few mountain streams debouch directly into the sea. The overwhelming majority of runoff water first collects in rivers and reaches the ocean via sluggish lower courses. Hence nearly all material carried into the sea is fine grained. Even small pebbles are relatively unimportant in bulk; clay particles greatly predominate. The Rhine, for example, carries no sand to the coast, because only clay and fine silt are found in the last few dozen kilometers of its course, except for sand washed in by tidal currents from the sandy beach. At Lobith where the Rhine passes the Dutch frontier only a million tons of coarse sand are carried along each year. This entire amount is dredged out to ensure even flow and to avoid silting up of the dyked-in river course.

The Mississippi dumps 1 km³ of sand and silt into the Gulf of Mexico each 3½ years, while the Nile carries one-tenth of that amount of sediment to the Mediterranean. It is estimated that all the rivers on the earth put together bring 12 km³ of sediment into the oceans per year. Spread out in an even layer over the entire surface of the sea floor this would form a layer 3 cm thick in 1000 years.

Some rivers are exceptionally turbid. Thus the Rio Grande River in the United States may carry 10% by volume of suspended matter. Less abnormal is the Fraser River of British Columbia. At low water 1 part dry weight per 100,000 parts of water is carried, and during floods 1 per 4000. The bottom load of the Rhine in its middle course is several times the amount carried in suspension; at the mouth of the Mississippi, on the other hand, it is but one-tenth. In this respect also marked variations are thus encountered.

Another highly important function of rivers is the supplying to the sea of dissolved matter that forms nutrient salts for plankton (phosphates and nitrates especially) or is used as building materials for tests and skeletons (lime and silica). The introduction of organic matter into the sea water by rivers has already been mentioned, and we must add floating vegetable remains such as pollen, seeds, and tree trunks.

It is often thought that the amount of silica carried to the sea in solution by rivers is but a small fraction as compared to the contributed lime. This, however, is not the case, for the yearly figures are respectively 320×10^6 tons of silica and 560×10^6 tons of lime.

But even less silica than lime is found dissolved in sea water (1 in 250,000). As a gradual increase does not take place an amount equal to that brought in by rivers is evidently deposited on the floor. As far as is known this deposition takes place in the form of plant and animal remains.

An interesting question is whether rivers or coastal erosion predominate in the delivery of sediment to the sea. In seeking for an answer one should avoid confusion with local rates of operation. On some coasts hanging valleys are met with in the cliffs, indicating that the retreat of the shoreline is so swift that even with their lowered base level (or, rather, shortened course) the streams are unable to keep up with marine planation (Fig. 112). The denudation of the whole drainage basin must be much slower still. Not only where the country rock is limestone or chalk and consequently surface erosion is reduced to a minimum, but also in impervious formations, this relation between coastal erosion and denudation may be observed locally.

However, the entire surface of the land is so much larger than the narrow coastal belt considered in the above comparison that a more penetrating quantitative analysis is needed for the solving of our problem as to the relative importance of terrestrial and marine erosion as sources of sediment.

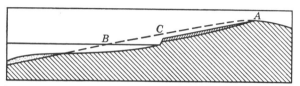

Fig. 112. Schematic representation of the shortening of a river by marine erosion.

It was stated above that the yearly contribution from rivers in undissolved matter is estimated at 12 km³. An estimate of the total effect of marine erosion can be arrived at as follows. The total length of coastline undergoing active erosion may be taken as 250,000 km. The cutting back will be set at 10 m per 1000 years, the average height of the cliffs at 25 m, plus 25 m below water as the depth to which the land is cut away. The resultant production of sedimentary material works out at 0.12 km³ per year. This is only 1% of the estimated contribution from rivers.

The figures assumed in this estimate of marine erosion are almost certainly too high (see p. 113). Although recession of cliffs in unconsolidated rock is generally 10 to 100 times the above value, the attack of firm rock is very much slower (see Shepard and Grant, 1947) and the average height of cliffs and depth of erosion are surely less. Barrell's estimate (1925) is 0.08 to 0.4 km³ per year. Some authors, like Bourcart (1945), believe that coastal erosion is of hardly any importance at all, and that platforms of marine erosion are due to subaerial denudation and have later been merely smoothed by the marine action. This opinion, however, does not take account of the action in unconsolidated country rock.

Even if abrasion is several times more active than our very liberal estimate, it remains far behind the present activity of continental denudation. Granting that the present rate of subaerial denudation is 10 times the average for the geological past, the conclusion is still warranted that marine erosion is of relatively small importance in the bulk production of marine sedimentary matter.

This conclusion is borne out by the investigation of marine sediments. Miss G. A. Neeb points out (personal communication) that the composition of the Moluccan sediments varies according to the types of rock cropping out in the drainage area of rivers flowing to the coast but appears to show no appreciable contribution from rocks exposed in the coastal cliffs.

GLACIERS AND ICE [1]

In arctic regions the glaciers descend to sea level and carry their morainic burden out to the sea floor. Surface moraines are lacking or poorly developed on most of these glaciers. Internal moraines are of greater importance, and their material remains incorporated in the icebergs floating away from the ice front. The basal moraines are by far the most bulky, and part of them is also carried away, frozen to the lower surface of the ice. The greater part, however, is probably deposited where the glacier starts to float and to spread out at the surface of the sea. Glacier streams are also active in dumping fluvioglacial deposits at the coast and spreading glacier-milk in the coastal waters. The part that remains frozen into the ice is carried along by the drifting bergs and is gradually scattered over wide areas as the ice slowly melts away. Wind and especially currents determine in which direction and at what speed floating ice is driven and where its load of sediment is deposited.

In our first chapter the present limits of drifting icebergs were mentioned. About 80 million km² of the ocean floors thus come under the influence of materials borne by ice. The relative proportion of rafted blocks and sand is small, however. During the Ice Age the sphere of influence of ice rafting was greatly extended towards lower latitudes. This is proved by the dredging of Scottish and Irish morainic boulders in the Bay of Biscay 300 km north of Cape Finistère and by the pebble of northern origin weighing 1 kg hauled up close to Madeira. Long cores obtained in the northern Atlantic likewise showed coarse-grained glacial strata, even containing pebbles, in localities where at present globigerina ooze is being deposited.

Detritus can also be carried along in ice floes, whether formed as ground ice in rivers and containing fluviatile sediments, or as floes

[1] See Andrée, 1925.

formed on the coast and enclosing beach sediments. It may also happen that on the setting in of a thaw tributaries wash sand and gravel onto the ice covering a river and that this ice is later broken up and floated seawards. Or dust storms may have contributed a small amount of sediment to river ice.

Ice floes are frequently driven onto the beach by wind, waves, and currents or by the pressure exerted by pack ice. Not only are the beach and shallow beach front plowed up and the sediments distorted, but large quantities of material may be pushed up above high-water line. Icebergs reach to depths of several hundreds of meters, and by reason of their great mass the disturbance caused in sediments where they happen to run aground may be severe.

Ice floes, because of their small mass, cannot drift nearly as far afield as great icebergs. On the other hand they may be formed at much lower latitudes. The Dutch rivers, for example, frequently carry out sediment enclosed in ice to the North Sea, thousands of kilometers south of the nearest glaciers that reach down to sea level and also far beyond the reach of icebergs. It is worth noting that this action of ice rafting is excluded up to polar regions in periods of mild climate, such as have occurred frequently in the geological past.

WEATHERING

Weathering on the sea floor is much less active than on dry land. The variations in temperature are much smaller and slower. Only in the shallow parts of the offshore and on beaches of cold climates can the important mechanical action of frost play a part. Burrowing, boring, and mud-feeding activities are carried on by benthonic animals, but these factors are probably not more intensive than on land.

Chemical weathering is also deprived of some important tools that are used on land. Most of the highly active acids, as humic acid, etc., are absent, and the sea water is slightly alkaline in reaction. The high concentration of potassium, sodium, calcium, and magnesium ions in sea water strongly counteracts solution of these elements from rock particles.

Another circumstance tending to retard weathering is that currents in submarine groundwater are almost entirely lacking. In finer sediment, groundwater is to all purposes stagnant and consequently saturated with all soluble materials. In coarser-grained deposits and especially in shallow water a certain degree of ventilation of the groundwater takes place.

Another very important cause for the insignificance of submarine weathering is found in the mineralogical nature of the deposits. In general the particles have been formed or liberated during the disintegration of rocks on land. Hence, they are either exceptionally resistant, like quartz and muscovite, or they have been newly developed, for instance clay minerals. Under external conditions they are therefore highly stable.

Taking the above into account it is not surprising to find so little evidence of weathering on the sea floor. For example, Miss Neeb (1943) showed that even the ash of the Indonesian volcano Tambora, thrown out a century ago, showed no signs of weathering whatever, although similar material on Java is attacked on land in a few years' time. Glacial pebbles are perfectly fresh when brought up from the sea floor, though they may show a coating of manganese oxide on the exposed upper surface. The many rock samples dredged off southern California included only a few weathered rocks, nearly all of volcanic material.

The possibility, however, that lava and ash erupted by submarine volcanoes and reacting with sea water while still at a high temperature may undergo intensive alteration has been suggested by several writers, and some "weathered" basaltic and andesitic pebbles and fragments of pumice have been reported from deep-sea samples. But the total mass of material involved can hardly be very large.

Dietz (1942) has suggested that possibly montmorillonite is slowly converted to illite on the sea floor by the absorption of potassium from sea water. But the alleged scarcity of montmorillonite in marine clays is not in accord with the results of other workers (Correns, 1939). Future investigations will have to solve this important question.

On the beach, weathering takes entirely different forms than under a permanent cover of water. The effects are generally masked, however, by the powerful abrasive action and swift reworking of the deposits by wave and current action. The result of solution may become evident, especially on limestone rock; this topic will be dealt with in detail when treating coral reefs. A curious phenomenon occurring locally is the development of rimmed solution pools in various kinds of rock with a hardened edge, as the result of deposition of lime during evaporation at low tide (Emery, 1946).

Recapitulating, we find that submarine weathering can hardly be considered an important source of, or influence on, sedimentary matter.

Worms and many other types of fouling organisms burrow in the material on the bottom and overturn it. The ingested sediment is deprived of part of the enclosed organic matter, and stratification is obliterated. The term "weathering" may be used in a wider sense to include this important action.

TRANSPORTATION OF SEDIMENT IN THE SEA

In the discussion of the various sources of sediment some information concerning the transportation has already been given. The loosening and the displacement of particles are processes so intimately connected that the one cannot be treated without some reference to the other. Thus the transportation by ice need not be dealt with again after what has already been said.

The following pages will show that, in spite of much general information that has been obtained on the transportation of sedimentary matter, there is ample justification for the following quotation from Trask (1941, p. 233): "Relatively little attention has been given to the laws governing movement of detritus in the ocean, and if any one single problem may be selected as being in the most urgent need of solution in the general field of sedimentation it is the conditions of transport of sediment in the sea."

From the moment the particles have been loosened or carried into the sea, two factors in transport have to be taken into account: first, the force of gravity, that attempts to pull them to or along the bottom, and then to stop them in the lowest position that can be reached; second, currents in the water, which may also exert forces with vertical components on sedimentary matter.

SLUMPING OF SEDIMENT AND THE ACTION OF GRAVITY

Turbidity Currents. Gravity constitutes the principal factor in two different types of movement affecting sedimentation. In the first type the churning up of sediment forms a suspension of higher density than that of the surrounding clear water. On a horizontal bottom the suspension will tend to spread and then deposit its load. On a slope it will start to flow, and in this manner a *turbidity current* (less correctly, a density current) can be set up. Daly was the first to draw attention to this possibility. Once the current is started, the turbulence in the flowing body retards the settling of the suspended sediment and the distance of transport is increased.

The churning up of sediment can be the result of wave action or it may accompany the sliding of an unconsolidated mass of sediment on a submarine slope (Bailey, 1938; Migliorini, 1944).

Mud flows are sometimes formed on land, for instance on slopes of volcanoes, or after cloudbursts in dry climates. If such a flow managed to reach the coast it could continue along the sea floor because the density would be higher than that of the sea water. It would gradually take up salt water by turbulent mixing and finally become indistinguishable from a turbidity current started on the sea floor. Sprigg has suggested that, when rivers contain sufficient suspended matter, they might be heavier than sea water and submerge at the outlet (see Chapter 7). Andrée (1920) reported that submarine cable ruptures are correlated with the rainy season along the East African and South American coasts. If this correlation is real it might possibly be attributed to the action of muddy rivers or mud flows running directly into the sea.

A slow turbidity current will drop suspended matter, will be diluted by turbulent mixing with clear water, and will gradually lose its motive force. It appears probable that if the velocity and turbulence exceed a certain limit the sediment will be retained and new material will be picked up from the bottom. The current would then accelerate and increase in volume and density until the bottom of the slope was reached. There the turbid water must spread out and deposit its load over a wide area.

Kuenen (1948) has shown that turbidity currents of high density can be made, experimentally, which attain surprising velocities on moderate slopes. In consequence of the high specific gravity the transporting power is raised very considerably. Under optimal conditions the maximum volume of blocks that can be moved should be several thousand times the equivalent for clear water. When the sediment content in the experimental currents is raised there is found to be a gradual but swift transition from a heavy liquid capable of turbulent flow to a paste of which the movement is more like sliding than flowing.

Computation shows that a current of sufficient velocity and turbulence to retain sand in suspension can result only on slopes that are at least moderate, unless the volume is very large. Hence, the action of turbidity currents in transporting sand and coarse detritus must be restricted to environments where the sea floor slopes several degrees or more. Lutite, on the other hand, does not require high velocities to be transported, and, according to Stetson and Smith, it appears probable that turbidity currents of low density carrying only clay and silt may form an important factor in the distribution of these finer fractions on the sea floor, especially down the continental slope. Up to the present the action of turbidity currents has been discussed only theoretically, and the currents have not yet been observed in nature, except in lakes and reservoirs. But it is probable that this type of current has played an important part in the periodic cleaning out of submarine canyons, or even that they are responsible for cutting these gorges in the continental slope. In Chapter 7 we will return to this aspect of turbidity currents.

These currents may also be an important factor in developing "graded bedding" (p. 366) and in the deposition of "deep-sea sands" (p. 360). Several other cases have become known in which sediments contain organic remains indicating shallower depths than the present site of deposition, or grain sizes too large to have been supplied by normal agents (Shepard, 1948). In all these instances turbidity currents or slumping may solve the problem, and where combined with graded bedding the former process is indicated.

Surf playing on beaches and bars of sand and finer grains tends to raise sediment. Each time sediment is churned up the water temporarily acquires excess density. Immediately gravity starts to act on the suspension and to pull the particles down any available bottom slope. Although currents due to other causes generally outweigh the influence of gravity, that force must add a component which is normally directed away from the beach. This action of suspended matter cannot yet be assessed quantitatively owing to lack of data on the amount of matter brought into suspension by surf. But it should be counted among the important factors regulating the distribution of sediment on the coast.

Slumping. In the second type of sediment transport in which gravity is the main factor, the particles are not carried along by a current but roll or slide down the slope.

On steep slopes such as small delta fronts in inland seas, screes or steep cliffs around coral reefs, etc., stones and fragments can tumble down separately one by one. A natural talus is thus formed, the declivity of which depends on local circumstances but which is always steep. Typical, steep deltas should be sought in protected bays or in lakes. Here the beds can slope at 10° or 20° and screes can attain 30°.

In open water, where waves and currents can reach the bottom at greater depths and where only fine particles are provided, the inclination of the bottom becomes very slight. The action of gravity on individual grains is then negligible and becomes entirely masked by other transporting agents.

A different type of movement is the sudden slumping of larger masses, which one might term submarine landslides. Both rock falls and mud slumps are known to occur. A slow slipping en masse of unconsolidated sediment can also be imagined, more akin to the creep on valley slopes. The structural evidence of slumping in fossil sediments will first be reviewed (for references see Fairbridge, 1946, 1947; Beets, 1946; Kuenen, 1948b).

Several coarse breccias have been attributed to submarine landslides. It is supposed that along steep slopes, as fault scarps, masses of rock have collapsed and tumbled down to form screes of coarse, angular material. Dixon (1931) and Moore (1934) have ascribed the emplacement in the Johns Valley Shale of huge slabs of older rock, measuring up to 100 m in diameter, to sliding on the muddy sea floor over distances of 30 km.

A more frequent occurrence appears to have been the slumping of unconsolidated sediments. A variety of structure due to sliding of soft muds has been recognized.

In some deposits small plications are observed that must have been formed during the sedimentation. This syngenetic origin is proved by the alternation with undisturbed strata, while often the anticlinal crests have been beheaded by sliding of the upper layer or by current and wave action. The thickness of the disturbed strata may be anything between a few centimeters and a few meters. It cannot be ascertained whether the movement occurred suddenly or by a gradual creep. Miniature nappes, wildly distorted and crumpled beds, and cracks due to stretching and complete brecciation have also been recorded. In other places the slumping proceeded beyond the stage of folding, and mud or silty sand was rolled into balls and spiral structures (Fig. 113). It may be inferred that in some places the stratum was entirely disrupted and a mud flow or even a diluted suspension ran down the slope. Kuenen suggested that turbidity currents of high density, referred to above, may originate in this way. The sediment must then have been spread out evenly at the bottom in a thin extensive layer (see p. 367).

Exceptionally fine and varied instances of large-scale fossil slumping have been described by O. T. Jones (1937, 1940, 1947) from the Silurian of north Wales. A great number of slumps were detected that had moved from north to south and had resulted in complicated folding, overfolding, contortion, rolling, and other forms of disturbance.   The anticlinal crests of folds had been cut away, and the next stratum had been deposited immediately on top, with the coarser material at the bottom grading into fine mudstones higher up.   The dis-

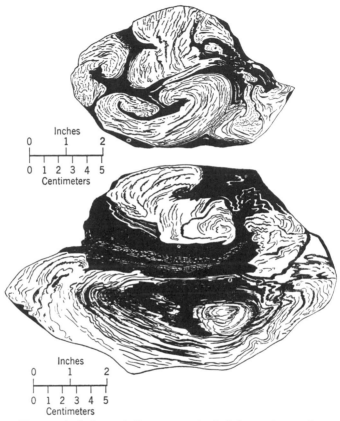

FIG. 113.   Two typical slump balls composed of shaly sandstone from a slump sheet of shale.   Carboniferous of southwest Wales.   (After Kuenen, 1948, Fig. 5, p. 370.)

turbed beds sometimes contained fossils from a shallower bathymetric zone than that of the undisturbed mudstones above and below.   The larger masses reach a thickness of over a hundred meters.   During the subsequent Caledonian orogenesis the slump planes below the slumps did not act as thrust planes but remained intact.

A rather different view on the action of gravity is advanced by Baldrey and Brown.   They described at length a number of intraformational disturbances in the Tertiary deposits along the western margin of South America. A "clay pebble" bed, contorted strata, thrusts, etc., are mentioned. They came to the conclusion that slumping was active during the sedimentation, but also that major internal slides occurred after thousands of meters of sediment had been deposited.

Others hold that intraformational corrugations are partly due to local overloading and squeezing out of unconsolidated material and that the plications were formed after a certain amount of sediment had already been deposited on the now-deformed stratum (Miller). The present writer does not agree, because in that event dragging of the folds should be evident both along the lower and upper margin of the distorted stratum. The influence of friction, however, is never observed on the upper side. This strongly suggests that there was no overburden at the time of deformation. Generally the folds are cut off sharply across the anticlinal crests.

Currents of water or swiftly flowing suspensions have also been invoked to explain intraformational corrugations by the same forces that produce wind waves. There are grave objections against this explanation. The Helmholz forces held responsible are extremely small and could not possibly deform a solid deposit. But if the deformed layers were still fluid during their distortion the wave would have flattened out before becoming fixed in a sedimentary structure. Moreover, most of the corrugations are much steeper than a wave can ever be and have frequently fallen over sideways.

A comparison with surf cannot be drawn, because with surf the steep shape and overturned crest are due to gradual deformation while the wave passes over a shelving bottom. In the explanation of folding by currents the deformed stratum is supposed to remain stationary and could therefore not develop shapes due to friction along the lower surface. As far as can be ascertained up to the present, surface slumping is by far the most probable explanation for almost all intraformational corrugations.

In spite of these and many other known instances, structural proof of fossil slumping is not very frequent. However, when more attention is given to the detailed structures of sediments in future field work, slumping will doubtless prove much less exceptional than is now generally realized. Especially in geosynclinal series many more pronounced slopes may have been developed locally. This would not be the first time that fairly common and obvious phenomena have been overlooked until the interest of field geologists had been awakened.

For example, the present writer came across many exposures with very clear and obvious signs of slumping in southern Wales. Here the Millstone Grit and Coal Measures are well exposed on the coast around Saundersfoot and have been accurately mapped and frequently visited by excursions. Still the evidence of slumping in the shape of balls, folds, slump sheets, etc., in shales and sandstones does not appear to have been recorded earlier. If the writer's interest in these structures had not previously been excited by the work of O. T. Jones,

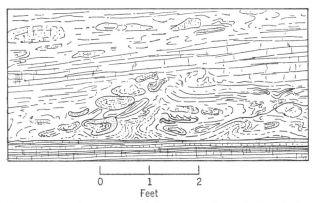

0   1   2
Feet

Fig. 114. Slump sheet of shale, containing sandy slump balls. Carboniferous of southwest Wales. (After Kuenen, 1948, Fig. 7, p. 373.)

he would doubtless have also passed by, without noticing (Kuenen, 1948; see Fig. 114).

Even so, it cannot be doubted that undisturbed beds greatly predominate over deposits that have undergone sliding. But it should be borne in mind that the great majority of known sediments have been formed in the shallow depths, where primary slopes are generally very slight. The activity of waves and currents continually tends to erase all inequalities in the relief and to spread out the sedimentary matter in flat, horizontal expanses. Parallel bedding planes are, therefore, the rule in fossil sediments, when only smaller areas are taken into account. A greater chance of finding evidence of slumping exists for fossil deposits in lakes, fiords, and other protected and restricted environments. But these are very scarce in the stratigraphical column.

In deeper water, beyond the 200-m depth line, the material can drop to the bottom undisturbed, and where a marked declivity occurs the deposits are originally laid down with a considerable slope. Here, however, the fine composition and high percentage of clay coupled with the considerable water content must render the muds highly mobile. The great extension of the slopes will further enlarge the chance of developing suspensions when sliding takes place. When these flows have come to rest, there will be little to show that we are not dealing with a normal direct deposit. It is therefore not surprising that among the fairly scarce deep-water sediments from the past only very few cases of slumping have been detected.

Several geologists have suggested that sliding of sediment from small depths to deeper areas has resulted in the incorporation of shallow-water strata between rocks originally deposited at depths of thousands of meters (Arn. Heim, Escher, Andrée, Horn). The Alpine Mesozoic radiolarites alternate with sediments that were evidently formed no deeper than a few hundred meters, and the authors mentioned reason that, if the radiolarites may be likened to the recent radiolarian ooze of the deep sea, the interstratification with shallow-water sediments could be explained by slumping of these sediments into deep-sea troughs. It can be shown, however, that the assumed interpretation of the radiolarites as deep-sea sediments is highly doubtful.

In the first place in the similar case of the Franciscan charts of California these are likewise interbedded with other types of sediment, some of them coarse detritals, but they are well bedded and certainly are not the result of slumping into the deep water (pointed out to the author by Dunbar).

In the second place normal pelagic radiolarian ooze cannot form so close in to the coast that sliding could bring along sediments from shallow water. Evidently the radiolarites were formed not far from land and have nothing to do with the recent radiolarian oozes which do not occur anywhere near the coast even if the depth is great (Grunau). But if in the formation of the Alpine radiolarites concentration of silica took place in an environment where terrigenous material must also have reached to the bottom in large quantities, no recent equivalent is known. This being so the radiolarites may just as well be shallow-water sediments. Hence, no proof can be given for great depths during the formation of the Alpine radiolarites, and consequently the action of sliding need not be invoked. As no evidence of slump structures is known, the hypothesis of shallow formation appears preferable. Moreover, the assumption that geosynclines were deep-sea troughs is probably incorrect, as we have already learned. Even in the deeper troughs the sediments were similar to those now accumulating in the Moluccas, and never true oceanic deep-sea deposits such as the recent red clay or radiolarian ooze (with the possible exception of the Mesozoic geosyncline of Timor and surroundings).

The fossil evidence of slumping having been reviewed, consideration can now be given to the action of gravity on recent sediment accumulating on the sea floor.

It is obvious that it must also be difficult to prove recent sliding by bottom sampling. Fine lamination suitable for showing contortions in a columnar sample is highly rare, and the samples are generally short. Large-scale disturbances cannot show up in tube samples.

The most convincing evidence known to the writer has been offered by Archanguelski. On the slope leading from the wave-cut shore terrace to the deep basin of the Black Sea the recent sediments are in many places absent on the upper part of the slope, leaving older deposits exposed either at isolated spots or along long continuous strips. On the lower slopes the slips were evidenced either by the total pinching out of individual beds or by their intense deformation. Fine illustrations of contorted lamination from core samples were given. Slumping is mentioned as having occurred wherever the inclination of the bottom attains 2° to 3°, occasionally even at 1°.

Indirect evidence of slumping has been obtained from time to time. Thus patches of coarse detrital material have been dredged by the *Travailleur* off the coast of Portugal from depths of 500 to 900 m though the normal sediment there was fine mud. The littoral origin was proved by the presence of a shallow-water, soft-shelled fauna. Again, sliding is the most probable explanation for this anomalous occurrence, although turbidity currents might also be invoked.

Indirect proof has been given by Bramlette and Bradley. In a series of long samples taken by Piggot in the northern Atlantic some strata were discovered which they attribute to slumping. The finer particles are absent. The lower contact is sharp, and sometimes also the upper. These strata contain Foraminifera indicating a warmer climate than that prevailing at the time of deposition. These tests were probably taken up by the slide from zones at some depth in the sediment higher up the slope that had been formed during an earlier, warmer period. The age determinations by Piggot and Urry later brought confirmation, because these layers were deposited at an abnormal rate, possibly instantaneously. It is noteworthy, however, that some of the beds are graded from coarsest at the base to finest at the top. This is not indicative of a slump, and the writers mentioned invoke a mechanism like the action of turbidity currents. On p. 366 the explanation of graded bedding by this mechanism will be given.

Some cases of abnormal stratification on the sea floor may possibly be explained by slumping, for instance the occurrence of red clay resting on a layer of a globigerina ooze (see p. 370).

In the deep basins of the Moluccas all factors favorable to slumping appear to be provided, such as steep slopes, swift sedimentation, and strong seismicity. Yet the *Snellius* expedition did not find any irrefutable proofs of sliding. But Kuenen (1943) observed that at the foot of steeper slopes the lime percentage is above the average for the depth zone sampled and agrees with the amount common at smaller depths. This may find its explanation in slumping.

On the other hand normal fine muds were found in thicknesses of half a meter and more on slopes of at least 15°, possibly even steeper. This shows that one must not lay too much stress on the activity of slumping, for even in a region of diversified bottom topography like the Moluccas slopes greater than 10° are quite exceptional.

A different type of evidence comes from the examination of submarine canyons. Shepard and Emery were able to demonstrate by soundings and other evidence, that sliding takes place off and on in some of the California submarine canyons. This evidence will be reviewed when dealing with the origin of the canyons in Chapter 7.

A considerable body of evidence has been brought together by Shepard and others showing that submarine slides are sometimes triggered by earthquakes. For instance, the sudden deepening of Sagami Bay during the earthquake of Tokyo in 1923 must evidently be attributed to sliding along the bottom.

This contention is substantiated by the frequent breaks of submarine cables during seaquakes. Several observations go to prove that in many cases the ruptures are not due to direct faulting of the sea floor but to sliding.

In the first place the surface over which the ruptures occur is often very extensive. In the second place portions of the cables are frequently found deeply buried under slumped sediment. In the third place many breaks may occur several hours after the shock and successively later at greater distances from the epicenter. This indicates a secondary cause, probably tsunamis. These oscillations may continue for many hours after the earthquake, and it is reasonable to suppose that they lead to slumping after a certain amount of erosion has been caused. As the oscillations are weaker at greater distances from the epicenter, they would require a longer time to cause a slump

(Shepard and Emery, 1941). In these instances the tsunamis may therefore be the cause of slumping, while they in turn are believed to have been caused by major slides in the epicentral area. On the other hand, Shepard has recently come to the opposite conclusion (personal communication). He thinks it unlikely that tsunamis cause an important slumping in deep water because, according to oceanographical computations, they exert very little force at depths. Neither does he believe that slumping can generate tsunamis. Fault movement seems to fit the character of the waves much better. It remains to be seen whether the time lag mentioned above can be reconciled with this view.

The steep slopes of submarine canyons, where inclinations of 45° occur locally, prove that the consolidated sediment can maintain higher gradients than the frontal slope of the continental terrace. Normal recent sediments have even been sampled clinging to the slopes of canyons (Stetson, 1936). Shepard (1948) reports recent sediment on slopes up to about 45° in La Jolla Canyon. These observations prove that in the sheltered positions on the canyon walls the primary slope of deposition may also greatly exceed that of the continental terrace. But on many parts these walls are bare, and it is not improbable that the sediment slides down regularly as soon as somewhat thicker strata have accumulated.

There is a school in orogenic geology holding that tectonic structures such as folding and thrusting should be attributed to sliding (Haarmann, van Bemmelen). These authors believe that after deposition and lithification large prisms of sediment are displaced by the action of gravity and are thereby deformed. They attribute all tectonic structures to sliding. Of recent years a number of alpine geologists assume that an important part of the thrusting in the northern Helvetic Alps is due to the action of gravity (Lugeon, Gangebin, et al.). It is not the place here to enter into these matters, because they are not directly connected with the process of sedimentation.

SETTLING

The velocity with which a particle sinks to the sea floor can be calculated theoretically or it can be measured experimentally. For the calculation the law of Stokes is used, which says that for a sphere the velocity of sinking depends on the specific gravity of the sphere and its diameter, likewise on the density of the liquid and its viscosity. Under given conditions $v = C \times r^2$, in which v is the velocity, C a constant, and r the radius. As the specific gravity of sea water is fairly constant and the changes in viscosity with temperature are also restricted (about 10% per 5°), the velocity for a given kind of material can be taken as roughly proportional to the square radius of the particle. Table 13 applies to quartz spheres in distilled water of 20°.

TABLE 13. VELOCITY OF SINKING OF QUARTZ SPHERES IN WATER AT 20° C

Diameter, mm	Velocity of sinking, cm/sec	Time for sinking 10 cm
1	6.6	1.5 seconds
0.5	4.4	2.3 seconds
0.1	0.8	13 seconds
0.03	0.09	2 minutes
0.008	0.005	½ hour
0.001	0.00009	1 day
0.0001	0.000001	3 months

Experimental tests roughly confirm these theoretical results up to sizes of 0.1 mm. But with larger diameters turbulent motion of the water is caused and the velocities are greatly retarded with respect to the calculated speed of settling. More complicated formulas have been worked out by several investigators (Oséen) to cover larger particles. Our Fig. 115 shows that Oséen's formula gives the same values as that of Stokes up to diameters of 0.2 mm, but that a grain of 0.4 mm is retarded almost twice and one of 4 mm 45 times. Details may be found in Krumbein and Pettijohn, 1938 (cf. also Nevin, 1946).

The specific gravity of the particle is also of importance, but for quartz, feldspar, and calcite this factor is almost equal. For dark constituents, ore, etc., the diameter for equal sinking velocity is smaller on account of the higher density.

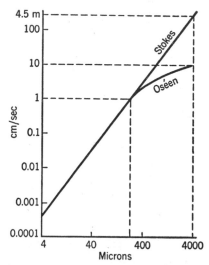

FIG. 115. Rate of sinking of quartz spheres in distilled water of 20° C. according to the formulas of Stokes and Oséen.

The shape of the sinking particle, however, is of much greater influence than the specific gravity, temperature, or salinity. The larger the divergence from sphericity and the rougher the surface, the greater will be the friction and consequently the slower the rate of settling. Hence the formula will apply fairly well for quartz grains, but for flakes of mica or clay minerals the formula gives much too large values for the settling velocity. Such disks tend to turn their flat side at right angles to the direction of movement, that is to say in a horizontal direction, resulting in a great resistance against settling. In the same way hollow tests, or shells with marked decorative irregularities and spines such as those of globigerinae or radiolarians, will sink to the bottom very slowly.

By way of example the measured (Thoulet) and calculated settling velocities of empty and broken globigerina tests are compared in Table 14.

TABLE 14. MEASURED AND CALCULATED SETTLING VELOCITIES OF GLOBIGERINA TESTS

Measurements roughly after Thoulet

Diameter, mm	¾	½	¼	⅛
Measured settling velocity, mm	3¾	2¾	1½	¾
Calculated settling velocity, mm	8	6	3	1½
Equivalent diameter	0.3	0.2	0.15	0.1
Days to sink 5000 m (measured)	1	2	4	8

In sedimentary analysis (Krumbein and Pettijohn, 1938) the following procedure avoids the difficulties due to shape and specific gravity of the grains. The mechanical composition of the finer fractions is always determined by a settling method. Either the fractions are split up by rising currents of different velocities (by this method the settling velocity is compared with an upward current of known velocity), or the particles are allowed to settle through a certain distance in standing water, the time of settling determining the settling velocity. The (apparent) size of the particles in each fraction is expressed as the diameter of a quartz sphere that would attain the same velocity. This diameter is calculated from Stokes's formula for the rate of settling. Hence the particles in a fraction show the same settling velocity as quartz spheres of the given radius. The size is thus given in so-called *equivalent diameters*, because the actual size is not considered. Some authors prefer only to note the time of settling and not to reduce to an equivalent diameter. These values of velocity may be more strictly exact, but they have the disadvantage of giving no indication as to the order of size of the fraction.

With the coarser fractions which are separated by sieving, the divergences from the spherical shape are generally not so large as greatly to influence the rate of settling. In any event the total time of settling, even in deep water, would vary only slightly on account of the high velocities.

The mechanical analyses having been made, the time required for settling in still water of a given depth can be directly calculated for each fraction. Combining this result with a given current velocity the distance to which particles will be moved during settling over a certain depth is readily computed.

However, this distance may be increased by the retarding influence of turbulent motion and by wave action, especially for small particles. Hence the above computation will give only the *minimum* distance of transport. In the following paragraphs these aspects of transport are further elaborated.

HORIZONTAL CURRENTS

Currents may transport particles either completely in suspension, or rolling along the bottom, or touching the bottom now and again (saltation). In the first case the velocity is equal to the average current velocity. In Chapter 1 a number of current velocities in nature were given, and in discussing erosion on p. 229 several instances of larger velocities are also mentioned. In open and deep water the currents at the surface seldom exceed 1 m per sec. Exceptionally swift currents such as the Gulf Stream may locally attain 3 m per sec.

In the deep sea, below 200 m, current velocities are generally not accurately known. They appear to be of the order of 5 to 20 cm per sec. The direction of flow in the various layers of the ocean is not the same. Hence, the average velocity between the upper limits of the deep sea and the bottom must fall far short of the velocity of each separate stratum and cannot exceed a few centimeters per second. Coarser grains can, therefore, not be moved more than 1 km and fine sand not more than a dozen kilometers from the point where it left the surface layers. For planktonic tests, these distances are greatly increased by the buoyancy of the organic matter and the fine projections. These have generally disappeared by decomposition and abrasion before the mechanical analyses is made. The divergences from the massive spherical shape are discounted by the method of analysis (equivalent diameter).

In shallow water on the shelf the rate of flow is frequently greater than in deep water. Thus the tidal currents in the North Sea may exceed 1 m per sec, and in restricted channels values of half a dozen meters per second have been observed. The currents sweeping over

the Agulhas Bank of 100-m depth attain 2 m per sec. Under favorable circumstances wind-driven currents may flow at 1 m per sec,
as in the entrances to the Zuider Zee in Holland. All these figures
apply only to the surface velocities. Figure 117, p. 255, gives an
approximate idea of the decrease downwards where a current sweeps
over a shallow bottom. In the Golden Gate the velocity at 1 m
above the bottom was found to be half the surface velocity. Revelle,
Fleming, and Shepard carried out measurements with three superimposed current meters suspended from a tripod. In a tideway the
following data were obtained:

> 126 cm above the bottom 26.3 cm/sec
> 51 cm above the bottom 21.3 cm/sec
> 21 cm above the bottom 15.6 cm/sec

In general the average velocity varies logarithmically with height
above the sea floor. The currents at greater depth in the Indonesian
basins attain velocities of a few centimeters to $\frac{1}{2}$ m per sec. The
higher values are encountered in straits forming the connection between basins and are due to tidal components. In La Jolla Canyon
at a depth of 560 m a maximum velocity of 23 cm per sec has been
measured 125 cm above the bottom. On the shelf off California the
velocities at 1 to 2 m above the bottom seldom exceed 10 cm per sec.
Apart from a few exceptions such currents give little evidence of
having tidal relations and appear in general to be related to the giant
eddies resulting from slope currents or internal waves (Shepard, 1948).

In Table 15 the relations between current and settling velocities and
displacement are shown. In this table the influence of turbulence has
not been taken into account. This factor must now be considered.

In Chapter 1 it was mentioned that all currents at sea show *turbulent motion*, because laminary flow is restricted to tubes and narrow
channels and to low velocities.

Only the vertical component of turbulence needs to be considered
in this connection. The action amounts to the continuous interchange
in place, now here, then there, of equal bodies of water, one moving
downward and the other upward. As only smaller particles of sediment with a slight mass leave the bottom and are carried in suspension, it may be assumed that they tend to follow closely the movement of the surrounding water. To this movement is then added the
acceleration of gravity directed downward.

Let us now consider a turbulent mass of water with a uniformly
distributed suspension of sediment of the same density as the water.

Obviously no alterations in the distribution of the suspended particles will be caused, as the upward and downward currents carry with them the same amounts, and the grains do not sink.

TABLE 15. SETTLING AND DISPLACEMENT IN A CURRENT OF 1 M/SEC AND 10 CM/SEC

Sediment	Diameter in mm	Settling velocity, cm/sec	100 m depth		
			Time for settling	Displacement	
				1 m/sec	10 cm/sec
Sand { coarse	2	25	7 minutes	0.5 km	42 m
{ fine	0.1	0.8	3 hours	10	1 km
Silt	0.06	0.35	8 hours	30	3
Clay { coarse	0.005	0.002	2 months	5,000	500
{ fine	0.0005	0.00002	14 years	500,000	50,000
Foraminifera (planktonic) { larger	0.5	6	½ hour	1½	170
{ smaller	0.02	0.05	3 days	250	25
Radiolarians	0.5	0.4	7 hours	25	2.5
Diatoms	0.04	0.15	1 day	80	8

But if the particles are heavier than the water they show a sinking movement superimposed on the turbulence. This must cause a decrease in the density of the suspension towards the top. Hence every turbulent mass of water moving upward will carry a greater number of particles than the equivalent sinking mass of water. It follows that no sooner does the concentration of the suspension increase downward than a net upward transport of particles by the turbulence will commence. The stronger the variation in concentration, the more effective will be this upward transportation. Finally a stationary condition is reached in which the sinking in consequence of gravity is exactly compensated by the upward transport by turbulence. The upward velocity of the churning movement must be greater, however, than the settling velocity of the particles.

This condition then remains stationary and can also be attained when the sediment does not descend but is churned up from the bottom. In the latter case the upward transport by turbulence is originally stronger than the influence of settling. In consequence of the strong concentration at the bottom more and more sediment is caught up and carried upward.

Because, in nature, the more frequent sedimentary particles are roughly of the same density, only the (equivalent) size plays a part.

The minute particles of which clay (lutite) is composed show exceedingly slow rates of settling. Hence the effect of slight turbulence is sufficient to counteract the motion due to gravity. The sediment is then distributed almost evenly right up to the surface. With sand the settling velocity approaches (if it does not exceed) that of the vertical movements of the water. Then a very strong upward decrease in concentration is required to attain a stationary condition. As the highest concentration is limited, the layer of water in which sufficient decrease in concentration is possible must be very thin. Even at a small distance above the bottom a concentration of zero is reached and the higher strata will receive no particles.

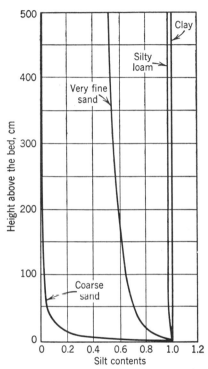

FIG. 116. Distribution of sediment (silt content) in stream or current with respect to height above stream bed, as computed from Schmidt's formula. (After Hjulström, in Trask, 1939, *Recent Marine Sediments*, Fig. 2, p. 20, American Association of Petroleum Geologists.)

If the concentration of the sediment at 2 cm above the bottom is considered 1, the concentration at every level above the bottom for a given intensity of turbulence and a given equivalent diameter of the particles can be established theoretically. Our Fig. 116 thus gives the curves for four grain sizes up to 5 m from the bottom with moderate turbulence. In a like manner the curves for various states of turbulence can be drawn.

In the present treatment, however, one very important element has so far been left out of account, namely, *the influence of the bottom on turbulence*. It has been tacitly assumed that the vertical component of turbulence remains equal down to the very bottom. But this cannot be so, as the solid bottom must hinder the upward and downward movements. Possibly this will tend to increase the horizontal component, but, however this may be, the vertical movements must decrease. The smoother the bottom, the more marked must be the decrease in vertical turbulence along it. In a very thin layer directly in contact with the bottom the flow must even approach a laminar movement (Fig. 117).

The scarce experimental data indicate that the bottom is in general rough in a hydrodynamic sense, but with a smooth deposit of fine

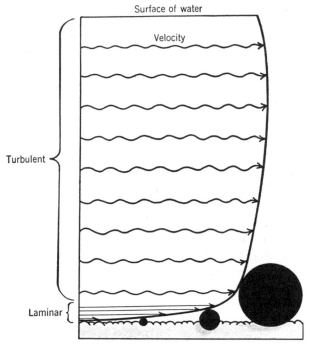

Fig. 117. Schematic section of a current, showing distribution of velocity and turbulence. Note greater velocity influencing larger particle on the bottom.

silt and a slow current a laminar sub-boundary layer immediately above the bottom may be expected.

If in the situation described above of sediment distributed evenly throughout a flowing body of water, a horizontal wall was suddenly introduced in the middle, then part of the sediment suspended just above the wall would be deprived of its supporting turbulence. It would then drop to the new bottom, thus causing a decrease in turbidity in a thin lamina of water. This low limit of turbidity would make itself felt upward through the current, because the decrease in density towards the top would have to be maintained and it starts at a lower value.

Where the turbulence is not able to lift sediment that has been dropped on the floor, all the suspended matter will finally come to rest on the bottom. But, even so, the average distance of transport from the point where the sediment was introduced will have been raised by the eddy diffusion.

The number of measurements in rivers and laboratories of the suspension of sediment by currents is very large, but the problem of distribution of turbulence over the cross section is so complicated and there are so many other variables to be taken into account that no general formula has been derived. For unknown conditions no quantitative predictions can therefore be made, and this is the case with almost all currents at sea. The turbulence in marine currents is held by some geologists to be too weak, except in strong tidal currents, to keep sand in suspension. Shepard (personal communication) doubts this contention, since there is so much evidence of sand being carried into basins to depths of several hundred meters off the California coast. There is also the possibility, however, that turbidity currents have caused this phenomenon.

Hence, the measurements carried out in the Vlie, the tidal passage between the islands of Texel and Vlieland on the Dutch coast, are of great importance. The current was measured at 15 cm and the sand content at 10 cm above the floor. Here it was found that a current of 1 m per sec is just able to lift sand of $\frac{1}{2}$-mm diameter; at $\frac{3}{4}$ m per sec a current lifts sand of $\frac{1}{3}$ mm; at $\frac{1}{2}$ m per sec, of $\frac{1}{4}$ mm. At 50 cm above the bottom only one-third of the amount at 10 cm was in suspension, and at 75 cm one-fourth. The grain size decreased from the bottom upward. During measurements in the Straits of Dover only a trace of sand was found and considerably more silt, in spite of velocities of 1 m per sec, at 15 cm above the bottom. Evidently this should be attributed to the absence of loose particles available to be caught up (van Veen, 1936).

On a submarine slope near Los Angeles Harbor in a depth of 350 m a maximum velocity of 36.7 cm per sec was measured above a silty bottom. It is surprising that the deposit did not consist of sand alone.

The finest organic tests and the lutite fraction can almost certainly be effectively retarded in their settling by the eddy diffusion of deep-sea currents, especially when it is increased by internal waves.

Thus distances of transport of a few hundred kilometers must be assumed for diatoms, while the finest fraction, that could be carried thousands of kilometers even without the action of turbulence, must, in general, be transported for unlimited distances and find a world-wide distribution. It is only in consequence of the flocculation in salt water, the action of organisms forming pellets, and the formation of larger flakes by organic slime that part of the clay carried out to sea from the continents is deposited in epicontinental seas. Otherwise practically all clay would have dropped in the deep sea during geological history.

An interesting investigation on the transport of mineral grains smaller than 0.11 mm by oceanic currents has been carried out by Correns (1947). The data are contained in Fig. 150, p. 350. Microcline and chipped augite, tourmaline, and zircon are supplied from the northern coast of the Gulf of Guinea and carried eastwards by the powerful Guinea Current. The South Equatorial Current brings along volcanic matter (glass and idiomorphic augite) from the volcanic islands. Rounded quartz is found at stations influenced by the northern coast, while the volcanic samples contain quartz chips, carried a great distance from the southern coast on account of their small size. The larger, rounded grains of quartz, zircon, tourmaline, and microcline supplied from the southern coast are deposited before reaching the stations with volcanic grains, because the South Equatorial Current is too weak to carry them any distance. Mixing of the supply from the two currents is shown at stations 234 and 238. No wind-borne grains occur in this region. The stations 222 and 238, at 3000-m depth, show the same minerals as the shelf stations 221 and 227, but finer grained. During the Pleistocene coarser grains were supplied than in the postglacial stratum at several stations. According to Correns this implies that the Guinea Current reached farther south beyond station 225 during the Ice Age.

The importance of this study is that it shows how only the powerful surface currents are able to influence the distribution of grains larger than submicroscopic. The deeper circulation of the water is too slow to have a marked effect.

In addition to transportation in suspension, displacement of sedimentary grains can take place by *jumping along the bottom*, so-called *saltation.*

This phenomenon is due to two causes: the pulsating force exerted by turbulent flow, and suction caused by the upward increase in velocity of the water in the film of laminar flow along the bottom. At a certain moment these two forces are sufficient to dislodge a particle and throw it upward. But after the first impulse is given the turbulent action above is insufficient to carry the grain farther upward. After taking a larger or smaller jump the grain again drops to the bottom. Frequently it rebounds or throws up another grain so that a new jump is made. Saltation is typical of sand and smaller bits of gravel; cobbles and boulders are too heavy to be lifted. Particles of colloidal dimensions, on the other hand, tend to stick together too much, as explained below, so that the particles are not dislodged until the turbulence is sufficient to keep them in suspension. Hence, no saltation of lutite particles can take place.

Finally transportation can take place by *rolling* or *sliding* along the bottom, and it is the coarse material that is moved in this manner. In rivers a large percentage, sometimes even the major part of the load, is transported in this way (bottom load). But in the sea the movement of fragments larger than the sand fraction is almost entirely restricted to the action of waves, which will be dealt with presently.

When discussing the ability of currents to transport debris a clear distinction should be made between the capacity, that is the maximum load that could be transported, the load actually moving, which is generally smaller than the capacity, and finally the maximum weight or size of particle that can be displaced. This maximum size is not necessarily available to the current. It also makes a very considerable difference whether the grains form a uniform, smooth bed, or whether solitary particles are found lying on top of a smooth bed of finer grain. In the latter case the maximum weight that can be moved is increased 10 times or more, according to experiments of the writer.

The tractional force exerted by flowing water is proportional to the square of the velocity, but the weight of a boulder that can be rolled along is proportional to the sixth power of the velocity, and the diameter to the third power. This relation is obvious, because while the weight increases with the third power of the radius, the surface on which the tractional force is exerted increases with the square of the radius. Thus, doubling the velocity causes the pressure per square centimeter to increase 2^2 times and with a block 2^6 times the weight the surface is 2^4 times as large. Hence the total force is $2^2 \times 2^4 = 64$ times as large, just balancing the increase in weight of $2^6 = 64$.

Now that the various factors in transportation of sediment by flowing water have been reviewed we may study the question of the minimum velocities at which bottom erosion of various types of deposits occurs and the velocities at which movement of already dislodged particles either along the bottom or in suspension continues. The answer must be even more difficult to find than for the simpler case of transport in suspension, treated above. For the present problems it is important whether the sediment is homogeneous or of greatly diversified grain size. Other factors to be considered are the shape of the particles, whether the water is clear or turbid, where the velocity is measured in the current, what the depth of the water is,

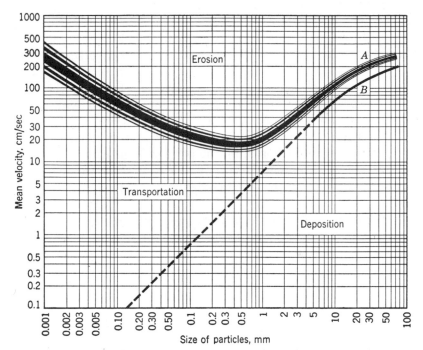

FIG. 118. Relationship between average current velocity in a river and sediments of uniform texture showing velocities necessary for erosion, transportation, or deposition. (After Hjulström, in Trask, 1939, *Recent Marine Sediments*, Fig. 1, p. 10, American Association of Petroleum Geologists.)

whether the bottom is hydrodynamically rough, etc. As the influence of these factors has not been studied separately we must be content with an approximate answer (Hjulström in Trask, 1939; Glangeaud, 1938).

From many tests in nature it follows that, for particles already held in suspension, the maximum size that can be kept in motion gradually diminishes with decreasing velocities (Fig. 118). For picking up materials from the bottom, that is for bottom erosion, much greater velocities are required, even for loose, uncemented sediments. But it was also found that it is not the finest fraction (lutite) than can be eroded by the weakest currents. Fine sand can be picked up more easily. For coarser material, again, greater velocities are needed, as would be expected. The reason that smaller particles are not more easily eroded than fine sand is that flakes of clay stick together more or less by adhesion and that the interstices between the grains are so tiny that the water can flow through them only very slowly in laminar motion. Moreover, the smooth surface of clay deposits is opposed to the development of turbulence in the bottom layer. This causes a decrease of the pulsating forces that are so effective in loosening particles and carrying them upward. The suction, already mentioned, is due to the greater velocity at the upper than at the lower edge of a grain. The difference must be much smaller with a small particle, and hence also the suction.

It is clearly to be seen in Fig. 117 how the greater increase upward in velocity close to the bottom in the layer of laminar flow must play an important part in this respect. In view of these various factors it is obvious that clay cannot be eroded at such low velocities as fine sand.

In Table 16 some data are brought together, showing the relation between the average velocity in the cross section of a river and the maximum uniform grain size that can be kept in motion or eroded from the bottom.

TABLE 16. MINIMUM VELOCITIES FOR EROSION AND DEPOSITION

Grain size, mm	Velocity for erosion, m/sec	Velocity for deposition, m/sec
10	1–1.5	0.7
5	0.5–1	0.4
1	0.15–0.25	0.08
0.5	0.12–0.22	0.04
0.1	0.15–0.3	0.007
0.01	0.5–1	<0.001
0.001	2–4	<0.001

Data obtained by experiments in shallow troughs are given in Table 17.

The traction tube, an ingenious and very simple apparatus for measuring bed velocities capable of moving various grain sizes, has been described by Nevin. It consists of a horizontal glass tube, half filled with sand. The great advantage over open troughs is that the velocity can be regulated irrespective of slope, and that relatively small amounts of water are required (Fig. 119).

Description	Mean diameter, mm	Depth	Velocity, m/sec	
Mud		Shallow	0.32	(*s*)
Fine sand	0.4	13 cm	0.26	(*m*)
Coarse sand		Shallow	0.49	(*s*)
Fine gravel	3.2	2.8 cm	0.46	(*m*)
Fine gravel	4.9	3.3 cm	0.65	(*m*)
Gravel	30	Shallow	1	(*s*)
Gravel	50	Shallow	1.5	(*s*)
Boulders	170	Shallow	3.5	(*s*)
Boulders	400	Shallow	5	(*s*)
Boulders	750	Shallow	12	(*s*)

s = surface velocity; *m* = mean velocity.

Rubey (1938) gives the following figures. At a "bed" velocity of 46 cm per sec gravel of ½-cm diameter is moved; at 1 m per sec pebbles of 4-cm diameter are moved; at 1½ m per sec, of 10-cm

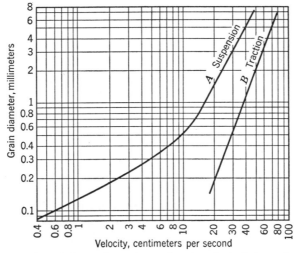

FIG. 119. Suspension and traction curves, showing the relation of grain size to the velocities of currents that support debris in suspension (vertical currents) and that carry debris along the bed by traction (horizontal currents). Curve *A* is based on data from elutriation tubes with turbulence; Curve *B*, on flume experiments and traction-tube experiments. (Simplified after Nevin, 1946, Plate 1, p. 674.)

diameter. According to Owens (see Steers, 1946), in water of moderate depth the "bottom speed" is, on an average, about 85% of that of the surface speed (Nevin gives 50%). Where sand exists in quantity all currents up to 75 cm per sec, according to the same investigator, are ineffectual in moving shingle, whereas above that velocity the current suddenly acquires the power of moving stones up to nearly 7½ cm in diameter over a sandy bottom.

It is further believed that sand is set in motion at smaller velocities in clear water than in muddy suspensions. This is explained by silt and clay becoming wedged between sand grains of the surface layer. Thereby the surface becomes hydrodynamically more smooth and approaches the state of a stratum of clay. On the other hand the presence of pebbles and boulders facilitates the erosion of sand because of the increased bottom turbulence.

The figures quoted show that there is still considerable divergence between the results of different workers, and that data obtained under natural conditions at sea are very scarce indeed.

THE COMBINED ACTION OF CURRENTS AND WAVE TURBULENCE

The transportation of sediment by currents at sea cannot be fully understood without taking into account the churning up of material by waves. In shallow seas wave turbulence is added to current action, and the fact that sand may be churned up and thrown on board ships from depths of a few dozen meters shows how strong the stirring action of storm waves may be. In depths exceeding 200 m, however, only the influence of current turbulence need be considered. This factor is insufficient except in some narrow straits to churn up anything coarser than very fine sand. Only during the short action of tsunamic disturbances may wave turbulence have temporarily reached down into the deeper zones of the sea and have influenced the otherwise undisturbed sedimentation.

The writer knows of very few experiments dealing with the influence of wave turbulence. For treating the problems of marine sedimentation this forms a serious gap in our knowledge. As, moreover, few measurements of turbidity at sea have been performed, very little is known about the relations between various conditions and the amount of suspended matter. On the Dutch coast samples taken during calm weather showed 0.3 g of sand and 1.3 g of clay per liter of water at the surface. At 1 m above the bottom 1 g of sand and 3 g of clay were measured. More exact data were obtained by field study of the Beach Erosion Board, U. S. Army Engineers. At the plunge point surf churned up 17 parts of sand per 1000 parts of water while 3 parts per 1000 occurred 40 to 50 m farther out from the beach. In oceanic waters far from the coast 0.07 to 0.5 g of very fine lutite per m³ or 66 tons to 500 tons per km³ have been measured. Roughly speaking, one may assume that the latter quantities are kept in suspension by the turbulence due to oceanic currents.

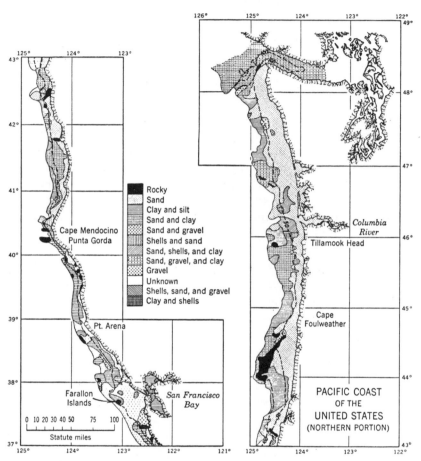

Fig. 120. Reconnaissance map of continental shelf sediments along Pacific Coast of United States. (After F. P. Shepard, in Trask, 1939, *Recent Marine Sediments*, Fig. 2, p. 224, American Association of Petroleum Geologists.)

Several investigators (Shepard, Correns, Trask, Stetson, Bramlette and Bradley) have remarked that the deposits are coarser grained on elevated portions of the sea floor and farther out on the continental shelf than in adjacent hollows and on the inner portions of the shelf (Fig. 120).

On some shelves the fine sediment reaches to dozens of kilometers off the land. In some places, on the other hand, it does not go very far, 400 m or less off the Tijuana River south of San Diego, for example (personal communication from Shepard).

Shepard (1941) found that on seamounts and ridges off the California coast coarse sand and even gravel and phosphate nodules form a covering, and in many cases rock bottom was proved. This held even where the eminence was several thousands of meters below the surface.

It has been suggested that the phenomena mentioned are due to the lowered sea level of the ice ages and that sedimentation has not yet advanced sufficiently from the coasts to provide materials at the edge of the continental shelf. During the low sea levels of the Pleistocene waves were able to churn up the sediment formerly deposited on the shelf and to disperse the finer fractions over the continental slope. Streams and wave action carried coarse material out to the edge of the shelf.

After sea level had returned to its present position clay and silt could again settle on the shelf. A veneer of fine sediment is thus supposed to be forming gradually from the coast outwards, but it has not yet reached the outer edge of the terrace.

For several reasons this explanation cannot be maintained. A thick stratum of fine blue mud has accumulated on the continental slope and on the deep-sea floor since the close of the Ice Age (see, for instance, the samples of the *Meteor* expedition from the equatorial Atlantic described by Schott and illustrated in our Fig. 161, p. 377). Hence, sedimentation of fine terrestrial detritus is proceeding over the entire sea floor, while only the outer parts of the shelf are avoided. This rule holds irrespective of the breadth of the continental terrace. If the above explanation were correct one would expect to find narrow terraces smothered entirely and broad terraces covered only along their inner margins. One would also expect that fine planktonic materials would have accumulated beyond the zone to which terrestrial clay had managed to progress.

Another reason why this opinion cannot be upheld is that the banks at depths of 2000 m were not swept more efficiently during moderate lowering of sea level, and yet they also are non-depositional environments at present.

The phenomenon must therefore be attributed to some agency that is operative at the present time and is restricted to, or at least concentrated at, the break in slope at the edge of the continental or insular shelf and of deep-lying seamounts.

Bramlette and Bradley (1940) proved that currents play a part at least in some places. They showed that on the Mid-Atlantic Rise at 1279-m depth the post-glacial layer is one-tenth as thick as in a neighboring station at 3745 m. Moreover, the amount of clay was much smaller, while the shards of volcanic glass were coarser. This last difference in grain size, especially, cannot be attributed to differences in supply from above but must result from subaqueous transport and selection by currents.

Current measurements off California showed that irregular eddy currents are of greater importance in agitating the waters than tidal flow. Repeatedly, on the continental terrace and over banks, velocities were encountered that were sufficient, theoretically, to carry silt and sand away or at any rate to prohibit deposition. But no correlation was found between measured velocities and either grain size of bottom sediment or amount of suspended matter just over the bottom.

The present author suggested that wave turbulence of long oceanic swell might be responsible. Possibly tsunamis also play a part. These waves may be supposed to churn up finer sand and silt, leaving coarser products, and to allow the suspended matter to be carried away to the deep sea by currents. The fact that, closer inshore, silt and clay are being deposited would then indicate that the force of the long waves reaching as deep as the bottom is partly spent at the outer edge of the shelf and the length of the waves is shortened by restriction of the oscillatory movement. These shortened waves, as they pass over the remainder of the shelf, no longer churn up sediment until the bottom begins to shelve more steeply on approaching the coast. Here a second zone of coarse deposits testifies to turbulent motion right down to the bottom (Kuenen, 1939).

Another factor of importance is that silt churned up close to the edge of the continental slope will tend to form turbidity flows that carry the lutite some way down the slope. At modest depths these flows should tend to spread out on meeting water of greater density. Farther inward on the horizontal shelf the churned-up silt cannot form a density flow and will settle to the bottom again.

It is clear, however, that this explanation by wave action cannot apply to deep-lying seamounts, except if tsunamis are invoked.

Fairbridge has suggested that the action of slumping might carry away silt deposited on the coarser glacial deposits of the shelf edge.

But this process can hardly be of general importance as it is not selective. It would leave fine material between the pebbles and in depressions of rocky areas. Moreover, the declivity of the areas in question is much slighter than that of the continental slope (1:100 as against 1:12, according to Fairbridge). The slope should be entirely clean if slumping on the shelf was a normal phenomenon. But fine deposits cloak most of the continental slope.

It is obvious from the foregoing discussion that we are not yet sufficiently informed to evaluate the relative importance of wave turbulence and irregular eddy currents in bringing sediment into suspension in these non-depositional environments. But the conclusion is warranted that any sudden break in slope, at whatever depth it is situated, causes appreciable turbulent motion which is able to churn up lutite, fine sand, and perhaps even coarse sand. Slow currents of only a few centimeters per second occur almost anywhere in the oceans and at all depths. These, together with turbidity currents, caused by the churned-up sediment, should sweep away all this sediment raised by turbulence and spread it out over wide areas in the neighborhood at greater depths.

Before leaving the problem of these peculiar environments the question must be answered where the coarse debris generally encountered there came from. Evidently transport is impossible under present conditions.

A century ago Austin (1850) had already established the existence in the outer English Channel of gravel banks, containing decayed shells of littoral species, rising to within 100 to 150 m of the surface and separated from the land by deeper areas covered with muddy sediment. Although he did not emphasize the action of waves or currents in keeping these banks clear of recent fine deposit, he gave what is probably the correct explanation of the source of the coarse material: "···· the indication of a coastline of no very distant geological period, buried under a great depth of water and removed to a greater distance from the nearest present coastline." Geologists now generally assume (Daly, etc.) that marine erosion and river transport during low sea levels of the glacial epochs is responsible. A large portion of the shelf was then worn down below the original profile of equilibrium, and coarse material was carried far out towards the edge of the continental terrace by the lengthened rivers. Since the subrecent rise of sea level the bottom nearer the coast is aggrading by finer sediment derived from the land. But, as Dunbar pointed out to the present writer, if very long waves or currents now expend part of their energy near the margin, they are operating to change the bottom profile, which will not be at equilibrium until the shelf slopes off somewhat more steeply towards its outer margin. As sea level is 20 to 40 m lower at present than it would be on an ice-free world, the writer considers it not improbable that formerly the shelf profile was lower with respect to preglacial wave base and that the terrace was originally built to fit the profile of equilibrium. Otherwise one must assume that crustal deformations have occurred and that no general explanation can be given either of the level or of the composition of the shelf margins.

A further general conclusion is warranted that on the open shelf currents are too sluggish to transport sand in the absence of waves. The turbulent action of waves must intervene, and it is just this combination of moderate current velocities and intensive wave action that results in the transport of sand fractions on the continental shelf. In some fossil sedimentation troughs the same combination will have occurred while others were more enclosed, both cases resulting in the spreading out of sediments in even, flat expanses on the sea floor.

In river transport waves play practically no part. At sea, where wave and eddy turbulence are almost always important, there is even greater need of collecting data on these factors than of correlating current velocities with sediment measurements.

TRANSPORTATION ON THE BOTTOM BY WAVES

The influence of turbulence was considered separately above because of its importance to current transport and on account of the impossibility of evaluating the relative influence of wave turbulence and current turbulence. In this section we propose to discuss transport by wave action alone, that is to say by rolling and saltation. (For the terminology of the features of the beach see Fig. 121.)

Under the influence of waves in shallow regions the water along the bottom moves in horizontal courses. In the case of oscillatory waves there are movements to and fro, which are slightly stronger in the direction of propagation of the wave because of the water moving faster and farther. As soon as the flow is strong enough the sediment is rolled back and forth, or it jumps both ways, with a small component in the direction of wave propagation. On many sea floors the long swell has the greater influence because it reaches deeper. The swell is always directed more or less towards the beach as this type of wave is formed in deep water only. Of storm waves, those formed by wind blowing in from the sea are also much stronger than those formed during offshore winds. Not only is the wind more powerful but the length of fetch is also greater. Obviously, therefore, the transporting power of waves must be stronger towards the coast than away from land when other factors are left out of account.

Where a wave runs into shallower water it becomes asymmetrical. The movement of the water along the bottom towards the coast is then swifter than the returning flow and, although of shorter duration, must exert a stronger action.

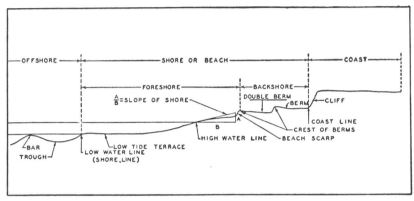

Fig. 121. Terminology applied to various parts of the beach profile. Berms are small impermanent terraces which are formed by deposition during calm weather and by erosion during storms. (After Shepard, 1948, *Submarine Geology*, Fig. 33, p. 82, Harper and Brothers.)

But there are also transporting agents active in the opposite direction. Where the bottom slopes, gravity must exert a transporting force downward, that is to say, in the majority of cases, away from the beach. Sediment raised by turbulence also comes under the influence of gravity, as explained above (p. 240). These gravitational effects may compensate the forward impulse of the oscillatory waves or even cause a net movement away from land. With an onshore wind, light materials, especially floating ones, are then thrown upon the beach and left high and dry when the tide falls (jetsam). With an offshore wind, friction carries more water away from the coast than is piled up against it by the weak oscillatory waves then running inwards. A hydraulic undertow then sucks the water up along the bottom back towards the beach. Hence during offshore winds more and different species of shells are carried up the beach, and collectors prefer these conditions for making their beach excursions.

It is generally held that the water carried landward by waves returns along the bottom by what is termed the *undertow*. Although the velocity cannot be great, all sediment held in suspension should have a component away from the beach added to whatever other forces are working on it. Although the existence of an undertow is assumed by most investigators, some doubt has recently arisen. A different type of seaward transport of the excess water piled against the shore by wind and waves has been detected.

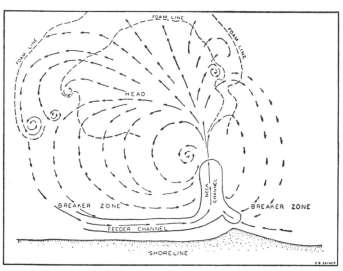

FIG. 122. Diagrammatic sketch of a rip current showing its component parts and direction of net water transport associated with the rip. Relative velocity indicated by length of arrows. (After Shepard, 1948, *Submarine Geology*, Fig. 20, p. 45, Harper and Brothers.)

According to Shepard et al. (1941) the water carried landward by large waves breaking on an exposed coast is returned by so-called *rip currents*. These flow principally at and near the surface and attain velocities of 1 m per sec out to distances of 300 m or more from the shore (Fig. 122). Geologically the currents are of importance, since they carry a suspended load of fine sediment out from the shore. Small channels in the sand are produced by the flow in the near-shore portions of these rip currents. Measurements to show whether an undertow actually occurs, and what its strength may be, are evidently needed.

Another important aspect of wave action is the strong local churning up of sand by breakers. At the so-called plunge point four to six times as much sediment is raised as in the immediate neighborhood. The result is a local excavation of the foreshore and the building of *sand banks*, sometimes called *bars* or *balls*, with *troughs* or *lows* between.

Most authors hold that the sand bank is built on the landward side of the plunge line, but Bagnold came to the opposite conclusion after an experimental investigation. He noted that the drift towards the shore by wave action stops just short of the plunge line and the load of sand is deposited. After a certain height is built up the plunge line shifts suddenly to seaward and a new outer slope is built up. The surf is then breaking on the outside of the old bank, and this would explain why most observers believe this bank to be due to the surf on its outer slope.

The importance of gravitative pull on water rendered turbid by churned-up sediment, mentioned on p. 240, may here be recalled.

The swash (or translation wave) forming inside the line of breakers moves the sediment farther forward than backward, and the sediment is thereby carried in steps towards the beach. The transporting power of the backwash is much less. Part of the water sinks into the beach, and the water runs back slowly under the influence only of gravity. It is mainly in consequence of the slope that transport is not restricted to a movement landwards.

Important contributions to our understanding of these alternating processes have been made by W. V. Lewis (see Steers, 1946). This investigator points to the development of two different types of waves. The destructive waves are irregular, steep, and close together. They break near the water line and plunge vertically, producing a relatively weak, ineffective swash but of large volume. The backwash is powerful because there is little time for the water to percolate into the beach, even when it is composed of shingle and not sand. This type of wave results from strong onshore winds and is frequently large in size. As a result the percolation is reduced relatively even further. The dominant backwash is the principal cause of the observed tendency to erode.

The constructive waves result from far-off winds and approach as long, regular undulations. They break farther out from the water line, and the water plunges obliquely forwards. Hence, the swash is powerful, though of relatively small volume, and there is time for considerable percolation. As a result the backwash is ineffective and material tends to be added to the beach (Fig. 123).

Whether a wave acts constructively or destructively depends not only on the nature of the wave but also on its size and on other factors such as the profile and composition of the beach. Hence, from a physical point of view, the distinction is not satisfactory although it is geologically significant. A more natural classification is used by oceanographers who distinguish between plunging and spilling breakers (see p. 83). In the plunging type, the back of the wave continues

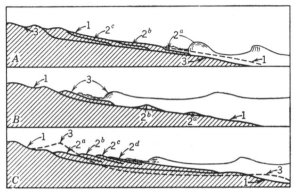

Fig. 123. Action of waves on a shingle beach according to W. V. Lewis. (*A*) *Destructive waves*, (1) original profile, (2^{a,b,c}) successive stages during rising water, (3) final stage after retreat. (*B*) *Constructive waves*, (1) original stage, (2^{a,b}) successive stages during rising water, (3) final stage at high water. (*C*) *Destructive waves* at spring tide, (1) original profile, (2^{a,b,c,d}) construction during falling tide, (3) result of destructive storm waves at spring tide. (Redrawn from Steers, 1946, Figs. 4–6, p. 51.)

well rounded up to the instant of breaking, whereas its front becomes deeply hollowed. The breaking takes place suddenly. This type tends to develop from swell, whereas the other, spilling type is more often associated with onshore winds. In the latter waves the backs of the crests, as well as the fronts, become concave as they rise to the angle of instability. Then the top starts to break continuously as the wave advances, gradually losing height.

It may be assumed that constructive waves generally spill while destructive waves tend to plunge, but large spilling waves can erode the beach and small plunging ones can build it up.

As the direction and strength of the winds are continually varying on most coasts, the profile of the beach is constantly being reworked to fit the new conditions. Lewis' results conform to the general experience that onshore storms generally erode the beach, whereas the normal action in steady calm weather is a gradual building up. An example is the yearly erosion during winter of the foreshore off La Jolla, California, and the return of the sediment in summer.

On some beaches all the sand is washed away in winter, leaving only rocks and boulders. The following summer the sand is brought back again.

According to Shepard (1948) the bars and troughs become much more pronounced during winter and tend to move out into deeper water. During calm weather they migrate shoreward again.

But it has also been observed, for instance in Florida, that the bar may migrate towards the beach under the influence of heavy surf and continue its shoreward progress after the storm has died down. Finally it merged with the beach.

Waves of the same size may cause erosion on one beach and outbuilding on another. The slope of the foreshore and the nature of the rip currents transporting sediment beyond the breakers may be different in the two cases and thus explain the opposing results.

A few, often three, bars are found running parallel to the shoreline, sometimes for distances of hundreds of kilometers. The crests are a few to many dozens of meters apart, while the depressions sink 1 or 2 m below the ridges. The bar closest to the shore may fall dry at low tide, thus enclosing a narrow lagoon parallel to the beach.

Kindle (1936) described "ridge and trough structures" from shallow water in bays and lakes with symmetrical profiles and wave lengths of 20 to 40 m. Although Kindle believes them to form a class apart, the present author is inclined to assume that they are normal bars and troughs.

The waves wash over the banks, and, especially in the frequent case of surf developing against the bank, large masses of water are carried to the landward side (Fig. 124). These masses must be brought back to open water by hydraulic currents. Over deeper banks there probably exists an undertow flowing seawards across the crest. But in shallow sand banks, especially where the crest is above average sea level, one or more openings are generally present. Through these a powerful current runs out carrying a large quantity of sand that had been washed into the hollow by the surf. These movements of the sand strongly influence the morphology of the beach and foreshore. It is doubtful, however, whether in the long run a permanent alteration in the shape is brought about. Only if longshore currents pick up the suspended sand will the continuous shifting of sediment result in a permanent displacement.

However, when longer periods are considered a gradual erosion or outbuilding of the shore may be established. The first process is characterized by a foreshore that is too steep, while in the case of gain the slope tends to be abnormally flat. On the other hand temporary erosion tends to flatten the foreshore while the reverse occurs after swift building up. An absolute balance is probably quite exceptional.

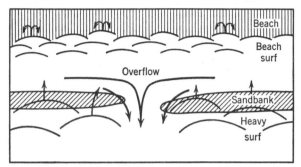

Fɪɢ. 124. Diagram showing the influence of sandbanks on surf and resulting currents.

The slope of the beach varies with the grain size of the material. Shepard (1948) gives the figures shown in Table 18.

TABLE 18

Beach type	Median diameter, mm	Slope
Fine sand	0.12	2°
Medium sand	0.25	4°
Coarse sand	0.5	8°
Gravel	2	12°
Cobble	64	20°

Naturally, the slope is strongly influenced by other factors as well. Thus in the Tenby area of southern Wales many sandy, less-exposed beaches show slopes of only 1°. Cobble beaches can attain up to 30°, and where they have been subsequently attacked by wave erosion even steeper angles are locally found, up to 50°.

Although a balance is struck between erosion and deposition on most shores, this does not mean that the same sand masses remain permanently in a given locality. Rivers and coastal erosion tend to supply new sand and an equal amount is permanently lost beyond the reach of the waves and deposited on the shelf or the continental slope.

A very important factor is introduced when the waves approach obliquely to the beach, the result of which is *coastal drifting*. Only exceptionally do swell or wind waves run dead on towards the coast. In spite of the tendency to curve round and approach with their crests parallel to the beach, this ideal is seldom reached. On the foreshore the grains are therefore dragged to and fro along courses that lie oblique to the water line. In consequence of the slight slope, gravity acts during the movement and causes the grains to diverge from their straight paths. The result is a small permanent displacement along the coast in the direction to which the waves tend (Fig. 125). Apart from possible movements up the beach or downward, oblique waves will therefore result in particles following a saw-shaped path at right angles to the slope. This is termed *longshore drifting.*

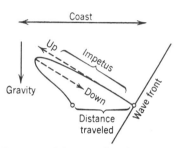

FIG. 125. Diagram showing movements due to coastal drifting.

On the beach a similar movement occurs in a slightly different form, so-called *beach drifting.* Here the pulsating flow of the translation waves rushes up the beach while gravity causes the water to wash back. The upward path is somewhat curved by the influence of gravity, especially towards the finish. The backwash is almost straight down the slope, because friction has absorbed the sideways component of the up run. At the top a rounded bend connects the two portions of the path (Fig. 126).

The finest particles are carried along bodily in this zigzagging course; the middling grains may be dropped where the water is almost stationary at the top if they happen to float in the tip of the wave. Otherwise they are carried down again by the backwash. Roughly speaking, therefore, the middle fractions also follow the path of the water pulses. But the coarser the fragments the more their movement is by rolling along the beach surface, and they must lag behind the rush of the water. The path followed is similar to that of the water but on a smaller scale.

Beach drifting thus results in a sideways, sawlike movement parallel to the beach, much like that of the longshore drifting. But whereas the finer particles outside the line of breakers are displaced a little farther than the very slight sideways shifting of the water, the sand raised on the beach follows the water almost exactly, while the pebbles lag behind. In neither case are the paths followed symmetrical parabolas, nor straight-sided triangles.

The importance of coastal drifting has often been underrated. But in general as much sediment is moved along a coast by drifting as by currents, and, the coarser the sediment, the more drifting predominates over current action. However, only a comparatively narrow strip comes under the former influence because drifting is effective only in very shallow waters. Not only has the lateral displacement of material from typical rock exposures on the beach been ascertained both along the beach and on the offshore, but also experiments with bricks have shown that surprising velocities are attained, such as 25 m per hour or even of 1 km per day. Steers by experiments on the fore-

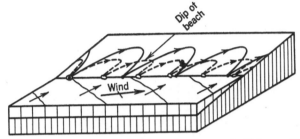

Fig. 126. Block diagram of beach drifting, showing path of large (dashed lines) and small (full lines) particles.

shore of Scolt Head Island in normal weather found 5–10 m average daily movement of brick fragments of pebble size, with a maximum of nearly 200 m. The wind varied during the experiments from 2 to 10 m per sec.

From the observation that rocks are sometimes carried up into the prevailing wind it has been wrongly concluded that coastal drifting cannot be of much importance. But the size of waves and hence the power to cause drifting is largely determined by the length of fetch. This quantity need not be largest for the prevailing wind. The most successful wind in drifting, the so-called dominant wind, is therefore frequently not the strongest or prevailing one, but the one sweeping over the widest stretch of water. This consideration explains why in an oblong basin drifting may proceed in opposite directions from a point on the longer coast (Fig. 127).

The problems of transport at sea are highly complicated, especially as to which factors predominate at a certain site—waves, tidal currents or other currents. The amount of material and the distance it is moved in a given period of time is another moot question. Opinions differ widely because sufficient data have not yet been collected.

A complicating factor is brought in by short-lived but powerful forces, as storms or tsunamis. These render observations highly uncertain because in a few hours' time more work may be performed and in a different sense than by long-continued action of the factors normally active at the spot in question. More and coarser-grained material may be dislodged and swept along in the same manner as has been observed with rivers in spate. But, during storms, observation at sea is rendered difficult or is even excluded. One has always to rely on instrumental observation, because the eye cannot reach the bot-

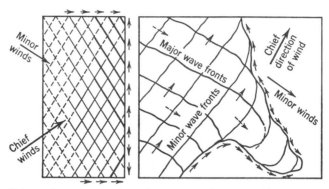

FIG. 127. Schematic representation of direction of beach drifting in oblong basin and in embayment.

tom. Tidal action makes the measurement of minor alterations in depth very difficult, and farther out it is generally impossible to fix positions with sufficient accuracy. Costs of investigation are high as soon as a vessel and crew are required. Our knowledge of these matters will therefore be increased but slowly.

RAFTING

The agents treated above may be looked upon as "normal" factors governing the distribution of sedimentary material over the sea floor. To these might be added swimming, crawling, floating, etc., of animals and plants whereby sedimentary source material is displaced before incorporation in the deposits. The problems involved in these migrations are mainly of marine biological nature. To the marine geologist they are of the greatest importance, because plant and animal detritus play so prominent a part in the formation of sediments. However, in order to limit the extent of this book this vast field will not be treated separately and the conception of "source" will be limited to the moment when the animal or plant has died, leaving treatment of earlier migrations to other writers. Displacements after death are by the "normal" agents dealt with above.

There are other agents playing a part in the displacement of sedimentary material that are of considerable interest, although seldom becoming quantitatively important. They may be conveniently classed under the heading of *rafting*.

Rafting can be brought about by floating ice (moraine in icebergs or sediment carried by ice floes) or by trees with the materials lodged among the roots. Particles from fine dust to large boulders may thus be carried for long distances and dropped into sediment of entirely different nature. Erratic boulders have frequently been dredged in polar deep-sea deposits and even beyond the present limit of icebergs, apparently having been carried there by bergs during the Ice Age (see p. 235).

Living animals and plants can also act as "rafts" in this sense. Emery, who has made a special study of this matter, has showed that marine mammals frequently carry pebbles and cobbles in their stomachs, sometimes in considerable numbers. The action of birds and other animals in collecting shells they had fed on, may be recalled here, although these accumulations are normally formed on dry land (Teichert and Serventy, 1947).

Kelp is a far more frequent agent in rafting stones and shells. Large waves may wrench these plants from their hold on the bottom and carry them to the beach with their "anchor" still attached. Large kelps with floats may even carry stones across deep water. Smaller algae and those without floats cannot lift stones, but they provide a hold for waves and currents whereby coastal drifting is greatly furthered, cases having been noted of displacements of 250 km from the point of origin. A few examples are also given by Emery of pebbles with kelp holdfasts still attached that were dredged from depths of nearly 250 m.

From these studies it may be concluded that individual pieces of stone found in fine-grained sediments, or among beach conglomerates where they do not belong, may have been carried to this contrasted environment by animals or plants.

ABRASION OF PARTICLES DURING TRANSPORTATION [1]

In dealing with problems relating to the abrasion of particles a distinction should be made between sphericity, the degree to which a

[1] See R. D. Russell, in Trask, 1939, Pettijohn, 1949.

spherical shape is approached, and roundness, the degree to which sharp angles are avoided. Thus an ikositetrahedron or other regular polyhedron is markedly spherical, but completely unrounded, while a cylinder with rounded ends (sausage shape) is completely rounded without approaching sphericity.

Many systems have been developed to classify fragments according to the amount of abrasion suffered, but owing to many failures to distinguish clearly between rounding and sphericity the results are generally unsatisfactory. The making of measurements or estimates for obtaining data naturally suffers from the lack of well-thought-out systems of classification. But even when the theoretical basis has been sound either the proposed techniques are too complicated for general application or often too few classes have been distinguished. Hence, detailed and trustworthy data are so rare that little has as yet been established satisfactorily concerning the action of various processes and the rate at which the effect is brought about. Yet the subject is of such importance and the result of some recent work is so promising that continued exertion will doubtless prove worth while.

Transportation in a river tends to abrade blocks and pebbles larger than 3 cm in diameter through rolling, grinding, and impact. Experiments with fragments in revolving cylinders have shown that the particles are quickly rounded and a fine flour of colloidal grain size is produced. Rock fragments lost upwards of 1% of their weight over a calculated distance of transport of 10 to 50 km. Smaller chips are knocked off, and sand may also be introduced from other sources. This finer fraction will not be rounded off by the grinding and impact (mortar action) of the larger blocks, but the particles will be broken now and again and become even more angular. According to Marshall's experiments sand is quickly eliminated by grinding (crushing) between pebbles. He concluded that "Sand cannot live on a beach where wave action keeps gravel in movement." This would lead to the conclusion that the rounding of sand is mainly restricted to localities where this fraction occurs to the exclusion of pebbles and boulders.

Actually, however, the sand may be in motion much of the time while coarser material is lying still. Under these conditions pebbles and boulders would be abraded and rounded by the sand blast of passing finer particles, which, in turn, must suffer rounding. As pebbles and boulders are generally heaped up against the beach while the sand occurs below low water line the total amount of sand undergoing crushing cannot be very large.

On the sea floor outside the zone of breakers transportation should lead to a certain, if small, amount of rounding because larger fragments are either absent or do not move about. Hence, all wear must result in increasing the roundness. Where sand is not carried back and forth or in circular paths, this distance of transportation by currents in sea is limited, just as in rivers. No pronounced influence on the shape can then be expected. But where the grains are moved to and fro as in some tidal currents, or in a closed circle as in inland seas and bays where counter eddies are produced by currents sweeping along the coast, the total distance traveled by a grain may attain enormous values. Where the grain size is not too small so that impact is strong, and where the movement is by rolling or saltation, it must be assumed that at least some wear and rounding off take place.

The rolling and jumping movements of the grains up and down the beach under the influence of surf should likewise result in rounding off. In windy regions or where ocean swell regularly reaches the shore the effect must eventually become pronounced. Quantitative data are entirely lacking to decide whether the beach or the foreshore is the more effective environment for rounding. Probably the action is more noticeable per unit of surface on the beach, but on the other hand the entire surface of this workshop is far smaller than that of those offshore areas where sand prevails.

It is generally assumed that wind is the most effective agent in the rounding of grains (Twenhofel, 1945). The greater velocity, and the smaller viscosity of air as compared to water, is thought to cause this difference. The velocity of transportation by rolling or saltation (no rounding off occurs during suspension) is about double for wind what it is for water. And for impact the effect is regulated by $\frac{1}{2}mv^2$ (m = mass, v = velocity). The specific gravity of the transporting agent, however, is of no consequence. Viscosity plays a part in impact when the grains approach very closely and the film between has to be broken through. In this respect only water noticeably weakens the impact. It is even believed that sand grains of less than $\frac{1}{2}$- or $\frac{3}{4}$-mm diameter do not collide with sufficient force in water to show much effect and grains smaller than $\frac{1}{4}$-mm appear to show none at all.

On the other hand breakers cause a churning motion in sand that probably strongly attacks the grains, not only in a single grain layer at the surface but down in the deposit to the depth of several grain diameters. This effect will also be felt by smaller particles. Moreover, solution will attack even such resistant minerals as quartz and help to remove slight protuberances and irregularities. In aeolian transport this action is entirely absent.

No definite conclusion can therefore be drawn from theoretical considerations whether wind or waves have the more marked effect in the rounding of sand grains in nature. It is probable, however, that aeolian action is effective on smaller grains than aqueous grinding.

It may be asked whether comparison of the roundness of sands that have been acted upon in the sea with those from aeolian environments could not readily solve these problems. It has already been pointed out that a frosted surface and sometimes a thin coating of iron oxide may be developed during aeolian transport. Cailleux (1942) showed that aeolian transport soon produces a fine scratching, giving quartz grains of all sizes this typical frosted appearance. In aqueous transport only grains larger than 1 mm collide with sufficient force to become frosted. On the other hand smaller frosted grains are quickly polished and rendered transparent by wave and river action. Hence, for the finer fractions this property can be used in distinguishing aeolian from aqueous transport.

Besides the investigation of sands from beaches and sand dune, ancient sands can therefore also be used for a comparison of shapes occurring in different environments. But the results of such a comparison would be far from convincing. In the first place the marked roundness of many aeolian and beach sands is due to selection, as will be shown later (p. 285). In the second place the shape of a grain is seldom determined by the last action it has suffered but rather by many different influences acting upon it during long series of sedimentary cycles. The rounding of quartz grains is certainly a very slow process, and increase of sphericity an even slower one. Most authors who have dealt with these matters are convinced that the very perfect state of rounding shown by some sandy sediments must be the result of more than one cycle of sedimentation. The problems of rounding are therefore not solved by determining the last medium of transport and then attributing the shape to this action. Evidently experimental work is a promising line of investigation, but so far only incidental and inconclusive results have been obtained along these lines.

Let us now consider the rounding of coarse fragments on the shore. As the distance of transportation in a river is moderate the rounding of pebbles and boulders cannot be continued to final, perfect stages. For each type of rock and each river system a limit is set to the rounding effect. The almost complete rounding and sphericity shown by boulders that become lodged in potholes are exceptions, but as such pieces are very rare they are not considered here.

On the shore, however, there is hardly a limit imposed on the distance a boulder can be rolled over its substratum, as it is carried up and down the beach by the waves.

Moreover the power developed by storm waves on a beach is enormous so that cobbles and even boulders are rolled and flung about and ground, the one against the other, with surprising energy. Each large wave piles the shingle up to its maximum angle of rest, and during the backwash the rolling of the fragments as the edifice is partly pulled down again causes a loud crunching roar. Boulders of tough rock, half a meter in diameter, are found to be entirely covered by cracks due to concussions. Whereas in mountain streams boulders are rolled comparatively carefully along the bed and the transport it limited to a single journey, the beach materials are violently hurled about and ground over one another incessantly by every storm during an indefinite period of time. No wonder, therefore, that on many pebble and cobble beaches one is struck by the remarkably regular shape of rounded homogeneous rock fragments.

Perfect spheres are sought in vain, because, even when homogeneous material is available, either the original fragment had an oblong shape or during the wear on the beach one axis happened to become somewhat longer than the others. As soon as this occurs the fragment must revolve round this longer axis while rolling. Henceforth there is no action tending to abrade the longer axis faster than the shorter ones. Consequently there is no return to a spherical shape. On the other hand the development of very oblong pebbles is excluded, because the outer ends become too vulnerable or the fragment is broken across before an extreme cigar shape is attained.

But the great majority of rocks are not homogeneous. Either joints or stratification divides them into homogeneous but flat or oblong bodies during disintegration. The rounding, however perfect, will not lead to sphericity but must then result in disks, triaxial ellipsoids, etc. If the hardness is irregularly distributed, even less regular shapes or dented forms will be produced.

Well and regularly rounded fragments larger than cobbles and small boulders are exceptional, because the blocks have generally been reduced in size considerably before an advanced stage of rounding has been attained.

The surf action on a beach does not appear to favor the development of larger fragments into rotation ellipsoids around the longer axis. A flat boulder tends to remain lying on its larger side and to shove about or rotate around its shorter axis. Upper and lower surface are thereby worn, and a rotational ellipsoid around the shorter axis presents the ideal shape. But when the size has been reduced to a few centimeters the breakers can lift the cobble and roll it about on the narrow edge. Then the flat shape is soon reduced and egg shapes are evolved. These revolve around the long axis and do not tend to revert to disks. On the other hand, when the original fragment is oblong in shape and not too large either a triaxial ellipsoid or a rotation ellipsoid around the longer axis tends to develop.

When an isolated boulder lies for a long time in a fixed position on a sandy beach the sand blast of wave action may wear the side facing the sea until a sharp ridge parallel to the shore is developed along the exposed surface of the block. Kuenen (1947) has termed such boulders aquafacts.

SORTING DURING TRANSPORTATION [1]

The sorting of grains during the transportation of sedimentary matter is of great importance. This action is never entirely absent, though in screes, mud slumping, and glacial transport it is of no great moment (Fig. 128).

The chief sorting activity of wind is in carrying away sand and finer fractions and leaving pebbles and coarser fragments in situ. A further separation is effected by the fact that medium and coarse sands are seldom carried bodily in suspension for any great distances. In general these fractions are moved by rolling and by saltation, but tornadoes and hurricanes can also lift coarse sand to great heights. Fine sand, dust, and lutite, however, may be churned up even by moderate winds and carried far away. Mud that has dried offers considerable resistance to wind action, but in the long run it tends to be disintegrated. In arid climates, where plants do not cloak the soil, the finer fractions are generally removed, leaving a mass of sand and rock. The dust and lutite travel until they are dropped into water or among vegetation.

It should not be concluded, however, that desert sand is always exceptionally well sorted. In the Sahara, sand grains of varying size are mixed, because very fine particles are also present.

In river transport matters are somewhat different. In the upper reaches large blocks are also transported; in the middle course, gravel

[1] See R. D. Russell in Trask, 1939.

often covers the bottom. In the lowlands sand is generally restricted
to the bottom and the levees, while silt and clay are deposited during
floods outside the bed of the river. A certain amount of sand and
clay is carried out to sea by traction along the bottom and suspended
in the waters. Naturally there are many variations in nature on this
general scheme, for the amount of water, the bottom slope, the nature
of available sediment, and tidal action all differ from case to case.
Artificial conditions due to human activity likewise cause abnormal
transport or deposition of sediment.

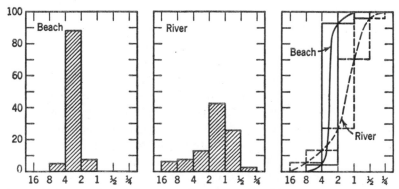

Fig. 128. Two methods of representing grain size: histograms and cumulative
curves. Note the more perfect sorting of the beach gravel from North Devon
as compared to the river gravel from Glencoe. (Redrawn from Hatch, Rastall,
and Black, 1938, Figs. 2, 3, 4, p. 44.)

The gradual decrease in size along a river course is due partly to
wear, partly to selection. This sorting results from a gradual decrease
in power to move debris by traction because the growing mass of
water is outbalanced by lessening of the slope. Pulsations in the transporting power are also of importance, for the smaller grains are kept
in motion continuously, while the larger fragments are shifted only
during spate and they consequently lag behind. It is true that slower
movement does not imply that ultimately somewhat coarser fractions
are not transported to the river's mouth, but the result is a concentration of the slower-moving particles along the course because more
is under way at each moment. When the river abandons its old bed
and seeks out a new one, the concentrate of coarser material is left
as a deposit and a new concentrate is gradually formed.

In the discussion of erosion and transportation by currents and
waves at sea many facts were mentioned that must lead to sorting on

the sea floor. Wherever grain fractions which exceed the maximum transporting power of prevailing forces are locally produced or are introduced from the surroundings, they must remain on the sea floor. Either they are worn to smaller sizes and then carried away, or they gradually accumulate.

Two extreme cases can be distinguished. If the size just exceeds the transporting power, all finer fractions are carried away and a pure concentrate of the coarse material is left behind. This generally happens on pebble or boulder beaches above low water line. It also occurs beyond the beach where sand tends to accumulate while pebbles and boulders are not supplied from the shore. On elevations of the deep-sea floor lutite and silt are often removed and either coarse material and hard rock of the substratum are laid bare or tests of planktonic origin form an organic deposit.

The other extreme is that transporting agents are absent. Then all sediment supplied accumulates. Sorting is much less pronounced and will depend only on the degree to which the supply is in itself already sorted. These conditions prevail over large basin-shaped areas of the deep-sea floor. Silt and lutite tend to predominate, and the sand fraction is generally restricted to organic tests dropping from the surface layers, because the transport of coarse sand to the deep sea does not take place (apart from rafted debris and, possibly, by occasional turbidity currents). Fine wind-borne sand, etc., may occur, however. Other environments in which all sediment supplied accumulates are encountered near the shore, for instance in lagoons.

In other cases fine and coarse fractions are deposited together, because the amount supplied exceeds the capacity of the transporting agents. This is generally true in tidal flats, behind offshore bars, on deltas, coral reef lagoons, etc. Then, again, in depressions of the shelf, fiords, estuaries, inland seas, etc., the mixing of coarse fractions and colloidal matter may occur.

Sorting also takes place on the beach. The gradual increase in grain size towards the beach as a consequence of increasing power of the waves along the shelving bottom has already been mentioned. Yet another factor operates to the same end. Oscillatory waves approaching the beach are subject to obstruction and friction along the bottom and take on an asymmetrical profile. The movement along the bottom is swifter toward the shore than away from it. Larger fragments will be shifted only by the incoming movement and will be carried gradually towards the shore. The finer particles follow both movements, but in consequence of gravity they may move further down than up the slope. In this manner the waves tend to concentrate the coarser fractions on the beach and to carry the finer out to sea.

Many shingle and cobble beaches are fairly steep (see p. 273). On the lower side they end slightly above low tide level, where an almost flat expanse of sand begins abruptly.

Sorting likewise takes place by longshore transportation. It has already been shown that both currents and drifting play a part. Whereas small pebbles and sand are influenced by both agents, the coarser fractions are transported only by drifting. A smaller pebble is shifted by weaker surf, and it moves farther with each wave than the larger blocks. Hence, it travels faster along the coast, and the coarse fraction is concentrated nearer to the point of origin.

As shingle occurs only on the upper parts of many beaches it is not worked on by waves except at high water. The lower, finer-grained parts of the beach are affected by currents and wave action especially at low water. If the currents are opposed in direction to the dominant winds the longshore transport of the shingle high up on the beach may be against that of the finer fractions lower down. A marked sorting will naturally result.

On the other hand the heavier fragments are worn away more swiftly than their lighter neighbors and only smaller pieces will remain after a long distance has been traveled. Similarly diminishing force of the waves along a coast will result in deposition of the larger pieces while the smaller continue on their way. Only when attached seaweed or porosity facilitate transportation a few larger fragments may pass beyond the normal limit set for their size.

Up to this stage only sorting according to size has been considered, but actually the shape is also an important factor. Flat pieces of rock are transported less easily than more nearly spherical ones and will therefore behave as if belonging to a coarser fraction. This may explain how flat pebbles are sometimes concentrated on the beach while the more spherical pieces are carried out beyond low water line. Difference in shape has greater influence with boulders than with pebbles, because small, flat disks can be rolled on their edge in the surf. Yet, for all pebbles, an oblong shape is more favorable to transport than a flat disk, while the spherical form is the most advantageous for rolling. In general it can be said that transportation is facilitated by approach to the spherical shape, resulting both in a higher velocity and in the movement of larger fragments.

The paradoxical observation has been made on beaches that the sand decreases in roundness as the length of transportation grows, whereas one would expect to find that the greater amount of rolling would have increased the roundness. The explanation is that the effect of transportation on the roundness is very slight, partly on account of displacement in suspension. As the lesser degree of roundness must increase the friction with the water, it should also facilitate this mode of transport. The more angular grains will then be carried farthest.

In aeolian transport it is held that as with pebbles in water rolling is again the principal mode of displacement. Hence, sphericity must aid the shifting of sand by wind. According to some authors this results in sorting on the dry beach and in deserts. The more spherical grains are said to be selected from the more angular and flatter ones and to be carried away to form dunes. If this is true the more complete rounding of many dune sands as compared to littoral sands might be partly due to sorting and not to a more active rounding effect of the aeolian environment. It will now be evident why a mere determination of sphericity in the laboratory cannot solve the problem of what is the most effective environment in the matter of rounding of sand grains.

However, Bagnold has recently shown that, although some of the sand is rolled along the ground, most of the transportation by wind takes places in the form of saltation. Whether selection according to sphericity takes place by saltation has not yet been ascertained. It does not appear improbable that spherical grains rebound farther and travel more swiftly than angular chips.

Sorting according to the mineralogy of grains can also be effected in the sea or on the beach. Minerals with abnormal properties will react in an abnormal way, resulting in concentration or wide scattering. Micas or other flaking minerals are carried away so easily that they tend to be scarce in beach sands. Heavy minerals, such as pyroxenes or magnetite, are sometimes concentrated, where quartz and feldspar are carried away. Small local concentrations are also frequent. For example, patches of dark purple sand are sometimes encountered on the otherwise light yellow beaches of the Dutch coast. They tend to be a few centimeters thick and several meters across, and are composed of almost pure garnet and pyroxene sand, comparatively rare constituents of the beach and dunes. On the beach of the Boulonnais in northern France glauconite, washed out of the chalk cliffs, regularly forms dark green patches on the white sands. In this case the low specific gravity is probably of importance. Again, in other places small chips of shells have become concentrated, obviously in consequence of their flat shape, which obstructs the displacement. On the beach at Bergen on the Dutch coast the sands are famed for the pure white color and perfect sorting of the quartz grains. It is not known what causes the absence of dark minerals and shell fragments in this locality, but selective transport is probably partly responsible.

A minor selective action is carried out by flotation (Emery, 1945). A thin film of dry sand grains may be picked up by the swash of waves, by water running out on the beach at low tide, or on the surface of rising pools, and float owing to surface tension. It soon collects in small patches that may be drifted by the wind or currents for a short distance. Floating sand cannot pass the zone of breakers, and the distance of transportation is therefore limited. But the shape, size, and specific gravity determine the ease with which a grain may float. Hence, angular and especially flaky minerals tend to become concentrated in swash marks and other patches where floating sand is deposited.

Very little is known concerning the concentration of mineral fractions on the sea floor. As far as can be judged from available samples it appears that there is far less selection than on the beach.

Taken all in all there is probably no other environment than the beach in which sorting according to size, shape, and composition is carried so far (Fig. 128, p. 283). The stretches of beach between promontories are frequently composed of coarse or fine gravel of remarkable uniformity in shape and size. Fine beach sands are often sorted to a degree that is not encountered elsewhere, not even in the desert. This is the more remarkable as the range in grain size is nowhere so large as on beaches in general, even if the scarcity of clay on the seashore is admitted. Mixed accumulations of strongly divergent fractions immediately beside or above others of different composition are by no means lacking on the shore. But, in spite of the occasional occurrence of well-sorted accumulations in fluviatile deposits, the beach is the environment in which sorting activity is most generally apparent.

On the sea floor the distribution of grain sizes does not vary so abruptly as on the narrow beach. Usually gradual transitions are developed over wide areas, while coarser fractions than sand are exceptions, apart from animal remains.[1] Uniformity, a consequence

[1] Except for the edge of the shelf (see p. 263).

of selection, is one of the major characteristics of marine deposits as compared with terrestrial accumulations of sediment. This property becomes even more pronounced as deeper regions of the sea floor are examined.

RHYTHMIC ACCUMULATIONS

Several types of rhythmic accumulations of sediment are found on the beach and the sea floor. They can be classified as ripple marks, larger rhythmic accumulations, and beach cusps.

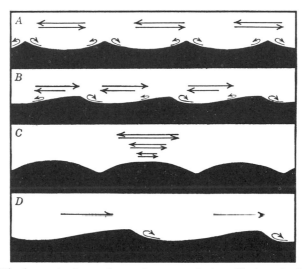

Fig. 129. Ripple marks in section. *A*, symmetrical oscillation ripple marks; *B*, asymmetrical oscillation ripple marks; *C*, symmetrical oscillation ripple marks with sharp troughs; *D*, current ripple marks.

Ripple Marks. Ripple marks are caused by waves and currents or their combination in granular deposits with no or little cohesion between the composing particles. It is generally held that mud and other cohesive sediments are never ripple-marked by water. But ripples formed in underlying sands may show through a thin coating of mud, and the sandy mud of tidal flats may show excellent ripple marking when animals have first formed mud pellets (personal communication, van Straaten).

Oscillation ripples caused by waves are symmetrical with sharp crests and rounded troughs (Fig. 129). Evans (1943) has found wave ripples with rounded crests and angular troughs, but this is certainly exceptional.

Wave ripples are often fairly regular and parallel over large areas of the bottom. The wavelength ranges from 0.8 to 50 cm; the amplitude (height) varies between one-third and one-ninth of the wavelength. Wave ripples commonly form in shallow water but have also been observed at depths of 200 m. The coarser grains are concentrated in the troughs.

The development is due to oscillation of the water to and fro along the bottom. A prominence occasions vortices alternately on its two sides. The opposing vortex current on the lee side carries the grains to the crest and deposits them there. The water oscillates over the entire surface of the bottom, and any point is as favorable to the initial development of a ripple as another. But as soon as a crest begins to develop it tends to grow laterally and thus to form a ridge parallel to the wave crests. At a certain distance on either side a new ridge is started owing to the deposition of grains at the farther side of vortices. In this manner a rhythmic pattern of parallel ridges spreads out from the original point of disturbance. These patches finally join and cover the bottom. As the neighboring patches will generally not fit with the troughs and ridges joining together, absolute regularity is not attained over wider areas.

The relations between depth, size of waves, and size of ripples have not yet been ascertained. On a gently sloping bottom the larger ripples are frequently found in middling depths with finer ripples both at greater depths and closer to the shore.

Asymmetrical oscillation ripples also occur, a fact overlooked by most writers. They are formed when the oscillatory currents are not of equal strength and duration in both directions. On a shelving foreshore, or when oscillatory waves have been somewhat altered to translation waves on approaching the coast, the possibility of the development of asymmetrical oscillation ripples is present. Nearly always the current towards the shore is stronger, although lasting a shorter time, and the steep side of the ridges faces that way. While symmetrical oscillation ripples are stationary, asymmetrical ones travel slowly in the direction of steepest slope (Evans, 1941).

A combination frequently occurring in nature is that of waves and currents. An undertow, a tidal current, or any other type of current, even when in itself too weak to move the sediment, may influence the development of the ripples when superimposed on wave motion. The result will be asymmetry of the ripple marks. It is probable that many of the asymmetrical ripples found on tidal flats owe their formation to this combination. They are sometimes referred to currents only, merely on the strength of their asymmetrical profile, but that alone is insufficient proof. Nevertheless, most ripples in enclosed tidal waters actually are true current ripples.

Currents flowing in one direction only may also result in the development of ripples. This happens as soon as the velocity surpasses a certain lower value ("first critical point"), sufficient to drag some of the surface particles along with it. The first critical point varies with the nature of the materials (between about 25 cm and 100 cm per second for sand and fine gravel). Current ripples travel downstream. They may consist of parallel, long, equidistant ridges at right angles to the current. They are asymmetrical in profile, with a steep lee side and a gentle upstream slope. The wavelength varies mainly between 1.5 and 30 cm. Where the flow is less regular, more especially in water only a few centimeters deep, the parallel ridges are replaced by short curved ridges with the convexity facing downstream or upstream. This type is called linguoid ripples. The coarsest particles involved in a set of current ripples are found in the troughs and the finest on the crests.

Evans' contention (1949) that current ripples are less regular than oscillation ripples may hold for stream beds but does not apply to tidal waters. The flat, uniform bottom over which the currents of tidal flats flow becomes covered with huge expanses of long, regular, and parallel ripples.

Current ripples are often ascribed to the operation of the general principle that a sinuous surface of contact between two moving fluids offers the minimum of friction for certain velocities. Although this may have some influence, the main cause should be sought in the formation of a vortex on the lee side that helps to build up the crest. The sand grains roll up the gentle slope and drop down the steep slope. As a result the ripples gradually travel downstream. It cannot be claimed, however, that the process is fully understood.

Above a certain velocity ("second critical point") the ripples disappear and the surface again becomes smooth. At the "third critical point" ripples again appear, but they are much larger and are termed regressive sand waves because they travel upstream. At even higher velocities when the water carries large quantities of sediment gigantic ripples called progressive sand waves are formed on the bottom. They are nearly symmetrical and move downstream. These two types of sand wave are not stable because a large proportion of the sand is in movement even down to depths of 50 cm in the bottom. They can be preserved only if the current slackens suddenly and drops the moving waves in a fixed position. Before the sand waves thus come to rest, they are modified by the current. Such modified forms are termed para ripples when slightly altered and meta ripples when strongly altered and changed to asymmetrical forms. The wavelength may attain many meters; the amplitude, 2 to 3 m.

Meta and para ripples may be seen in tidal channels and on the beds of large rivers after a period of spate.

A rare type of ripple is sometimes formed by a thin sheet of water, for instance swash or backwash, flowing over a smooth surface of sand. The pattern is rhomboid, and hence these are termed rhomboid ripples.

On sandy beaches ripple marks are very common, especially during periods of mild wave action. They are generally attributed either to oscillation waves or to currents. The true cause is somewhat complicated, however. As pointed out above, Evans (1941) has showed that the ripples may be asymmetrical owing to the unequal strength of the oscillatory currents caused by the deformed waves on shelving bottoms. But according to observations made by the present author inside the plunge point of breakers the ripples are not of the oscillation type but are true current-formed ripples. After the wave has broken, a large volume of water rushes towards the beach. During this flow in one direction a set of current ripples is fully developed. Then the water either flows back before the next wave sends a new swash towards the beach, or several waves follow quickly on each other, forming a pulsating beachward flow, until finally the direction is reversed and the whole mass of water returns. If the water escapes sideways there is no return flow. The ripples formed by the shoreward current are first nearly or entirely erased and a new set is formed fronting towards the sea. The ultimate cause of these alternating systems of ripples is surf action, but the mechanism is purely one of currents. Admittedly these currents alternate, but this is also true of tidal currents, and there is no reason for calling the resulting ripples oscillation ripples. The essential point is that the currents last long enough in one direction to form the ripples, while with oscillation ripples many oscillations are needed before the ripples are well established.

On tidal beaches the comparatively narrow zone in which the ripples are formed is shifted up and down the beach, and, as the waves tend to be larger than on lake shores, the importance of the mechanism is much greater than on the non-tidal beaches studied by Evans.

Many of the ripples exposed at low tides are due to the process described, or to the longshore flow out of beach troughs.

For lack of a better name they may be called surf ripples. Especially favorable localities for the development of surf ripples are the shallow oblong depressions behind sand banks which are submerged at high tide but fall dry at low tide.

A different type of ripple, which has been described by Timmermans, is generated by backwash above the level of maximum wave retreat. The thin film of the backwash sometimes stands up in ridges of water a few centimeters high, parallel to the beach, and when the water has retreated broad, flat ripples are seen to have been formed with narrow and shallow troughs in between, often some 30 cm apart. Shepard, who has also observed this phenomenon, suggests use of the term backwash ripples (personal communication).

A number of more intricate ripple patterns are also met with in nature. They may be conveniently classed as "compound ripples." In the first place an oscillation ripple mark may be altered by later waves running in a different direction. Second, currents and waves running in different directions may cause a combined pattern. Third, current ripples may be superimposed on older current ripples formed by a flow in a different direction. And fourth, both current and oscillation ripples may be deformed by alteration in the strength of the generating agent. As the system of ripples is seldom preserved when the force increases, the patterns we find are generally due to decreasing force. One form is that of major oscillation ripples with smaller crests in the troughs, formed by decreasing waves. Further complications are introduced when ripples are laid dry during ebb tide. Sharp crests may sag as they emerge above water or capillary waves nibble at their flanks; water may trickle along the troughs and produce linguoid ripples; blown sand may be checked on the wet surface, forming a thin crust altering the profile and characteristic sorting.

According to van Straaten (personal communication) longitudinal ripples of great regularity are formed by currents in sand or mud under special conditions, sometimes combined with transverse current ripples.

The following classification of water ripple marks may be offered:

I. Ripples formed by currents in one direction.
    (*a*) Current ripples, formed between first and second critical velocities. Asymmetrical.
        (1) Normal current ripples, tidal flats, stream beds, marine currents, turbidity currents (?); (2) surf ripples; (3) linguoid

ripples; (4) rhomboid ripples; (5) longitudinal ripples; (6) backwash ripples.

(*b*) Sand waves, formed above third critical velocity.
   (1) Regressive; (2) progressive (much sediment in suspension).

(*c*) Meta and para ripples. Formed from sand waves by falling velocities.

II. Ripples formed by oscillation currents.
   (*a*) Symmetrical oscillation ripples.
      (1) Angular crests; (2) angular troughs (rare).
   (*b*) Asymmetrical oscillation ripples.
      (1) On shelving bottom (probably due to one of the following causes).
      (2) By asymmetrical oscillation currents.
      (3) Combination with undertow or other currents.

III. Compound ripple marks.
   (*a*) Reticular compound ripples.
      (1) Two directions of oscillation formed one after the other; (2) two directions of current following each other; (3) oscillation together with current; (4) oscillation and current following the one on the other; (5) longitudinal and transverse current ripples formed simultaneously.
   (*b*) Parallel compound ripples.
      (1) By falling velocity of current; (2) by decrease in wave size.

A different classification can be followed in which wave ripples are substituted for oscillation ripples. These should then include surf ripples, backwash ripples, and most rhomboid ripples.

Larger Rhythmic Accumulations. Para and meta ripples may attain sizes to be measured in meters. Several other forms of large-scale rhythmic accumulations are known. The sand banks and troughs encountered on many sandy coasts are the main representatives of this class. They were mentioned on an earlier page (269). Their origin, like that of various other types of large-scale rhythmic accumulations (e.g., Rich, 1948), is not yet fully understood.

Beach Cusps. Beaches sometimes show festoons of regularly spaced, crescentic accumulations of materials which may range in size from sand to cobbles. These formations are now generally termed beach cusps (Figs. 130 and 131). The projecting parts are more or less triangular with a rounded apex extending into the water and with curved bays between. The basal parts of the triangle are sometimes horizontal with the apex sloping down the beach. Generally the cusps are more coarse grained than the remainder of the beach material and either merge gradually into the beach or are set off sharply therefrom. The height may be very slight but may also attain more than a meter, and the distance between is a few centimeters to several dozens of meters. The apex may protrude several meters, and the relative depth of the bays is also variable. In front of the bays the foreshore is sometimes built out under water in a delta shape.

Although cusps may develop on many types of beach, they are most frequent on slightly concave stretches of the coast. Observa-

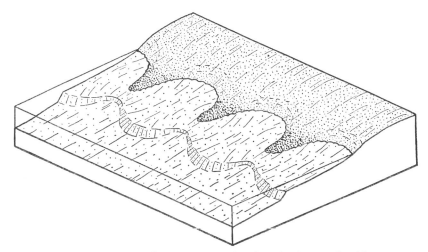

FIG. 130. Block diagram of beach cusps, showing the horns (in this case consisting of coarse material) and the submarine deltas corresponding to the embayments. (Mainly according to Timmermans, after Kuenen, 1948(a), *J. Geol.*, Vol. 56, Fig. 1, p. 35.)

tion has shown that they may be formed or destroyed again in a few hours' time, and small ones even more quickly. Each change in size of the waves results in the development of a new series of cusps to fit the altered conditions. According to Johnson (1919) the interspace is roughly doubled for a doubling of the wave height.

Evans showed by measurement that the interspace generally varies about 50%, occasionally over 100%. Although these variations are appreciable they confirm the essentially rhythmic nature of the phenomenon.

Many attempts have been made to explain the formation of beach cusps. Several authors (Johnson, Evans) have emphasized the importance of erosion in the forming of the embayments, while Kuenen argued that concomitant deposition on the cusps is of equal moment. According to the last writer the process may be pictured roughly as follows.

On a smooth beach a regular train of waves will cause a succession of swash flows. These flows encounter slight depressions and start to erode them, while the backwash carries some sediment out of the embayment to build deltas opposite them. As long as the depth of water in the bay is so slight that the water passing in and out is able

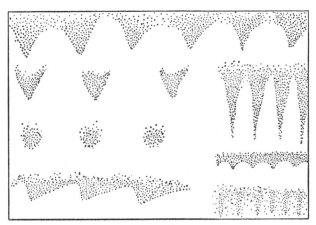

Fig. 131. Variations in the shapes of beach cusps. (After Johnson, 1919, *Shore Processes and Shoreline Development*, Fig. 141, p. 465, John Wiley & Sons.)

to carry the sediment along, the enlargement will continue both horizontally and vertically. As the channel becomes deeper and its sideways slopes steeper the breadth also tends to increase. But when the depth at the outer side approaches a certain limit, erosion gradually slackens because the currents set up by the waves become too weak to shift the sediment. Refraction of the swash as it fans out in the embayments results in transport of material towards the sides and prograding of the cusps (Fig. 132). The coarse material tends to be pushed back up the beach of the embayment and out along the developing cusps. Growth of the bays and prograding of the cusps must gradually decrease when the maximum depth in the central area of the bay has been attained.

In the meantime adjacent channels have undergone the same process. Where these are so close together that the two natural spheres of growth overlap, a rivalry develops. This should tend to push the

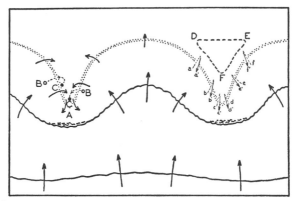

Fig. 132. Diagram showing the refraction of the swash. Pebbles are rolled from *B* to *C*. At *A* the powerful backwash of the foregoing wave impedes the swash and increases the refraction. *a–f*, slope; *a'–f'*, direction of backwash due to the piling up of water over the area *DEF*. (After Kuenen, 1948(*a*), *J. Geol.*, Vol. 56, Fig. 2, p. 37.)

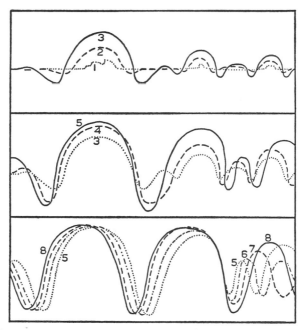

Fig. 133. Successive stages in the development of cusps from irregular indentures of the beach to an almost regular, rhythmic pattern. (After Kuenen, 1948(*a*), *J. Geol.*, Vol. 56, Fig. 3, p. 39.)

bays farther apart, because the material eroded from the one and dumped on the intervening cusp must tend to encumber the growth of the other. The erosion in the latter will be shifted slightly to the opposite side and thus cause the entire bay to move away (Fig. 133).

Where two neighboring bays are farther apart their adjacent cusps will not coalesce and will leave a slight space in between. In this space diffraction begins and a new bay will start to form.

As long as the maximum depth of water in a bay has not been attained the tendency to enlarge will be greater than in an adjacent,

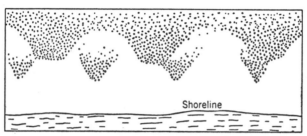

Shoreline

Fig. 134. Partially eroded older cusps and respaced later series. (After Johnson, 1919, *Shore Processes and Shoreline Development,* Fig. 142, p. 466, John Wiley & Sons.)

shallower indenture. The larger one will grow at the cost of the smaller one. This relation is reversed when the depth approaches its maximum value. Then a smaller bay is more powerfully eroded and tends to encroach on its overgrown neighbors. In this manner a balance will be struck when all bays have attained the maximum depth in relation to the size of waves playing on them. They will push each other aside or obliterate each other until this stage is attained and a regular rhythmic pattern has been evolved.

This working hypothesis appears to explain the main features of cuspate beaches: the regularity of the pattern, the dependence of size on the size of the waves, and the accumulation of coarse material in the horns. But several problems remain to be solved. It is not clear why cusps are a comparatively rare phenomenon. On the shore of lakes their formation appears to depend on the breaching of a ridge (Evans). The relations between slope of the beach, height of the tide, size of waves, grain size of the beach material, and forms of the cusps are unknown, and there is an almost complete lack of quantitative data.

Bibliography

ANDRÉE, K. *Geologie des Meeresbodens*, Bd. 2, 689 pp., Bornträger, Leipzig, 1920.
Das Meer und seine geologische Tätigkeit, in W. SALOMON, *Grundzüge der Geologie*, Bd. 1, pp. 361–533, Schweizerbart, Stuttgart, 1925.

ARCHANGUELSKY, A. D. Slides of Sediments on the Black Sea Bottom and the Importance of this Phenomenon for Geology, *Bull. Soc. Natur. Moscow*, Sect. Geol., T. 8, Nov. Ser. T. 38, pp. 32–80, 1930.

AUSTIN, R. A. C. On the Valley of the English Channel, *Quart. J. Geol. Soc. London*, Vol. 6, pp. 69–97, 1850.

BAGNOLD, R. A. Lecture to the Geol. Soc. London, April 16, 1947.

BAILEY, E. B. New Light on Sedimentation and Tectonics, *Geol. Mag.*, Vol. 67, pp. 77–92, 1930.
Sedimentation in Relation to Tectonics, *Bull. Geol. Soc. Am.*, Vol. 47, pp. 1713–1726, 1936.
American Gleanings, 1936, *Trans. Geol. Soc. Glasgow*, Vol. 20, pp. 1–16, 1938.

BAILEY, E. B., L. W. COLLET, and R. M. FIELD. Paleozoic Submarine Landslips near Quebec City, *J. Geol.*, Vol. 36, pp. 577–614, 1928.

BALDREY, R. A. Slip-Planes and Breccia Zones in the Tertiary Rocks of Peru, *Quart. J. Geol. Soc. London*, Vol. 94, pp. 347–358, 1938.

BARTH, T. F. W., C. W. CORRENS, and P. ESKOLA. *Die Entstehung der Gesteine*, 422 pp., Springer, Berlin, 1939.

BEETS, C. Miocene Submarine Disturbances of Strata in Northern Italy, *J. Geol.*, Vol. 54, pp. 229–245, 1946.

BOURCART, J. Sédiments quaternaires conservés sur la grève de la région de Roscoff (Finistère), *Compt. rend. acad. sci.*, Vol. 221, pp. 357–359, 1945.

BOURCART, J., et J. JACQUET. Sur la répartition des sédiments dans la baie du Mont Saint-Michel, *Compt. rend. acad. sci. Paris*, pp. 1507–1508, 1946.

BRAMLETTE, M. N., and W. H. BRADLEY. Lithology and Geological Interpretations, 34 pp., in Geology and Biology of North Atlantic Deep-Sea Cores, *U. S. Geol. Surv. Prof. Paper* 196, 1940-1942.

BRONGERSMA-SANDERS, M. The Importance of Upwelling Water to Vertebrate Paleontology and Oil Geology, *Verh. Kon. Ned. Akad. van Wetensch. Amsterdam, Afd. Nat.*, Sec. 2, Dl. 45, 4, 112 pp., 1948.

BROWN, C. B. On a Theory of Gravitational Sliding Applied to the Tertiary of Ancon, Ecuador, *Quart. J. Geol. Soc. London*, Vol. 94, pp. 359–370, 1938.

CAILLEUX, A. *Les actions éoliennes periglaciaires en Europe*, 176 pp., Soc. Géol. Paris, 1942.

CORRENS, C. W. Die Sedimente des äquatorialen Atlantischen Ozeans, *Meteor*, Bd. 3, T. 3, Lf. 2, 298 pp., 1937.
See BARTH et al., 1939.
Leitminerale im Golf von Guinea, *Nachr. Akad. Wiss. Göttingen, Math.-Phys. Kl.*, pp. 1–3, 1947.

CORRENS, C. W., et al. *Tiefseebuch*, 144 pp., Mittler, Berlin, 1934.

DEMAREST, D. F. Rhomboid Ripple Marks and Their Relationship to Beach Slope, *J. Sed. Petr.*, Vol. 17, pp. 18–22, 1947.

DIETZ, R. S. Clay Minerals in Recent Marine Sediments, *Am. Min.*, Vol. 27, pp. 219–220, 1942.

DIETZ, R. S., K. O. EMERY, and F. P. SHEPARD. Phosphorite Deposits on the Sea Floor off Southern California, *Bull. Geol. Soc. Am.*, Vol. 53, pp. 815–848, 1942.

DIXON, E. E. L. The Ouachita Basin of Oklahoma vis-à-vis the Craven Lowlands of Yorkshire, *Geol. Mag.*, Vol. 68, pp. 337–344, 1931.

EMERY, K. O. Transportation of Rock Particles by Sea Mammals, *J. Sed. Petr.*, Vol. 11, pp. 92–93, 1941.

Transportation of Rock by Kelp, *Bull. Geol. Soc. Am.*, Vol. 52, pp. 855–862, 1941.

Transportation of Marine Beach Sand by Flotation, *J. Sed. Petr.*, Vol. 15, pp. 84–87, 1945.

Marine Solution Basins, *J. Geol.*, Vol. 54, pp. 209–228, 1946.

EMERY, K. O., and F. P. SHEPARD. Lithology of the Sea Floor off Southern California, *Bull. Geol. Soc. Am.*, Vol. 56, pp. 431–478, 1945.

EVANS, O. F. Classification and Origin of Beach Cusps, *J. Geol.*, Vol. 46, pp. 615–627, 1938.

The Classification of Wave-Formed Ripple Marks, *J. Sed. Petr.*, Vol. 11, pp. 37–41, 1941.

Effect of Change of Wave Size on the Size and Shape of Ripple Marks, *J. Sed. Petr.*, Vol. 13, pp. 35–39, 1943.

Further Observations on the Origin of Beach Cusps, *J. Sed. Petr.*, Vol. 53, pp. 403–404, 1945.

Ripple Marks as an Aid in Determining Depositional Environment and Rock Sequence, *J. Sed. Petr.*, Vol. 19, pp. 82–86, 1949.

EVANS, O. F., and R. L. INGRAM. An Experimental Study of the Influence of Grain Size on the Size of Oscillation Ripple Marks, *J. Sed. Petr.*, Vol. 13, pp. 117–120, 1943.

FAIRBRIDGE, R. W. Submarine Slumping and Location of Oil Bodies, *Bull. Am. Ass. Petr. Geol.*, Vol. 30, pp. 84–92, 1946.

Coarse Sediments on the Edge of the Continental Shelf, *Am. J. Sci.*, Vol. 245, pp. 146–153, 1947.

Possible Causes of Intraformational Disturbances in the Carboniferous Varve Rocks of Australia, *J. Proc. Royal Soc. New South Wales*, Vol. 81, pp. 99–121, 1947.

GLANGEAUD, L. Études quantitatives et expérimentales sur l'érosion et le transport par les eaux courantes, *Rev. Géogr. phys. et géol. dyn.*, Vol. 11, pp. 323–370, 1938.

GRANT, U. S. Waves as a Sand-Transporting Agent, *Am. J. Sci.*, Vol. 241, pp. 117–123, 1943.

GRUNAU, H. Geologie von Arosa mit besonderer Berüksichtigung des Radiolarit Problems, Diss. Bern, 108 pp., 1947.

HÄNTZSCHEL, W. Bau und Bildung von Grosz-Rippeln im Wattenmeer, *Senckenbergiana*, Bd. 20, pp. 1–42, 1938.

HATCH, F. H., R. H. RASTALL, and M. BLACK. *The Petrology of the Sedimentary Rocks*, 383 pp., Allen and Unwin, London, 1938.

HEIM, ARN. Ueber submarine Denudation und chemische Sedimente, *Geol. Rundschau*, Bd. 15, pp. 1–47, 1924.

JONES, O. T. On the Sliding or Slumping of Submarine Sediments in Denbighshire, North Wales, during the Ludlow Period, *Quart. J. Geol. Soc. London*, Vol. 93, pp. 241–283, 1937.

The Geology of the Colwyn Bay District: A Study of Submarine Slumping during the Salopian Period, *Quart. J. Geol. Soc. London*, Vol. 95, pp. 335–382, 1940.

The Geology of the Silurian Rocks West and South of the Carneddau Range, Radnorshore, *Quart. J. Geol. Soc. London*, Vol. 103, pp. 1–36, 1947.

JOHNSON, D. W. *Shore Processes and Shoreline Development*, 584 pp., Wiley, New York, 1919.

The New England-Acadian Shoreline, 608 pp., Wiley, New York, 1925.

KINDLE, E. M. Notes on Shallow-Water Sand Structures, *J. Geol.*, Vol. 44, pp. 861–869, 1936.

KRUMBEIN, W. C. Measurement and Geological Significance of Shape and Roundness of Sedimentary Particles, *J. Sed. Petr.*, pp. 64–72, 1941.

KRUMBEIN, W. C., and F. J. PETTIJOHN. *Manual of Sedimentary Petrography*, 549 pp., Appleton-Century, New York, 1938.

KUENEN, PH. H. Geological Interpretation of the Bathymetrical Results, *The Snellius Expedition*, Vol. 5, part 1, 123 pp., Brill, Leyden, 1935.

Water-Faceted Boulders, *Am. J. Sci.*, Vol. 245, pp. 779–783, 1947.

(*a*) The Formation of Beach Cusps, *J. Geol.*, Vol. 56, pp. 34–40, 1948.

(*b*) Slumping in the Carboniferous of Pembrokeshire, *Quart. J. Geol. Soc. London*, Vol. 104, pp. 365–385, 1948.

(*c*) Turbidity Currents of High Density, Eighteenth Sess. Intern. Geol. Congr., 1948.

(*d*) Troebelingsstromingen van hoog soortelijk Gewicht, *Versl. K. Nederl. Akad. Wet. Amsterdam.*

(*e*) De Kringloop van het Water, 408 pp., Leopold, The Hague, 1948.

KUENEN, PH. H., and G. A. NEEB. Bottom Samples, *The Snellius Expedition*, Vol. 5, part 3, 265 pp., Brill, Leyden, 1943.

KUENEN, PH. H., and I. M. v. D. VLERK. *Geheimschrift der Aarde*, 370 pp., de Haan, Utrecht, 1948.

MARR, J. E. *Deposition of the Sedimentary Rocks*, 245 pp., Cambridge University Press, 1929.

MIGLIORINI, C. Sul modo di formazione dei complessi tipo Macigno, *Boll. soc. geol. italiana*, Vol. 62, pp. 48–49, 1944.

MILLER, W. J. Intraformational Corrugated Rocks, *J. Geol.*, Vol. 30, pp. 587–610, 1922.

MILNER, H. B. *Sedimentary Petrography*, 3d ed., 666 pp., Murby, London, 1940.

MOORE, R. C. The Origin and Age of the Boulder-Bearing Johns Valley Shale in the Ouachita Mountains of Arkansas and Oklahoma, *Am. J. Sci.*, Vol. 227, pp. 432–453, 1934.

MURRAY, J., and J. HJORT. *The Depths of the Ocean*, 821 pp., Macmillan, London, 1912.

NEEB, G. A. The Composition and Distribution of the Samples. *See* Kuenen and Neeb, 1943.

NEVIN, C. Competency of Moving Water to Transport Debris, *Bull. Geol. Soc. Am.*, Vol. 57, pp. 651–674, 1946.

PETTIJOHN, F. J. *Sedimentary Rocks*, 526 pp., Harper, New York, 1949.

PETTIJOHN, F. J., and J. G. LUNDAHL. Shape and Roundness of Lake Erie Beach Sands, *J. Sed. Petr.*, Vol. 13, pp. 69–81, 1943.

PRATJE, O. Die Sedimente des südatlantischen Ozeans, *Meteor*, Bd. 3, T. 2, Lf. 1, 56 pp., 1935.

RETTGER, R. E. Experiments on Soft-Rock Deformation, *Bull. Am. Assoc. Petr. Geol.*, Vol. 19, pp. 271–292, 1935.

RICH, J. L. Submarine Sedimentary Features on Bahama Banks and Their Bearing on Distribution Patterns of Lenticular Oil Sands, *Bull. Am. Assoc. Petr. Geol.*, Vol. 32, pp. 767–779, 1948.

RUBEY, W. W. The Force Required to Move Particles on a Stream Bed, *U. S. Geol. Surv. Prof. Paper* 189-E, pp. 120–141, 1938.

SCHOTT, G. *Geographie des Atlantischen Ozeans*, 438 pp., C. Boysen, Hamburg, 1942.

SCHOTT, W. Die Foraminiferen in dem aequatorialen Teil des Atlantischen Ozeans, *Meteor*, Bd. 3, T. 3, Lf. 13, pp. 43–134, 1935.

SHEPARD, F. P. Non-Depositional Physiographic Environments off the California Coast, *Bull. Geol. Soc. Am.*, Vol. 52, pp. 1869–1886, 1941.
  Submarine Geology, 348 pp., Harper, New York, 1948.

SHEPARD, F. P., K. O. EMERY, and E. C. LaFOND. Rip Currents: A Process of Geological Importance, *J. Geol.*, Vol. 49, pp. 337–369, 1941.

SHEPARD, F. P., and U. S. GRANT. Wave Erosion along the Southern California Coast, *Bull. Geol. Soc. Am.*, Vol. 58, pp. 919–926, 1947.

STEERS, J. A. *The Coastline of England and Wales*, 644 pp., Cambridge University Press, 1946.

STETSON, H. C. Geology and Paleontology of the Georges Bank Canyons, *Bull. Geol. Soc. Am.*, Vol. 47, pp. 339–440, 1936.

STETSON, H. C., and J. F. SMITH. Behavior of Suspension Currents and Mud Slides on the Continental Slope, *Am. J. Sci.*, Vol. 35, pp. 1–13, 1938.

SVERDRUP, H. U., M. W. JOHNSON, and R. H. FLEMING. *The Oceans, Their Physics, Chemistry, and General Biology*, 1060 pp., Prentice-Hall, New York, 1942.

TEICHERT, C., and D. L. SERVENTY. Deposits of Shells Transported by Birds, *Am. J. Sci.*, Vol. 245, pp. 322–328, 1947.

TIMMERMANS, P. D. Proeven over de Invloed van Golven op een Strand (English summary), *Leidsche Geol. Med.*, dl. 6, pp. 231–386, 1935.

TRASK, P. D. Sedimentation, chapter in *Geology 1888–1938*, 50th Anniv. Vol., Geol. Soc. Am., pp. 223–239, 1941.

TRASK, P. D., et al. *Recent Marine Sediments, a Symposium*, 736 pp., Am. Assoc. Petr. Geol., Tulsa, 1939.

TWENHOFEL, W. H. *Treatise on Sedimentation*, 926 pp., Williams & Wilkins, Baltimore, 1932.
  Principles of Sedimentation, 610 pp., McGraw-Hill, New York, 1939.
  The Rounding of Sand Grains, *J. Sed. Petr.*, Vol. 15, pp. 59–71, 1945.

VEEN, J. VAN. *Onderzoekingen in de Hoofden*, 252 pp., Landsdrukkerij, The Hague, 1936.

VERBEEK, R. D. M. *Krakatau*, 546 pp., Landsdrukkerij, Batavia, 1885.

The Formation
of Marine Sediments

INFLUENCE OF BOTTOM SHAPES

THE MARINE PROFILE OF EQUILIBRIUM

It is a well-known fact that the great majority of fossil sediments are of marine origin. This is the logical consequence of weathering and erosion that denude the dry land, whereas the denudation products are carried to the marine environment and ultimately find a resting place on the floor of the sea. Yet it would be wrong to conclude that sedimentation is going on everywhere in the sea. In earlier chapters it was pointed out that at many sites currents and waves sweep the bottom clean and that here and there even erosion takes place. The question must now be considered whether erosion and sedimentation occur over the sea floor according to simple rules or whether an apparently arbitrary or even a continually varying distribution of these two conditions prevails.

In the foregoing chapter the profile of equilibrium was mentioned, and this concept can also serve as a useful introduction to the study of sedimentation. But it will soon become evident that the conditions on the sea floor are highly complicated as compared to rivers. Hence the profile of equilibrium is of more theoretical than practical value. In a river the profile of equilibrium is reached when transporting power and sedimentary load are balanced everywhere. Physiographic youth has then made place for the stage of mature erosion. This equilibrium profile is a slightly concave line showing a relatively steep slope at the source and approaching sea level at the mouth. The precise form of the curve is different for each river and depends on precipitation, the nature of the rocks, the size and shape of the drainage area, the number of tributaries, the difference in level between

source and mouth, etc. Many river beds show a close approach to
the ideal flowing curve of equilibrium.

Theoretically a similar, but more complicated, profile of equilibrium
should develop on the sea floor. This line is concave upwards at the
shoreward end, passing to a horizontal stretch further out. But
thence it gradually merges with the part where deposition is going
on, and the profile again bends downwards. For rivers there is no
counterpart to this convex part of the marine profile of equilibrium.

Normally the concave part is undergoing erosion. It is so adjusted
that at each point the supply of sediment by local erosion and the
material received from higher up together equal the amount lost by
the transporting forces. The closer inshore, the more plentiful the
supply of sediment and the coarser the grain size. During transportation the particles are subjected to wear, and part of the finer material
thus formed goes into suspension. In fact, this variation in size and
amount of material forms one of the chief causes for the curvature
of the profile. The horizontal part develops at a depth where the
combined action of waves and currents is just able to transport the
supply of sediment but no active abrasion of the sea floor is possible.
At greater depth the supply exceeds transporting power and aggrading takes place.

On closer inspection numerous factors are found to introduce complications. At the landward end the supply is due partly to the
erosive action of the sea, more especially to surf pounding on the
shore. Another source is the weathering of the cliffs back of the
beach. Then there is local supply by rivers, glaciers, etc. But the
supply at any point on the beach need not all be transported outward along the sea floor. A large proportion can be carried sideways along the beach. Large quantities of sand may be thrown up
on the beach and blown away inland by the wind. Prograding of the
coast may result where the supply exceeds the capacity of transporting agents.

Minor irregularities of the profile are caused by the development
of sand bars or coral reefs.

Beyond the horizontal part the profile normally shows an S- or
Z-shaped curve, convex upwards at the top and concave upwards at
the lower end. Slumping or other complicating factors may continually disturb the development of this aggrading part of the profile.
Where abundant coarse sediment is provided, a break in slope will
occur at the higher end of this part of the profile with a steep, straight
scree slope beyond, ending more or less abruptly at the lower end.

Whereas sea level provides a common base level for all rivers, the horizontal part of the marine profile of equilibrium varies in depth according to local conditions. The size of incoming waves varies with the climate (wind) and the length of fetch, and current action also depends on local conditions. Hence, the depth to which erosion is possible must also vary from one locality to another.

By the time equilibrium is attained, the profile is normally a very flat one. The flatness of the curve is affected by many factors. In this respect also the strength of waves and currents are important.

Obviously the nature of the country rock has great influence on the shape of the profile. The degree of cohesion and solubility, the size of the debris into which it disintegrates, and the hardness of its constituents all count in the rate of supply, in the transport, and in the abrasion of detritus.

The length of time since the profile was established is no less important. When a river has reached its profile of equilibrium, erosion does not come to a standstill. The bed continues to sink lower and lower while a peneplain gradually develops. Neither does the marine profile of equilibrium mark a final stage of development. Erosion continues to carry the coastline landwards, and the sea floor continues to be aggraded farther out. With rivers the profile approaches a horizontal line while the length remains constant. With the marine profile the vertical range remains unaltered but the length increases.

Up to this point our treatment of the marine profile of equilibrium has been entirely theoretical. But when one seeks to apply it in nature its value is found to be doubtful. Obviously, any relative change in the position of sea level will entirely upset any approach to equilibrium previously attained. Deposition or erosion can soon adjust the profile of a river when diastrophic action has upset equilibrium. But the vast area of the sea floor renders adjustment by sedimentation a lengthy process, and submarine erosion acts very slowly. During the Ice Age sea level repeatedly swung up and down many dozens of meters. Warping of the continental margins is continually changing the level of the land. Hence, conditions on all coasts have been fundamentally altered recently, and we are left in doubt whether the phenomena we now find represent an approach to equilibrium or merely a stage in major readjustments.

The continental shelf and slope are generally looked upon as conforming closely to the marine profile of equilibrium for open oceanic coasts. However, as previously noted (p. 263), recent investigations have shown that "hard bottom" (rock and coarse detritus) tends to occur more especially along the outer edge of the shelf. This absence of recent sediment on an area situated between environments closer to the shore and farther out which show deposition can hardly represent an advanced stage of adjustment under the conditions now prevailing. Neither can the continental terrace have been formed under similar conditions, because oil wells, dredging, and seismic reconnaissance on the shelf along the east coast of the United States have revealed a thick pile of sediment underlying the non-depositional edge

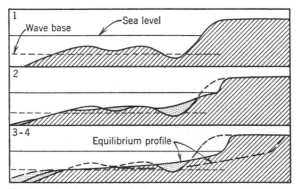

Fig. 135. Gradual development of the equilibrium profile on a steep coast.

of the shelf. Most profiles of the continental terrace show an abrupt break in slope, some even more than one. It is not yet certain whether this is due to recent changes in level or whether the break in slope is a natural feature of a fully adjusted profile of equilibrium.

When an irregular land surface is drowned the new sea floor will not conform to the profile of equilibrium. The elevations must represent sites of erosion and can never form an environment of permanent deposition. Only fractions of coarser grain than that belonging to this position may remain in place after having been accidentally brought there by ice, slumping, exceptionally violent wave action, etc. But eventually even this coarse material will disappear, because wave energy will concentrate on these elevated portions (Fig. 135).

The depressions reaching below the profile of equilibrium, on the other hand, tend to form traps for sediment, offering it a more or less permanent resting place. Areas lying above the profile but nevertheless forming a depression in an elevated region may form temporary environments of sedimentation, but erosion will ultimately set in when the higher surroundings have at last given way to the erosive action.

It is sometimes held that all sediments deposited below the concave part of the profile are permanent and will never be attacked by erosion as long as earth movements or a lowering of sea level does not intervene. But this is not entirely correct, because the profile of equilibrium itself is gradually displaced landwards by the erosion. Sedimentary matter is not ultimately safeguarded from marine erosion in the prevailing cycle until it has been deposited below the greatest depth to which waves and currents can reach at that particular position, that is, the top level of aggradation. In this case bottom erosion, while gradually shifting landward, can never reach the deposit.

Beyond the continental shelf sedimentation prevails. Some exceptions to this statement must be noted, however. In the first place there are a few smaller areas in these deeper zones where tidal and eddy currents or tsunamic waves are sufficiently strong to prohibit all deposition. The sills between deep-sea basins, even when lying at 1000- to 2000-m depth, are generally swept clean and covered by a coating of manganese oxide or a deposit of gravel. Even banks, guyots, and ridges at hundreds of meters' depth in the open ocean are frequently cloaked with coarser material, such as globigerina ooze, shards of volcanic glass, sand, or even concretions and gravel. It was pointed out in an earlier chapter that this is evidently due to the removal of finer fractions by currents.

Some permanent currents beyond the shelf reach the bottom with sufficient force to sweep away all particles finer than the coarse sand fraction. The Florida Current, for instance, impinges on the continental slope and the adjoining Blake Plateau lying at 1000-m depth. It prohibits the settling of fine sediment, leaving relatively coarse globigerina ooze.

A further exception must be made for areas where the slope is sufficiently steep for slumping to take place now and again. There can be no question then of permanent deposition. The problem of slumping was considered in the foregoing chapter.

There is an apparent contradiction between the findings that many if not most fossil sediments were deposited in quite shallow water, while base level for erosion tends to lie at a depth of several dozens of meters. Several matters should be taken into account, however.

In the first place sedimentation may occur on areas of the sea floor which are above the profile of equilibrium, as long as they are protected by surrounding shallow areas. Offshore bars, rock ledges, reefs, or wide expanses of shallow water on the seaward side may all in turn lend such protection. If subsidence of the area in question takes place it will lead to continuous sedimentation and thus result in the permanent burial of shallow-water deposits. This explanation applies to many geosynclinal prisms.

In the second place the supply of sedimentary matter may exceed the transporting power of waves and currents. In this event accumulation takes place, even if the bottom lies far above the effective depth of wave action at the site in question and although the sediment is continually churned up and shifted about. This process of accumulation may continue until the deposit emerges above sea level and makes place for terrestrial sediments via brack-water strata. The case of delta formations may here be recalled. In basins that are nearly or entirely cut off from the sea this process will generally take place. No profile of equilibrium can then develop.

In the third place the effective depth of wave turbulence is large only on *open* oceanic coasts. In inland seas, like the North Sea, waves of great size and oceanic swell cannot develop and affect the bottom to depths greater than a few dozen meters. It must be assumed that, in general, fine-grained, fossil sediments were deposited in inland seas. The particles sank beyond the reach of waves in relatively shallow depths. This follows from the combined properties of fine lamination, which excludes wave action, and the occurrence of animals living at shallow depths, which excludes deep water.

In the fourth place the climate in former periods may in many places have been characterized by weak winds, so that even a considerable length of fetch did not result in large waves.

The profile of equilibrium is not a sharp line. The conditions are continually changing, for during stormy weather it lies deeper than normally. In consequence of crustal unrest or movements of sea level it moves up and down. Variations in supply by alterations in the course of rivers or tidal creeks necessitate adaptations in the slope and position of the sea floor to ensure the regular transport of sediment away from the shore out into deep water. Alterations in the fauna or flora, the climate, etc., will find expression in supply, deposition, or transport. In short, nearly all factors playing a part in sedimentation are liable to show variations and to cause concomitant adaptations of the profile of equilibrium. These variations will find clearest expression in sedimentation, when intermittent subsidence takes place and the sea floor is fairly well adjusted to equilibrium. For then sedimentation and standstill or even erosion will continually alternate

while a thick pile of deposits accumulates, in which the varying interplay is recorded by separate laminae and beds, showing variation in
grain size, composition, structure, etc., and divided by diastems.

The term "diastem" signifies a certain type of interruption in the
sedimentation (Fig. 136). The terminology of these phenomena is

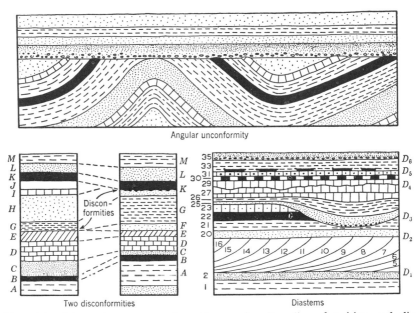

Angular unconformity

Two disconformities   Diastems

FIG. 136. Schematic representation of unconformity, disconformities, and diastems. D_1 and D_2 inferred from cross-bedding; D_3, from channel fill; D_4, from
erosion; D_5, from attached shells; D_6, from intraformational conglomerate.

somewhat confused. According to general custom "angular unconformity" denotes a long break in sedimentation, during which the
lower series has been tilted and eroded. Hence, the lower beds are
not parallel to those above. The term "disconformity" is employed
when the beds below and above the break are parallel and the time
interval which elapsed after the lower stratum was laid down and
before the next one covered it was of the length of at least a stratigraphical stage. Consolidation and erosion have generally taken place
in the meantime. The beds are parallel, however, and the contact is
therefore conformable. When the interval was of shorter duration
the term "diastem" is used. Consolidation has generally not occurred,
and frequently no erosion either. The break in deposition can often

only be inferred. It may have been as short as the interval between tides, or the duration of a storm. Commonly, however, it has been much longer (Barrell, 1917).

Diastems may have several causes. The following may be enumerated. (1) Elevation of the sea floor or sinking of sea level. It is not necessary that emergence take place, as is often assumed, because less depth may already have resulted in non-deposition or even erosion. (2) Reaching of wave base by the sea floor, in consequence of accumulation. (3) Increase in the transporting capacity of waves and currents, for example by the disappearance of obstacles or by variations in climate. (4) Decrease in that capacity in adjoining areas resulting in the falling off of supply. (5) Lessening of supply, for instance by the alteration of river courses, negative shifting of the strand line, or exhaustion of the source of sediment. (6) Slumping. (7) Interruption of production of animal tests by variations in ecological conditions.

Barrell has shown that normally the sum of the time intervals recorded by sedimentation is much shorter than the sum of the lost intervals as long as the supply of sediment is larger than the space made available by crustal downwarping. This has doubtless been true, even in most geosynclinal series; otherwise the depth could not have remained small for long periods at a time. Figure 137 applies to the normal case in which sedimentation keeps the basin filled to wave base. It shows that sedimentation occupies a fair proportion of the whole time, but that owing to scour and removal to deep water much of the deposit is continually being destroyed. Many minor diastems, due to storms, variations in supply, and other incidental causes, are intercalated between major diastems due mainly to climatic changes and physiographic alterations especially in the surroundings. Larger diastrophic oscillations result in disconformities.

In deep-sea deposits diastems must be rare. The accumulation, instead of being by swift steps, divided by long intervals of nondeposition or even scour, is a leisurely but continuous process. Even if the rate varies considerably, the record of past time should be practically unbroken, especially in depression of the deep-sea floor.

Diastems may be detected in sedimentary series by the occurrence of bedding planes, by sudden alterations in composition, by the presence of broken or of attached shells, and many other phenomena. But these may also develop without the presence of any true break in deposition and cannot be taken as proof. On the other hand countless diastems must occur in fossil sediments without showing up in any way, and they will thus escape observation. Their existence is inferred when the total thickness of a formation falls far short of the amount found by multiplying the rate of sedimentation by the length of time. This rate of sedimentation is seldom known, but it is sometimes indicated by the nature of the deposit, e.g., volcanic deposits

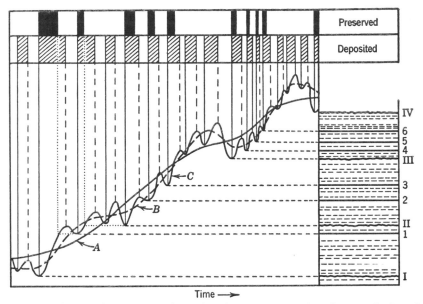

Fig. 137. Schematic representation of sedimentary record. *A*, general rise of top level of sedimentation, determining thickness of sedimentary series, shown on the right; *B*, oscillations due mainly to diastrophism, giving disconformities I–IV; *C*, minor oscillations due mainly to climatic and physiographic changes, giving major diastems 1–6. Minor diastems due to incidental causes. At the top of the diagram the time occupied by deposition and the time ultimately recorded are shown in black.

from an eruption, or by the preservation of fossils of perishable organisms which must have been quickly buried.

COASTAL TOPOGRAPHY AND SEDIMENTATION

It is especially during the stages prior to the development of the profile of equilibrium that the topography of the land and the type of coast have a predominant influence on sedimentation. In the case of submergence of a country in a youthful stage of erosion the water is frequently deep to within a short distance of the shore, thus allowing a powerful erosive action by the waves. Deep bays will be found running far inland, and there will be steep cliffs, coarse and varied sediments, and an irregular sea bottom. Inlets and depressions will permit the local accumulation of sediment. When a more mature stage of development has been attained and the marine profile of equilibrium has been established the coast will present a flowing curve lying some distance inland from the original position.

In the old age of coastal development the waves roll in over a wide platform and arrive at the shore with much-reduced erosive power. The deep erosion platform is covered by a veneer of loose particles which move very slowly out to the area of aggradation. Only in the event of subsidence will a new series of strata come to rest and be deposited unconformably on the platform.

In passing it may be pointed out that opinion is strongly divided on the question of how far marine agents are able to develop a smooth platform of erosion in hard rocks. Some investigators are convinced that a broad area is quickly smoothed; others hold that a slow relative subsidence of the land is required to allow extensive leveling. There are also those who deny any appreciable planation by the sea. According to them, all peneplanes are the result of subaerial denudation. A flat sea floor should then be the result of submergence of a peneplane or the smothering of uneven topography by sediments. Future investigations will have to show which opinion is correct.

Where a very flat landscape is submerged to smaller depths than base level of erosion, the new sea floor will show slighter declivity than the profile of equilibrium. As a result the waves will throw up an offshore bar, cutting off a lagoon. Provided there is sufficient time, erosion and wave attack will gradually push the bar landwards and consume the lagoonal deposits formed behind the bar.

A coast due to emergence will frequently pass through the same stages of development. The reason is that the almost horizontal section of the former profile of equilibrium, provided it was already developed, will reach to the beach in the new cycle. The new profile will therefore have to be cut downward until the necessary steep section close to the beach has been developed. Emergence will cause a seaward migration of all zones of the profile of equilibrium.

The study of physiographic forms of the coast and foreshore and their evolution forms a separate branch of geomorphology to which full justice cannot be given here. The reader is referred to the classical monographs by D. W. Johnson.

THE ENVIRONMENTS OF MARINE SEDIMENTATION

GENERAL CONSIDERATIONS

In connection with the diverse conditions obtaining where sedimentation is proceeding, a number of different *environments* may be distinguished. The term "environment" embraces the sum total of the conditions that prevail while the sediment is being deposited; in this connection it is used mainly in a restricted sense, as applying to the surroundings directly over the deposit, and not to the adjoining areas of the sea floor or land. Each factor involved has its own distribution in the seas, and, although the limits of several factors may happen to coincide at a certain point, the general rule is that the conditions as to depth, temperature, currents, etc., vary independently. Hence, the distribution of environments over the sea floor must vary according to which factor is used to define the extent. The marine environment covers the whole area occupied by the oceans and seas. The deep-sea environment is limited to the regions beyond the 200-m depth line. The marine-glacial environment covers all parts and depths of the sea floor where morainal material forms the dominant constituent of the deposits. Delta environments are developed where river-borne material is deposited in excess of other sedimentary matter. Many other examples of overlapping environments could be given.

A term extensively used in geological literature is *facies*. This word denotes the sum of the characters (lithological, structural, paleontological, and the variability) exhibited by a deposit that are regarded as criteria of the conditions that controlled the formation. It therefore applies to the physical expression of a deposit at the time it was being formed. Characters evolved at a later date by diagenesis, weathering, metamorphism, or tectonic action may not be used to define the facies.[1]

There are a large number of factors controlling the formation, and according to circumstances the geologist may wish to lay emphasis on different aspects of sedimentary conditions. He may want to express either the environment, the composition or source of the material, the ecological, the physiographic, or other aspects. Hence, various types of facies are mutually exclusive, while others are collateral. Thus a rock may be developed either in marine or in ter-

---

[1] R. C. Moore (*Geol. Soc. Am. Memoir* 39, 1949) has suggested the term *lithofacies* for denoting what is here called facies. Facies can then be restricted to emphasize differences between contrasting parts of a single stratigraphic unit.

restrial facies, but in both cases it could also be in glacial or any other climatic facies. Though a sediment cannot show at the same time conglomeratic and muddy facies, it may in both cases show either beach or else shallow-water facies. Geosynclinal facies is contrasted to epicontinental facies, but in both a great variety of rock types may occur and all types of climate may have prevailed at the time of deposition.

The terms environment and facies are related, but, whereas the environment deals with the actual conditions prevailing in the area under consideration, facies refers to characteristics of a deposit. These may reflect the environment, and when we understand all the factors involved in sedimentation we may interpret the former environment by studying the facies.

In the practice of geological investigation this deduction of environment from facies is of the greatest importance. When dealing on later pages with the principal marine environments it will be shown that few factors are restricted to any single type of environment, and the characteristics which they induce in the sediments are seldom of precise diagnostic value. Hence it will always be necessary to use as large a combination as possible of different features of a rock to determine the sedimentary environment. Frequently it will be advisable to combine the results for several successive beds, because a single bed may show insufficient distinctive features.

The most general classification of the sea floor into different environments is according to depth zones: the littoral (between tide levels), neritic (low tide level to 200-m depth), bathyal (between 200 and 1000 m), and abyssal (below 1000 m) zones. In Fig. 138 the main features concerning conditions and resulting sedimentary products of these environments according to depth zones are summarized. Most of the matter contained in this diagram has been dealt with on the preceding pages and need not be repeated here; the sediments will be discussed presently.

A classification according to coastal distance can also be employed, namely in beach, shelf, hemipelagic, and (eu)pelagic environments. This classification runs more or less parallel to the depth classification. It is therefore added *pro parte* in our figure. In general the slope of the sea floor is slight, seldom exceeding a few degrees, especially when averages over larger distances are considered. From this it follows that greater depths must be sought at greater distances from the coast. Thus the bathyal zone is almost never found as near as a few kilometers from the shore, and the abyssal zone must be looked for at dozens to hundreds of kilometers from the coast. Hence, deep-sea deposits formed beyond the 200-m line are generally also of hemipelagic or

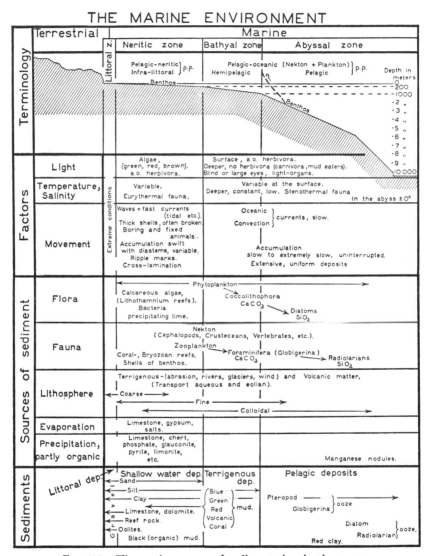

FIG. 138. The environments of sedimentation in the ocean.

pelagic nature; that is to say, they show little direct influence from the neighboring land. This means that coarser and frequently also relatively fine sedimentary detritus from the continents are reduced to the minimum, while the finest clay particles, remains of planktonic organisms, volcanic dust, etc., predominate in the pelagic deposits.

Frequently it is tacitly assumed, however, that the two sets of environments listed above are identical and merely represent a different terminology. This is not correct and may lead to misconceptions. It was pointed out earlier that the Indonesian deep-sea depressions contain hemipelagic sediments down to depths greater than 7000 m. On the other hand oceanic banks and ridges such as the Whale Ridge in the southern Atlantic are covered by bathyal deposits of purely pelagic nature.

Another subdivision sometimes used lays more stress on the bottom and less on the waters covering it. It runs as follows: eulittoral zone either between tide levels or down to the limit of attached plants (generally 40–60 m); sublittoral zone down to 200, or 400 m, or to the edge of the continental platform; anchibenthic zone down to about 1000 m; and abyssal-benthic zone at still greater depths.

Stratigraphers customarily use a classification according to depth zones. It should not be forgotten, however, that sometimes very little can be deduced, from fossil sediments deposited below wave base, about the depths of the environment in which they were laid down. The distance to the coast, on the other hand, may sometimes be roughly ascertained, or is at least indicated to a certain extent, either by paleogeographical data or by features of the sediments themselves. Thus most of the characteristics typical of so-called deep-sea deposits are due to their great distance from the coasts, that is to their pelagic nature, and not to the great depths in which they were laid down. For example, globigerina ooze can be formed at all depths, even in the neritic zone, but is very scarce close to the shore. In dealing with the problem of fossil deep-sea deposits, such as radiolarian ooze and red clay, generally only the question of depth, instead of the eupelagic nature, is discussed. This happens in spite of the fact that the relevant characteristics of recent deep-sea deposits are due to the great coastal distance.

It might even be suggested that the entire term "deep-sea" deposits be abandoned, but it would be preferable to hold strictly to the original proposal of Murray and Renard to include the bathyal as well as the abyssal sediments in the deep-sea deposits. This would reduce the number of ambiguous cases to the minimum. On the other hand the objection remains that stratigraphers would never describe deposits in a basin of a few hundred meters' depth as deep-sea sediments. They intend to imply by this term a depth of several thousands of meters and an eupelagic character. It is only when dealing with recent sediments, where the depth is accurately known, that the term deep-sea deposits can be employed in the correct sense. In any event geologists would do well to realize the essential points of difference when using terms like deep-sea, hemipelagic, and eupelagic deposits.

Natland (1933) was able to show that the Foraminifera collected off southern California can be divided into five assemblages characteristic of different depth zones, and other organisms may provide similar indications of depth (see Shepard, 1948). It should therefore ultimately be possible to determine the depth at which a recent deposit containing suitable organic remains was laid down. But it will prove very difficult to apply this method to fossil sediments, especially those of pre-Tertiary age.

The danger involved in interpreting pelagic deposits as abyssal ones is brought out by an attempt of Cayeux's to explain the alternation of ancient shallow water and pelagic sediments to great vertical movements of the sea floor. As Woolnough (1942) and Rutten (1949) have pointed out, small variations in level during the past, when the continents generally showed but slight relief, can explain the observed alternations.

In the present volume the environments which will be treated separately are as follows (see Fig. 138):

1. Pelagic-abyssal environment, coastal distance at least several hundreds of kilometers, depths greater than 1000 m. Main types of sediments: red clay, a fine-grained lutite with less than 30% lime, radiolarian and diatom ooze of much the same character but with abundant siliceous skeletons or frustules, globigerina ooze with more than 30% lime, mostly planktonic Foraminifera, the remainder lutite.

2. Hemipelagic-abyssal environment, coastal distance less than several hundred kilometers, depth greater than 1000 m. Main types of sediment differ from those of the pelagic-abyssal environment, by admixture of terrestrial mineral grains of silt or fine sand grade sizes.

3. Bathyal environment, depth 200–1000 m, coastal distance normally a few dozen to a few hundred kilometers. Main types of sediment: blue mud, a fine, dark mud with less than 30% lime, abundant terrestrial mineral grains, various related muds such as calcareous mud.

4. Neritic environment, depth from low tide to 200 m, coastal distance seldom more than a few hundred kilometers. Main types of sediment: coarse to fine terrestrial material, with admixture of marine organic remains, mainly calcareous. In tropical waters calcareous

matter tends to be more abundant, giving locally coral sand or mud, oölites, etc.

5. Several special environments mainly of neritic character such as delta, tidal flat, and lagoon environments.

6. Littoral or beach environment, between low tide and the highest limit reached by storm waves. Wide diversity of deposits including the coarsest boulder deposits, sands, muds, and organic deposits. Some authors include the neritic zone in the littoral environment, but this tends to cause confusion.

7. Euxinic environment, depth varying, characterized by poor ventilation of bottom water, resulting in absence of bottom fauna. Deposits mainly fine grained with high content of decomposable organic matter.

THE DEPOSITION OF SAND AND MUD IN MARINE ENVIRONMENT

The deposition of sand and coarser fractions does not call for separate treatment here. As soon as the transporting agents are no longer able to move the grains they come to rest. Minor complications in connection with ripple marking have already been reviewed, and "cross bedding" will be treated below (p. 363).

But special problems arise when fine fractions are involved in the transport and deposition.

Where sand and lutite are transported together the coarser grains will settle more easily. Generally the coarser fractions accumulate while the fine ones are still being carried away. Hence, sand and lutite tend to accumulate in different environments, or at different times in the same environment. But there are also exceptions to this rule. One of these results in so-called graded bedding, which will be investigated later (p. 366). Another is found where the transporting agents cannot cope with the supply and deposition is too swift to allow of sorting.

In sea water the fine particles generally form a much-diluted suspension. In more or less stagnant water below wave base, individual flakes can settle on the bottom and gradually accumulate, for instance in the form of red clay in the deep sea, or between Foraminifera in globigerina ooze. But the sedimentation of mud is not restricted to the deep sea and also takes place at or near sea level. This deposition of mud in estuaries and lagoons, on tidal flats and beaches, is a complicated problem.

It is generally held that clay and colloidal fractions are precipitated by the electrolytic action of sea water where they are carried out to sea by rivers. The coagulated lutite forms particles of sufficient size to sink to the bottom and make a deposit of mud. Bourcart and Francis-Boeuf (1942) have shown, however, that in estuaries the main mass of mud is deposited not where salinity commences but in localities where the mechanical action of tidal currents is favorable. This happens where the water is at rest for a sufficient length of time at each turn of the tide for settling to take place. The mud in suspension occurs mainly in the form of a loose, flaky, or frothy mass in which organic matter, sand grains, and colloidal fractions are contained. The flakes have a specific gravity approaching that of water and are carried for a long time in suspension. They can settle only when the waters are not agitated by waves or currents. Once deposited, they stick to the bottom, and only powerful action can bring them back into suspension. The sand fraction in these estuarine muds is composed of quartz grains, other minerals, and plankton skeletons. The organic matter is in various stages of decomposition and acts as a binding agent. It varies in amount between 2 and 20%. There is also a varying amount of iron present in various forms, such as the monosulfide and hydrogels, which also act as binding matter according to the authors mentioned. It is the presence of these binding materials that gives these muds their specific properties and is the main cause of the mixing of finer and coarser fractions in one and the same deposit in estuaries.

Other investigators have pointed to the importance of the large numbers of mud-feeding animals thriving on tidal mud flats. The vital activities of these organisms also have important results on the sedimentation of fine materials. The excreted mud is generally coagulated by slimy substances, so that pellets are formed that are less mobile than the separate particles. In fact, the lutite is converted to grains belonging in the sand fraction and can therefore accumulate in water with marked transporting power. These "mud grains" soon fuse into a firm deposit of mud. Worms and lamellibranchia are most active in this respect.

Plant life also assists in catching and retaining silt and mud. For this reason various types of plants are used along the northwestern coasts of Europe for speeding the accumulation of mud against the dykes and thus furthering the reclaiming of new fertile "polders." On tropical coasts mangrove vegetation forms a highly effective mud trap.

A peculiar action of vegetation has been noted where algal threads attach themselves to the mussels growing in beds on the sandy flats of inland tidal waters. Abundant mud is caught in the fine network and tends to smother the mussels. The animals react by working themselves upward to the surface, where the process of mud catchment continues. In this manner a foot or more of mud may accumulate under a thin covering of living shells, which lend protection from erosive forces.

In consequence of the mechanical action of waves, scouring currents, etc., a large proportion of the fine deposits formed in tidal waters is again disintegrated into small pieces. These are shifted more or less in the manner of sand grains and redeposited. After becoming firmly pressed together and compacted again, little remains to show that we are dealing with what was originally a medium-grained deposit from a mechanical point of view.

THE PELAGIC-ABYSSAL ENVIRONMENT

The pelagic-abyssal environment covers no less than 250×10^6 km², half the area of the earth.

The lutite forming the colloidal groundmass of the sediments is more or less uniform throughout the environment, although the color varies with the degree of oxidation. Hence the larger particles are chiefly responsible for causing the various types of sediment. These larger particles are almost exclusively supplied by planktonic organisms, and this circumstance explains much concerning the composition and distribution of pelagic-abyssal deposits.

Important variations in the nature of the deposits from one area to another are caused by differences in the properties of the surface layers of the ocean waters and consequently also in the planktonic skeletons produced there. Thus the diatoms occur in mass only in high latitudes and areas of upwelling, fertile waters, while radiolarians and planktonic Foraminifera show their maximum development towards the equator. Furthermore, in general, planktonic life decreases in intensity away from the coast, mainly on account of lack of nutrient salts. Concomitantly the supply of terrigenous inorganic material falls off oceanward, but more rapidly. Consequently the planktonic admixture gains in importance in spite of its absolute decrease. The distribution of currents is more arbitrary than that of coastal distance, being greatly dependent on the topographic relief of the sea floor. Where ridges and banks occur, currents and waves tend to become active, resulting in the absence of colloidal particles, sometimes even of sand grains. The purest examples of globigerina ooze are therefore found on elevations of the bottom far out in the ocean.

One of the most important factors governing the development of recent pelagic-abyssal types of sediment is the solution of lime and silica. This follows readily from the significant part played by planktonic skeletons, which are of calcareous or siliceous nature. The solution of lime will be dealt with later (p. 354). Siliceous tests also undergo solution but at a considerably slower rate. Hence, under certain conditions, all traces of lime may have disappeared from an ooze while radiolarians and diatoms are still profuse.

Although other materials, such as volcanic ash, coral detritus, silt from large rivers, and desert dust, are supplied locally to the surface waters, these products show only gradual and slow variations over wide areas of the ocean floors. The great depth provides ample opportunity for currents to scatter these fine materials far and wide before they reach the bottom, in spite of the low velocities of oceanic circulations. As currents running in different directions have to be passed by the sinking particles on the way down, the scattering tends to be more regional than linear. Calculations on the distance of transportation to be expected were given previously (p. 253).

The foregoing discussion will have made clear that, although strongly contrasted oozes are encountered on the ocean floors, the areas over which appreciable variations occur must be measured not in hundreds but in tens of thousands or even millions of square kilometers. The boundaries must also be exceedingly vague. The pelagic-abyssal type is by far the most uniform of all marine environments from a regional point of view.

It has been held by some authors that in a vertical sense the variations in this facies must also be small and gradual even to the exclusion of stratification. In posing this contention a very important factor has been entirely overlooked, however. The extremely low rate of sedimentation prevailing on the ocean bottom counteracts the slowness of variations from one type to another. The stratification on the sea floor will be dealt with below, but it may be noted here that, in the Atlantic Ocean, beds with high and low lime percentages alternate in thicknesses of only a few centimeters. On the other hand bedding is absent in many cores 1 or 2 m long from such areas as the Moluccan deep-sea basins and off the California coast where the land is not far off. This is due to a much swifter rate of accumulation. (See also p. 384.)

THE HEMIPELAGIC-ABYSSAL ENVIRONMENT

This environment is typical of most, but not all, deep-sea depressions. In these basins depths attaining several thousands of meters are commonly combined with a relatively small distance to the coast, a few kilometers to several hundreds of kilometers only. Solution of lime is generally active, but exceptions occur in poorly ventilated basins, as for instance the Sulu Sea north of Borneo. In the nature of the deposits the terrestrial influence tends to prevail, and the muds resemble those of the bathyal zone more than the oozes of the pelagic facies. As pointed out earlier, paleogeographers are likely to make the mistake of supposing that great depth alone is sufficient to ensure the development of pelagic sediments such as red clay and radiolarian ooze, or on the other hand to ascribe all hemipelagic deposits to depths of 1000 or at most 2000 m. The possibility of hemipelagic-abyssal conditions should not be lost sight of in reconstructing paleogeographic conditions. The deposits forming in the Moluccan area have been studied in detail by Miss Neeb (1943) and may be taken as an example of this group of sediments (see p. 337).

THE BATHYAL ENVIRONMENT

This environment is developed over an area of about 40×10^6 km² at the present time. Our Fig. 138, p. 314, shows that there is a strong resemblance to the abyssal environment. But the variability is considerably wider. This is due partly to the smaller coastal distance and stronger inclination of the bottom, partly to the smaller basins and the transitions to the highly variable neritic environments. Owing to the moderate distance to the coast in most cases and to the comparatively small depths, the strongly divergent influences of rocky or sandy coasts, rivers, volcanoes, deserts, etc., can make themselves felt in the bathyal zone. The lesser depth and shorter time required for settling reduces the scattering of particles by currents as compared to abyssal environments. Although swifter currents occur here and there, they tend to influence only narrow strips of the sea floor.

In the moderate depths of the bathyal zone the differences in level due to slopes have a much more pronounced influence on conditions than the same differences in level in the abyssal zone. For example, the solution of lime, the temperature, the amount of light, and disturbance by waves and currents, etc., do not differ perceptibly between 5000 and 5500 m depth, but they may change entirely between 200 and 700 m. As, moreover, the slopes are in general steeper in the shallower parts of the deep sea, the variations in conditions may occur over shorter distances. Basins are commonly much smaller and depth zones much narrower in the bathyal than in the abyssal zone, and this automatically leads to swifter transitions from one condition to another.

At its shallow margin the bathyal zone merges into the neritic zone. Here the effects of penetrating light and of wave turbulence begin to make themselves felt. In short, the diversity of conditions prevailing in the neritic zone reaches down into the upper parts of the bathyal zone.

It was already pointed out that the boundary between the abyssal and bathyal zones is chosen arbitrarily at 1000 m and does not correspond to a natural division. In many places 2000 m would represent a better limit. It might even be preferable to take 3000 to 4000 m as the limit of the true deep-sea floor if it were not that echo sounding has of recent years destroyed the illusion that a steep continental slope abuts abruptly against an undiversified and flat deep-sea floor.

The upper limit of the bathyal zone corresponds roughly to the edge of the continental shelf. Although this morphological break in slope is also often found to be vague and to vary between 100 and 300 m in depth, the limit of the bathyal zone cannot be chosen more advantageously than at 200 m, as long as this figure is taken *cum grano salis.*

No attempt will be made here to distinguish between a hemipelagic-bathyal and a pelagic-bathyal environment, because the latter differs only very slightly from the pelagic-abyssal environment and is of rare occurrence.

THE NERITIC ENVIRONMENT

This type of environment at present covers 30×10^6 km², that is, about 10% of the marine area of the earth. The neritic facies is the most important for stratigraphy, because the great majority of fossil sediments were deposited under neritic conditions.

Conditions in the neritic zone are marked by great variability. Light penetrates in greater or lesser degree to the sea floor and renders plant life possible, but the intensity and nature of the growth are highly variable. The temperature does not vary daily, but the seasons make themselves felt throughout the neritic zone. The climatic zones are thus projected downwards onto the sea floor, especially through the medium of planktonic organic remains. The neritic zone is found both at hundreds of kilometers from the coast and right up against the foot of plunging cliffs at the margin of the land. In exposed positions, such as the edge of the continental terrace opposite the ocean, the deepest parts of the neritic zone can be reached by wave turbulence. But in enclosed basins and in windless climates even comparatively shallow bottoms are not noticeably stirred.

The greater part of detritus deriving from the land is deposited in the neritic zone except for the fine silt and colloidal fractions which are largely removed to deeper water. Volcanoes, rivers, glaciers, coral reefs, dust storms, and coastal erosion all serve as sources and deliver their products to coastal waters. These raw materials for the formation of sediments contrast markedly with one another and with the marine contribution. Moreover, they are in general distributed over limited areas and thus cause rather sharply demarcated sedimentary units. The delta, lagoon, tidal flat, and estuarine environments are all special forms of the neritic environment. They are dealt with below, and it will be shown that marked differences are found among all of them.

Finally the action of currents is also most important in the neritic zone. Not only are tidal and other currents strongest in shallow waters, but most of them reach the bottom and may locally sweep the finer fractions away. In the deep sea, on the other hand, the function of currents tends to be restricted to scattering during the sinking and seldom results in the churning up of materials that have once reached the bottom.

Many organisms, especially benthonic life, react strongly to external conditions. For example, some forms such as reef corals cannot thrive in turbid waters. These fastidious animals also require sufficient light and agitated waters, a high temperature, normal salinity, and a firm substratum to attach themselves to. But, although it may be less apparent, each kind of benthonic animal and plant is adapted to a limited range of climate, of depth, and of bottom sediment, etc., and its distribution is controlled by these factors. These requirements may be quite different from those of reef builders. It is only because the requirements of reef builders are so conspicuous that so much emphasis has been laid on the special conditions prevailing around coral reefs.

The widely variable benthos adds to the diversity of material available for sedimentation in the neritic zone.

In answer to the question how fossil neritic sediments may be recognized a number of characteristics can be enumerated. But none of these is always shown, and not one is entirely absent in other environments. Neither the great variation in grain size from very coarse to finest clay nor the occurrence of false bedding, current and wave ripple marks, fixed animals, or diastems can constitute more than strong evidence of shallow depths. All these features may occur occasionally far into the bathyal environment. Thus strong currents may sweep the sills between deep-sea basins; tsunamis may agitate the bottom water now and then even in oceanic depths; while submarine slumps, faulting, etc., may cause all manner of irregularities in the sedimentation at greater depths.

Differences between the neritic and littoral zones will be mentioned in connection with the latter.

A remarkable characteristic of recent neritic sedimentation, already referred to in Chapter 4, is the increase in grain size along the outer edge of the continental terrace.

We will now turn to the various special environments of the neritic zone.

THE DELTA ENVIRONMENT

The most typical deltas are formed by small streams in lakes and protected embayments (Fig. 139). Three types of strata are formed.

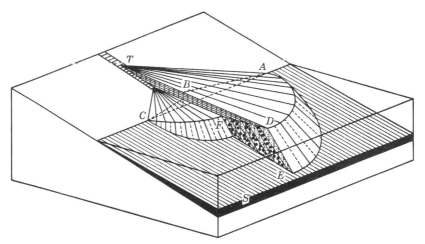

Fig. 139. Schematic block diagram of the growth stages of a small delta in a lake or inland sea. *TBA*, deposited beyond shoreline; *TDF*, top-set beds; *FDE*, fore-set beds; *S*, bottom-set beds.

The fore-set beds are deposited on the steep subaqueous slope. The bottom-set beds are part of the normal deposits forming on the floor of the lake or inlet. The fore-set beds gradually extend the delta front over the bottom-set beds. The fore-set beds, in turn, are covered by the top-set beds as the river extends its course to the edge of the delta front.

Large, lowland rivers carry only fine sediment to the coast. Either no delta develops, or the sediment is dropped over wide areas. Hence the fore-set beds slope much less steeply, while the top-set beds are much attacked by wave action. The differences between the various types of bed are then much less distinct. In general the rule holds

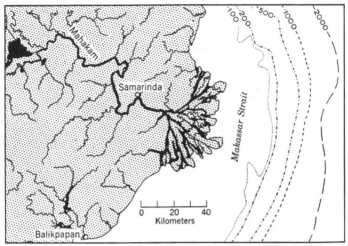

FIG. 140. Map of the Mahakan Delta on the east coast of Borneo with broad estuarine distributaries. Depths in meters.

that, the larger a delta is, the smaller are the surface slopes and the finer the sedimentary particles.

The marine delta environment is characterized by the interplay of marine and terrestrial influences. The inorganic material is almost entirely supplied from land by the river that forms the delta. But it may be submitted to wear, sorting, drifting, etc., by waves and currents before it is finally deposited. The organic sedimentary materials, both vegetable and animal, as also tests and skeletons, are partly supplied by the river, e.g., mammalian bodies, trees, humic colloids, etc. The remainder is derived from plants and animals that lived in the lagoons and open waters of the delta, e.g., molluscans, foraminiferans, echinoderms, seaweeds, etc.

With deltas forming in the sea the deposition is in part purely marine, such as that of the fore-set beds, in part purely terrestrial such as that of the inner portions of the top-set beds. Bars of sandy material may begin to develop beyond the coastline, but they frequently change to islands with dunes and are ultimately incorporated in the land. The lagoons enclosed between such offshore bars and levees are originally of normal salinity. Later, however, the water becomes brackish and finally entirely fresh. In this manner, with the growth of the delta, the irregular boundary between terrestrial and marine sedimentation is gradually pushed out seawards. Matters may be complicated by subsidence that goes on permanently over the entire area of a large delta. During outbuilding the river tends to alter its

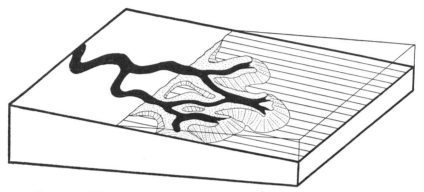

Fig. 141.   Schematic block diagram of the Mississippi type of delta.

course, and as soon as a stretch of the delta front is abandoned, erosion sets in and part of the deposits is reworked and deposited farther out in the fore-set and bottom-set beds.

A typical delta is that of the Nile. The subaerial part, with an area of more than 100,000 km², is formed by a low land covered by small lakes, meandering distributaries, and with lagoons along the coast. Along the beach a relatively steep slope runs down to 5 or 10 m. Outwards follows a submarine plane, several dozens of kilometers broad, reaching to depths of about 200 m. Then a steeper area commences where the fore-set beds appear to be forming, sloping 1½° down to depths of 1000 m. The bottom-set beds are found beyond in depths of 1000 to 2000 m.

The Mississippi Delta is similar in many respects, but the distributaries build out levees far into the sea, causing a peculiar shape that has been aptly termed "birdfoot delta" (Figs. 141 and 142). The main requisite for the development of this type is a gently sloping sea floor in front of the river mouth on which the levees can be built up quickly.

As the physiographical development continues the river carries out to the sea less and finer sediment while the increasing circumference of the delta calls for ever larger amounts of material in order that the delta be prograded the same distance into the sea. The growth proceeds at a diminishing rate until finally the destructive marine agents gain the upper hand. The delta then falls a prey to marine erosion

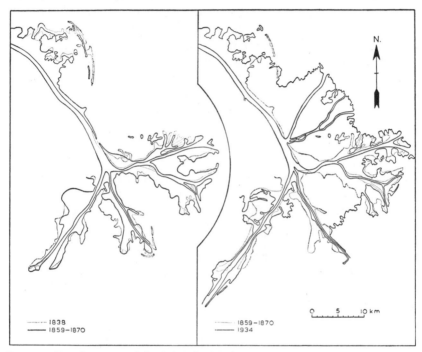

Fig. 142. Development of the Mississippi Delta, according to chart of U. S. Coast and Geodetic Survey.

and is gradually planed off. Only the bottom-sets and the deeper lying fore-sets will ultimately remain.

The modern investigations of the Mississippi Delta (Russell et al., 1936; Russell, 1948), however, have shown that subsidence may intervene and result in the safe conservation of delta deposits in the earth's crust. Probably the increasing weight of the delta causes subsidence of the entire crust, while compaction of the deeply buried strata adds to the sinking movement of the surface. Locally the rate of subsidence of the Mississippi Delta attains no less than 2 to 3 m per century. The amount of sediment added to this delta is estimated at 2×10^6 tons per day. At the mouth of important distributaries the delta front is built up and the coastline is carried gradually seawards to the edge of the shelf because accumulation outweighs subsidence and marine erosion. Owing to increasing length the grade of the river becomes gradually smaller and the bed is aggraded by the deposition of sediment. Finally the river breaks through its own levees and forms a new bed beside the abandoned course or it seeks an entirely new short cut to the coast over the delta. Around the old mouth the supply of sediment is suddenly cut off. Waves and currents build an offshore bar. In the meantime the secular subsidence continues, and the bar is converted into a row of islands. Ultimately these are submerged together with the lagoons and levees behind, and the new coastline is established a great distance back of its original position.

This interplay of growth and loss shifts from one point to another along the periphery of the delta. The ultimate result is an almost stationary condition as to horizontal extension of the delta. But the entire volume of the structure is steadily enlarged, and the strata are becoming gradually more compact. Thus the thickness of the Tertiary column of the Mississippi Delta is estimated at 10,000 m and the Quaternary at 1000 m. This vast accumulation lies in a geosynclinal (?) depression in an east-to-west direction along the Gulf coast of the southern states.

Evidently in a large delta the great weight causes isostatic and compactional subsidence, to which geosynclinal subsidence may be added. The normal sequence of the physiographic delta cycle, consisting of growth followed by erosion, will not be developed. The occurrence of widespread and thick series of delta deposits in the stratigraphical column in which top-set beds are also incorporated thus finds a natural explanation.

The foregoing discussion explains why the deposits of a delta, especially the top-set beds of a large one, are the most variable formations known to geologists. There is an intimate intermingling of marine, fluviatile, lagunal, terrestrial, and limnic environments. The distributaries are continually changing their courses, cutting off new lagoons, scouring out fresh channels now here, now there, filling up old lagoons, and pushing the beach outwards. False bedding is frequent. Birds drop marine shells in terrestrial and lagoonal environments. The river washes terrestrial material out into the marine environment. During spate the river causes freshening of the waters in brackish lagoons and along the coast, and the result is mass destruction of life.

Marine erosion is nibbling at the top-set beds and pushing back the coastline. Bars may be thrown up temporarily, only to be destroyed later. Invasions by sea water into brackish and fresh lagoons and across dry land are the result of subsidence or tsunamic waves. Slumping frequently displaces and distorts the strata because many deposits are laid down at steep angles.

A separate type of delta is represented by *tidal deltas* (Fig. 143). The river is replaced by an opening in an offshore bar or similar nar-

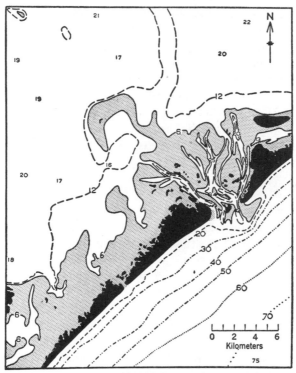

Fig. 143. Double tidal delta of Ocracoke Inlet, on the east coast of the United States. Depths in fathoms.

rows in which strong tidal currents sweep in and out. Some of the sediment is eroded from the walls and floor of the tidal channel, but the greater part is provided by coastal drifting that carries material from the adjoining beach and foreshore into the tidal channel. The lagoon will also supply a certain amount of fine terrestrial and planktonic sediment.

In two important aspects the tidal deltas differ morphologically from the normal type of river delta. The surface cannot emerge above sea level because the tidal currents are the active elements. The entire structure must remain almost purely marine in origin. Furthermore many tidal deltas are double. One part is built in the lagoon at the inner end of the tidal channel by the flood tide; the other part is due to the ebb tide and develops in front of the offshore bar. Generally the second is of smaller extent, because the sea floor lies deeper than the lagoon bottom and more sediment is lost by current and wave action in the open sea. In other places no distinct delta is formed on the inner side because the deposits cover the entire floor of the lagoon. The tidal flats in their entire extent form the equivalent of the inner delta. This is the situation, for instance, in the tidal flats between the Dutch and German coasts and the islands to the north (Figs. 38, 111).

Frequently the channels in these deltas are much deeper than the surrounding sea floor. An example is furnished by the Marsdiep to the north of Holland, which is 47 m deep, while the adjoining North Sea does not attain greater depths than 30 m. Fine examples of double tidal deltas are found along the eastern coast of the United States, e.g., at Ocracoke Inlet (Fig. 143).

THE TIDAL FLAT AND ESTUARINE ENVIRONMENTS

It was pointed out above that tidal deltas and tidal mud flats cannot be sharply distinguished. The latter environment is characterized by the simultaneous deposition of clay and sand in tidal waters that partly emerge during low tide. Mud flats in estuaries strongly resemble these. The tidal flats are typically developed behind the breached offshore bar of the North Sea Islands. A branching system of main channels divides up into smaller creeks (so-called *prielen*) that function alternately as distributaries during flood tide and as tributaries during ebb tide. Along their winding paths the smaller channels bring the water almost to the center (or inner margin) of the emerged flats and carry it away again when the water begins to drop. They are reminiscent of the capillary blood vessels of the skin only that in the circulatory system a separate set of tributaries carries the liquid back to the main reservoir. Instead of an alternating flow in opposite directions there is a constant direction of transport in the circulation of the blood.

Owing to the unconsolidated nature of the deposits, the walls of the channels are easily eroded by the currents and waves. Scour along the outer walls of a curve and concomitant deposition on the convex bank, cutting off of meanders, silting up of abandoned channels, beheading, and all similar processes are constantly taking place. Slumping on the newly formed steep banks also happens frequently. These alterations, by which the channels are continuously wandering over the expanses of mud and sand, result in an uninterrupted reworking of the sediments. The renewed deposition often takes the form of laminae at the maximum angle of rest, where deeper depressions are filled up by material washed in sideways off the flats. Elsewhere the mud is precipitated in horizontal strata from the overlying waters. Roughly speaking, the finer fractions are deposited around high water mark in the center of the flats, because wave turbulence and current velocity are at the minimum there. The sand fraction comes to rest near low water line, while in between a mixture is laid down. But these rules are followed only very roughly.

Subrecent tidal flats may show up vividly on aerial photographs. The typical system of dendritic, winding channels is seen clearly against the adjoining flats, because their ultimate fill is of slightly different composition, generally being coarser in grain. Exceptionally fine examples can be seen from the air by the naked eye in certain seasons in the reclaimed lands of the former Zuider Zee of the Netherlands. Elsewhere they have been detected as sandy ridges meandering across the former mudflats of the low country behind the Dutch coast. The compaction of the clay of the flats (and peat formed during a regression) was so much stronger than of the sandy fill in the tidal creeks that the surface of the flats now lies 1–2 m lower.

Estuaries frequently contain extensive mud flats, similar to those behind offshore bars. The amount of scour in such estuaries depends not only on the range of the tides but also on the size of the basin lying farther inland, because the volume of water running in and out determines the size and depth of the channels. Reclamation of land reduces the inflow and outflow and results in further accumulation at the head of the tidal basin. Loss of land tends to strengthen the tidal currents and to initiate further scour. This is especially true in estuaries that do not end in a river but in a dead end, such as those found in the southwest of Holland.

The French school of marine geologists is actively pursuing the study of the estuarine environment. Some of their interesting results are mentioned (p. 317) in connection with the deposition of mud. (See Bourcart, Francis Boeuf, Glangeaud.)

THE LAGOON ENVIRONMENT

In general the lagoon environment is characterized by exceptionally calm waters, because the enclosing bars keep out larger waves. Hence the bottom is churned up only if the water is shallow. But even then the suspended matter is deposited again as soon as the waves subside, because it cannot be carried elsewhere. Tidal and wind-driven currents may sweep part of the sediment out of a lagoon, but this action is seldom of more than transitory importance. Fine sediments with a high percentage of organic matter abound.

Depending on the communications with the open sea, the water may be either fresh, brackish, salt, or alternately fresher and more saline. It goes without saying that the climate and the conditions prevailing on the adjoining land and in the adjacent sea play a major part in determining the nature of lagoon deposits. A coral-reef lagoon, for instance, will contain entirely different deposits from a delta lagoon in an arctic or mild climate. In many lagoons algae flourish and finally become mixed with other sedimentary matter.

The final stage of marine sedimentation ends when the lagoon floor emerges and terrestrial deposition sets in. Compaction or a relative rise of sea level or tsunamic waves may cause marine invasions, and a repetition of terrestrial and marine conditions is sometimes met with.

THE LITTORAL ENVIRONMENT

At present the littoral environment covers the modest area of roughly 150,000 km². The dominant factor is the surf, which is responsible for a number of typical features. Coarse, strongly rounded material, thick-walled shells, and organisms occupying boreholes are the rule on rocky shores, that is to say on most coasts undergoing active marine erosion. But in embayments, behind offshore bars and barrier reefs and all other protected areas, and furthermore where the country rock is composed of poorly consolidated or unconsolidated sediments, sandy beaches or even silty flats will prevail. But here also stout shells are usual.

The agitated waters of most beaches and the sudden alternation of unconsolidated deposits and hard rock in the land back of the beach undergoing erosion together result in abrupt changes in grain size of the beach materials. Coarse piles of boulders may directly adjoin fine gravel or sand, and angular screes may come to rest on well-rounded cobbles or sand. Seaweed or driftwood often lie in a narrow strip beside or between deposits containing no organic matter. Lamellibranchia are generally represented by loose shells, and double specimens are very rare. The selective action of the surf is expressed in many beach deposits. Heaps of shells and monomineralic concentrations (beach ore, etc.) are obvious examples.

But the littoral environment presents some further properties that are highly characteristic. The tides or variations in water level due to atmospheric influences cause alternate submergence and emergence of the beach. This may result in drying out, that may lead to sun-cracks and the formation of rock salt crystals. Rain pits, fulgurites, wind ripple marks, footprints, and many other indefinable tracks of crustaceans, worms, etc., may give valuable evidence of temporary emergence of the littoral environment. Currents of water running over a sand bank in a thin sheet call forth a typical current pattern, strongly recalling the markings on a lepidodendron trunk on a large scale. This pattern is restricted almost entirely to the littoral zone.

Cailleux (1938) found that on a sandy beach scattered pebbles and cobbles are orientated roughly with the larger axis parallel to the wave fronts. When coarse material has accumulated to the exclusion of the sand fraction this rule is not so clearly followed but it still holds in general. Where a pebble beach consists of flat stones these are frequently found overlapping and sloping down towards the water. Cobble beaches attain surprisingly steep slopes, local values of over 45° having been observed.

Rounding and sorting of particles on the beach and beach drifting were described in the foregoing chapter; coral reefs will be dealt with separately in Chapter 6.

From the above summary it follows that of the deposits of all marine environments those of the littoral zone can show the most characteristic features.

The grain size may show extreme and abrupt variations; the fossils may be highly characteristic; bedding planes can show all manner of distinctive markings; and irregular lamination with cross bedding can occur. Concussion marks on boulders, worn shells, interbedding with land or brack-water deposits may give further valuable indications.

The littoral facies should therefore be recognizable with greater certainty in a stratigraphic series than most others. Still, very often doubt remains, especially in the case of fine-grained deposits, or when the strand line shifted to and fro during alternating transgressions and regressions, for then one has to decide whether one is dealing with littoral, shallow neritic, or delta deposits for each individual stratum. Conclusive evidence need not be available for each separate bed.

Very few of the distinctive characteristics, however, are restricted to littoral deposits. Several may occur in shallow neritic sediments, and others are frequent in terrestrial formations. This is especially true of features due to temporary drying out, because over most of the littoral zone flooding is repeated at too short intervals to permit mud cracks, etc. Only where seasonal variations in sea level occur in combination with a very low coastal plain may flooding occur at long intervals, leading to thorough drying in between.

It is also obvious that an advancing sea will generally rework its own littoral deposits before final deposition can occur. The littoral deposits left by a retreating sea are likely to be destroyed before becoming covered by later sediment. The chance of shore formations being preserved is therefore only slight.

Bourcart showed that some fossil beach conglomerates and also boulder tracts dredged in deeper water off the Atlantic coast of Europe are reworked river deposits. This follows from the varied composition. Instead of consisting of reworked fragments of the underlying rock formations, they contain a great variety of rock types, among which vein quartz may predominate. Bourcart believes that the boulders were carried to the coast and scattered along the beach by coastal drifting. The same explanation might be offered for the non-local composition of many recent cobble beaches. In glaciated regions the reworking of a cover of boulder clay to form a cobble beach is a common feature. Bourcart also pointed out that many basal conglomerates resting on a surface of marine abrasion show the same polymict composition derived from the waste products of extensive inland areas.

On the other hand many pebble and cobble beaches are composed entirely of local material, identical with the rock exposed in the adjoining cliff sections. It would evidently be wrong to suppose that beach material is always dominantly composed of reworked de-nudation products from the land.

The littoral environment presents special characteristics where man-grove vegetation occurs. The force of the waves is entirely broken, and all properties due to their activity are lacking. The closely spaced roots tend to entrap lutite, and in this manner fine deposits are formed on open coasts. In a fossil state, when the roots have rotted away, such a deposit would hardly suggest a littoral facies.

Flat, low-lying areas of great extent may be occasionally or repeat-edly invaded by the sea. It is merely a matter of definition whether they are to be incorporated in the beach or not, but this possibility should at any rate be borne in mind when interpreting fossil deposits showing evidence of temporary marine invasions.

An area illustrating this point is the Rann of Cutch to the south-east of the Indus Delta. According to Lyell (1868), a former land area of 5000 km² was inundated by the sea and converted into a lagoon after the earthquake of 1819, while a low ridge was formed in the neighborhood. But the remainder of the Rann, 17,000 km², is frequently invaded by the sea when the monsoon winds raise the water in the Gulf of Cutch and the creeks at Luckput. On evaporation of the sea water a crust of salt is left. The Rann is also likely to be flooded occasionally in some parts by river water of the Indus.

Another cause of temporary flooding by the sea is found in tsunamis, which may spread over vast areas, carrying marine shells far inland. Large deltas are especially liable to this kind of marine deluge, as Grabau (1940) has pointed out. He coined the term "marining" for very short-lived spreading of marine waters over a surface of primarily floodplain or delta deposits, and he called the resulting sediments "huangho" deposits after the Huang Ho of China, the best-known modern example.

THE EUXINIC ENVIRONMENT

Poorly ventilated basins are characterized by deficiency in oxygen and in extreme cases by the presence of hydrogen sulfide in the water. In Chapter 1 the oceanographical aspects were discussed. The green or black muds, rich in decomposable organic matter, that form on the bottom are of special interest to geologists as constituting potential source beds of petroleum. This facies is termed "euxinic." It is also of importance to paleontologists on account of the absence of scavengers, resulting in the fossilization of vertebrates, etc., in undisturbed, frequently highly complete condition in the euxinic sapropel. At present euxinic conditions have developed in basins of varying depths, such as Norwegian fiords and the Black Sea.

The sediments of the Black Sea have been described by Archanguelsky. They vary from calcareous mud with 62% lime in the deeper portions to gray clay with 16% lime closer in shore, where a stronger dilution of the planktonic matter by terrigenous particles takes place. There also occurs a black sapropelitic mud with 11% lime and 30% organic matter. Much of the lime is found in the form of drewite, a biochemical precipitate of calcium carbonate; pyrite is also plentiful. Occasionally thin laminae of sand, attaining a thickness of 2 cm, are encountered. The sediments show a very fine lamination due to the annual cycle in planktonic growth. Macrostratification is also found, caused by shifting of the margins between the various types of sediment. The change is frequently accompanied by a thin lamina of sand. These phenomena are ascribed to variations in the supply of clastic matter by rivers, but the present writer believes that turbidity currents of high density could also be invoked. In many samples contortions due to submarine slumping were encountered, even on slopes of only a few degrees.

CLASSIFICATION AND DISTRIBUTION OF MARINE SEDIMENTS

The classification and characteristics of marine deposits can be reviewed without the need of repeating all that has already been brought out in discussing the principal marine environments. The deposits themselves can be grouped according to several principles. For instance, a purely lithological classification is often used. But it is also customary to adopt a classification for fossil sediments based on the grouping in environments treated above. For recent sediments the distance to the coast should be somewhat more emphasized, as has already been pointed out. The following classification of recent marine sediments can be given.

Mixed marine and terrestrial sediments.
    Littoral sediments.
    Delta sediments.
    Lagoon sediments.
    Estuarine sediments.
Marine sediments.
    Shelf sediments.
    Deep-sea sediments.
        Hemipelagic and terrigenous sediments:
            Blue, red, yellow, green, coral, calcareous, and volcanic muds.
        (Eu)Pelagic sediments:
            Calcareous oozes: globigerina, pteropod, coccolith oozes.
            Siliceous oozes: radiolarian, diatom oozes.
            Red clay.

A slightly different classification, that will not be followed here, is also satisfactory (for details see Revelle, 1944).

Terrigenous deposits.
    Organic muds.
    Inorganic muds.
Pelagic deposits.
    Inorganic deposits (red clay).
    Organic deposits or oozes.
        Calcium carbonate oozes.
            Globigerina, pteropod, coccolith.
        Siliceous oozes.
            Radiolarian, diatom.

MIXED MARINE AND TERRESTRIAL SEDIMENTS

These sediments have already been reviewed sufficiently in the discussions of the various environments in which they are formed.

MARINE SEDIMENTS

Shelf Sediments. For these sediments also the reader is referred to the above treatment of the neritic environment.

Large tracts of the shelf are covered by sediments identical or strongly related to the terrigenous sediments of the bathyal and abyssal zone described below (e.g., Bourcart, 1947). These deposits will not be dealt with separately here.

However, one feature of recent marine sediments from the neritic zone needs special attention. Although deposits rich in lime are common among the fossil representatives, they are much less frequent on the present sea floor, especially in the temperate and cold regions. But even in tropical waters lime is rare, except in the neighborhood of coral reefs where calcareous sand and mud are generally forming on the sea floor.

One of the few recent calcareous deposits forming in higher latitudes is the so-called *tangue* of the bay of Mont Saint Michel on the western coast of France. Bourcart has shown that the lime may reach 75% and is derived from a great variety of organisms that belong in depths of 10 to 30 m. A subrecent deposit of these calcareous elements on the foreshore is undergoing erosion, and the resulting fine products are carried to the shallow regions of the bay and deposited there in the form of a fine gray mud.

Another, different type of recent calcareous deposit of limited extent is found in the Irish Sea. It consists of calcareous algae, echinoderms, and molluscs (Herdman, 1895).

Two explanations for this contrast between recent and fossil neritic sediments may be offered. It is possible that the spread of warm climates to high latitudes in the geological past favored the formation of calcareous deposits. But even then the scarcity of equivalents from the Indonesian seas remains unexplained.

A different cause may be found in the loss of lime by deposition in the deep sea since the Cretaceous, resulting in a lower concentration in the surface waters of the oceans. This hypothetical view will be treated later (p. 392).

Hemipelagic or Terrigenous Sediments. For many types of sediment belonging in this class the term hemipelagic is most appropriate, because they contain mainly pelagic and but little terrigenous matter. Some, however, are almost free of planktonic remains, and for these the term terrigenous is more suitable. Submicroscopic particles, although deriving largely from the land, are here classed as pelagic matter because they are carried to midocean.

It was pointed out above that the hemipelagic deposits are roughly equivalent to bathyal sediment. But, whereas the sediments accumulating at depths of several thousands of meters in the Indonesian and West Indian deep-sea depressions, even the typical blue muds and volcanic muds, should actually be incorporated in the abyssal deposits, there is no objection against classifying them as hemipelagic sediments, because the adjacent islands play a predominant part in their formation. For the depth at which accumulation of these sediments is taking place proves to be of minor importance, and does not appear to influence the nature of the deposits fundamentally. It is only bottom-living microorganisms that may differ according to the depth.

Blue mud is the most common representative of the terrigenous deposits. It consists of fine terrigenous material with an admixture of pelagic products, such as planktonic Foraminifera. In general it accumulates at moderate distances from land, where coarse fractions are lacking owing to the absence of strong currents, and where the production of lime is not dominant. The highest percentage of lime allowed is 35 parts of calcium carbonate in 100; otherwise the term calcareous mud is used. The color is lead-gray to dark blue-gray in moist condition, changing to light yellowish gray or bluish gray on drying. This tint is due to the low degree of oxidation of the contained iron compounds (hydrotroilite, ferrous sulfide) and finely divided organic matter. The upper layer of 0.5 to a few centimeters thick is dark reddish brown, owing to the oxidized state. In the interior of the deposits reduction takes place to ferrous sulfide, which ultimately forms marcasite or pyrite. It is found that in general the color becomes darker with increasing content of organic matter, while lime tends to cause lighter shades.

The predominance of terrigenous matter is not due to lack of planktonic tests, for these are plentiful at moderate distances from the coast. The abundant supply of material from the land is evidently responsible for a dilution of planktonic products. This contention is borne out by the observed high rate of sedimentation as compared to that of the organic oozes forming at greater distance from the coast. Illustrations of the point in question are to be found

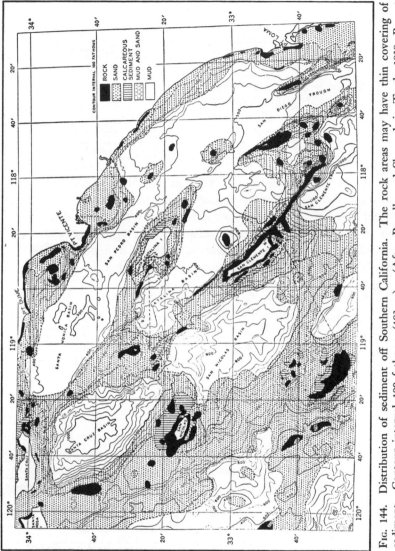

Fig. 144. Distribution of sediment off Southern California. The rock areas may have thin covering of sediment. Contour interval 100 fathoms (183 m). (After Revelle and Shepard, in Trask, 1939, *Recent Marine Sediments*, Fig. 1, p. 247, American Association of Petroleum Geologists.)

in the series of bottom samples collected by the *Meteor* expedition (see Fig. 161, p. 377).

Some general aspects of the production and loss of lime are dealt with on a later page in connection with the calcareous oozes (p. 352).

Examination of the *Snellius* samples from the Moluccan area led Miss Neeb (1943) to a classification under five headings, according to the nature of the source rocks for the terrigenous components: (1) crystalline schists, (2) acid igneous rocks, (3) basic metamorphic rocks, (4) quartziferous sediments, and (5) basic ancient volcanic rocks, subdivided into alkali and calc-alkali rocks. The distribution on the sea floor was found to be in accordance with what is known of the geological structure of the surrounding islands. The expectation was confirmed that, whereas the coarser fractions are carried only a short distance along the bottom, the finer fractions of sand are transported in suspension and attain greater distances even across deep depressions. An example is found in the series of stations 119–124 taken at right angles to the southeastern coast of Timor and ending on the Sahul Shelf across the Timor Trough, a depression 2600 m deep. Table 19 and Fig. 145 together illustrate the data obtained.

TABLE 19. GRAIN SIZE OF SAMPLES IN SECTION ACROSS TIMOR TROUGH

	Station No.					
	119	120	121	122	123	124
% minerals > 20 μ	9.8	5.1	3.7	1.0	0.5	0.4
% lutite < 2 μ	30.0	33.9	37.6	39.2	27.1	21.5
% $CaCO_3$	17.0	27.1	27.5	46.1	54.0	76.6
Coastal distance, km	10	60	90	120	150	160
Depth, m	600	2050	2300	1150	450	400

Recognizable chips of rock are found only in sample 119, namely, andesite and chlorite schist. The graph shows that the percentage of determinable mineral grains (planktonic matter not included) shows no relation to the bottom profile but decreases regularly with increasing distance from the coast. This strongly indicates transportation in suspension and not by rolling or sliding, or a sudden decrease in grain size beyond the deepest point of the section would occur. The lutite fraction shows an increase in amount which continues beyond the deep until shallow water is reached. Whether falling off in lutite is due to dilution by lime or to agitation of the bottom waters remains an open question that could be answered only if the rate of accumulation were known. The lime content, due chiefly to planktonic

Foraminifera, shows a gradual increase with coastal distance. This is probably the result of decreasing dilution by terrigenous matter, for an increase in supply is not probable.

Coral Mud and Sand. Where coral reefs fringe the coast, erosion cannot supply terrigenous material, and sediment provided by rivers must also be of minor importance, because otherwise the corals could not thrive. The amount of terrigenous matter must be even smaller along a barrier reef or an atoll. On the other hand, coral reefs produce a large quantity of calcareous matter deriving from the corals

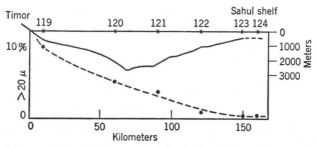

Fig. 145. Stations of the *Snellius* expedition south of Timor to Sahul Shelf, showing gradual decrease of mineral grains larger than 0.02 mm away from the coast, independent of the slope of the bottom. (Data from Neeb, 1943.)

themselves and from associated benthonic and planktonic life. Calcareous particles are formed from corals by the surf, by fishes and other organisms feeding on them, and by benthonic animals such as holothurians that feed on the mud, the particles being triturated in their intestines. Together with bits of lime-secreting algae and the shells and broken tests of molluscs, Foraminifera, echinoderms, etc., the coral detritus is scattered in the neighborhood of the reefs. It accumulates to form an almost pure lime sand or mud. In this manner the blue mud is replaced by *coral mud,* so called even when the percentage of particles that can be directly referred to corals is unimportant. Between the area covered by coral mud and the margin of the reefs there is generally a zone of coarser calcareous sand, called *coral sand,* a shelf sediment; with distance from the reefs the percentage of reef detritus gradually decreases, making place for planktonic or terrigenous matter. In this way coral mud may grade either into blue mud or globigerina ooze, volcanic mud, etc.

Calcareous Mud. In some hemipelagic environments, as the Mediterranean, the Red Sea, and the Caribbean Sea, a type of deposit accumulates that resembles both blue mud and coral mud, and that is generally termed *calcareous mud*. But it differs from the blue mud by containing a high percentage of lime, and from the coral mud by lack of coral detritus. Neither should it be grouped with the pelagic calcareous oozes, such as globigerina ooze, because the terrigenous material is relatively coarse grained and the lime need not be of planktonic origin. The majority of the deposits from the Moluccan area described by Böggild as globigerina ooze might have been classified as calcareous mud, especially as much of the lime is of terrestrial and benthonic origin.

Miss Neeb made a distinction, in the Moluccan muds with more than 30% lime, between globigerina ooze in which pelagic Foraminifera form more than half the calcareous matter and terrigenous mud in which particles predominate that are supposed to have come from the disintegration of limestones on the islands. Revelle (1944) suggested the term globigerina mud for this type of sediment. All transitions between the two types of sediment, calcareous mud and globigerina ooze, occur, and if the percentage of Foraminifera is large the characteristic difference is in the size of the mineral grains. Some of the Moluccan oozes are almost pure globigerina accumulations, for instance the sediment in the Sulu Sea.

In some lagoons of larger atols a calciferous ooze is encountered, rich in globigerinas and pteropods and containing fine needles of calcium carbonate that appear to have been formed by chemical precipitation. Although these lagoonal muds resemble pelagic calcareous deposits, the presence of shallow-water organisms is distinctive.

Volcanic Mud. Volcanic activity, especially explosive eruptions, may produce such large quantities of dust that the ash not only forms an important addition to blue mud accumulating in the neighborhood of a volcano but may even predominate over normal terrigenous material. The resultant sediment is called *volcanic mud*. The color is generally dark; the grain somewhat coarser than that of most blue muds. Good examples have been described by Miss Neeb (1943) from the *Snellius* samples, taken around volcanic islands in Indonesia. She was able to map the boundary where the percentage of ash sinks below 50 and the volcanic mud merges into the blue mud or globigerina ooze. Also she could indicate the boundary where the ash content falls below 3%, marking the outer limit of terrigenous-volcanic mud. Other lines show where the admixture of ash in other types of sediment falls below the value of 3% or becomes zero (Fig. 146).

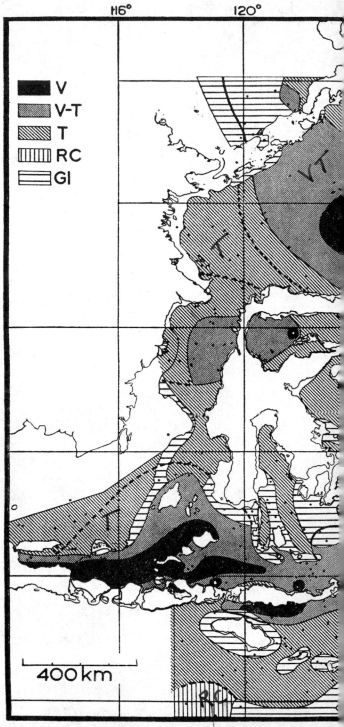

FIG. 146. Deep-sea deposits of the Moluccas. *V*, volcanic mud;
Gl, calcareous mud, mostly globigerina ooze. Full-drawn line
of volcanic ash. Shelf sediments white. Soundings

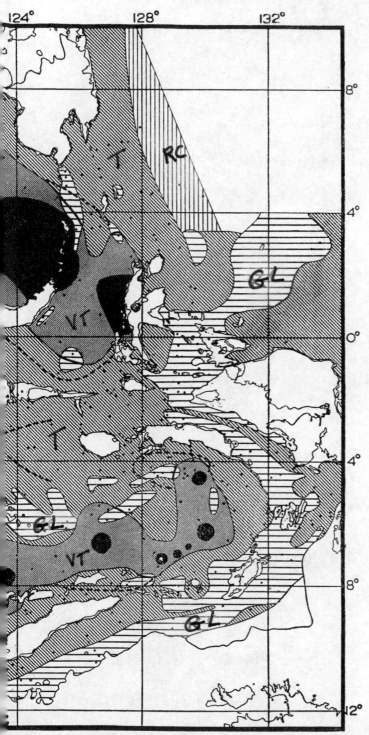

T, volcanic-terrigenous mud; T, terrigenous mud; RC, red clay;
mit of 3% volcanic ash in globigerina ooze. Dashed line = limit
ted by dot. (Simplified from Neeb, 1943, Plate I.)

The ash of several volcanoes in this area could be recognized by some distinctive features. The Batu Tara ash northeast of Flores shows clear crystals of leucite. The Una Una ash (Gulf of Tomini, Celebes) from the 1898 eruption is characterized by small biotite crystals and a low glass content. It has been recognized in the muds of Makassar Strait at the other side of the northern arm of Celebes

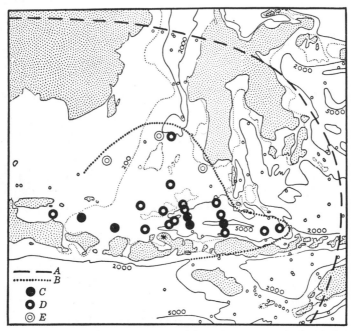

Fig. 147. Distribution of Tambora ash of 1815 in bottom samples. *A*, limit of ash fall; *B*, limit in samples; *C*, 60–80% ash; *D*, 3–30% ash; *E*, less than 3% ash. (Redrawn from Neeb, 1943, Plate II.)

(Fig. 105, p. 213). In this locality it must have been introduced directly from an ash cloud, because transportation by currents is excluded.

The ash thrown out by the Tambora on Sumbawa during the well-known eruption of 1815 is recognizable by a high percentage of glass and brown biotite. The distribution over a wide area is strongly influenced by aeolian transport, for it is absent to the south of the Lesser Sunda Islands (Fig. 147). But transport by currents could also be proved in an easterly direction (see also p. 372).

X-ray analysis of the lutite fraction contained in the *Snellius* samples of terrigenous and other muds brought to light some interesting facts.

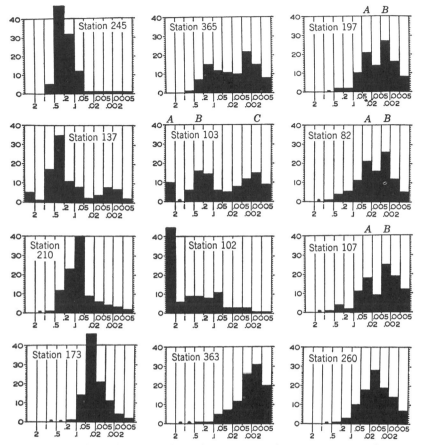

Fɪɢ. 148. Mechanical composition of a number of bottom samples from the Moluccas (see Neeb, 1943). The fractions are expressed in millimeters. Good sorting at stations 245, 137, 210, 173, 102, and 363. Poor sorting at stations 365 and especially 103. Very regular distribution at 260.

St. 245. Pure volcanic mud with marked maximum of ash. Near the volcano Gn. Api, Wetar, 4450 m. (Cf. st. 173.)

St. 137. Globigerina ooze, strong maximum of unbroken shells, coarse and fine terrigenous fractions. Sill between Rotti and Sawu, 450 m.

St. 210. Terrigenous mud, well sorted, fairly coarse. Southwest of Buru, 4900 m.

St. 173. Volcanic mud, pure with maximum of Tambora ash, much finer than st. 245. North of Lombok, 1500 m.

St. 365. Terrigenous-volcanic mud. Poorly sorted mixture of lutite and ash. Weber Trough, east of Serua, 6300 m.

St. 103. Globigerina ooze, poorly sorted. *B*, globigerinas; *A*, coarse and *C*,

(Continued on facing page.)

$$\mu = \frac{1}{1000} \, mm = 10^{-6} \, m.$$

It showed that the fine fraction contains hardly any volcanic material. Evidently volcanic explosions do not produce shards of submicroscopic dimensions smaller than about 5 μ in appreciable quantity. The lutite fraction consists of terrigenous and calcareous matter. From this result it follows that grain-size analysis may be useful in determining the source of the material, for it is known that all particles smaller than 5 μ are of non-volcanic origin. For instance, microscopic examination of a very fine-grained terrigenous mud in which a small amount of slightly coarser volcanic ash is contained will show only volcanic matter. All the lutite is washed away before making the slide for optical examination, and one might be led to describe the sample as a volcanic mud, although, actually, the non-volcanic material greatly predominates (Fig. 148).

This conclusion enabled Miss Neeb to ascertain the boundaries of 50, 3, and 0% volcanic admixture referred to above and to give a trustworthy account of the influence each separate volcano exerts on the sediments in its surroundings.

Glacial Marine Sediments. A separate type of blue mud is developed mainly around the Antarctic continent. The place of clay minerals is taken by rock flour (silt fraction) produced by the land ice. The shells of the unexpectedly rich benthonic life are dissolved, so that the lime percentage is almost nil. Surprisingly, diatom frustules are also scarce although these organisms are plentiful in the surface waters of the region. Probably they are carried away before reaching the bottom by surface currents due to the melting of ice. The resulting deposit is termed *glacial marine sediment*. It is rich in stones dropped by icebergs. Glacial marine sediments of similar composition grading into normal blue muds or deep-sea oozes are also

---

fine terrigenous fractions. Close to the shore of Groot Kei, 600 m. (Cf. the well-sorted st. 102 and 363.)

St. 102. Terrigenous mud, very coarse, little lutite. Close inshore to Groot Kei, 350 m. (Cf. st. 103.)

St. 363. Terrigenous mud, very fine. East slope Weber Trough, 950 m. Far from the coast but not deep.

St. 197. Terrigenous-volcanic mud. *A*, fine Tambora ash; *B*, lutite. North of Flores, 5100 m. (Cf. the almost identical diagrams, st. 82 and 107.)

St. 82. Hemipelagic globigerina ooze (36% $CaCO_3$); globigerina ooze according to Neeb. *A*, pelagic Foraminifera; *B*, terrigenous lutite. Northeast of Obi, 1000 m. (Cf. st. 197.)

St. 107. Globigerina ooze. *A*, broken shells; *B*, terrigenous lutite. East of Tenimber Islands, 400 m.

St. 260. Terrigenous mud; rather fine grain. Mindanao Trough, 7950 m.

found in the north polar arctic seas. During the Pleistocene this type of deposit covered considerable areas that are now receiving no glacial matter or only inconsiderable amounts.

Glacial marine sediments deposited close to the termination of a glacier tend to consist almost entirely of glacial materials. An example of recently elevated glacial marine sediments has been described from Alaska by Russell (1893). They consist of stratified morainic matter, with sandy clay containing large quantities of glaciated boulders distributed irregularly throughout the 1500 m of sediment. In finer portions seashells are numerous and boulders with attached cases of annelids also occur. These stones must have remained exposed on the bottom of the sea for some time before being wholly buried.

The typical muds forming in poorly ventilated basins, such as the Black Sea, were mentioned earlier. The main characteristics are the high organic content, the presence of hydrogen sulfide, and the richness in ferrous sulfide. The color is gray, owing to a considerable admixture of calcium carbonate.

Yellow mud and red mud are merely special types of blue mud that owe their exceptional color to the climatic conditions of the adjoining land. For example, the Yellow River carries enormous quantities of fine yellow sediment from the deserts and regions of loess in China out into the China Sea. The resulting yellow mud on the sea floor hardly differs from normal blue mud except in its brilliant color and the nature of the iron compounds. In environments receiving sediment from lands covered by lateritic soil the deposits also tend to show a reddish brown hue or even bright red colors. Neither of the types of terrigenous muds mentioned has a wide distribution on the sea floor.

TABLE 20. AREAS COVERED BY HEMIPELAGIC SEDIMENTS

Type of deposit	Area, millions of square km	Percentage of sea floor
Blue mud	56	15
Volcanic mud	2	0.5
Red + yellow mud	0.5	0.2
Green mud	4	1
Coral mud	10	3
Total	73	20

Green mud is similar to blue mud except that it is green. The color is occasionally due to chlorophyll or green terrigenous minerals but usually to the presence of glauconite, in which event the term glauco-

nite mud is more appropriate. According to Revelle, glauconite muds are generally found off coasts lacking important rivers. Glauconite is often associated with phosphorite nodules in areas of slow deposition or none.

Pelagic Sediments. The pelagic (or eupelagic) sediments are characterized by the absence of terrestrial mineral grains larger than the colloidal fraction. The most common constituents are clay minerals and remains of planktonic unicellular organisms.

The term "pelagic sediments" corresponds very nearly to "abyssal sediments," because on the floor of the deep sea beyond the bathyal zone the direct influence of the continents in the form of microscopic mineral grains is seldom evident. But where strong currents or winds carry continental waste far out to sea, or wherever large rivers spread their turbid waters to dozens of kilometers from the coast, the terrigenous admixture is found far beyond the 1000-m-depth curve. The same holds for inland seas or along steep continental slopes. It has already been pointed out that, in the abyssal depths of the Moluccan deep-sea depressions, no true pelagic deposits are accumulating, not even below the 5000-m line. Conversely, pure pelagic sediments are found on banks of less than 1000-m depth in midocean. These exceptions clearly demonstrate the necessity of distinguishing sharply between pelagic and abyssal deposits.

The finest terrigenous matter, the colloidal lutite particles, do not flocculate when diluted sufficiently. This explains why a minute quantity is found even in the purest waters of midocean. Sea water in midocean of average depth contains 75 mg of clay in each column of 1 cm² cross section. On deposition this would form a layer 0.3 mm thick. Owing to their relatively large surface the flakes are carried in suspension almost indefinitely by ocean currents and the circulation of the deep sea. Not until a particle happens to be carried by a slow bottom current along the deep-sea floor does it find opportunity of settling somewhere. Meanwhile in the course of hundreds of years it may have been carried through all the oceans before it dropped to the bottom. Hence, the finest fractions of pelagic deposits bear a universal character and should be practically identical everywhere, provided that conditions of deposition are otherwise equal.

Naturally this does not exclude a certain amount of sorting according to different environments. Thus Revelle found an appreciable difference between the lutite fraction of red clays on the one hand and globigerina ooze on the other. But the evidence he obtained favored the view that the particles are supplied by the continents and not by weathering of volcanic matter on the sea floor. Correns was even able to show that in the equatorial Atlantic the mineralogical nature of the lutite shows regional variations which do not conform

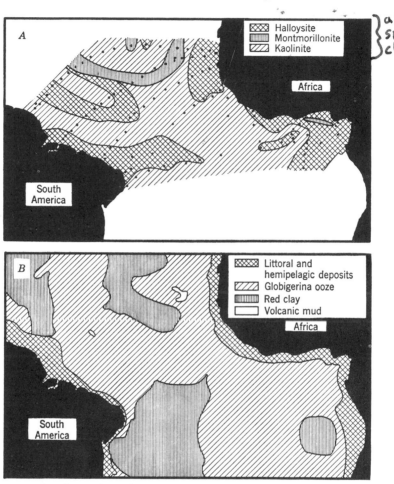

) all simile
} species;
) clay min·

Fig. 149.   *A.* Distribution of clay minerals in recent deep-sea samples of the equatorial Atlantic. (Redrawn from Correns and Schott, 1937, Fig. 105, p. 284.) *B.* Distribution of recent deep-sea deposits in the equatorial Atlantic; cf. Fig. 150. (Redrawn from Schott, 1942, Plate VI.)

to the distribution of the red clays, globigerina oozes, and the blue muds of that region (Fig. 149). He attempted to explain this by differences in neighboring sources. This would imply, however, that in many cases the clay particles were not carried more than a few hundred kilometers by oceanic currents, and that the rate of accumulation should vary with the abundance of local sources. These deductions cannot be granted, and the present author is inclined to assume tentatively a selective deposition from a more or less uniform supply in the bottom waters, or local diagenetic alterations of clay minerals on the sea floor (see p. 237). Moreover, Correns himself showed that grains of 0.1-mm. diameter are carried by surface currents at least 2000 km away from the southern coast of the Gulf of Guinea (Fig. 150). The lutite, then, should be spread out far and wide and mixed with the clay fraction of other sources long before reaching the ocean bed.

On the sea floor this fine material is diluted by truly pelagic matter of organic origin and further by volcanic ash, terrestrial and cosmic dust, etc. Depending on which of these materials predominates, different types of pelagic deposit are formed. Like the hemipelagic muds, the pelagic oozes are again classified according to the coarser fractions, because only these can be conveniently studied under the microscope.

It is not generally realized that the often-reproduced illustrations of deep-sea deposits given by Murray and Philippi are of washed samples from which the colloidal fractions have been removed. Less clear, but more truly representative, are the photomicrographs of the actual samples given by Correns (1939). (Compare with the photomicrographs of hemipelagic samples given by Neeb, 1943.)

Calcareous Oozes. The pelagic sedimentary particles consist for the greater part of tests of plankton organisms. Among these the principal representatives in warmer waters are Foraminifera, coccoliths, and rhabdoliths (minute calcareous disks forming the protective structure of Coccolithophoridae, a kind of calcareous algae) and siliceous tests of radiolarians. In colder climates the siliceous frustules of diatoms are paramount. In those deep-sea regions where the tests of globigerinas, the most important planktonic Foraminifera, do not dissolve either during settling or on the bottom, a calcareous ooze is formed, called *globigerina ooze.* Obviously globigerina ooze may grade laterally into blue mud or other types of mud near the coast. Generally 30% of foraminiferal tests is taken as the lower limit for globigerina ooze. Schott proposed counting the number of individuals larger than 0.1 mm and taking 6000 per cubic centimeter as the lower limit justifying the term globigerina ooze. Although there is something to be said for this method, it is time consuming and requires careful treatment so as not to crush the tests. It would also be inconvenient to

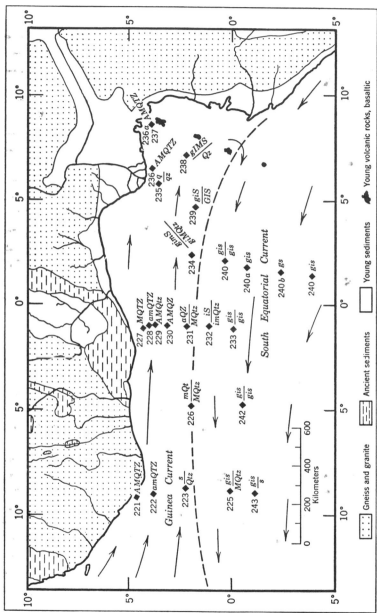

FIG. 150. Relation between surface currents and distribution of mineral grains in the Gulf of Guinea. Guide minerals: *A*, chipped augite; *I*, idiomorphic augite; *T*, tourmaline; *Z*, zircon; *M*, microcline; *S*, rounded quartz; *G*, volcanic glass. Capital letters denote grains larger than 0.11 mm. Below the dashes the Pleistocene composition is shown. (According to Correns, simplified, 1947.)

change the original definition after half a century of use. A minor alteration was made by Miss Neeb in describing the *Snellius* samples, namely of taking 30% *lime* instead of *Foraminifera* as a limit, but with the condition that more than half the calcareous matter is composed of planktonic Foraminifera (see p. 342). This is far simpler than counting the tests and more accurate than estimating the percentage

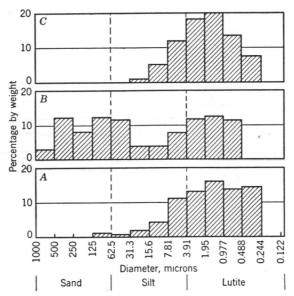

Fig. 151. Three mechanical analyses of deep-sea deposits according to Revelle (1944). *A*, blue mud, depth 4480 m, $CaCO_3$ 0.25%; *B*, globigerina ooze, depth 2851 m, $CaCO_3$ 86%; *C*, red clay, depth 4756 m, $CaCO_3$ 1.0%.

of Foraminifera. But a drawback is that muds are included in the globigerina ooze which belong to the hemipelagic muds on account of an appreciable admixture of terrigenous particles coarser than the lutite fraction. As pointed out earlier (p. 342), Revelle suggested the term globigerina mud for this type of deposit.

According to Arn. Heim, there is a general tendency to overestimate the percentage of tests. He contends that more than 90% of recent and fossil calcareous sediments consist of a fine calcium carbonate silt which has been formed by chemical precipitation. Although this estimate is probably much exaggerated there certainly is frequently a large measure of uncertainty as to the amount of lime represented by tests still recognizable and by lime in submicroscopic particles.

This uncertainty demonstrates that estimating the number of tests cannot form a sound basis for determinations (see also p. 220).

The average amount of lime in globigerina ooze varies from 30% to well over 90%, the general average being 65%. The higher values tend to occur in depths of 1000 m or less, the lower values at 4000 to 5000 m. Globigerina ooze is seldom found at greater depths. The color is light, from milky white in dried condition to gray or yellow when moist. When the composition approaches that of some other type of sediment the color also tends to change to the color of that deposit. Usually this means that it becomes darker, generally gray, green, blue, or red.

In tropical globigerina oozes several species of planktonic forms are commonly encountered (maximum about 20). In colder waters the number decreases, and finally only one or two kinds with small tests are found. In the Atlantic Ocean the percentage of lime in the deposits is higher at the equator than around the tropics. A slight increase occurs at 40° northern and southern latitude.

Besides planktonic Foraminifera benthonic types are represented, and coccoliths, pteropods, heteropods, etc., also play an important part, especially in warmer regions.

Although the shells of the pteropods and heteropods hardly ever predominate and seldom attain 30% in weight of the sediment, they are conspicuous on account of their large size. Samples with a fair amount of these shells are termed *pteropod ooze*. The content of lime is found to vary between about 50 and 90% with an average of 80%. The higher percentages are most frequent in about 2000-m depth, and this type of ooze appears to be limited to depths between roughly 1500 and 3000 m.

Coccolith ooze with a high percentage of coccoliths and rhabdoliths is very rare.

Lime Percentage of Pelagic Deposits. The percentage of lime contained in a pelagic sediment is of such great importance that a brief survey of the factors involved will be given here, although most of them are mentioned also in other connections (Fig. 152). The lime percentage depends on a number of factors. In the first place it is influenced by the rate at which lime is supplied, especially from the surface waters. This follows among others from the correlation established by Trask between the properties of the surface waters and the lime percentage of the deposits on the bottom. The percentage in the deposits increases with the salinity and with the temperature of surface waters. Both correlations result in higher lime content of

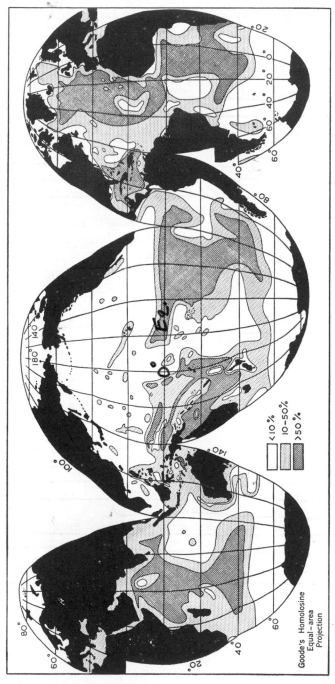

FIG. 152. Percentage of calcium carbonate in marine sediments. (Slightly modified from Sverdrup et al, 1942, *The Oceans*, Fig. 258, p. 1003, Prentice-Hall.)

pelagic sediments in tropical regions than in polar areas. Production is also at a peak where upwelling water brings a rich supply of nutrients into the photosynthetic zone. Although production is mainly due to planktonic organisms, there might theoretically be additional supply by precipitation from oversaturated surface water. Another factor in lime production is the mass destruction of life where warm and cold surface currents meet and the tests produced by growth of organisms over a wide area are concentrated after their death on a relatively small patch of the sea floor.

In the second place dilution by other sedimentary matter helps in determining the lime content. Broadly speaking this admixture increases towards the coast, especially where large rivers debouch or deserts deliver dust. Volcanoes, whether subaerial or submarine, may also strongly dilute calcareous matter. Oceanic currents are seldom sufficiently turbulent to hold globigerina tests in suspension, but they may carry away clay particles where they sweep along the floor. In such positions a pure globigerina ooze accumulates owing to the lack of pollution by fine terrigenous matter. This frequently occurs on submarine ridges, seamounts, and other topographic highs.

In the third place solution influences the lime content. This factor comes into play during settling of calcareous tests and on the sea floor. Roughly half the number of tests produced by planktonic Foraminifera are abandoned by the animal while reproducing. The other half either passes through the digestive organs of plankton-feeding animals (where it is dissolved?) or dies and sinks to the sea floor. In the latter case solution may be retarded during the settling, owing to protective covering by organic matter. But solution is also active on the sea floor, inasmuch as the bottom waters are hardly ever perfectly stagnant or saturated. Decomposition of organic matter contained in the sediment produces carbon dioxide, which, in turn, results in activating the solution of calcium carbonate.

The author is inclined to assume that by far the greater amount of solution takes place on the sea floor and not during the settling because the time of settling is so much shorter than the time left before a test becomes covered and protected from further attack on the sea floor.

The theory of lime solution is not yet satisfactorily established. It was pointed out in an earlier chapter that the distribution of carbonic acid in sea water is yet insufficiently known, and this is the main factor determining the solution of calcium carbonate. A detailed discussion of these matters is given by Sverdrup et al. (1942).

Solution is found to be more active with increasing depth, partly because the distance of settling is longer, partly because the solvent action becomes more powerful owing to the lower temperature and salinity at great depths, and probably also to higher pressure.

Theoretically solution of lime should also increase with the velocity of the bottom current. It is observed, however, that in general the

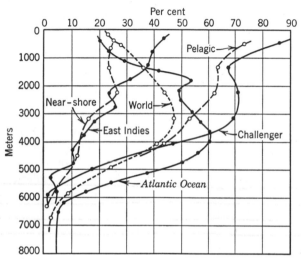

Fig. 153. Relation between depth and lime content of deep-sea deposits. The line for Indonesia was constructed from all available data, the Atlantic from data given by Pia (1933), the world average from data given by Trask (1937). This author gave separate data for pelagic (more than 800 km) and near-shore deposits (less than 800 km from the coast), making allowance in each group for unequal distribution of samples by taking an equal number from each representative area. In combining these two groups for obtaining a world average the present writer gave different weights for each depth to near-shore and pelagic deposits respectively as follows: 90 m 1:0; 315 m 20:1; 450 m 10:1; 1350 m 2:1; 2250 m 1:1; 3150 m 1:5; 4050 m 1:10; 4950 m 1:25; 5850 m 0:1; 6750 m 0:1.

lime content of deep-sea deposits is greater on elevations, where stronger currents prevail and the lutite fractions are washed away, leaving very pure globigerina ooze. On the other hand it cannot be doubted that solution is excluded where the bottom water is stagnant, because a fresh supply of solvent is required to replace the water that has become saturated.

Plotting the average lime content of marine deposits against depth brings out several interesting facts (Fig. 153). The percentage is much lower for near-shore than for pelagic deposits. In the Indonesian basins the lime content is high in depths to 2000 m but normal in the deeps as compared to the average for near-shore deep-sea sediments. The tropical climate explains the former relation (see p. 379), because production must be high. Abnormally active solution and a relatively large amount of terrestrial particles must account for the swift drop in lime with depth.

This forms one of the problems awaiting further research, for in the oceans there is no appreciable falling off until depths of 4000 m are reached. Neither this observation nor the reason for a different relation in the hemipelagic abyssal basins is yet understood. It is not probable that dilution by terrigenous matter is solely responsible for the lower lime content in the Moluccan region, for then the abnormally high percentages of the Sulu Sea (some 50% lime in 4500-m depth as against 4% in the Celebes Sea at the same average depth) could be explained only by the scarcity of volcanic matter and the absence of large rivers flowing into this sea. These two factors, however, are certainly insufficient to account for the observed difference. There is much to be said for the supposition that solution is more active in the basins than in the oceans at depths beyond 3000 m. The poor ventilation and hence slow solution in the Sulu Basin would then account satisfactorily for the abnormal composition of its bottom deposits.

The *Challenger* samples appear to conform fairly well with a world average for pelagic deposits obtained at a later date. Below 3000 m the Atlantic sediments are exceptionally rich in lime. It is not known whether this is due to high production, poor ventilation, low carbon dioxide content of the water, or low contribution of non-calcareous matter. The last suggestion at first sight appears improbable, for, although the supply of volcanic dust may be below the average, the contribution from the land is certainly larger than in the other oceans. It should be borne in mind, however, that large areas of moderate depth occurring on the Mid-Atlantic Rise are far from land and are probably swept by currents. The currents, by carrying away the non-calcareous lutite, tend to leave pure globigerina oozes with a high lime content. The fact that in less than 1000 m the Atlantic is slightly deficient in lime may be attributed to the large number of great rivers discharging detritus into this ocean.

Sverdrup et al. (1942) gives separate curves for the pelagic deposits of various parts of the oceans. These bring out the marked differences between these basins. Thus the northern Pacific is poorer in lime than the average of all oceans for the same depth.

The relation between lime and depth is a very irregular one because the percentage in a deposit results from so many independent variables besides depth. Instructive instances are discussed by Revelle (1944). He showed that samples which contain many individuals and many species of benthonic Foraminifera are usually, other things being equal, those of relatively low content of pelagic Foraminifera (hence, low lime content) and higher organic matter. Areas in which the surface water is rich in plankton also have rich bottom faunas. Hence, Revelle is of the opinion that the variations in the bottom faunas are chiefly dependent on varying rates of accumulation of available organic matter. The low carbonate contents of deposits which support large communities of bottom-living organisms might be explained by the fact that more carbon dioxide would be produced by metabolism and decomposition; hence conditions would be more favorable for the solution of carbonates. The churning over of the bottom deposits would also favor solution.

Another example of the complications involved is given by the same author. The irregular band of sediments poor in carbonate along the South American Pacific coast is probably due to at least three factors: (1) the masking effect of terrigenous materials; (2) the relatively low temperature of the surface waters of the Peruvian Current; (3) the large amount of organic matter in the water and on the bottom.

Pelagic Deposits Poor in Lime. Towards the poles the production of lime falls, while diatoms (siliceous algae) predominate in the plankton. Decreasing salinity appears to be one of the reasons, because diatoms are also abundant near the mouth of large rivers. Possibly the solution of lime is also more active where the descending currents of polar regions must show a strong solvent action. Together the solution of lime and the more abundant supply of diatom frustules produce a siliceous pelagic sediment, called *diatom ooze.* It is most strongly developed around the Antarctic, but is also important in other areas of upwelling water where nutrients are plentiful, as in the Gulf of California. This type of deposit contains 2–40% calcium carbonate and 3–25% mineral grains, partly carried by ice. The percentage of frustules may reach more than 90. The color is light yellow to gray, and the deposit is generally found to be of a feltlike consistency. The demarcation line between diatom and globigerina oozes is found to follow the line where the surface waters converge and sink downwards obliquely to a depth of 800 or 1000 m, flowing thence towards the equator (south Atlantic intermediate current). The diatoms thrive in the polar surface waters; the Foraminifera, in the so-called mixed water of intermediate latitudes. The diatom frustules are carried along for a while by the northward sinking current, so that the boundary line between the two types of deep-sea ooze lies somewhat north of the convergence line.

Microscopic examination of diatom ooze shows that the thin-walled frustules are dissolved, for only the more massive types such as Coscinodiscus and Synedra are contained in the samples.

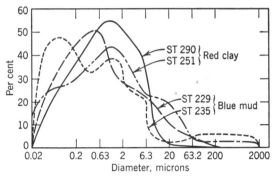

FIG. 154. Equal area distribution curves of grain size in red clay and blue mud of four *Meteor* stations. (According to Correns, in Barth, Correns, and Eskola, 1939, Fig. 33, p. 172.)

At lower latitudes other types of siliceous organisms predominate, namely radiolarians. These are always entirely overshadowed by Foraminifera in the living plankton. It is only in environments where solution of lime on the bottom is more active than elsewhere that the siliceous tests (hydrated silica) can predominate in the sediment. The term *radiolarian ooze* is applied when these tests form more than 20% of the sample. The maximum content observed is 60 to 70%. Among the genera found in the deposits those belonging to the order of the Acantharia are absent, owing to the solubility of the strontium sulfate contained in the shells, as also those belonging to the Phaeodaria that produce very thin skeletons. The maximum lime content of radiolarian ooze is 20%. The finest waste products from the continents and volcanic ash play a more prominent part in radiolarian ooze than in globigerina ooze. It may be looked upon as a special type of red clay in which siliceous shells happen to be more prominent. The color resembles that of red clay, but is often somewhat lighter.

Radiolarite is a fossil siliceous sediment containing radiolarians. It may form the chief component of thick stratigraphical prisms. In the Devonian and Carboniferous of Australia, for instance, series 3000 m thick have been mapped. These formations, however, were evidently deposited in shallow water. The problem of the radiolarites is not yet solved in other places, for the Alpine Mesozoic representatives are ascribed by some investigators to a deep-sea environment, while this contention is strongly opposed by others. In any event it is highly improbable that we are dealing with true pelagic deposits,

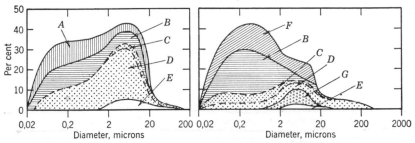

Fig. 155. Distribution curves showing composition and grain size of red clay, *Meteor* station 305, and blue mud, *Meteor* station 222. *A*, montmorillonite; *B*, mica; *C*, feldspar; *D*, quartz; *E*, rest; *F*, halloysite; *G*, siliceous tests. (According to Correns, in Barth, Correns, and Eskola, 1939, Figs. 38 and 39, p. 178.)

because they were formed in a geosyncline at moderate distances from the coast (see p. 245).

Over vast areas of the deep-sea floor not only calcareous matter but also the opaline siliceous matter forming radiolarian shells and diatom frustules is attacked by solution. There remains only a fine lutite of reddish brown to chocolate color, called *red clay*. One of the chief characteristics is the slow rate of accumulation, which results in a relative concentration of accessories that are otherwise scarce in sediments showing swifter growth. These accessories have already been mentioned in a former chapter: meteoric dust, sharks' teeth, ear bones of whales, manganese nodules, cobbles rafted by ice and trees, fragments of pumice, etc. Dredging can bring to light only superficial material, yet it has shown the presence of Tertiary sharks' teeth. In such localities accumulation must approach zero, but they are certainly not representative of all red clay deposits (see p. 382).

The percentage of lime in red clay varies between 0 and 30 but is generally very low. The color is bright to brownish red or chocolate brown, owing to the presence of ferric hydroxide or oxide and a small amount of manganese oxide. Formerly, when only microscopic examination was possible, the conclusion was drawn that red clay consists almost exclusively of volcanic matter. More recent X-ray analysis has shown, however, that the bulk is formed by clay minerals, characteristic of subaerial weathering and of the same nature as those in blue mud and globigerina ooze. These are the fine products of subaerial chemical weathering on land that have traveled for long ages in the oceanic circulation currents before finally settling in the pelagic regions of the deep sea.

Although manganese nodules are occasionally found in globigerina ooze, and more frequently in radiolarian ooze, they are typical for red clay. The size varies from microscopic pellets to chunks of 15-cm diameter. Red clay is mainly found in the Pacific. It occupies nearly as large an area of the ocean floor as globigerina ooze.

Finally attention is drawn to the so-called *deep-sea sands*. These are normal pelagic sediments with a considerable admixture (up to 50%) of fine sand, composed of continental minerals that cannot be ascribed to volcanic action. The deep-sea sands have been encountered especially in deep depressions of the Atlantic (north of Bermuda, Romanche Deep, Cape Trough, along the Whale Ridge, etc.) and in the basins west of southern California. The composition cannot be attributed to direct supply from the land, because broad areas of normal pelagic deposits without continental sand lie between. Rafting by ice is excluded for the situations in tropical regions, and the well-sorted grain size also opposes this explanation. Several characteristics point to a neritic source, as for instance the presence of glauconite, fishes' teeth, and sponge spicula and the high degree of sorting. A possible explanation by turbidity currents is offered above (p. 240), and confirmatory evidence is given elsewhere in connection with abnormal stratification (p. 370).

Data on the lime content of pelagic sediments were presented above. To these may be added the average for all pelagic deposits, namely 37%, and of all terrigenous deposits, 25%. The average for the Pacific is 19%, and for the Atlantic 41%.

Distribution of Marine Sediments. In Fig. 156 and Tables 21 and 22 some data on the distribution of marine sediments are assembled.

For a more detailed discussion the reader is referred to G. Schott (1936, 1942), Trask (1939), Sverdrup et al. (1942), and to the reports of expeditions.

32, 13, 70

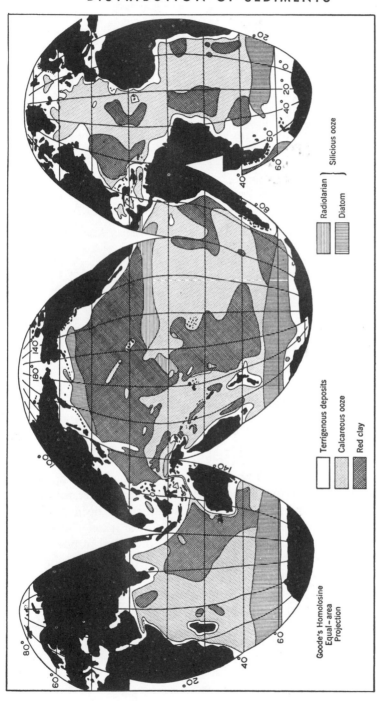

Goode's Homolosine
Equal-area
Projection

Terrigenous deposits

Calcareous ooze

Red clay

Radiolarian

Diatom

Silicious ooze

Fig. 156. Distribution of the various types of pelagic sediments. (After Sverdrup et al., 1942, *The Oceans*, Fig. 253, p. 975, Prentice-Hall.)

TABLE 21. AREAS COVERED BY MARINE SEDIMENTS

Type of deposit	Area, millions of km²	Percentage of sea floor	Average depth, m
Shelf sediments	30	8	<100
Hemipelagic	63	18	±2300
Pelagic	268	74	4300
Globigerina ooze	126 } 128	35 } 36	3600
Pteropod ooze	2	1	2000
Red clay	102	28	5400
Diatom ooze **S.pole**	31 } 38	9 } 10	3900
Radiolarian ooze **near eq.**	7	2	5300

TABLE 22. DISTRIBUTION OF THE PELAGIC SEDIMENTS IN THE OCEANS IN PERCENTAGE
(AFTER SVERDRUP ET AL., 1942)

Type of sediment	Indian Ocean	Pacific Ocean	Atlantic Ocean
Calcareous ooze	54.3	36.2	67.5
Siliceous ooze	20.4	14.7	6.7
Red clay	25.3	49.1	25.8
	100.0	100.0	1.000

Ocean	Calcareous ooze	Siliceous ooze	Red clay
Indian Ocean	26.9	33.9	15.7
Pacific Ocean	40.6	55.3	68.7
Atlantic Ocean	32.5	10.8	15.6
	100.0	100.0	100.0

See beginning of chap.

FURTHER ASPECTS OF SEDIMENTATION

STRATIFICATION

General Considerations. The occurrence of stratification in marine sediments is an important subject and merits separate treatment.

A sedimentary deposit is said to be stratified or bedded when it shows successive beds, layers, or strata due to the manner in which it was formed. The more or less well-defined divisional planes between the separate units are not all of the same character. In some cases there is merely a break in physical continuity of the deposit, but otherwise the bed above and below are of identical character. The beds then either lie on each other without any cohesion, or they can be easily split apart. In other cases there is an abrupt or gradual change from one type of rock to another, e.g., from sand to clay or from limestone to marl. There need be no break in physical continuity in the shape of a fracture plane. It may also be that the successive beds differ only in one characteristic, such as color, grain size, fossil content, etc., but are otherwise alike.

Not unfrequently a bedding plane is rendered more conspicuous by one or more of the following types of marking: tracks and trails, rock salt pseudomorphs, rain pits, ripple and swash marks, drying cracks, air bubble markings, boring holes, attached organisms. Frequently the cause of cleavage along the bedding planes is obvious, for instance when a thin film of clay occurs between limestone beds or where a stratum composed of mica flakes divides sandstone layers. But often there is no apparent cause for this property.

Various terms are applied to the individual layers of a bedded series according to their thickness. Layers up to 1 cm in thickness are called *laminae*, while thicker layers are called *beds*. The term stratum is applied either to thick beds or to a series of beds well marked off from preceding or following beds.

The horizontal extension of each bed is generally very large compared to the thickness, while the thickness is constant. Lenticular or irregular shapes of which the upper and lower surface are not parallel are also found. Normally the bedding planes are parallel to each other and to the upper and lower surface of the whole series. Where they lie at a distinct angle to the general stratification the terms *false bedding, current bedding,* or *cross bedding* are applied.

The sand and coarser grades are moved along the bottom and not in suspension. When they suddenly reach a steep slope the grains roll down it and form a kind of scree. The surface of the scree is protected from the current, and the grains roll down it only under the influence of gravity. By building outwards in the direction of the current the break in slope at the upper end of the scree is maintained. At the lower end there is normally a gradual decrease in slope to horizontal. Hence the laminae are concave upwards (Fig. 157, *A*). This type of current bedding is most frequent where a thin sheet of water, for instance the water trickling out of a sandy beach at low tide, flows into a deeper pool or where gravel is being shifted.

In other places the laminae are convex at the upper and concave at the lower end. However, as the upper part is usually eroded away again before the next system of current laminae is deposited on top, the remaining part is much like the type described above, but the laminae start even more abruptly at the upper end. This type of current bedding is probably developed in somewhat deeper water, because the velocity of the current is not so drastically reduced at the point where deeper water is reached (Fig. 157, *B*).

Current bedding is an important aid in determining the original position of strata where there is lack of stratigraphical evidence, especially in the pre-Cambrian and with complicated tectonic structures. The concavity of the current bedding is originally upwards

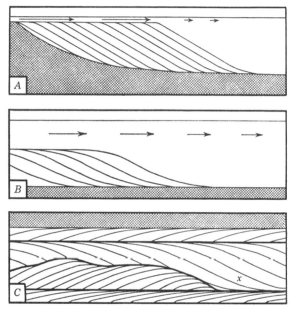

Fig. 157. Schematic sections of current bedding. *A*, formed by very shallow current entering deep pool; *B*, formed in deeper water, e.g., on a sand bank; *C*, partly truncated laminae, now inverted. At *x*, locality where misinterpretation of original top is possible.

and therefore gives the direction in which the beds are younging. Care should be taken, however, to use only such parts of current-bedded series as show evidence of concavity together with a clear-cut break in slope at the other end of the laminae. Otherwise the upper convex part may be mistaken for concavity the other way up (Fig. 157, *C*). Luckily the convex laminae hardly ever show a break in slope at the lower end but do show a more or less pronounced concave slope back to horizontal. On account of the possible misinterpretation of upper convexity for a lower concavity it is safer not to rely on a single observation but to search for several examples in a single exposure.

Other phenomena that may indicate the directions of younging are (1) graded bedding (p. 366) and (2) washouts (Fig. 158). Washouts are channels eroded in deposits during the accumulation. They may be characterized by unconformable contacts at their edges, a coarser fill than the surrounding deposit, or the inward slope of their sides. See also Shrock (1948) for many other guides to interpreting the sequence in sedimentary deposits.

The ultimate cause of stratification is to be sought either in interruptions of deposition or in variations in the quantity or nature of

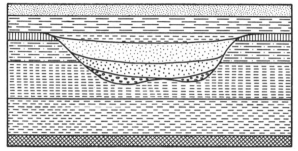

FIG. 158. Diagram of a washout in section.

the supply of sedimentary matter. During a standstill in accumulation, especially if it is of some duration, alterations may occur in the deposit, for instance lithification. Erosion may, but need not, accompany the halt in deposition. Even if identical material is supplied on resumption of deposition, a break in the physical continuity of the rock may result and lead to the development of a bedding plane.

Normally, however, an interruption will not lead to a bedding plane unless renewed deposition begins with a different type of sediment. In the latter case the interruption is not necessary to cause bedding.

So many different causes for stratification are possible that not all of them can be enumerated. Some of the more frequent are variations of currents and waves, of organic growth, or of colloidal precipitation. Further causes are volcanic eruptions, dust storms, and slumping. Changes in climate, in the position of sea level, or in the physiography of the coast and land may also cause stratification either directly or by influencing neighboring areas. In short, all factors bearing on sedimentation are open to variations and may thus cause stratification.

A peculiar type of bedding is sometimes encountered in which the coarser material lies at the bottom and grades upwards into finer sediment. It is aptly called *graded bedding*. The coarse fraction is generally sand or silt, but gravel, cobbles, or even boulders have been found at the base.

The cause of graded bedding is not always obvious. Currents strong enough to transport the coarser particles involved should have eroded the fine-grained upper part of the preceding bed and should have formed ripple marks on their own floor. But many graded beds are found covering an older graded bed without signs of erosion or ripple marking at the contact. Generally current bedding and graded bedding are mutually exclusive, and this also indicates that graded bedding is not due to normal current transport.

The materials thrown out of a volcano into the sea tend to accumulate in a graded bed on the bottom, because the larger particles sink more quickly than the smaller ones. The churning up of poorly sorted sediment may have caused some graded deposits, again because the finer particles took longer to settle to the bottom. The lower contact should show signs of erosion and wave ripple marks.

Bailey (1936), who has focused attention on graded bedding, suggested that the slipping of sediment down a slope, e.g., owing to a seaquake, may represent another, not infrequent cause of graded bedding. Slumping of sediment cannot result in the type of sorting shown by graded bedding, and it is not probable that tsunamic waves can carry much coarse material far out to sea and then drop it to the bottom. Hence the present author is of the opinion that many graded beds were deposited by turbidity currents of high density (Kuenen, 1948; Kuenen and Migliorini, in press).

While the turbidity current is flowing down a channel or a flat slope on an even grade it may be eroding the bottom because it is increasing in volume and gathering speed. This depends on the nature of the bottom deposit, on the slope, and on the shape and size of the flow. Where the slope begins to decrease, the current may cease to erode, even when passing over unconsolidated material, but without depositing any of its load. Farther along, deposition will begin. The turbidity flow should first drop the coarser and gradually finer and finer particles until the silt and mud finally come to rest. This should cause grading in a horizontal sense. But after the main mass of the flow has passed a certain spot and dropped coarse particles, it will be followed by more dilute suspension, carrying finer sediment alone. This part of the flow will drop finer grains on top of the first deposit. This process should continue until particles of the silt fraction and then lutite are laid on top. In this manner vertical grading at a certain spot will be produced. But some fine matter should be lodged between the coarser grains, and each stratum of a graded bed formed in this manner should show a not very high degree of sorting. This explains the observation that normally graded sandstones are muddy graywackes.

On a wide, horizontal expanse the resultant graded bedding should include all fractions from the largest to the finest particles supplied, including lutite. On a slight slope the muddy water containing only lutite need not drop its load, even though the current is very slow. Hence the deposit need not include the finer fractions. It is even conceivable that a turbidity current coming down into a trough might cross to the other side and deposit its coarser load while rising up the opposite slope owing to its momentum. But the muddy water will finally flow back slowly into the depression, carrying the still-suspended finer fractions with it.

As a turbidity current of high density has an exceedingly high power of transport compared to its velocity, it should be able to continue carrying quite coarse fractions after the velocity has sunk to a low value. This mechanism enables us to account for a curious feature of graded bedding, namely, that relatively coarse grains are supplied without any erosion, or only slight attack, of the bed over which they are being transported.

Where a turbidity current has deposited its load it may soon be followed by another, and a series of graded beds would gradually be built up, the one directly on top of the other. In other cases the graded bed might be followed by material deposited by normal direct sedimentation. In deep water a coarse layer would then be covered by a normal deep-sea deposit. Turbidity currents of high density might thus provide the clue to some curious sequences of this type noted in fossil deposits, and to the occurrence of deep-sea sands, described above (p. 360).

The stratification of sediments which are originally deposited with marked bedding may sometimes be rendered less clear or even be entirely destroyed by the action of burrowing animals at the time of deposition. (Special cases are discussed on pp. 373 and 406.) But the widespread occurrence of bedding and even of fine lamination in fossil sediments and recent deposits (viz., *Snellius* station 330, depth 4456 m, containing 74 layers in a core 152 cm long, and station 301, depth 5200 m, with 23 layers in a core 77 cm long) shows that this action has been of limited importance. The frequency of bedding is rather surprising in view of the rich bottom life of the seas, and the cause is not properly understood.

Now and again stratification may be rhythmic in nature and display cycles. Instances are known of the regular alternation of coarse and fine beds, of lime and clay, of sand and marl, and many other repetitions. Threefold repetitions of various rocks are likewise found in some rock series. In several cases the cause is to be sought in exceptional storms, that result in the churning up and the resettling first of sand and later of silt and clay; in others, in the cycle of seasons, the rhythm of tides, etc. Other possible causes of rhythmic stratification are: (1) longer climatic periods, such as "Brückner's period" (the existence of which is not admitted by all investigators); (2) the precession of the equinoxes (21,000 years); and (3) the variation in the eccentricity of the earth's path around the sun (91,000 years).

Highly complex cycles in the Pennsylvanian system in the central and eastern states of the United States have been described by Wanless and Weller as *cyclothems*. A complete cyclothem is composed of the following members in descending order:

Marine sediments:
   8   Shale with "ironstone" nodules and bands.
   7   Limestone with marine fossils.
   6   Black shale with large concretions.
Continental sediments:
   5   Coal.
   4   Underclay.
   3   Limestone without marine fossils.
   2   Sandy shale.
   1   Sandstone unconformable on lower beds.

These cyclothems are traceable over wide areas and are found to be of remarkable constancy. The authors mentioned attribute them to diastrophic movements which must have affected the entire eastern half of North America. Later, Wanless and Shepard (1936) suggested eustatic movements of sea level in connection with glacial stages of the Upper Paleozoic as the major cause.

Stratification in Recent Sediments. Present knowledge concerning stratification of recent marine deposits is limited by the technique of sampling. Earlier instruments either disturbed the strata or took samples only a few inches long. Hence, the impression was gained that uniformity is the rule. When longer and longer samples were obtained variations in color and composition were repeatedly encountered. In the Atlantic deep sea, for instance, Philippi (1910) discovered widespread stratification that was later shown to obtain over the entire Atlantic (Schott, 1939). In modern samples of a few meters' length stratification is even found to be a rule to which there are few exceptions. One of these, a core of red clay 246 cm long, was taken a few hundred kilometers off the coast of California.

The most typical arrangement for *pelagic deposits* is a stratum of globigerina ooze 20 to 40 cm thick resting on red clay of similar thickness, and this alternation is probably repeated several times at greater depths (Fig. 161, p. 377). In the red clay certain Foraminifera indicative of warm surface waters are absent though occurring in the underlying and covering stratum of globigerina ooze. They are replaced by forms belonging to higher latitudes. This indicates lower surface temperatures during the deposition of the red clay. The lower lime content of this stratum is apparently due both to smaller supply of lime and to a more pronounced bottom current with strong solvent action. These relations point to a colder climate during the accumulation of the red clay, and the conclusion is warranted that this stratum represents the last Ice Age. The lower globigerina ooze can be attributed to the last interglacial or interstadial period.

In the long samples obtained by Piggot from the northern Atlantic as many as four cold periods are represented (Figs. 159 and 160). Age determination by radioactive methods indicates that these are all stages of the last Ice Age (Wisconsin = Würm), because the oldest stratum was deposited not more than 70,000 years ago. In the Caribbean the same investigator took a long sample of globigerina ooze that proved to contain several strata with Foraminifera indicating about five warmer and colder periods. The age determinations described on a later page show that the second (Mindel-Risz) Interglacial period was reached. Further investigations are needed, especially of the very long samples Pettersson has collected, before a correlation between glacial variations of climate and strata on the ocean floor can be established with any certainty.

Closer to the continents the buried stratum of red clay is replaced by blue mud and the thickness increases (Fig. 161, p. 377). The direct influence of the land becomes gradually more noticeable. In cores taken in the regions where blue mud and red clay are accumulating at the present time no stratification is visible, but examination of the contained Foraminifera generally shows the presence of the stratum with cold-water forms. Close to the foot of the continental slope the postglacial stratum becomes so thick that samples of less than 1 to

1½ m no longer reach the deposits of the Ice Age. The same stratification has been observed in the western Indian Ocean, and the
phenomenon may be universal.

It is more difficult to find an explanation for the opposite sequence,
in which red clay is found resting on a layer of globigerina ooze
(Philippi, 1910; Murray and Hjort, 1912). The suggestion has been

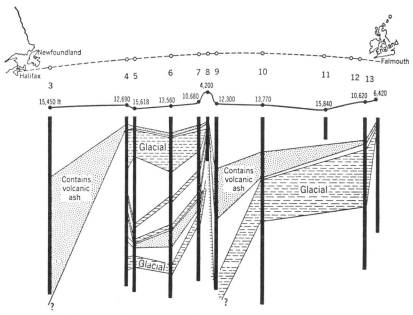

FIG. 159. North Atlantic cores, showing depth and location and the relation of
the glacial and volcanic strata. (After Piggot, 1938, *Scientific Monthly*, Vol. 46,
Fig. 6, p. 214.)

offered that swift subsidence of the sea floor took place from the
level in which globigerina ooze may accumulate to depths in which
solution of lime causes the formation of red clay. But this hypothesis
requires movements of questionable magnitude and speed. It seems
more probable that the globigerina ooze accumulated at lesser depths
somewhere in the neighborhood and slumped down into depths where
only red clay could form in situ. After the slump, normal accumulation of red clay continued on top and formed the upper layer of the
samples. Until the topographic forms around the sites of such abnormal stratification have been accurately ascertained no definite
answer can be given. The explanation offered here is even more
probable for the cases in which three or more strata with different

lime content have been encountered in one sample. Otherwise repeated changes of depth of 1000 or 2000 m would have to be assumed
during a few tens of thousands of years. The combination of abnormal stratification with deep-sea sands has been found in more than

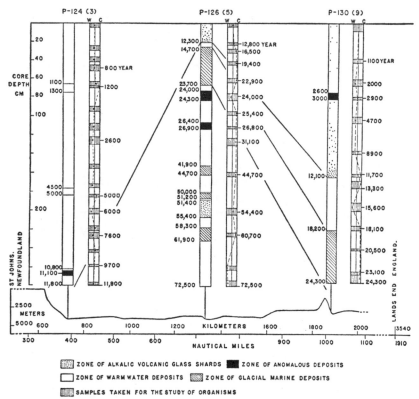

Fig. 160. Chronology of three North Atlantic cores. The right-hand profiles
show the fluctuations in the temperature of the surface waters at the site of
each core as deduced from planktonic tests. (After Piggot and Urry, 1942, *Bull.
Geol. Soc. Am.*, Vol. 53, Fig. 2, p. 1195.)

one case, and this lends support to the explanation of these sands by
turbidity currents given on an earlier page (240), because both phenomena may be attributed to the presence of topographic highs at
not too great a distance.

No glacial stratification was found in the samples 1½ to 2 m long
that the *Snellius* expedition took in the Moluccan area. This might
be due to lack of change in the tropical climate of this region during
the Pleistocene. However this may be, another factor is that sedi-

mentation goes on at so high a speed that much longer samples would be needed to pierce through the postglacial layer in most if not all localities. For instance, Kaoe Bay between the northern arms of Halmahera is 500 m deep, but the entrance is only 50 m deep. During glacial low sea level this basin must have changed to a lake in which deposits quite different from present ones accumulated. The samples of 148- and 168-cm length failed to reach these fresh-water deposits. In a later paragraph evidence will be presented for assuming an accumulation of many meters since the close of the Ice Age even in the wide Moluccan basins. In Kaoe Bay a few dozen meters may have been deposited.

Apart from the Quaternary stratification just discussed little is known concerning the formation of strata in hemipelagic and pelagic sediments. Alterations in color and composition are met with here and there, but nothing can be said as to which of all the possible causes is responsible in any particular deposit. In the Moluccan deep-sea basins alterations in color have been observed that were sometimes repeated many times. But these cases were always found to be of local occurrence and no cause was evident. Only when coarse layers of volcanic ash and pumice were encountered in the neighborhood of active volcanoes was the explanation obvious. Similar occurrences in the northern Atlantic must be attributed to violent prehistoric eruptions probably on Iceland.

In connection with the latter volcanic stratum an interesting feature of deep-sea sedimentation has been treated by Bramlette and Bradley (1940). These authors pointed out that the volcanic ash is not concentrated in thin layers, but part occurs in one or several ill-defined strata, while the remainder is scattered at random through a considerable thickness of the sediment above. This cannot be attributed to differential settling of the shards, because they are mixed in with a layer representing nearly all of postglacial time, although the size of the ash particles is such that they should have reached the bottom in five years.

A similar case has been noted by Miss Neeb in the Moluccas. The ash deriving from the Tambora eruption (see p. 343), although thrown out 115 years prior to the collecting of the bottom samples, is found right up to the surface of the deposit. According to their size the grains should settle to the bottom in a few years' time at the most. As there is an increasing admixture of clay from the bottom of the volcanic stratum to the surface (some 20 to 30 cm thick in a few samples) it cannot be doubted that accumulation of non-volcanic matter has gradually proceeded since the eruption to an amount of at least a dozen centimeters. Hence, part of the ash is mixed with material that has settled to the bottom recently. Neither can the ash in the upper part of the samples be referred to material still washing off the neighboring islands, because it is fresh, while similar ash on Java is known to weather in a few dozen years. The suggestion offered was that turbulent currents have retarded the settling. Not only, however, is turbulence of sufficient strength highly improbable, but the currents causing this turbulence would have swept all suspended ash away and scattered it far and wide.

A more plausible explanation is offered by Bramlette and Bradley, who attribute this phenomenon to mud-feeding animals. The newly deposited ash is supposed to have passed through the intestines, and succeeding generations of the animals must have picked up progressively fewer shards as the sediment became more and more diluted by the continual influx of the constituents belonging to the normal sedimentation. Each time an animal scooped up mud and later excreted it on the sea floor, most of the particles were deposited at a level a little above the original position. The same should apply to coarse grains deriving from glacial layers and scattered through the foraminiferal marl above. The authors mentioned attribute this activity especially to holothurians and further to echinoids, annelids, and ophiurids.

This explanation is the most logical one that has yet been suggested. But, as pointed out above (p. 369), the general—not to say universal—occurrence of clear-cut stratification in deep-sea deposits could not be accounted for if the action of burrowing organisms were of general importance. Neither is there any apparent reason why they should be more abundant where ash deposits occur. Hence confirmation of the explanation offered is needed before it can be accepted without reserve.

Search in fossil and recent marine sediments for a yearly rhythm, equivalent to the varves in glacial fresh-water deposits, has nearly always been made in vain. The only occurrence of marine varves known to the author is described by Moore from the Clyde Sea (1931). But they are caused by biological factors. The scarcity of marine varves due to inorganic precipitation is attributed by Fraser (1929) to the flocculation of clay in sea water, causing it to sink as rapidly as fine sand. Moreover, in shallow marine environments disturbance by waves and burrowing benthonic life may have destroyed varves. Kuenen (1943) attributed the absence of a yearly rhythm in the Moluccan deep-sea depressions to the great length of time required for the finer fractions to settle to the bottom, that must run to years or even centuries. Meanwhile convection and tidal currents will have completely effaced differences between seasonal supply of terrigenous matter. The planktonic supply is probably not markedly rhythmic.

In the quiet deep of the Black Sea this need not be true, because the waters are practically stagnant. The fine and regular stratification found at depths exceeding 200 m caused by the alternation of lighter and darker laminae has therefore been attributed to seasonal variations (see p. 335). A few other examples of marine varves have been described (see p. 380). A yearly rhythm has been encountered in the Gulf of California due to the periodic upwelling of water with abundance of nutrient salts. This results in seasonal plankton development and stratification of the bottom deposit.

Practically no data have been obtained concerning stratification of the shelf deposits. This is due partly to the fact that oceanographic expeditions have seldom operated in shallow waters, partly to the frequent coarse grain that renders sampling by normal tubes ineffective. The use of heavy equipment may lead to interesting results. The neglect of shallow waters by oceanographic expeditions in the hunt for spectacular results in the deep sea is not justified when the far greater importance of neritic sediments to stratigraphy than of bathyal and abyssal deposits is taken into account. It is high time that marine geology concentrated on the systematic exploration of shallow inland seas such as the Gulf of Maine and the Irish Sea.

RADIOACTIVITY [1]

The average radium content of acid igneous rocks (granites) is of the order of 2.5×10^{-12} gram per gram of rock, and of basalts 1.0×10^{-12} gram per gram, while sedimentary rocks contain less, from 0.2 to 0.8×10^{-12} gram per gram. But the radioactivity of pelagic deposits is considerably greater. Although different investigators have not arrived at the same values, they all agree that the ocean bottom is strongly radioactive. Piggot found in 1933 an average of 6.5×10^{-12} gram Ra per gram for 28 samples. Red clay is richest, containing 9.5×10^{-12} gram Ra per gram as the average of 13 samples. Pettersson (1943) found 13.5×10^{-12} in 19 samples of red clay, 13.1×10^{-12} gram Ra per gram in two radiolarian oozes and 3.3×10^{-12} gram Ra

[1] See especially Evans; Piggot and Urry.

per gram in 7 samples of globigerina ooze. But he points out that there is a wide range and that some samples of red clay fall well within the range of acid igneous rocks. The outer layer of manganese nodules is even more radioactive and attains values around 50×10^{-12} with a maximum of 135×10^{-12} gram Ra per gram. Evans and Kip reported 2.5×10^{-12} gram Ra per gram in terrigenous muds. Five terrigenous muds with and without volcanic ash from the Moluccan area (analyzed by the latter workers) contained an average of 2.2×10^{-12} gram Ra per gram, of which the sample from 10,050 m in the Mindanao Trough showed the lowest value, 1.38×10^{-12} gram Ra per gram, although the depth of water was twice that of the other samples. Pettersson also arrived at the conclusion that activity is independent of depth.

We cannot enter here deeply into the problem of what causes the strong activity of the sea floor, but a few general aspects may be mentioned. In the first place, it is conceivable that the radioactive elements are precipitated independently on the ocean floor directly from the sea water, the sedimentary particles acting merely as dilutent. Evidence against this conception is to be found in the activity of the Moluccan muds, which are accumulating some 50 times as quickly as oceanic pelagic deposits, but in which no dilution of the radioactive matter appears to occur. Russell arrived at the same conclusion from a study of fossil sediments, but he pointed out that with very swift accumulation insufficient radioactive elements may be present to cause high activity.

Studies by the same author and by Beers have shown that the bulk of the radioactive elements are deposited from solution together with organic compounds. Hence marine oil shales are strongly radioactive.

Recent work by Piggot and Urry has shown that in long samples the activity decreases with depth in the deposit and soon attains normal low values for fossil sediments. Pettersson showed that the same generalization applied to manganese nodules, the strong activity of the surface quickly diminishing inwards. From this it follows that the abnormal activity of the superficial layer must be due to the short-lived elements ionium and/or radium. The final low values are caused by a normal percentage of uranium. When the sediment is freshly deposited it contains more of the strongly active but short-lived daughter elements than are generated spontaneously by the parent element uranium. Very little is known concerning the distribution of other radioactive elements such as thorium and potassium, and they will be left out of account in the following.

In the course of time the short-lived elements in excess of radioactive equilibrium are lost by spontaneous disintegration until no more is left than is in radioactive equilibrium with the uranium. Uranium disintegrates so slowly that no appreciable reduction in activity takes place in the few hundred thousands of years represented in the longest samples of red clay yet examined. In some samples it proved to be ionium; in others, radium that had been deposited in excess of radioactive equilibrium.

Pettersson (1943) showed that the radium and ionium content of sea water is far below radioactive equilibrium. The conclusion is warranted that the excess of these elements in deep-sea sediment is due to the sedimentary particles picking up certain amounts of radium and ionium and carrying them to the sea floor. The ionium and radium generated by the uranium dissolved in sea water is continuously being adsorbed to these particles and carried to the sea floor, there to disintegrate relatively quickly.

In the next paragraph an account will be given of the manner in which ages can be calculated from these data.

In complete accordance with the results just mentioned, Evans found that a Cretaceous deposit from Timor, that is generally held to be a fossil red clay with manganese nodules, shows normal low activity. If, as seems probable, this red clay was also strongly radioactive at the time of deposition, the normal amount of uranium is all that remained soon after.

RATE OF SEDIMENTATION

Several methods have been proposed for ascertaining the rate of accumulation of recent marine sediments. Twenhofel used the amount of matter suspended in sea water, but as the rate of settling and the degree of turbulence are unknown the results are more in the nature of a shrewd guess than an actual calculation. Nevertheless he arrived at figures comparable to those derived from other methods.

Theoretically sediment traps could be used to demonstrate the rate of accumulation. This method has been followed with success in Alpine lakes, but at sea the technical difficulties are formidable. Moreover, the conditions in a trap differ from those on the adjoining sea floor, because benthonic life is hampered and because a trap will tend to catch more of the suspended matter than a flat expanse without a rim, while on the other hand particles rolling along the bottom are excluded.

An estimate has been based on the degree to which transoceanic telegraph cables become covered by sediment in the course of years. But a heavy cable sinks deeply into the soft deposit and gives no indication of the amount of subsequent covering. No wonder the result arrived at of 250 cm per century of globigerina ooze is preposterously large.

Schwinner (1936) estimated the yearly fall of meteoric dust at 500 tons. Using the number of cosmic nickel-iron and silicate spher-

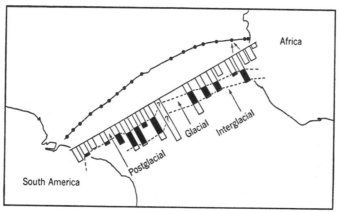

Fɪɢ. 161. The post-glacial, glacial, and interglacial stratum of deep-sea deposits encountered in one of the *Meteor* traverses of the tropical Atlantic. (Data from Schott, 1935.)

ules in pelagic deposits he calculated the following rates of accumulation: 0.2 cm per 1000 years for red clay and 4 cm per 1000 years for globigerina ooze. He introduced a correction on account of supposed oxidation and decay of the spherules. But Murray and Renard showed that a shell of magnetic oxide of iron occurs around a nucleus of native iron and that a small pit due to contraction is preserved. These observations are a strong indication of the absence of decay. These two authors state expressly that the percentage of cosmic spherules mentioned by them appertains to localities where accumulation is apparently exceptionally slow. Hence, the conclusion may be drawn that the average rate of accumulation is larger, perhaps two or more times that calculated by Schwinner.

Lohmann chose the production of coccoliths as a basis for estimating the rate of accumulation and found 0.1 cm per 1000 years for an ooze with 50–70% coccoliths. Application of the same method to normal globigerina ooze, with only $\frac{1}{10}$ to $\frac{1}{20}$ of the coccolith content, gives a rate of accumulation of 1 to 2 cm per 1000 years.

More trustworthy results were obtained by W. Schott (in Trask et al., 1939) on the basis of glacial stratification in the tropical Atlantic and southwestern Indian Ocean. The occurrence of glacial and interglacial strata on the ocean floor (Fig. 161) was briefly discussed above (p. 369). Taking the length of postglacial time as 20,000 years and averaging the thickness of the equivalent stratum, Schott arrived at the rates of accumulation shown in Table 23.

TABLE 23. ACCUMULATION OF RECENT DEEP-SEA SEDIMENTS (SCHOTT)

		Blue mud	Globigerina ooze	Diatom ooze	Red clay
Average thickness, postglacial	Atlantic Ocean	36	24		17
	Indian Ocean		12	11	
Smallest, average, and largest rate in cm per 1000 years	Atlantic Ocean	0.9 1.8 3.3	0.5 1.2 2.1		<0.5 <0.9 1.3
	Indian Ocean		0.3 0.6 1.0	0.3 0.5 0.7	

According to Schott the lower values in the southwestern Indian Ocean are due to a smaller contribution of terrigenous matter. But the thickness of the stratum increases towards the equator in this basin. At its southern limit the globigerina ooze attains 6 cm and increases to 15 or 20 cm at 40° southern latitude. A value of 24 cm, equivalent to that of the tropical Atlantic, may be assumed in the Indian Ocean around the equator. This might be expected in any event for a pelagic organic deposit, which must be fairly independent of supply from the land. It may be surmised that "postglacial" time has been shorter in the south. The gradual improvement of the climate would result in a slow migration of the boundary of globigerina ooze away from the tropical regions.

Schott is of the opinion that the glacial stratum accumulated more swiftly, at 2.1 and 3.3 cm per 1000 years for globigerina ooze and blue mud, respectively. But little is known concerning the length of that period, and a faster accumulation of an organic ooze during the cold period does not seem very likely. Recently Pettersson took very long samples in the Tyrrhenian Sea, from which an average rate of sedimentation of about 10 or 50 cm in 1000 years could be deduced from glacial strata.

In principle the same method was applied by Miss Neeb to obtain the rate of sedimentation in Indonesia. It has already been shown that no glacial stratification has been found in this area, but in two cases dating of a stratum due to a volcanic eruption was possible. In several samples the ash thrown out by the Tambora in 1815 and by the Una Una in 1899 was detected. Four Tambora samples showed an average accumulation in 115 years of 23 cm of sediment, of which half is volcanic ash, one-third terrigenous mud, and one-tenth lime. The rate of accumulation per 1000 years works out at 200 cm total, 100 cm ash, 75 cm terrigenous mud, 20 cm calcium carbonate. A Una Una sample gave 2 cm of terrigenous matter in 30 years or 66 cm per 1000 years. The contribution by globigerina tests in the latter sample amounted to 2.4 cm per 1000 years. As tests form about one-third of the bulk of a normal globigerina ooze the rate of accumulation of such a sediment in the Moluccas would work out at 7 cm per 1000 years. Miss Neeb found only 1 mm of globigerina ooze on the Tambora ash of one station (corresponding to 9 mm per 1000 years), but this low value may be due to unavoidable inaccuracy of the measurement.

The values thus found for blue muds are much larger than those of oceanic samples. But the bulk of lime deposited is also 10 times as much as that accumulating in globigerina ooze in an equivalent number of years in the Atlantic. This forms a welcome confirmation of a swift accumulation of the Moluccan deposits. Probably the average of 90 cm of terrigenous matter in the examined samples is above the average for the whole region, because the investigated samples were taken in the neighborhood of larger islands (north of the Lesser Sunda Islands and east of Borneo). But for the whole archipelago one would hardly expect an average less than half the amount obtained. Confirmation is found in a calculation of the accumulation given by Kuenen (1943) based on the rate of denudation. This gave 50 cm of terrigenous matter and 15 cm of lime, together 65 cm, per 1000 years. The volcanic contribution being added, the rate becomes roughly 75 cm per 1000 years. This is 50 times the values obtained for the Atlantic by Schott.

These large figures for the Moluccan area are the combined result of swift denudation (high relief, tropical climate), small distance from the coasts, narrow insular terraces, volcanic action, and high productivity of lime-secreting organisms. The last contention is based on Trask's results mentioned earlier and the high productivity of Foraminifera established by Myers (1942, see below). There is also a fair amount of detrital lime introduced by rivers, according to Miss Neeb. This explains why the average lime content of Indonesian samples is as high as 20% in spite of the vast amounts of inorganic matter settling in the depressions.

Revelle and Shepard (Trask, 1939) estimated the sedimentation off the southern California coast at 30 cm per 1000 years from the denudation on land. In the opinion of the writer this figure is too high because loss to the oceans to provide for deep-sea sedimentation was not taken into account. For prehistoric times, before human intervention increased denudation, a value of 20 cm per 1000 years may be assumed.

Yet another estimate of accumulation can be made for the Black Sea (Trask, 1939, p. 448). A yearly rhythm produces alternating laminae 0.1 mm thick, two of which together represent one year (see pp. 335 and 374). Hence, the rate of sedimentation works out at 20 cm per 1000 years. In the northern Caucasus similar fossil strata are found. Taking the laminae as yearly rhythmic deposits, the length of the period from Middle Oligocene to Middle Miocene would be 7 million years. This is certainly the correct order of magnitude and forms a confirmation of the interpretation offered. A yearly rhythm in the Gulf of California led Shepard (1948) to assume a rate of accumulation of 1 m in 1000 years.

In the Clyde Sea, Moore (1931) detected varves in the mud indicating a rate of sedimentation of 1 cm in 2.1 years, or 500 cm per 1000 years, while Strøm reports varves showing a figure of 150 cm per 1000 years in Drammens Fiord, Norway.

An interesting method of measuring the rate of sedimentation has recently been applied by Myers (1942). By quantitative catches of Foraminifera the rate of production is evaluated. Study of the bottom deposit at the same spot shows the rate at which the sediment is being deposited. It may be expected that this method, which appears to give values of some accuracy, will in the future develop into a valuable source of information on recent rates of deep-sea sedimentation.

The last method for estimating the rate of marine sedimentation to be dealt with is based on radioactive measurements and has been successfully applied by Piggot and Urry. Their findings on the decrease in radioactivity with depth in long samples has been mentioned above. It was found to be due to ionium and radium occurring in the surface layer in excess of radioactive equilibrium with the contained uranium. Disintegration of this extra amount gradually reduces the activity until equilibrium is attained. Now the half-life, the period in which any given quantity of a radioactive element is reduced to one-half by spontaneous disintegration, is 82,000 years for ionium and 1700 years for radium. Mathematical analysis of the curve showing the decrease in activity with depth in the deposit shows how much time has elapsed since each part was deposited on the sea floor. The only major uncertainty is the assumption that, throughout the time represented by the entire length of the sample, the radioactive elements were deposited in the same ratio to each other. However, the flowing curve found by the investigators mentioned strongly supports this assumption.

The oldest stratum reached by the sampler in the northern Atlantic must have been deposited over 70,000 years ago (Figs. 159 and 160, pp. 370 and 371). Four layers were encountered of which the contained Foraminifera demonstrated cold surface waters. These cannot be correlated with the ice ages but must represent stadial variations of climate during the last (Würm = Wisconsin) Ice Age. For an identical layer of volcanic ash in two samples, ages of 12,300 and 12,100 years were calculated, although at the one locality 8 times as much had been subsequently deposited as at the other. This excellent correlation confirms the reliability of the method.

The average rate of accumulation for a sample taken at the lower side of the continental slope at the end of the Labrador Current was found to be 24 cm per 1000 years. This is a position on the sea floor where a high figure might be expected. Alongside the Mid-Atlantic Rise 11 cm and in the center of the western basin in an impure globigerina ooze 4 cm per 1000 years was calculated. A sample of globigerina ooze from the Caribbean Sea was found to show slower accumulation, namely 0.6 cm per 1000 years, while a red clay from the Pacific taken 500 km from the California coast yielded a value of 0.5 cm per 1000 years.

This excellent method for calculating rates of sedimentation cannot be applied to swiftly accumulating deposits. With these the radioactive elements are so strongly diluted by materials of normal activity that the decrease with age becomes imperceptible. The fairly high radioactive values found in the *Snellius* samples from the Moluccas (2.2×10^{-12} gram Ra per gram) show, however, that success is not excluded even where as much as 50 cm or more is accumulating in 1000 years.

Pettersson examined a couple of manganese nodules and showed, by radioactivity analysis, that they contained radium in excess of radioactive equilibrium. Besides, he contended that a slightly faster growth upwards, proved by greater thickness of growth laminae, had been caused by the incorporation of clay. From this he calculated the rate of sedimentation of red clay at the site in question at ½ mm per 1000 years. The present writer cannot accept this figure as representative, because there are other ways of explaining the eccentric growth. Moreover, it is probable that nodules form where a bottom current retards sedimentation. Particles would tend to be swept off the rounded and protruding nodule so that, even if one accepts Pettersson's explanation of the eccentric growth, the nodule would receive less sediment than the surrounding floor, and the figure would also appertain to an environment of exceptionally slow sedimentation. In passing it may be noted that the rate of growth of the nodules examined is of the order of 1 mm per 1000 years in all directions.

An important point must be emphasized here. It might be held that the rate of sedimentation of red clay is far above the average at moderate distances from the coasts on account of the short distance to the source of sedimentary matter. Thus the sample examined by Piggot, that came from a few hundred kilometers off the Californian coast, would give a figure greatly in excess of the average for the Pacific. But two matters should be borne in mind.

If the proximity and productivity of the continents played an important part, the narrow Atlantic into which many of the largest rivers of the world debouch should be characterized by abnormally rapid accumulation. This is hardly compatible with the high lime content, which is almost double the world average in depths between 4000 and 6000 m (see p. 355), or with the constant thickness of the postglacial layer of red clay found across the southern Atlantic. In the second place it was emphasized earlier that the finest particles of which red clay is formed take many dozens or even hundreds of years to sink to the bottom. During this long descent currents will spread the particles far and wide. The actual route along which a flake of clay travels to reach the ocean floor would show a length many times the circumference of the earth. Hence a sediment of red clay contains particles deriving from all over the world, and there is no reason why one site should receive more than another, as far as the distance to the neighboring land is concerned. The only influence of importance is the velocity of the bottom currents over the various environments. These doubtless show considerable variation, but not in any way related to coastal distance. Volcanic dust will also reach the bottom in larger quantities near volcanoes, because the average grain size is not so small as to allow of long distances of transport. Deposition of red clay is certainly not uniform and is very slow where sharks' teeth, manganese nodules, etc., come to the fore, but it is highly doubtful that the sites in the central parts of the ocean show on an average a lower rate of deposition than the margins.

All stratigraphical methods applied to core samples from the sea floor are in need of a correction. While the sampling tube sinks into the deposit the sample has to slide into the interior. Friction must be overcome, and the result is that the sediment is partly squeezed sideways. The length of the sample is thereby reduced, and the amount of loss probably increases as the sampler cuts more deeply into the bottom. Finally no sediment can be forced into the tube, and the apparatus sinks further as a solid bar. Various estimates have been made of the shortening of the sample as compared to the strata on the sea floor; some 20 to 40% appears to be a fair estimate of the reduction involved (Piggot, 1941; Emery and Dietz, 1941). Hence, all deduced values of the sedimentation rate should be increased by a factor of 25 to 65%. We will assume 40%. The new piston sampler developed by Kullenberg does not show this drawback.

Another important factor is the very large pore space of recent sediments as compared to lithified and compacted fossil deposits. In general 50 to 80% of water by volume is contained in fresh samples of muds and oozes, whereas in fossil rocks the pore space is generally only 10 to 20%. Before a comparison can be made between the rate of accumulation of recent and fossil sediments the values deduced for the former should be divided by a factor of 2 to 3.

In order to show the surprisingly good correspondence between the results of the various independent methods for estimating the rate of recent deep-sea sedimentation the results are brought together in Table 24.

The comparatively low value for red clay derived from the meteorite method may be partly due to the exceptional material used, as pointed out above. The high value for globigerina ooze in the Moluccas has been explained by local conditions. The great variability for blue muds showing values in the ratio 1 in 50 and attaining 200 times that for red clay is doubtless real and due to the highly diverging conditions under which this sediment forms.

In the foregoing discussion rates of sedimentation have been expressed per 1000 years. It would be of interest to know how large the average interval of time is between the deposition of successive grains settling above each other on the sea floor. In a globigerina ooze deposited at a rate of 1 cm per 1000 years, the smaller tests, which are roughly 0.1 mm, accumulate by one every 10 years (leaving out

TABLE 24. RATE OF ACCUMULATION IN CM PER 1000 YEARS OF RECENT MARINE DEPOSITS

Method	Red clay	Globigerina ooze	Terrigenous mud	Diatom ooze
Meteorites	0.4	4		
Coccoliths		1-2		
Postglacial	0.9	1.0	1.8	0.5
Unshortened *	1.3	1.4	2.5	0.7
Radioactive	0.5	0.6 (4)	10 (max. 24)	
Unshortened *	0.7	0.8 (5.6)	14 (max. 29)	
Black Sea			20	
Unshortened *			28	
Moluccas		7	95	
Unshortened *		9	133	
Calculated			70	
Off. California, calculated			20	
Clyde Sea			500 (shallow)	
Tyrrhenian sea, postglacial			10 or 50	
Gulf of California			100	

* Increased by 40% to discount shortening of the sample while penetrating the corer.

of account solution and disintegration). In making a similar estimate for lutite deposits such as red clay and blue mud, the difficulty arises that it is not known in how far the degree of coagulation of the colloidal particles when the mechanical analysis is made corresponds to that when the original deposition took place. The dispersion applied before analysis may be stronger or weaker than in the sea during deposition. The mechanical analyses of the *Meteor* and *Carnegie* samples show that, under the treatments applied, the bulk of the samples broke down to particles averaging roughly 1 micron (Fig. 151, p. 351; Figs. 154 and 155, pp. 358 and 359). On the doubtful assumption that this also represents the composition during sedimentation it follows that one particle of average size is deposited every month in red clay (1 cm per 1000 years) and one every 3 days in blue muds in the oceans (10 cm per 1000 years) and one every half day in terrigenous mud in the Moluccan basins (50 cm per 1000 years). The interval between the settling of finer particles must, of course, be smaller. There are so many uncertainties as to shape, size, and number of the particles that the figures arrived at can serve to give only a very rough idea of time intervals.

In shallow waters the accumulation is far less regular, as was pointed out in the discussion of the profile of equilibrium. The amount of sedimentation in a given period depends mainly on the rate of subsidence that provides the opportunity for accumulation. The supply of sedimentary matter is generally of lesser importance, as it is in excess of the available space. In other cases the supply is irregular in the extreme, and swift accumulation is followed by much longer periods of non-deposition. Hence, measurements in shallow environments have only local significance. Thus in a lagoon of the Mississippi delta 30 cm of silt was once deposited in 4 days, but naturally this amount is hundreds of times larger than the average for the whole delta. Another surprisingly large local value has been measured on the delta of the Fraser River in Canada, where 7 m per year was observed.

By way of comparison some data on fossil sedimentation basins and geosynclines according to Umbgrove are given in Table 25. It should be borne in mind that in these fossil sediments compaction is almost complete.

TABLE 25. MAXIMUM RATE OF SEDIMENTATION IN SOME BASINS AND GEOSYNCLINES (ACCORDING TO UMBGROVE, 1945)

Type of depression	Formation	Duration, millions of years	Maximum thickness, meters	Average sedimentation, cm per 1000 years
5 geosynclines in Indonesia	Neogene	30	5200	17
4 geosynclines in Indonesia	Tertiary	60	9000	15
Basin of Paris	Jurassic	50	1200	2.4
North Sea	Post-Carboniferous	220	8000	3.6
	Permian	38	500	1.3
	Triassic	38	1300	3.4
	Jurassic	44	1500	3.4
	Pleistocene + Holocene	0.6	300	5 *
	Riss to Recent	0.2	80	4 *
	Holocene	0.02	22	11 *
Gulf Coast Basin	Lower Cretaceous to Pleistocene	100	8000	8

* Compaction not yet completed.

Many interesting figures on rates of accumulation of fossil sediments have been compiled by Schuchert (1931).

TOTAL VOLUME OF OCEANIC SEDIMENTS

In a former chapter the conclusion was reached that the ocean basins are permanent features of the earth's crust. If this assumption is accepted an interesting question arises as to the total volume and thickness of the deep-sea deposits that have accumulated in these major sediment traps during the history of the earth. It would lead us too far into the field of geochemistry to treat this matter in any detail, but some aspects prove to be of general importance.

Opinion on the thickness of oceanic deposits differs strongly. On the one hand the dredging of Tertiary sharks' teeth from the surface of red clay has led some geologists to assume that only a few meters of sediment have accumulated in the large oceanic basins since the beginning of geological time. Others have concluded that globigerina ooze is deposited at the rate of 2½ meters per 1000 years, and that would lead to the assumption of dozens of kilometers for the total thickness of pelagic deposits. Obviously this is all mere guesswork and has not brought us any nearer to a solution of our problem. Luckily a number of data are now at hand from which more trustworthy figures can be obtained, and the results of different lines of attack are in satisfactory agreement. Still, the result is only a rough estimate in need of further confirmation or revision.

In the first place the present rate of accumulation can be multiplied by the age of the oceans. Table 25 shows that present accumulation is of the order of 1 cm per 1000 years. The present topography of the continents is more diversified and lies at a higher level with respect to sea level than formerly. This must result in a higher production of sedimentary matter in recent times than was usual during the past. As, moreover, the area of inland seas that could entrap sedimentary matter is at a minimum, the amount delivered to the deep sea must be larger than what was normal in former ages. As first approximation an average value of ½ to ¾ cm per 1000 years beyond the continental shelf may be assumed. Minus pore space, this would correspond to ⅙ cm of solid sediment per 1000 years. For the whole geological past, estimated at 2×10^9 years, a total thickness of 3 km is obtained. The volume of all extracontinental sediments then adds up to 9×10^8 km³, calculated free of pore space.

A second line of reasoning is as follows. All sediments are formed from weathered older rocks, ultimately from igneous rocks. From the average composition of shale, sandstone, and limestone on the one hand and igneous rocks on the other the ratio can be calculated in which the sedimentary rocks are produced. The result is 20:3:2 for shale : sandstone : limestone, according to Clarke. However, measurement of a large number of sections on the continents shows a very different ratio for fossil rocks, namely 20:12:14. Obviously a large amount of the sand produced by weathering and most of the clay have been washed off the continental blocks and deposited in the deep sea. If all lime had been retained on the continents, then 74% of all weathering products would have found a permanent grave in the ocean basins. To this amount should be added 12½ times the mass of all lime deposited in the deep sea.

The total mass of sediment on the continents can be estimated from the thickness of sediments deposited since the end of the pre-Cambrian. The average thickness for the North American continent is 0.8 km. Although the pre-Cambrian lasted three times as long, much of the sedimentary rock formed in that period has been denuded and re-deposited. The average for all sedimentary rocks may be evaluated at 1.2 km solid, and the volume at 2×10^8 km³. The mass of deep-sea sediments should then be $3 \times 2 \times 10^8 = 6 \times 10^8$ km³. On the strength of figures to be given later the addition in connection with deep-sea lime will be put at $12\frac{1}{2} \times \frac{1}{5} \times 10^8$ km³ or $2\frac{1}{2} \times 10^8$ km³. The total mass calculated without pore space for the oceanic sediments adds up to $8\frac{1}{2} \times 10^8$ km³.

The third method is based on denudation and volcanic activity (Fig. 162). From drilling results and the examination of exposures, Moss concluded that two-thirds of the surface of the United States is covered by Cambrian sediments. Part of the remaining area has received as much sediment in later periods as was denuded from it since the end of the pre-Cambrian. Therefore only about one-sixth of the area has made a net contribution to sedimentation since the beginning of the Cambrian. For the whole continent it may be assumed that one-third of the area has made its contribution. The production of a stratum measuring 650 m (free of pore space) over the entire surface calls for a denudation of 2 km. Besides this a great mass of terrigenous mud has been deposited on the continental slope. The area is roughly 10% of that of the earth, or twice that of the producing regions. Estimating the average thickness at 1200 m (free of pore space), an additional 2½ km of denudation is called for since the pre-Cambrian. It does not appear probable that the total denudation from the pre-Cambrian areas has exceeded the calculated 4½ km. This corresponds to a yearly amount of ⅙ km³.

However, there is another important source of sedimentary matter— the volcanoes. These are estimated by Sapper to have delivered 1 km³ per year since about A.D. 1500. Free of pore space this contribution probably does not exceed ¾ km³ yearly. As present activity probably exceeds the average, the figure of ½ km³ will be assumed. This volume corresponds to the yearly amount available for deep-sea sedi-

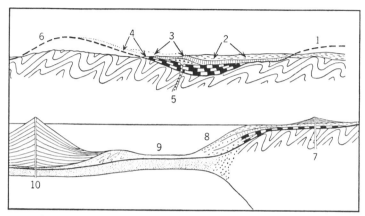

Fig. 162. Diagram illustrating sources of Post Algonkian sediments. 1–6, land surface at beginning of Cambrian; 2, Tertiary sediments; 3, Mesozoic sediments; 4, Paleozoic sediments; 5, intrusive rocks; 7, Recent volcano; 8, continental slope; 9, deep-sea sediments; 10, Recent volcano sunk by regional isostatic compensation and pressure on deep-sea deposits.

mentation beyond the continental slope. Naturally this does not imply that all volcanic matter was transported to the pelagic environments; it merely shows the volume. Since the pre-Cambrian the volume of deep-sea sedimentation works out at $2\frac{1}{2} \times 10^8$ km³, and since the beginning of geological time 10×10^8 km³ (free of pore space). We must add the $2\frac{1}{2} \times 10^8$ km³ stored in the continental slopes. For all oceanic sedimentation $12\frac{1}{2} \times 10^8$ km³ is found.

The fourth method takes the loss of sodium to the ocean waters during the sedimentary cycle as a basis for calculation. This element is excluded from the new minerals formed by chemical weathering and is leached out and carried to the sea. The total mass of sodium in the oceans should correspond to the loss during weathering, if we may ·postulate a sodium-free ocean at the beginning of geological time.

Table 26 shows the average composition of the principal rocks. Volcanoes have contributed more to the production of sediment than corresponds to the present content of volcanic rocks in the earth's crust, in consequence of the elevation, unconsolidated nature, and explosive activity. Hence, greater weight is given to volcanic rocks in the composition of our source material by adding an amount equal to that of all igneous rocks and taking the average. The result is found in column VII. The average composition of the more important sedimentary rocks (mainly from analyses of composite samples by Clarke) is presented in columns I to VI. Taking the ratio of red clay, blue mud, and globigerina ooze as 8:2:1, and combining this with continental sediment in the ratio 3:1, the composition of column VIII is found (for details see Kuenen, 1941, 1946).

TABLE 26. AVERAGE COMPOSITION OF ROCKS

	I	II	III	IV	V	VI	VII	VIII	IX *
	Shale	Sand-stone	Lime-stone	Red clay	Terrig-enous clay	Globig-erina ooze	Source	All sedi-ment	% differ-ence
SiO₂	58.11	78.31	5.19	54.48	57.05	26.64	57.83	58.16	+½
Al₂O₃	15.40	4.76	0.81	15.94	17.22	9.75	15.68	15.93	+1½
F₂O₃	6.70	1.40	0.54	9.60	7.60	3.75	8.17	8.54	+5
MnO	Trace	Trace	0.05	0.99	0.12	0.27	0.17	0.64	? †
MgO	2.44	1.16	7.89	3.31	2.17	1.38	3.77	3.58	−5
CaO	3.10	5.50	42.57	1.96	2.04	28.87	5.87	6.26	+7
Na₂O	1.30	0.45	0.05	2.05	1.05	0.98	3.47	1.89	−45
K₂O	3.24	1.32	0.33	2.85	2.25	1.32	2.59	2.82	+9
TiO₂	0.65	0.25	0.06	0.98	1.27	0.29	0.98	0.94	−5
P₂O₅	0.17	0.08	0.04	0.30	0.21	0.18	0.28	0.26	−8

* Differences between columns VII and VIII in percentage of each constituent of the source material.

† Large discrepancy, explained in text.

Comparison of columns VII and VIII gives the differences between source and computed total mass of sediment. These amounts, expressed in percentage of each oxide in the source, have been entered in the last column. In choosing the amounts of the three types of deep-sea sediment an attempt was made to render the figures of this last column as small as possible. It will be seen that the discrepancy between source and sediment is insignificant. By varying the ratios also for continental sediments the difference for any particular oxide can be reduced to zero. But it was not found possible to obtain a better overall result than that presented here.

The only two elements showing large discrepancies in column IX of Table 26 are manganese and sodium. The peculiar process of sedimentation of manganese by chemical precipitation, instead of by settling, appears to account for the apparently large amount of this element in sediments. In order to obtain a correct figure one would have to compose a composite sample for analysis in which the amount from each station corresponded to the rate of sedimentation in that particular locality. Actually, however, a composite sample was analyzed by Clarke in which equal amounts were taken from each station. The result is that the samples which come from slowly accumulating deposits are overemphasized. This does not make much difference for the oxides contained in mineral grains. But the precipitated manganese, which is concentrated to high values in the slowly accumulating samples, comes out too high in the final figures.

For Na_2O the loss in the sedimentary cycle is 45%, or 1.58% of the total weight of the source. The ocean waters and salt deposits together contain 2.02×10^{16} tons of Na_2O. It can now be calculated how much source rock was weathered to give this amount: $100 \div 1.58 \times 2.02 \times 10^{16}$ ton $= 128 \times 10^{16}$ tons. At a specific gravity of 2.71, the volume works out at 4.74×10^8 km³. To this amount should be added 12% for carbon dioxide contained in the lime and for water chemically bound. Hence the volume is raised to 5.3×10^8 km³ free of pore space.

A review of possible sources of error indicates that the calculated volume is probably too small. Our former estimate tended to show that volcanic matter forms more than half of all sediment on earth. As extrusive rocks contain less sodium than the average for igneous rocks, this element may be overestimated in our computation for the source. It has further been observed that the connate water contained in the pore space of rocks taken from bore holes is frequently of considerably higher salinity than normal sea water. If the same relation prevails in the thick stratum of sediment below the ocean floor, then the loss of sodium in the sedimentary cycle would be that much less than was found from the above calculation. The result would be an increase in the total mass of sediment. These and other considerations lead to a most probable volume of 7×10^8 km³. Subtracting continental sediments leaves a volume of 5×10^8 km³ for deep-sea deposits.

A fifth method for evaluating the mass of deep-sea sediment is based on the TiO_2 and P_2O_5 content of rocks. The source material contains

0.98% TiO_2, while the continental rocks show a much lower percentage. For shale, sandstone, and limestone the respective amounts are 0.65, 0.25, and 0.06%. The same applies to globigerina ooze, with only 0.29%. On the other hand red clay and blue mud are relatively rich in TiO_2, showing 0.98 and 1.27% respectively. A large amount of blue mud must be assumed to compensate the continental sediments and the globigerina ooze, while the amount of red clay is irrelevant.

The percentages of P_2O_5 in continental deposits are 0.17, 0.08, and 0.04, the source rocks containing 0.28%. Blue mud and globigerina ooze are also below the last figure with, respectively, 0.21 and 0.18%. From these figures a very large amount of red clay, that contains 0.30% of P_2O_5, can be deduced as necessary to compensate the low percentage in all other sediments.

The values for titanium and phosphorus are hardly sufficiently trustworthy to permit an exact calculation of the total amounts of sediment. But two facts emerge from the above analysis. First, the total mass of deep-sea deposits must be several times as large as that of continental deposits, for all types of the latter are deficient in TiO_2 and P_2O_5 and no combination of these deposits can explain the geochemistry of titanium and phosphorus. Second, a welcome confirmation is found of the reliability of the geochemical computations. The source and sediments of our table show a fair measure of agreement for the major constituents for which the calculations were made. The two remaining elements are likewise found to be in good agreement when the various types of sediment are combined in the same ratio.

Summarizing the outcome of the different and in part independent methods for estimating the total mass of deep-sea deposits contained in the earth's crust, the following result is obtained:

From the rate of recent accumulation	9×10^8 km³
From the ratio shale : sandstone : limestone	$8\frac{1}{2} \times 10^8$ km³
From denudation and volcanism	$12\frac{1}{2} \times 10^8$ km³
From the sodium content of the oceans	5×10^8 km³
From the geochemistry of TiO_2 and P_2O_5	Several times 2×10^8 km³

Theoretically an estimate of deep-sea sedimentation could also be based on the total production from the continents. The contribution from rivers is estimated at 12 km³ per year, and the combined amount from marine erosion, volcanic dust dropped directly in the sea, windborne dust, and dissolved silica and lime may be placed at $1\frac{1}{2}$ km³ per year. The total of $13\frac{1}{2}$ km³ per year spread out on the sea floor works out at 3 cm (solid) per 1000 years. But unhappily insufficient data exist to estimate the proportions of deep-sea and shallow-water deposition or to compare the figures for recent times with the average for the geological past. All we can do is to calculate whether results from other methods are contradicted by the above figure.

Taking the area of the deep sea below 1000-m depth as five-sixths of that of the ocean, and an average solid deposition of $\frac{1}{6}$ cm per 1000 years, and then subtracting this amount from $13\frac{1}{2} \times 1000$ km³, the rate of accumulation in water less than 1000 m deep works out at 20 cm solid per 1000 years, or 80 cm with pore space. The last figure appears considerably above what would be expected from available data, because so much of the shallow seas are a non-depositional environment or show only slow accumulation. Hence an estimated present oceanic sedimentation of $\frac{1}{6}$ cm solid—or well over $\frac{1}{2}$ cm with pore space—certainly does not exceed what present denudation would lead one to expect.

It is also worth while to realize that our estimate of total pelagic sedimentation corresponds to a yearly amount of only $\frac{2}{5}$ km³, whereas the estimated present supply to the oceans from rivers alone is 12 km³ or 30 times as great.

A paper by Weibull (1947) tells of an entirely new and highly important method of actually measuring the thickness of sedimentary strata on the sea floor. He uses an adapted method of echo sounding, giving additional echoes from strata in the bottom deposit. So far the preliminary results in the Mediterranean show thicknesses of hundreds of meters to 2700 m.[1]

The geoeconomy of calcium, silica, and manganese needs separate treatment. Taking into account the area and rate of accumulation of globigerina ooze, the CaO of all recent sediments amounts to $12\frac{1}{2}\%$. Sverdrup et al. (1942) arrived at the slightly lower figure of 19% $CaCO_3$, corresponding to 11% CaO in carbon dioxide-free state. The amount of CaO in the source is but 5.87%. For obtaining agreement in our table a much smaller amount of globigerina ooze had to be assumed, namely 9% instead of the 50% in recent deep-sea deposits. Obviously very different relations as to the accumulation of lime must have prevailed in former ages. Twenhofel solved the difficulty by pointing out that before the Cretaceous pelagic Foraminifera did not exist and hence far less lime was deposited in the deep sea then than

---

[1] For the preliminary computations Weibull assumed that the rate of propagation of sound waves in the sediment equals that in water. Probably it is higher, and the thickness of sediment should be multiplied by the same factor.

since. The following picture of the geoeconomy of calcium is arrived at.

During the pre-Cambrian there were hardly any organisms secreting lime. The calcium liberated by weathering and accumulating in the ocean waters in excess of saturation must have been precipitated. As there are few limestones amongst pre-Cambrian sediments, it appears most likely that accumulation took place in part on the deep-sea floor. The suggestion offered by Hills (1947) that the pre-Cambrian ocean contained hydrogen chloride, and that no calcium carbonate could be secreted, is not borne out by any facts of pre-Cambrian sedimentation.

After the advent during the Cambrian of organisms secreting lime in shallow waters inorganic precipitation in the deep sea came to an end and practically all the lime supplied to the oceans from the continents was deposited in shallow waters on the continents. Gradually the amount of limestone incorporated in the continental masses increased. During the Paleozoic and Mesozoic eras a gradual rise occurred in the proportion of limestone deposited. The part played by limestone attained a maximum during the Cretaceous. The lime budget was continuously gaining in bulk, for the amount of CaO liberated by denudation from limestones and carried to the oceans by rivers increased steadily. Probably precipitation in epicontinental seas gradually grew in importance. But, during the Cretaceous, pelagic Foraminifera began to extract large quantities of lime from the oceans and to deposit their tests in the deep sea. Not only the supply of CaO newly liberated from igneous rocks was called upon, but also the part derived from the solution of limestone. Gradually the hoard put by on the continents during the Paleozoic and Mesozoic eras is thus taken out of circulation and frozen on the floor of the oceans. Computation from the data given above shows that in another 100 to 150 million years the whole of the accumulated capital of lime will have been squandered by pelagic Foraminifera. A shortage of CaO will then set in and necessitate some kind of adaptation of future life on earth. The precipitation of lime in the deep sea will also be reduced to the supply from weathering igneous rocks.

Two curious facts find a ready explanation in the above deductions. In the first place the present relative scarcity of calcareous deposits in shallow waters, as compared to former periods, is a striking feature of recent marine sedimentation. The total amount of $CaCO_3$ accumulating on the sea floor depends on the rate of increment from rivers of dissolved calcium to the oceans. As the present discharge of rivers would require no more than ½ to 1 million years to make up an amount of lime equal to that already present in the sea water, the lag between discharge and deposition cannot be large from a geological point of view.

Since the Cretaceous pelagic Foraminifera extract such large amounts of CaO from the seas that oversaturation is hardly anywhere attained. Hence, inorganic precipitation can at present occur only in a few favorable places. The bulk of lime is now deposited in the deep sea, whereas formerly it went to shallow-water sediments. On a previous page (p. 220) it was pointed out that the problem of how the structureless groundmass of many fossil limestones was generated remains as yet unsolved. Our deductions now point to the probability of inorganic or bacteriological precipitation in shallow seas when the waters were oversaturated with lime.

The second feature that can now be explained is the gradual relative decrease of magnesium in carbonate rocks during the past. Daly showed that from the Devonian up to the Cretaceous the proportion of magnesium in carbonate rocks gradually fell and then began to rise again.

TABLE 27.   THE RATIO $CaCO_3$ TO $MgCO_3$ IN CARBONATE ROCKS
(ACCORDING TO DALY)

Pre-Devonian	2.39:1
Devonian	4.49:1
Carboniferous	8.89:1
Cretaceous	40.23:1
Tertiary	37.92:1
Quaternary and Recent	25.00:1

The persistent accumulation of calcium up to the Cretaceous, followed by a decrease, is brought out in Table 27. Again, the activity of pelagic Foraminifera can be traced in these data.

As the formation of red clay was stimulated by the low temperatures of the Pleistocene it appears possible that the warm Tertiary periods were characterized by a marked development of calcareous deposits. The amount of $CaCO_3$ available in ocean waters is limited, however. It is therefore not probable that there was sufficient supply of calcareous tests to cause total absence of red clays. Over a long period of time there cannot be a much stronger sedimentation of lime than is at present taking place, but the Tertiary red clays may have shown a somewhat higher percentage of lime, or a smaller extent, while globigerina oozes were somewhat lower in lime content.

The geoeconomy of *silica* is somewhat different. The weathering of igneous rocks produces clay, quartz, and dissolved matter. It has been shown that most of the clay is washed away and ultimately deposited in the deep sea.

The physical properties of quartz, however, result in the production of comparatively large grains. These particles are in general too heavy to be readily transported to the ocean basins. Hence, this mineral is gradually concentrated on the continents. But, as pointed out earlier, a not inconsiderable amount of silica goes into solution, especially in connection with the weathering of feldspars. The annual supply of dissolved SiO_2 to the oceans is 320×10^6 tons, or roughly $0.1 \ km^3$. A fair percentage of this material is extracted from the sea water by sponges, radiolarians, and diatoms and deposited in the deep sea. However, this amount is negligible as compared to the total supply to the seas of SiO_2 in the shape of quartz. This quantity can be estimated at $\frac{4}{25} \times 12\frac{1}{2} \ km^3$ per year, or $2 \ km^3$. This is about 20 times the loss of amorphous SiO_2 to the deep sea.

The quartz deriving from denudation has been gradually accumulating on the continents from the beginning of geological time, while clay was being lost to the deep sea. Hence, the continents are slowly becoming more and more thickly veneered by quartz sands, and there is no reason to expect a relaxation of this process in the future.

Whereas *manganese* of the source rocks averages 0.17%, it forms only 0.01% in continental sediments and is evidently leached out and carried to the sea in solution. Several facts strongly indicate that precipitation in the deep sea forms the counterpart of this leaching from continental sediments. (1) Blue mud contains about as much as the source, while globigerina ooze has double that amount and red clay six times. There is concentration in the deposits accumulating slowly in the deep sea. (2) Manganese oxide forms nodules in the pelagic sediments. (3) It is a matter of observation that all hard surfaces, whether pebbles, rocky bottom, coral fragments, or shells, that remain for a sufficiently long time uncovered on the sea floor become coated with a similar substance. This takes place in all depths, at least below a few hundred meters. (4) Roughly speaking, the same amount is deposited per unit of surface and of time in areas of red clay and of globigerina ooze, but there are great local variations, as Pettersson (1945) has shown. Although it is possible, as this author has suggested, that the sedimentary particles absorb some manganese before reaching the sea floor, the enumerated arguments point rather towards direct precipitation on the deep-sea floor. The rate at which the manganese oxide is precipitated should be strongly influenced by the alkalinity of the water, the oxygen content, and the rate of flow. There is nothing in the great variation in the rate of accumulation against the assumption of precipitation.

It has been suggested that the manganese in deep-sea deposits is derived from basic lavas on neighboring lands or on the sea floor. Even granting that a large percentage of manganese could be leached out of hot lavas and precipitated elsewhere, a simple calculation shows that impossibly large volumes of lava would have to be assumed.

In conclusion of these geoeconomical computations an estimate can be made of the thickness of the sedimentary cover of the deep-sea floor. To begin with, the obtained volume must be recalculated to allow for pore space. The average thickness is then found to attain about 3 km for red clay. To this amount must be added 200 m of globigerina ooze covering about half the area of the deep sea. The continental slopes should be composed of a wedge of sediment with a maximum thickness of about 5 km, while the average thickness of the sedimentary veneer on the continents is 1½ km.

Doubtless, future investigation will bring significant amplifications and corrections of these estimates. They should be regarded merely as first approximations. But because of the agreement among the different methods it does not appear likely that drastic revision, as for instance a reduction or multiplication by a factor of 10, will prove necessary.

It was pointed out above that in the near future geophysical prospecting methods will be applied to the ocean floor. This may result in actually proving the thickness of the sedimentary cover, if a sharp transition to the original crystalline crust exists. At any rate a minimum value should be obtained.

Now that a rough estimate has been obtained for the magnitude of suboceanic sediments, a number of important questions may be viewed.

1. When dealing with the isostatic balance between continents and ocean basins, it is always assumed that the floor of the Pacific is formed by sima. Now an average cover of sediments amounting to perhaps 3 km in thickness may be tentatively assumed, of which the specific gravity is even lower than that of the continental granites. From this it follows that in order to obtain isostatic balance between the major topographic features of the earth's crust the granite part of the continental blocks must be either 3 to 4 km thicker than generally assumed or that the average specific gravity must be somewhat less.

2. If the earth's crust is gradually thickening in consequence of cooling, as some geologists assume, the rate at which heat is lost by the oceanic sections and hence the increase in thickness of the crystalline crust must be smaller than if no appreciable sedimentation had taken place. If the loss of heat is balanced by radioactive generation, a melting of the lower surface of the crust beneath the blanket of oceanic deposits must be taking place.

3. A volcanic cone built on top of the thick prism of soft oceanic deposits must tend to subside in consequence of compaction and plastic deformation of its substratum (see Fig. 162, p. 388). A subsidence of several hundreds of meters may be expected. It is difficult to say, however, whether this process is so slow as to result in subsidence of the cone long after the constructive period has come to a close or whether it keeps up with the growth of the cone and merely results in a slower rate of upbuilding than if the substratum were firm, unyielding rock. In the former case the long-continued subsidence might in part explain the growth of atolls and barrier reefs as postulated in Darwin's theory. On the Hawaiian island Lanai, marine sediments occur 350 m above sea level. This proves that elevation of volcanic islands of the Pacific does take place, but does not disprove, however, that a general slow subsidence of volcanic masses occurs to which tectonic movements both positive and negative may be added.

4. Subsidence of volcanic cones should also occur in consequence of oceanic sedimentation that takes place after the structure was finished. Hess (1946) has pointed out that the earth's crust is not sufficiently strong to carry the weight of accumulating oceanic deposits. Sinking of the suboceanic crust and rise of the continental blocks must accompany sedimentation. The height of sea level with respect to the surface of the continents is a complicated problem that will be dealt with in a later chapter. As first approximation it may be assumed that sea level remains in the same position relative to the land surface. But a volcanic cone will sink, together with the floor on which it rests. It will sink absolutely, with respect to the center of the earth and also with respect to sea level. The earlier in the earth's history the volcano was built, the farther it will have been submerged. The part emerging when the volcanic activity died out was quickly planed off by marine erosion. From then on, the decapitated cone gradually subsided as sedimentation forced down the suboceanic crust. According to Hess the countless guyots recently detected in the Pacific by echo sounding represent so many pre-Cambrian volcanic cones. Their summit depths vary between 940 and 1730 m at least,

but future soundings may be expected to detect even deeper summits, as indications have already been obtained of guyots having depths between 2000 and 3400 m.

It is remarkable that guyots of less than 940-m depth appear to be absent or at least very scarce. Hess accounts for this by upward growth of decapitated cones through the activity of lime-secreting organisms. These first appeared in Cambrian times. Earlier cones had by then become too deeply submerged to allow the establishment of lime-secreting benthonic animals. In this manner the less ancient cones managed to keep in contact with the surface by organic growth and thus form atolls, instead of becoming submerged to depths intermediate between 940 m and sea level. Atolls must crown a cap of limestone erected on a submerged foundation in the form of a guyot.

The next question is whether this picture tallies with the quantitative deductions on the amount of deep-sea sedimentation. It was shown that sedimentation beyond the limits of the continents was of the order of 8×10^8 km³, representing an average layer of 2½ km, solid. Assuming that the area of the continents has remained roughly constant, sea level should have risen by the same amount relative to the original surface of the ocean floor. Since the beginning of the Cambrian about 600 m may be assumed. To this amount should be added the rise due to volume increase of the oceans from the production of juvenile water. This last amount is estimated in the next chapter at 175 m. Together a figure of 775 m is obtained. Some further corrections must be made. In the first place the melting of all land ice would add some 30 m to the depth of the oceans. On the other hand the abraded level of the guyots should have been a few dozen meters below sea level. These amounts compensate each other. As the secretion of lime did not come into full swing until late in Cambrian times, the growth of lime caps probably started less than 500 million years ago. Hence the figure 775 m is on the high side.

Although no great trust can be placed in the calculated amount of depression, it does appear rather doubtful that this factor alone can account for the submergence of nearly 1000 m. The present writer ventures to suggest that 500 to 600 m of this amount is due to the relative rise of sea level and 400 to 500 m to compaction. The compaction would probably take place rather swiftly, for instance in a few hundred thousands to a couple of millions of years. Isostatic subsidence is not probable. But on the evidence of gradual compensational uplift of the zone with the marked negative anomalies in Indonesia treated in an earlier chapter the possibility of a similar but

opposite local deformation of the crust under the weight of a volcanic cone must be reckoned with. It might occupy several to many
millions of years. (See also p. 477.)

5. The theory of continental drift can be applied only if the postulate is made of a plastic sea floor that yields to the pressure of a sliding
continent. Although geophysical evidence is strongly opposed to this
contention, the fact remains that the solid crust of the ocean floor
cannot be sampled. Hence, appeal can always be made to our lack
of knowledge, when postulating properties for the suboceanic crust.
Now that a thick cover of pelagic deposits has been deduced, however,
a new difficulty to continental drift becomes apparent. These deposits
have a much lower specific gravity than the underlying sima and are
certainly not in a suitable physical condition to spread out laterally
when the advancing American continents swept westwards. These
advancing continental icebergs should act as a skimmer moving across
the Pacific pool of sima and crowd together the superficial layer of
sediment against their blunt bows. The western ranges of America
are not composed of deep-sea sediments and cannot represent this
Pacific cover. The westward drift of South America is supposed to
have reached 3000 km, and the deep-sea deposits skimmed off the sima
should amount to 9000 km^3 per km length of coast. Complete isostatic adjustment of this mass would still leave a volume of 1000 to
2000 km^3 above the ocean floor. If this mass of scum were to form a
plateau at sea level its breadth would reach 300 km. Far from en-
countering anything of this sort, a deep-sea trough is found along the
Pacific coast of South America.

DECOMPOSABLE ORGANIC MATTER [1]

The amount of decomposable organic matter contained in marine
sediments is a problem of great importance to mankind, for practically
all petroleum is obtained from fossil marine sediments and has been
formed out of organic remains deposited together with the inorganic
constituents. Moreover, the organic matter plays a prominent part
as food of benthonic animals. The diagenetic alteration of animal and
plant remains to oil will not be considered in this volume, and attention will be restricted to sedimentation, the first phase in the chain of
events leading to the formation of oil pools.

Since the hypothesis of inorganic generation of oil has been abandoned and the impossibility has been realized of attributing the oil to

[1] Trask, 1932, 1939; Trask and Patnode, 1942.

the burial of large schools of whales, there no longer exists doubt that the chief source must lie with marine planktonic life. Some rare exceptions may occur in which fresh-water deposits have functioned as source beds of petroleum, but the vast majority of oil fields show marine facies.

In the foregoing chapter it was pointed out that the small size of most planktonic organisms is compensated by the vast numbers in which such forms as Foraminifera, pteropods, radiolarians, diatoms, and all manner of Algae swarm in the surface layers of the seas. It was also emphasized that coastal waters and high latitudes are in general far more fertile than the warmer central areas of the oceans. The question now is the percentage of organic matter contained in various types of deposit.

The amount of decomposable organic matter contained in a sample may be found by determining the percentage of organic carbon or of nitrogen. But with the nature of the organic matter the ratio of these elements to each other and to the total varies considerably. For the time being one must use an average factor of multiplication for estimating the total organic content from one or both of the elements. With carbon, 1.8, and with nitrogen, 18, are factors suggested by Trask (1939). On the other hand, Wiseman and Bennett (1940) found the carbon-to-nitrogen ratio in the Arabian Sea to vary between 5 and 34. They prefer to give these quantities separately, and they attach little importance to the calculated total of organic matter. The average ratio of carbon to nitrogen found by various investigators seems to be 10 or somewhat more. The rough approximations obtained by the procedure followed by Trask and his co-workers are sufficiently accurate for our purpose.

Two generalizations have been established: the organic content increases (1) with decreasing grain size of the sediment, and (2) with approach to the coast. More than 1000 km offshore the content is insignificant, generally below 1%. It increases to about 2½% at 100 to 200 km from land, and remains fairly constant over the remaining area around the land. This correlation with distance is due mainly to differences in productivity of planktonic life.

The high content of fine-grained deposits is the result of two factors. The lutite contained in a deposit safeguards the enclosed organic matter against oxidation far more perfectly than does coarse sand. The wider pores between large grains allow water to circulate and to introduce a fresh supply of oxygen into the deposit. Hence the organic matter is attacked after deposition and carried away.

A second cause of the high percentage in fine deposits is to be sought in the nature of the sedimentary environments in which they accumulate. The deposition of lutite cannot occur where currents and waves sweep the bottom except off very large rivers. Lutite in a general way requires quiet bottom waters. Here both the fine particles and the light organic matter can accumulate together. The absence of effective ventilation is another favorable property of sedimentary environments in which lutite is accumulating, for both oxidation and benthonic life feeding on the mud are reduced to the minimum.

The abnormal wealth in organic matter that characterizes green and black muds deposited in the euxinic environment of entirely stagnant basins is readily explained. The black muds settling in Norwegian fiords with stagnant waters may contain as much as 10 or even 20% of decomposable organic matter. The black muds of the Black Sea are even richer, attaining no less than 35%, while the gray laminae of the same basin have 3 to 10%. The green mud of the Kaoe Bay on the coast of Halmahera, shows just over 3%.

In direct connection with the foregoing matters Trask found that depressions in and along the continental terrace contain fine deposits rich in organic matter (Fig. 163; see also Fig. 144, p. 339). The best-known example is the Channel Island region off the California coast. Several basins are found there 1000 to 2000 m deep, divided by ridges of less than 1000 m, crowned here and there by islands. Most of these islands are surrounded by rocky bottom, while the ridges show sand and sandy silt. In the basins, however, fine mud is accumulating. The organic content on the ridges is from zero to 5% and in the basins from 5 to 10%.

From data obtained with the *Snellius* samples in the Moluccan area Kuenen (1943) showed that the organic content decreases with rising percentage of lime and with decreasing depth (Fig. 164). But these variations are mainly due to concomitant fall in the percentage of lutite, or in other words to the correlation of organic matter with clay content. The latter relation is almost entirely responsible for the percentage of decomposable organic matter in these hemipelagic abyssal deposits. Yet there remains 0.5% in samples without any clay at all. A percentage of 2½ corresponds to 70% clay. This explains the high content of 2½% in the shallow samples from the Java Sea, where fine-grained deposits were sampled in waters of less than 100-m depth.

Deposits exceptionally rich in organic matter are encountered in areas where upwelling waters fertilize the surface layers of the oceans.

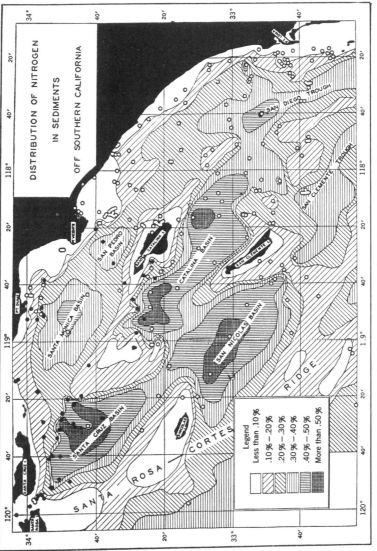

Fig. 163. Relation between organic nitrogen content in sediments and relief features off Southern California (cf. Fig. 144, p. 339). (After Revelle and Shepard, in Trask, 1939, *Recent Marine Sediments*, Fig. 8, p. 262, American Association of Petroleum Geologists.)

An example occurs in Whale Bay on the west coast of Africa. Twice yearly an immensely rich plankton crop of dinoflagellates grows there (Brongersma-Sanders, 1948). These organisms secrete a poisonous substance that kills off the fish fauna. Dead fish and plankton settle on the bottom together and form a sapropele-like deposit rich in hydrogen sulfide. Benthonic life is not able to colonize this area, and only anaerobic bacteria are encountered. In consequence of this peculiar cycle extensive deposits are formed on the sea floor with an

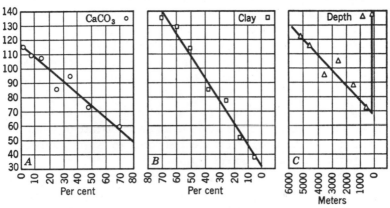

FIG. 164. Relation between organic matter (expressed in 1/1000% nitrogen) and various factors in the Moluccas. (After Kuenen, 1943, Fig. 3, p. 18.)

exceptionally high organic content. Off the Californian coast and elsewhere similar conditions, though less extreme, are brought about probably by upwelling of relatively deep water. Possibly the green mud, rich in hydrogen sulfide, covering the bottom of the Gulf of Oman is due to the same cause.

THE INFLUENCE OF SEVERAL FACTORS ON SEDIMENTATION [1]

Climate. Climate has much less direct influence on marine than on terrestrial sedimentation. The water forms a protective screen between the atmosphere and the sea floor, and the deeper the water the more uniform are the conditions on the bottom. The influences of frost, drought, etc., are entirely or almost entirely excluded. The temperature is nearly constant, and wind can have only an indirect influence by generating currents and waves. The color, grain size,

[1] See Twenhofel, 1932, 1939.

and chemical composition of marine sediments are therefore practically independent of direct atmospheric influences.

This does not mean, however, that marine sediments are not influenced by the climate *in*directly. Actually the nature of terrigenous matter, especially the products of weathering, delivered to the sea depends largely on the climate of adjacent lands. The closer inshore a deposit is accumulating and the shallower the water, the more obvious will be the part played by the climate of the coastal area. Some aspects may be dealt with more in detail.

The most important climatic factor in marine sedimentation is the temperature. Thus the possibility of annual convection (and hence the fertilization of surface waters that controls the production of plankton) is mainly a question of variation in temperature. Besides, the extraction of lime from sea water is controlled to a large extent by the temperature and is adversely influenced when it is low. For silica the opposite relation to temperature holds. In marine environments adjacent to deserts a not inconsiderable admixture of wind-borne dust is introduced. Coral reefs are restricted to warm climates, and glacial marine deposits to arctic regions.

In general a gradual transition from tropical to arctic marine sediments can be traced both in deep and shallow waters. Nevertheless it is seldom possible to deduce the climatic conditions under which a fossil sediment was deposited by comparison with recent deposits. In all latitudes the entire range of grain size is represented on the sea floor, and all transitions from angular to perfectly rounded particles are met with. Red colors in terrestrial sediments are restricted to low latitudes, but nothing of the kind can be said of marine deposits. In all climates the reduced state of iron in blue muds causes a dark gray to blue tint, below a thin superficial stratum of reddish brown oxidized mud. Red clay can also be formed in high latitudes. The only correlation between warm climates and red deposits is found where lateritic soil is carried to the sea in large quantities and causes the formation of red mud.

Only exceptionally will morainic material still bear evidence of its origin when once incorporated in marine sediments. Larger pieces of rock generally lose their typical surface markings long before they have passed through the grinding mill of surf along the shore. The finer elements of boulder clay are washed out and sorted before they settle permanently on the sea floor. Coarse pieces may be rafted by ice, but tree stubs may perform a similar action with boulders in warm waters. Only in the rare event that striated glacial boulders are rafted directly to an environment where attack by abrasive agents is excluded can pertinent proof of arctic conditions be preserved.

On the whole, enclosed organic remains give the most reliable evidence on climatic conditions in former ages. But, the farther back one proceeds in the geological past, the less trustworthy are deductions based on organic evidence. Whereas Mesozoic coral reefs can be held as definitely proving tropical conditions, a similar deduction for the Paleozoic is open to doubt. The invasion of arctic climates by *Elephas* and *Rhinoceros* during the Pleistocene is a striking instance of the dangers surrounding deductions based on the present-day distribution of life in the climatic zones.

But, although admitting that the climate of the past cannot be easily deduced from the nature of fossil sediments, one can fully appreciate the changes wrought in marine sediments at any given locality by a fluctuation of the climatic conditions. The world-wide alterations in marine sedimentation caused by the ice ages may be recalled to emphasize this aspect of our problem. In the same manner all variations in temperature, precipitation, or wind will find more or less well-marked expression in the deposits accumulating in the neighborhood of the region undergoing such fluctuations. The magnitude of supply, the relative amount of colloidal matter, and the nature and amount of organic contributions are all subject to the climate of the environment of sedimentation itself or of the regions supplying sedimentary matter.

Relative Rise and Fall of the Strand Line. In dealing with the profile of equilibrium, submergence and emergence of the coast were mentioned. No strict rules can be established as to the result of such changes. Shifting of the strand line may be caused by eustatic movements of sea level, by movements of the crust, by erosion, or by sedimentation. When the relative movement of the land is downward the first consequence is the washing away of the soil and the production of fine sedimentary matter. Later, marine erosion may attack the underlying country rock and produce coarse detritus. The increased depth allows larger waves to reach protruding parts of the shore and to help in the onslaught on the land. As the coast is pushed farther inland the force of the waves diminishes and hence also the size of the erosion products. Where transgression takes place without the intervention of subsidence, the stage of coarse detritus is omitted and only fine material is dumped on the foreset beds of the terrace. Hence, marine erosion need not always be accompanied by the formation of a basal conglomerate.

Especially where the relative subsidence of the coast is fast enough to carry the new profile of equilibrium above the old sea floor, there is a chance of a basal conglomerate forming the lowest stratum of a new stratigraphical series. Naturally the country rock or rivers should provide suitable material for the development of cobbles or boulders. Where the subsidence is slow no conglomerate need be formed, or, if that does happen, it will often be destroyed in a later stage of the marine erosion. The scarcity of basal conglomerates in the stratigraphical prisms indicates that in general relative subsidence is comparatively slow.

With a receding sea the depth will generally be too small for the direct establishment of a profile of equilibrium. Erosion will set in, and this may cause the deposition of coarse material farther out. The consequences will often be marine erosion of earlier deposits and a slight unconformity where renewed sedimentation takes place. A possible stage of development is the temporary building of offshore bars.

A different sequence of events results when a rise of the land accompanies the sinking of the sea floor, a frequent combination in geosynclinal regions. A shifting of the strand line need not occur, but rejuvenation of the erosion and a continual creation of space to accommodate the erosion products are the result. As a rule the movements are intermittent and a rhythmical alternation of finer and coarser sediment will be deposited in the basin. The relative amount of lime will also show variations on account of the irregular degree of dilution by terrigenous matter and on account of differences in the supply of calcareous tests resulting from varying ecological conditions (depth, salinity, turbidity, etc.). Thus sudden changes in the relief explain the rhythmical series in geosynclinal prisms that may show countless repetitions of identical groups of strata.

Organisms. Mud-feeding animals play an important part in sedimentation by consuming organic matter contained in the bottom deposits and by reworking the sediment. For example, on sand flats around the British coasts lobworms burrow to depths of half a meter. It has been estimated that, where they occur in larger numbers, an amount equivalent to a layer of half a meter of sediment passes through their digestive channels every two years. This reworking was mentioned before (pp. 367 and 373) in connection mainly with deep-sea deposits. Some remarks on shallow sediments may be added.

Some investigators are of the opinion that all sedimentary matter of the shelf is thus passed through the intestines of mud-feeding animals, a large part of it several times. But this opinion doubtless greatly exaggerates the importance of reworking. There are certainly very many exceptions, for instance where accumulation is abnormally swift, or where the ecological conditions are unfavorable to benthonic life. It may be observed that even our most richly fossiliferous formations show excellent stratification although deposited in an environment swarming with life.

A striking instance of stratification in recent shallow sediments is the widespread lamination discovered by Häntzschel in the tidal flats of Germany.

The crushing and trituration of shells and tests is brought about by many organisms. Some fishes consume lamellibranchia and spit out the shells again intact; others chew up the shells to small fragments. Crustaceans break shells with their nippers. Sponges (*Cliona*), gasteropods, and Algae drill small holes in the shells. Wood, bones, etc., are sometimes riddled with narrow- or wide-bore holes by lamellibranchia, *Lepas*, etc. In this manner mechanical and chemical destruction is aided.

One of the results of these actions is that well-preserved remains and a high percentage of decomposable organic matter may be expected only in environments showing either swift accumulation or an abnormal supply of organic remains, or offering adverse conditions to benthonic life (poor ventilation). An example is the occurrence in mass of graptolites in black bituminous shales, which appear to have accumulated in poorly ventilated basins. The graptolites must have settled to the bottom in other environments also, but they have not been preserved on account of carrion eaters.

The role played by bacteria in the mud is now gradually becoming better known. Aerobic forms are profuse in the upper 5 to 10 cm of marine deposits, while anaerobic bacteria are found to depths of 40 or 60 cm. Farther down they quickly disappear, but the enzymes left by former individuals, that died as sedimentation proceeded, continue to act on the organic matter. Oxidation of the organic matter consumes the oxygen contained in the enclosed sea water at shallow depths in the deposit. Practically no new supply to lower strata takes place. The reduction of the deposit increases with depth, while the reducing capacity diminishes as the result of the bacterial activity.

Many types of bacteria occur that can decompose all kinds of organic matter, leaving substances that are more and more closely related to petroleum. Concomitantly they synthesize new protoplasm from waste organic matter. This new protoplasm in turn serves as nourishment for bottom-dwelling animals. It is obvious that bacterial activity is of the greatest importance for the economy of organic matter in the bottom deposits of the sea.

SOME REMARKS ON THE INTERPRETATION OF FOSSIL DEPOSITS

The problem of ascertaining the conditions of deposition of fossil sediments, and the processes by which they were formed, is of the greatest importance not only from a theoretical point of view but also for economic purposes such as oil geology. The distinction between terrestrial, fluviatile, lacustrine, and marine environments is generally a simple matter. Usually the fossils give sufficient indication. But when they are absent, or when more details on the nature and extent of a fossil sedimentation basin are required, great difficulties may arise. Beach and delta facies are often easily recognized, but desert deposits may show similar characteristics (cross bedding, ripple marks, the results of temporary emergence and drying out, etc.). The difficulty of ascertaining the depth of marine sedimentation has already been referred to. Climatic indications are often wanting, and the distance to the coast is seldom directly obvious. The direction from which supply has come and the nature of the transport, whether by wind, rivers, marine currents, or waves, are hard to ascertain. All properties should then be taken into account in the hope of finding pertinent evidence.

Up to the present our knowledge of the properties of recent sediments formed under various conditions is still very elementary. One of the reasons is that oceanographical expeditions have concentrated almost exclusively on the deep sea, the much more important shallow regions having been grossly neglected. However, the growing number of oceanographic stations working on shallow-water programs and the interest gradually awakening among oil geologists in recent sedimentation may lead to improvement. Laboratory investigations of sedimentation problems are now being carried out in many centers. An example is de Sitter's investigation of facies in the south Sumatra oil field by means of Foraminifera and mineral grains. An instance of what may be attained by detailed study of a single property is the examination by Doeglas of the grain size of sands and silts (1946). He showed that a large number of fractions should be determined and the results plotted on arithmetic probability paper. The amount of the extreme fractions proves to be of special importance in ascertaining whether a deposit has been formed under uniform or varying conditions. Deep-sea, aeolian, tidal-flat, beach, and river deposits each have characteristic size frequency distributions. On the other hand mechanical analysis alone can seldom prove the original environment. A vast program of research, especially the regional treatment of various environments, will have to be carried out before the interpretation of fossil deposits by means of mechanical analysis can be undertaken with chances of success.

The same need for data on other properties such as grain shape, organic content, enclosed animal and plant remains, etc., and their relation to transporting agents was felt in the course of our survey of marine sediments and their environment. Here a most attractive field of endeavor is offered to geologists. To treat this vast subject would require a separate chapter and would lead to much repetition of matters dealt with in the present and former chapter. The reader is referred to separate treatises such as those of Twenhofel; Barth et al.; and Pratje (1938); Pettijohn (1949).

Bibliography

ANDRÉE, K. Sedimentbildung am Meeresboden, *Geol. Rundschau*, Vol. 3, pp. 324–338, 1912; Vol. 7, pp. 123–170, 249–301, 329–337, 1916/17; Vol. 8, pp. 36–79, 1917.

Geologie des Meeresbodens, Bd. 2, 689 pp., Bornträger, Leipzig, 1920.

Das Meer und seine geologische Tätigkeit, in W. SALOMON, *Grundzüge der Geologie*, Bd. 1, p. 361–533, 1925.

ARCHANGUELSKY, A. D. On the Black Sea Sediments and Their Importance for the Study of Sedimentary Rocks, *Bull. Soc. Nat. Moscow*, Sec. Geol., T. V., Nouv. Ser., T. 35, pp. 199–289, 1927.

BAILEY, E. B. Sedimentation in Relation to Tectonics, *Bull. Geol. Soc. Am.*, Vol. 47, pp. 1713–1726, 1936.

BARRELL, J. Rhythms and the Measurement of Geological Time, *Bull. Geol. Soc. Am.*, Vol. 28, pp. 745–904, 1917.

Marine and Terrestrial Conglomerates, *Bull. Geol. Soc. Am.*, Vol. 36, pp. 279–341, 1925.

BEERS, R. F. Radioactivity and Organic Content of some Paleozoic Shales, *Bull. Am. Assoc. Petr. Geol.*, Vol. 29, pp. 1–22, 1945.

BOURCART, J. La sédimentation dans la Manche, in *La géologie des terrains récents dans l'ouest de l'Europe*, Sess. Extr. Soc. Belges de Géol., September 1946, pp. 14–43, 1947.

Sur les vases du plateau continental français, *Compt. rend. acad. sci.*, Vol. 225, pp. 137–139, 1947.

BOURCART, J., and C. FRANCIS-BOEUF. *La vase*, 67 pp., Hermann, Paris, 1942.

BRAJNIKOV, B., C. FRANCIS-BOEUF, and V. ROMANOVSKY. *Techniques d'étude des sédiments*, 110 pp., Hermann, Paris, 1943.

BRAMLETTE, M. N., and W. H. BRADLEY. Lithology and Geological Interpretations, in Geology and Biology of North Atlantic Deep-Sea Cores, *U. S. Geol. Surv. Prof. Paper* 196, 1940–1942.

BRONGERSMA-SANDERS, M. The Importance of Upwelling Water to Vertebrate Paleontology and Oil Geology, *Verh. Kon. Ned. Akad. Wet. Amsterdam,* Afd. Nat., Sec. 2, Dl. 45, 4, 112 pp., 1948.

CAILLEUX, A. La disposition individuelle des galets dans les formations détritiques, *Rév. géogr. phys. et géol. dyn.,* Vol. 11, pp. 171–196, 1938.

CLARKE, F. W. The Data of Geochemistry, *Bull. U. S. Geol. Surv.* 770, 841 pp., 1924.

CORRENS, C. W. Leitminerale im Golf von Guinea, *Nachr. Akad. Wiss. Göttingen,* Math.-Phys. Kl., pp. 1–3, 1947.

CORRENS, C. W. In T. F. W. BARTH, C. W. CORRENS, and P. ESKOLA, *Die Entstehung der Gesteine,* 422 pp., Springer, Berlin, 1939.

CORRENS, C. W., and W. SCHOTT. Die Sedimente des äquatorialen Atlantischen Ozeans, *Meteor,* Bd. 3, T. 3, Lf. 1, 2, 298 pp., de Gruyter, Berlin-Leipzig, 1935 and 1937.

DIETZ, R. S. Clay Minerals in Recent Marine Sediments, *Am. Min.,* Vol. 27, pp. 219–220, 1942.

DIETZ, R. S., K. O. EMERY, and F. P. SHEPARD. Phosphorite Deposits on the Sea Floor off Southern California, *Bull. Geol. Soc. Am.,* Vol. 53, pp. 815–848, 1942.

DIRCKSEN, R. *Das Wattenmeer,* 220 pp., Bruckmann, Munich, 1942.

DOEGLAS, D. J. Interpretation of the Results of Mechanical Analyses, *J. Sed. Petr.,* Vol. 16, pp. 19–40, 1946.

EHRHARDT, A. *Das Watt,* 96 plates, Ellerman, Hamburg, 1937.

EMERY, K. O., and R. S. DIETZ. Gravity Coring Instrument and Mechanics of Sediment Coring, *Bull. Geol. Soc. Am.,* Vol. 52, pp. 1685–1714, 1941.

EMERY, K. O., and F. P. SHEPARD. Lithology of the Sea Floor off Southern California, *Bull. Geol. Soc. Am.,* Vol. 36, pp. 431–478, 1945.

ESCHER, B. G. Beschouwingen over het Opvullings-Mechanisme van Diepzee-Slenken, *Verh. Geol. Mijnb. Gen. Nederl.,* Vol. 3, pp. 79–88, 1916.

EVANS, R. D., and A. F. KIP. Radium Content of Marine Sediments from the East Indies, etc., *Am. J. Sci.,* Vol. 36, pp. 321–336, 1938.

FRANCIS-BOEUF, C. Recherches sur le milieu fluvio-marin et les dépôts d'estuaire, *Ann. Inst. Océan.,* Vol. 23, pp. 149–344, 1947.

FRASER, H. J. An Experimental Study of Varve Deposition, *Proc. Trans. Royal Soc. Canada,* Vol. 23, Section IV, pp. 49–60, 1929.

GLANGEAUD, L. Transport et sédimentation dans l'estuaire et à l'embouchure de la Gironde, *Bull. soc. geol. France,* 5e Sér., T. 8, pp. 599–631, 1938.

Sur la formation et la répartition des faciès vaseux dans les estuaires, *Compt. rend. acad. sci.,* T. 213, pp. 1022–1024, 1941.

GRABAU, A. W. *The Rhythm of the Ages,* 561 pp., Vetch, Peiping, 1940.

HÄNTZSCHEL, W. Die Schichtungsformen recenter Flachmeer-Ablagerungen im Jade Gebiet, *Senckenbergiana,* Bd. 18, pp. 316–356, 1936.

HERDMAN, W. A., et al. The Marine Zoology, Botany, and Geology of the Irish Sea, *Report British Assoc. Adv. Sci.,* pp. 455–467, 1895.

HESS, H. H. Drowned Ancient Islands of the Pacific Basin, *Am. J. Sci.,* Vol. 244, pp. 772–791, 1946.

HILLS, G. F. S. *The Formation of the Continents by Convection,* 102 pp., Arnold, London, 1947.

JOHNSTON, J., and P. D. WILLIAMSON. The Rôle of Inorganic Agencies in the Deposition of Calcium Carbonate, *J. Geol.*, Vol. 24, pp. 729–750, 1916.

KUENEN, PH. H. On the Total Amount of Sedimentation in the Deep Sea, *Am. J. Sci.*, Vol. 34, pp. 457–468, 1937.

The Cause of Coarse Deposits at the Outer Edge of the Shelf, *Geol. en Mijnb.*, pp. 36–39, 1939.

Geochemical Calculations concerning the Total Mass of Sediments in the Earth, *Am. J. Sci.*, pp. 161–190, 1941.

Rate and Mass of Deep-Sea Sedimentation, *Am. J. Sci.*, Vol. 244, pp. 563–572, 1946.

De Kringloop van het Water, 408 pp., Leopold, The Hague, 1948.

KUENEN, PH. H., and G. A. NEEB. Bottom Samples, *The Snellius Expedition*, Vol. 5, part 3, 268 pp., Brill, Leyden, 1943.

KUENEN, PH. H., and I. M. V. D. VLERK. *Geheimschrift der Aarde*, 370 pp., de Haan, Utrecht, 1948.

KUENEN, PH. H., and C. I. MIGLIORINI. Turbidity Currents as a Cause of Graded Bedding (in press).

LYELL, C. *Principles of Geology*, Vol. II, 649 pp., 10th ed., 1868.

MARR, J. E. *Deposition of the Sedimentary Rocks*, 245 pp., Cambridge University Press, 1947.

MARSHALL, P. The Wearing of Beach Gravel, *Trans. Proc. New Zealand Inst.*, Vol. 58, pp. 507–532, 1928.

MOORE, H. B. The Muds of the Clyde Sea Area. III Chemical and Physical Conditions; Rate and Nature of Sedimentation, and Fauna, *J. Marine Biol. Assoc. U. K.*, Vol. 17, pp. 325–358, 1931.

MURRAY, J., and J. HJORT. *The Depths of the Ocean*, 821 pp., Macmillan, London, 1912.

MURRAY, J., and E. PHILIPPI. Die Grundproben der "Deutschen Tiefsee-Expedition," *Wiss. Ergebn. Valdivia*, Bd. 10, pp. 77–206, 1908.

MURRAY, J., and A. F. RENARD. Deep-Sea Deposits, *Challenger Reports*, 525 pp., Longmans, London, 1898.

MYERS, E. H. Rate at Which Foraminifera are Contributed to Marine Sediments, *J. Sed. Petr.*, Vol. 12, pp. 92–95, 1942.

NATLAND, M. The Temperature and Depth Distribution of Some Recent and Fossil Foraminifera in the Southern California Region, *Scripps Inst., Tech. Ser. Bull.*, Vol. 3, pp. 225–230, 1933.

NEEB, G. A. The Composition and Distribution of the Samples. *See* Kuenen and Neeb, 1943.

NEVIN, C. Competency of Moving Water to Transport Debris, *Bull. Geol. Soc. Am.*, Vol. 57, pp. 651–674, 1946.

PETTERSSON, H. Manganese Nodules and the Chronology of the Ocean Floor, *Göteborgs K. Vet. Vit. Samh. Hand. Sjätte Földjen*, Ser. B, Bd. 2, No. 8, pp. 1–43, 1943.

Iron and Manganese on the Ocean Floor, *ibid.*, Bd. 3, No. 8, pp. 1–37, 1945.

Three Sediment Cores from the Tyrrhenian Sea, *ibid.*, Bd. 5, No. 13, pp. 1–94, 1948.

PETTIJOHN, F. J. *Sedimentary Rocks*, 526 pp., Harpers, New York, 1949.

PHILIPPI, E. Die Grundproben der deutschen Südpolar-Expedition, 1901–03, II, *Geographie und Geologie*, Bd. 6, pp. 411–616, 1910.

PHLEGER, F. B. Foraminifera of Three Submarine Cores from the Tyrrhenian Sea, *Göteborgs K. Vet. Vit. Samh. Hand. Sjätte Följden*, Ser. B, Bd. 5, No. 5, pp. 1–19, 1947.

Foraminifera of a Submarine Core from the Caribbean Sea, *ibid.*, Bd. 5, No. 14, pp. 1–9, 1948.

PHLEGER, F. B., and H. PETTERSSON. Foraminifera of Three Submarine Cores from the Tyrrhenian Sea, *ibid.*, Bd. 5, No. 5, pp. 1-19, 1947.

PIA, J. Die rezenten Kalksteine, *Zeitschr. f. Krist., Min., Petrogr.*, Abt. B, Erg. Band, 420 pp., 1933.

PIGGOT, C. S. Core Samples of the Ocean Bottom and Their Significance, *Sci. Monthly*, Vol. 46, pp. 201–217, 1938.

Factors Involved in Submarine Core Sampling, *Bull. Geol. Soc. Am.*, Vol. 52, pp. 1513–1524, 1941.

PIGGOT, C. S., and W. M. D. URRY. Time Relations in Ocean Sediments, *Bull. Geol. Soc. Am.*, Vol. 53, pp. 1187–1210, 1942.

PRATJE, O. Die Sedimente des südatlantischen Ozeans, *Meteor*, Bd. 3, T. 2, Lf. 1, 56 pp., 1935.

Die Ausdeutbarkeit der Sedimente, *Geol. Rundschau*, Bd. 29, pp. 168–174, 1938.

REVELLE, R. R. Marine Bottom Samples Collected in the Pacific Ocean by the *Carnegie* on its Seventh Cruise, *Carnegie Inst. Wash.*, Pub. 556, part 1, 180 pp., 1944.

RUSSELL, I. C. Second Expedition to Mount Saint Elias, in 1891, *13th Ann. Rept. U. S. Geol. Surv.*, pp. 7–91 (see pp. 24–26), 1893.

RUSSELL, R. J. Coast of Louisiana, *Bull. Soc. Belge Géol.*, Vol. 57, pp. 380–394, 1948.

RUSSELL, R. J., et al. Lower Mississippi River Delta, Louis. Geol. Surv., *Geol. Bull.*, Vol. 8, 454 pp., 1936.

RUSSELL, W. L. Relation of Radioactivity, Organic Content, and Sedimentation, *Bull. Am. Assoc. Petr. Geol.*, Vol. 29, pp. 1470–1494, 1945.

RUTTEN, M. G. Actualism in Epirogenetic Oceans, *Geol. en Mijnb.*, Vol. 11, pp. 222–228, 1949.

SCHOTT, G. *Geographie des Indischen und Stillen Ozeans*, 413 pp., Boysen, Hamburg, 1935.

Geographie des Atlantischen Ozeans, 438 pp., Boysen, Hamburg, 1942.

SCHOTT, W. Die Foraminiferen in dem aequatorialen Teil des Atlantischen Ozeans, *Meteor*, Bd. III, T. 3, Lf. 1, B, pp. 43–134, 1935.

Rate of Sedimentation of Recent Deep-Sea Sediments, in Trask et al., pp. 409–415, 1939.

SCHUCHERT, C. Geochronology, or the Age of the Earth on the Basis of Sediments and Life, *Bull. Nat. Research Council*, No. 80, pp. 10–64, 1931.

SCHWINNER, R. *Lehrbuch der physikalischen Geologie*, Bd. 1, 356 pp., 1936.

Sediment-Heft, *Geol. Rundschau*, Bd. 29, pp. 145–461, 1938.

SHEPARD, F. P., and K. O. EMERY. Submarine Topography off the California Coast, *Geol. Soc. Am.*, Spec. Paper 31, 171 pp., 1941.

SHROCK, R. R. *Sequence in Layered Rocks*, 507 pp., McGraw-Hill, New York, 1948.

SITTER, L. U. DE. Facies analyse, *Geol. en. Mijnb.*, Vol. 3, pp. 225–237, 1941.

SVERDRUP, H. U., M. W. JOHNSON, and R. H. FLEMING. *The Oceans*, 1087 pp., Prentice-Hall, New York, 1942.

TERCIER, J. Dépôts marins actuels et séries géologiques, *Eclog. Geol. Helv.*, Vol. 32, pp. 47–100, 1939.

TRASK, P. D. *Origin and Environment of Source Sediments of Petroleum*, 323 pp., Gulf, Houston, Texas, 1932.

Relation of Salinity to the Calcium Carbonate Content of Marine Sediment, *U. S. Geol. Surv. Prof. Paper* 186-N, pp. 273–299, 1937.

TRASK, P. D., and H. W. PATNODE. *Source Beds of Petroleum*, 566 pp., Am. Assoc. Petr. Geol., Tulsa, 1942.

TRASK, P. D., et al. *Recent Marine Sediments, A Symposium*, 736 pp., Am. Assoc. Petr. Geol., Tulsa, 1939.

TWENHOFEL, W. H. *Treatise on Sedimentation*, 926 pp., Williams & Wilkins, Baltimore, 1932.

Principles of Sedimentation, 610 pp., McGraw-Hill, 1932.

UMBGROVE, J. H. F. Periodal Events in the North Sea Basin, *Geol. Mag.*, Vol. 82, pp. 237–244, 1945.

WANLESS, H. R., and F. P. SHEPARD. Sea Level and Climatic Changes Related to Late Paleozoic Cycles, *Bull. Geol. Soc. Am.*, Vol. 47, pp. 1177–1206, 2008–2014, 1936.

WANLESS, H. R., and J. M. WELLER. Correlation and Extent of Pennsylvanian Cyclothems, *Bull. Geol. Soc. Am.*, Vol. 43, pp. 1003–1016, 1932.

WEIBULL, W. The Thickness of Ocean Sediments Measured by a Reflection Method, *Medd. Ocean. Inst. Göteborg*, Vol. 12, pp. 2–17, 1947.

WISEMAN, J. D. H., and H. BENNETT. The Distribution of Organic Carbon and Nitrogen in Sediments from the Arabian Sea, *John Murray Expedition*, Vol. 3, 4, pp. 193–221, 1940.

WOOLNOUGH, W. G. Geological Extrapolation and Pseud-Abyssal Sediments, *Bull. Am. Assoc. Petr. Geol.*, Vol. 26, pp. 765–792, 1942.

ZO BELL, C. B. *Marine Microbiology*, 240 pp., Waltham, Mass., 1946.

Coral Reefs

BIOLOGICAL DATA AND CLASSIFICATION OF REEFS

BIOLOGICAL DATA

The problems related to coral reefs are both biological and geological in nature. Biologists are mainly concerned with systematics of the animals and plants, and with physiological, ecological, and related problems. Geologists are chiefly interested in the development of the reefs and their growth forms as a whole, the formation and destruction of islands, the influence of changes in level, etc. Biological aspects will be treated in this volume only as a necessary foundation for attacking the geological problems.

The coral polyp (Fig. 165) feeds by catching small animals (planktonic) that pass into the stomach by the action of cilia that produce a constant flow of water down one end of the elongated mouth into the animal and out of the other end of the mouth. The polyps of reef-forming corals contain symbiotic unicellular algae, zooxanthellae, that are found mainly in the cells of the inner covering of the animal, the so-called entoderm, especially towards the upper parts, except in the tentacles. These algae receive the requisite nutrients and carbon dioxide from the host. The host in turn receives oxygen from the algae. Probably the algae deliver carbohydrates and can also be used by the polyps as nourishment.

At night the polyps expand with outstretched tentacles and show the most brilliant colors. The feeding by plankton is then most important. During daytime the animals are partly retracted, and the parts containing algae are exposed most advantageously to the light so as to ensure the metabolism of these plants.

The restriction of reef corals to small depths is evidently due to the need of the symbiotic algae for light. In dark, overshadowed localities or in dark cages corals lose their bright colors and finally die, even when the depth is small and all other factors are favorable.

Propagation is by small larvae developing from fertilized egg cells. The larvae swarm forth from the internal cavity and lead a planktonic mode of life during a short time. For a few days or a week they are carried by surface currents until they meet a solid substratum, to which they attach themselves. Here they develop into a new polyp.

The growth of a colony is due to asexual propagation by way of budding or fission. All polyps thus formed remain in contact with

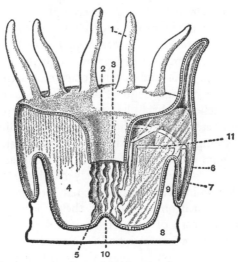

FIG. 165. Semi-diagrammatic view of half a simple coral polyp in extended condition. The calcareous skeleton is shown with a dark line. (After Woods, 1947, Fig. 26, p. 80, Cambridge University Press).

each other, and in many respects they may be considered parts of a single individual. According to the position and the manner of fission, very different forms of colonies are evolved.

In budding, the polyps may spread apart to form shrublike colonies in which each corallite is circular in section and has its independent wall; or they may spread apart but still be connected by a sheet of common tissue (coenosarc) which also secretes lime to fill the space between corallites so that the skeleton presents scattered calyces upon a smooth surface of solid calcite; or polyps may be so crowded that they assume a polygonal form against each other and the corallites take on a prismatic shape. The brain corals present a special case in that the budding is by vertical fission which begins at the oral disc and is not complete at the base. Thus long rows of polyps develop with separate mouths and circlets of tentacles and mesenteries, but with a common base that leaves a meandering furrow on the surface of the skeleton resembling the pattern of the human brain.

The mushroom coral, *Fungia*, is peculiar in being a solitary form. The short body spreads out on the top of a stony column to form a circular cushionlike skeleton. This column is absorbed by the living tissue, and the head breaks off and lies unattached on the bottom, continuing its growth and forming perhaps a heavy disc a few dozen centimeters across. Meantime, another disc grows out on the broken column, itself to be cut off when large enough.

Colonies as a whole show strongly divergent growth forms. Some are dome-shaped (*Maeandrina, Goniastraea, Porites*), and may attain several meters in diameter. Others grow in thick branching forms, the twigs blunt at the ends and several centimeters thick, the whole colony up to a meter or more high (*Porites, Pocillopora*). There are also found more delicate shrublike growths with pointed branches one to a few centimeters thick at their base, or branching horizontally with short erect stumpy branches, the whole colony attaining a meter in diameter (*Acropora*). Other genera develop broad leafy plates a few millimeters thick, growing up obliquely like loose cabbages (*Montipora*). Some branching corals grow as flat incrustations on surface reefs, adopting this form on account of the impossibility of upward growth in the strong rush of very shallow and rough waters on the windward side of exposed coral islands. The number of genera and of various growth forms, which may vary widely in each genus or even species, is far too large to be enumerated here.

Some factors that influence the growth of reef corals will now be discussed. Reef corals require sea water of high *temperature* that will not fall below 20°, while the average must be a few degrees higher. But they do not grow in profusion until the temperature is between 25° and 30°. For example, the temperature in Indonesia, a region famed for its wonderful reefs, is about 27° to 28°. Temperatures above 30° are above the optimum for reef corals. In open water such temperatures hardly ever occur. But in shallow pools on the reef during daytime the temperature may run up well above 30°. Such high and swiftly varying temperatures are not merely harmful to most species but actually deadly. Hence only a poor fauna composed of a few hardy species is encountered under such extreme conditions.

It is obvious that temperature strongly limits the distribution of reef corals. They seldom occur beyond the tropics, and they show a greater development in the western than in the eastern parts of all three oceans, because in the eastern parts cold waters rise from below and lower the temperature of the surface waters. Another factor is the westerly trend of surface currents in low latitudes that carry the larvae away from the eastern shores and towards more westerly parts of the oceans. Colonization by new individuals is always more effective in the direction in which the prevailing currents flow, and the farther to the west an island lies in the ocean the greater the variety of its coral population tends to be.

It has already been pointed out that *light* is essential to the growth of corals on account of the symbiotic algae. Light decreases quickly with *depth*, owing to absorption by the water and by floating plankton and mineral particles. In exceptionally clear water a few species of reef-forming corals manage to remain alive in depths of 100 m, but for most reef corals the limit is 70 to 80 m. With the normal degree of turbidity occurring around coral islands the reefs do not flourish in greater depths than 50 to 60 m, perhaps even less. The less clear the waters, the shallower the reef limit lies.

Table 28, showing results of dredging on reefs of the Indian Ocean, demonstrates the influence of depths on coral life. The optimum

TABLE 28. DISTRIBUTION OF CORALS WITH DEPTH IN THE INDIAN OCEAN
(STANLEY GARDINER)

	Depth, m					
	29–36	37–45	46–54	55–63	64–72	73–90
Number of dredgings	29	65	55	33	31	23
Number of species	36	61	22	15	15	1
Number of genera	16	19	13	8	8	1

conditions, however, are found much closer to the surface, as is demonstrated by counting the number of colonies per square meter. On an Australian reef the maximum number of 25 per m² was found at a depth of only 50 cm below low tide level, while at 5 m only 1 to 2 were counted. The results of such countings vary widely according to the place where they are carried out. Moreover, the size of the colonies generally increases with depth. Although nothing definite has as yet been proved, the depth at which the greatest weight of coral is added to each square meter of reef surface per year may be assumed at a few meters below sea level.

The need of light is also responsible for the development of overhanging slopes on reefs. These are frequently found both on the outer face and on the lagoon side of reefs and likewise around isolated small knolls of coral, so-called coral heads. The intensive development of colonies close to the surface causes extension of the reef at this level, and the result is an overshadowed portion of the slope where corals cannot thrive. The development of screes out of broken-off pieces may finally build the slope outwards and upwards and thus form a suitable substratum to which new colonies may become attached.

Deep-sea corals are entirely independent of light, but then they lack symbiotic algae. They occur widely separated and are not able to build up reefs.

A free supply of *oxygen* is likewise required by reef corals during the night. In the daytime the algae produce sufficient oxygen for the corals to live on. Hence, currents and wave action are favorable to growth as long as turbidity remains low. Verwey calculated that with a flow of 10 cm per sec all oxygen would be consumed from a layer of water 1 m thick passing along a reef for a distance of 250 m during the night. In open waters it may be assumed that the supply of oxygen is always sufficient. Whether corals are ever killed outright by insufficient ventilation of the surrounding waters is not known for certain. But in quiet inland seas deficiency of oxygen must hamper growth more frequently than insufficient supply of food.

The Madreporaria are marine animals, and normal *salinity* is most favorable to their development. They cannot thrive close to the mouths of larger rivers, owing to the low salinity and the turbidity of the surface waters. Heavy tropical downpours also cause freshening of a thin superficial layer of the sea, especially during calm weather. The portions of a reef that emerge during low tide are then exposed to adverse conditions. Therefore only a few hardy species can grow above normal low-tide level. The great profusion of flourishing corals exposed during exceptionally low tides is a matter of wonder, considering the general sensitivity of corals to waters of low salinity.

During spate even small streams carry enormous quantities of turbid fresh waters out to sea. At first sight it appears surprising that flourishing reefs are found directly off the mouths of small rivers. The explanation is simple, however; the low density of the drainage water causes it to spread out in a thin cover below which the corals remain in water of normal salinity. The blue wake of a motor launch churning through a brown expanse of floodwaters along the coast demonstrates how thin this turbid sheet actually is.

The deleterious influence of *silt* to reef corals has already been mentioned. Silt not only restricts the penetration of light but also hampers growth when it settles on the colonies. Nevertheless, many quickly growing, branching forms are found to be comparatively impervious to silt, and among massive forms some are found to possess to a remarkable degree the ability to clean silt off their surface. Thus it has been found by experiment that a type of *Maeandrina* was able to remove all sediment from its surface in a few hours after it had been completely covered.

Where corals are absent in somewhat turbid waters the cause often lies not so much in the suspended silt as in the absence of a *suitable foundation* on the muddy sea floor. The reef patches in the Bay of Batavia illustrate this relation. Several circular reefs a few hundred meters in diameter rise from the muddy sea floor and are crowned by small islands—Edam, Enkhuizen, etc. On the lower parts of the surrounding slopes no live corals are found, because fine calcareous mud and want of light render coral life impossible. It is only because of the existing topographical eminence that a suitable foundation closer to the surface is offered to the corals. A new reef cannot start to grow on the adjacent sea floor, but an artificial foundation would certainly become coated with colonies in a few years' time and develop into a reef patch similar to the existing ones. In fact, reefs could flourish almost anywhere on the wide expanse of the Sunda Shelf. The scarcity of coral reefs and islands is simply due to the inability of corals to grow up the first few meters from the muddy sea floor. It is not known of what the foundations of the reefs in the Bay of Batavia and the Spermonde Archipelago to the northwest are formed. Probably some slight topographical eminence was available that was swept clean of silt, thus offering coral larvae a firm substratum to initiate reef growth.

When the reefs began to grow, the coastline of Java with its silty rivers had not advanced as far as the present position. Hence conditions for growth on the bottom may have been less unfavorable at that time.

At Emmahaven on the west coast of Sumatra a fringing reef has been pierced by nine bore holes (Umbgrove). It was found that the reef rests on the muddy bottom of the bay and starts with a layer of mud mixed with coral debris, formed of branching types of growth (Fig. 166). The more cohesive reef lying on top contains also massive types of coral colonies. Whether the corals began to grow over a wide area of the muddy bottom or the reef gradually advanced over the mud by shedding debris which served as substratum for later corals has not been ascertained.

The *rate of growth* of corals and especially of reefs as a whole is
a matter of particular importance to theories of atoll and barrier formation. Many workers have investigated rates of coral growth. Two
methods have been followed: sometimes the growth of corals has been
investigated at intervals in channels that had been cleaned; other investigators have weighed individual colonies set out on the reefs and
then have determined the increase in size and weight after a certain
length of time. The first method was applied by Stanley Gardiner
in the Maldives, where, on a surface of $3\frac{1}{2}$ square meters, in the course

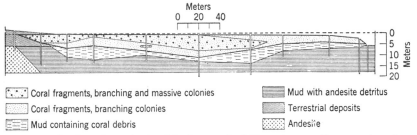

Meters
0   20   40

Coral fragments, branching and massive colonies   Mud with andesite detritus
Coral fragments, branching colonies   Terrestrial deposits
Mud containing coral debris   Andesite

Fig. 166. Section through the fringing reef of Emmahaven, Sumatra, based on
borings. Illustrating growth of a reef on a muddy substratum, probably by outgrowth on scree. Vertical twice horizontal scale. (Modified after Umbgrove,
1931, Plate 4.)

of 3 years 45 colonies averaging $\frac{1}{2}$ kg and $7\frac{1}{2}$ cm high had grown
on the walls of a channel. But only 13 per cent of the area was covered by them. In the Bay of Batavia the second method was applied
by Boschma to 46 species of coral. With an average initial weight of
280 grams the yearly increase was 300%, with a lowest figure of 20%
and a maximum of 1200%. The branching forms were found to grow
faster, for all species showing an increase of more than 400% were
branching. The massive forms grew more slowly, as all species that
had increased less than 100% were massive or only slightly branching.
This difference is probably due to the relatively large surface of the
strongly branching growth forms. It is also to be expected that large
old colonies should show lower percentages of increase. Similar results have been obtained elsewhere in the Atlantic and Pacific.

As a general average of all measurements it can be assumed that
coral colonies grow at the rate of $2\frac{1}{2}$ cm per year (i.e., a meter in 40
years) under favorable conditions and for part of their life. But it
is obvious that reefs as a whole must grow much more slowly.
Branches break off for several reasons, being then either lodged be-

tween the colonies or carried upwards to the beach or else rolling down the slope to greater depths. Solution and wear attack dead pieces of coral, so that part of their mass is lost to the reefs as building materials. Furthermore, the whole reef is not covered by living corals and the patches in between are occupied partly by organisms without a calcareous skeleton, partly by lime-secreting algae that appear to grow much less rapidly than Madreporaria. The space between the branches of each staghorn type and between the separate colonies, as also the sandy patches found where larger open spaces occur between living portions of the reef, must all be built up by detritus deriving from the growing parts and from other organisms. Now and again an entire reef is killed by sediment during typhoons or dies off for unknown reasons. The dead corals are quickly overgrown by algae, and judging by general appearances it must take a long time before such a reef is again colonized by new coral patches.

Little has been discovered of the growth rate of reefs by direct measurement. Sluiter found that a new reef established on Krakatau after the eruption of 1883 had grown to a thickness of 20 cm in 5 years, or 4 cm per year. Other investigators have estimated reef growth at 0.1 to 5 cm per year. In general, the higher of these figures applies to favorable conditions and probably does not take account of the openwork structure of the branching colonies. Though the general surface may rise a considerable amount in a few years from a massive substratum at a given locality, the upbuilding of the compact rock mass is a much slower process, as pointed out above. The present writer is therefore inclined to put the average for a whole reef and for a longer period at considerably lower than 1 cm per year.

The decreases in depth sometimes observed during renewed hydrographical surveys are no trustworthy indication of reef growth because they do not exceed possible errors of observation. A sounding on a flat firm bottom under favorable conditions may be exact within 0.5 m, but the irregularities of a reef surface, errors in position, and the reduction to datum level introduce larger inexactitudes. Assuming a rate of growth of 2 cm per year, a decrease in depth could not be established beyond doubt within a century. But accurate surveys have not been in existence long enough to warrant any definite conclusion at present. It may be assumed for the time being that, while some reefs are almost stationary, others are growing upwards at a rate of ½ to 2 m per century.

Besides Madreporaria a large variety of *other organisms* play an important part in the building of coral reefs. Most important are the family of red algae called Corallinaceae, generally termed nullipores, encrusting corallines, or *Lithothamnion*. But other genera, as *Lithophyllum* and *Archaeolithothamnion*, are also of importance. These calcareous algae form extensive encrustations in strongly agitated waters on the outer edge of the reef flat. These films are more resistant to solution and mechanical wear than the skeletons of corals, partly owing to a high content (about 18%) of magnesium carbonate. Although spreading outwards at a rate of several centimeters per year at their edges, such encrustations are generally only a few centimeters thick in the old central parts. Their chief activity from a geological point of view is therefore not the adding of mass to the reef but the cementing and binding of branching corals and loose detritus. The nullipores are able to grow well above low-tide level but must be continually moistened by spray. Dead corals are quickly covered by a veneer, and new colonies cannot settle on the living surface of the algae. Hence, all along the outer edge of oceanic reefs the shallow parts are covered by these encrustations in smooth or slightly mammillated surfaces. Often a rim, the *Lithothamnion ridge*, rises to a meter or more above the surrounding reef. Seawards the reef surface dips below low-tide level, where a zone of several meters' breadth occurs, deeply channeled and entirely covered by encrusting corallines to the exclusion of practically all other sedentary organisms (Fig. 167). At depths of 6 to 7 m the corals begin to appear and soon gain the upper hand, although nullipores are found incidentally to considerable depths. Despite the strengthening influence of the encrustations on the reef structure in the breaker zone, there can be little doubt that, for the reef mass as a whole, growth is greatly retarded by the presence of these almost stationary veneers. The toothed reef edge of Funafuti is dealt with in the Funafuti report (Armstrong et al., 1904), while a detailed and profusely illustrated description and analyses of the *Lithothamnion* growths and reef types of Bikini Atoll has been given by Tracey, Ladd, and Hoffmeister (1948).

Green algae such as *Halimeda* occur in dense growths on the floor of some lagoons. They contribute a vast amount of small calcareous plates to the sediment collecting on the bottom.

A number of animals closely resembling the true reef coral may also play a part. *Millepora* and *Heliopora* build branching calcareous skeletons, the latter with a peculiar blue color. *Tubipora* has a calcareous skeleton of bright red consisting of parallel tubes held in place by thin sheets of the same material at right angles to the tubes and at a few millimeters' or centimeters' distance. All these forms are representatives of the Cnidaria. The spicules embedded in the fleshy tissue of the abundant gorgonians and pennatulids contribute to the mass of detritus.

A host of gastropods, lamellibranchs (among others the giant tridacnas), echinoderms, Foraminifera, etc., produce calcareous tests that on death become intermingled with the detritus of sedentary organ-

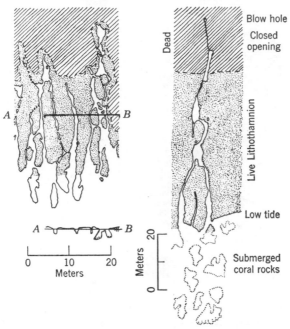

FIG. 167. Lithothamnion edge of Funafuti Atoll, showing buttresses and trenches. (Redrawn after Funafuti Report, 1904, Plates 17 and 19.)

isms and help to fill in the crevasses between fixed animals and plants. On the other hand fishes and boring organisms cause damage to the reef structure and living corals, while holothurians and other mud-feeders assist the mechanical wear of detritus, especially in the lagoons.

CLASSIFICATION OF REEFS AND THEIR COMPONENT PARTS

Fringing reefs grow directly against rocky coasts. The breadth varies from zero at the first colonization of a newly invaded coast to hundreds of meters. Commonly tropical coasts show an uninterrupted fringing reef; in other places many open spaces are left off the mouths of rivers and in other unfavorable localities.

Barrier reefs are separated from the coast by a lagoon that is too deep under the ruling conditions to allow of coral growth (Fig. 168). Although some barriers are found off continental coasts, the majority are developed around volcanic islands. Lagoons may range from 20 to more than 100 m in depth and from narrow channels to dozens of

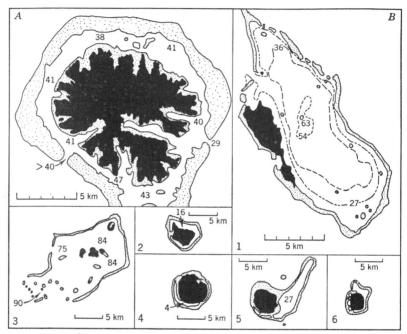

FIG. 168. Seven barrier reefs (depths in meters). *A*, Tahaa, Society Islands, typical barrier reef with strongly embayed island and fringing reef. *B*, Fiji Islands: (1) Wakaya, strongly asymmetrical barrier reef with wide lagoon, passing into fringing reef; (2) Naitomba; (3) Budd Reef, an almost-atoll with incomplete barrier, deep lagoon, and half a dozen lagoon reefs; (4) Mango, narrow lagoon, partly fringing reef; (5) Kanathea, asymmetrical barrier, partly fringing reef; (6) Vanua Vatu, barrier joined to island by several patches of reef.

kilometers in breadth. Generally barrier reefs follow the coast for long distances, often with short interruptions. Some barriers pass sideways into a fringing reef by joining the coast. The breadth of the reefs is of the order of 500 m, but occasionally barriers a few kilometers broad are encountered. The interruptions are termed passes or passages. These vary from narrow and shallow channels that can be negotiated only by small launches to broad and deep gaps that serve as entrances to the lagoon for large ocean steamers. In many cases the reefs curve inwards and jut out into the lagoon for a few hundred meters at both sides of a pass. In the lagoon may be found smaller or larger numbers of reef patches, generally rising to the surface, while the coast is commonly bordered by a fringing reef.

Atolls are reef rings around a lagoon in which there are no islands of non-coral origin (Fig. 169). In other respects they are similar to barrier reefs. The average depth of the lagoons is 45 m, according to Shepard.

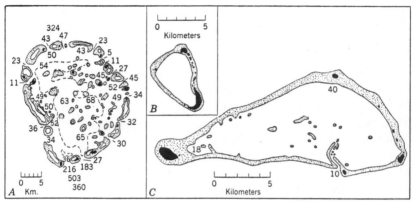

Fig. 169. Three atolls (depths in meters). *A*, Nilandu Atoll, Maldive Archipelago. Rim consists of faros (depth 20–30 m). Many lagoon reefs, correlated with large number of passes in the rim. *B*, Etal Atoll, Caroline Islands. Rim closed, no lagoon reefs shown on chart. *C*, Ngatik Atoll, Caroline Islands. Rim with only one passage showing horns, few lagoon reefs.

The same author points to the results of recent detailed investigations of Pacific atolls, especially in the Marshalls, in which a vast number of coral pinnacles are encountered, strewn throughout the lagoon. He proposes to distinguish these as a separate type of reef formation. Emery's chart of Eniwetok atoll (1948) is the finest record of atoll topography yet produced. It illustrates the feature under discussion most clearly. Future work will have to show whether the occurrence of these pinnacles is the general rule in lagoons. The present writer believes that, in those Indonesian atolls that show a well-developed rim, coral growth in the lagoon is not profuse, and this appears to apply in many other areas also.

There are some atolls and barriers in which the reef is discontinuous along a considerable part of the circumference. Closer study of the chart nearly always reveals a number of shallower soundings along the edge of the lagoon floor. Evidently, then, the rim is present in embryonic form. Most small atolls have only one or two passes or even none, while most of the larger atolls have several to a few dozen passes crossing their reefs.

Almost-atolls are atolls with a minute non-coral island, generally of volcanic origin.

Reefs of great extent without lagoons are marked on some charts. Some of these have later been found to be atolls without passes, but in Indonesia a few solid reef masses occur.

Faros are small atoll-shaped reefs with lagoons a few to 30 meters deep, forming part of a barrier or atoll rim (Figs. 197 and 200). In some instances the rim consists of a row of round or oblong faros with hardly any normal reefs in between.

Reef patches is the term for all coral growths that have grown up independently in lagoons of barriers and atolls. They vary in extent from expanses measuring several kilometers across to pillars or even mushroom-shaped growths consisting of a single large colony. The smaller representatives are called knolls.

Bank-inset reefs are situated on locally unrimmed continental or island shelves or offshore banks and well inside the outer edges of these submarine flats.

Drowned reefs are situated at such depths that reef growth is excluded or at least greatly hampered. Death of the reef or subsidence might explain the origin of such formations.

Uplifted reefs are of widespread occurrence, especially uplifted fringing reefs.

The following major elements can generally be distinguished on a coral reef.

The Reef Flat. The reef flat is a stony expanse of dead reef rock with a flat surface. It generally becomes partly or entirely dry at low tide. Patches of sand and debris and a few widely scattered colonies of the more hardy species of coral diversify the featureless horizontal surface of many reef flats. Shallow pools are a normal feature on some; others are crossed by irregular gullies or are riddled with potholes (Fig. 170). The landward side of fringing reefs generally merges into a sandy beach or accumulations of debris; sometimes it shelves upwards, ending in a notch in vertical limestone cliffs.

Boat Channel. Between fringing reefs and the shore a depression of the reef flat is often encountered running parallel to the beach. The water driven over the reef flat by wind and surf flows away sideways through this channel. A typical representative is several meters broad and a few meters deep with a sandy bottom, but smaller and much larger examples are known, so that no sharp distinction can be made between a broad boat channel and a narrow barrier lagoon.

Seaward Slope. The unlovely reef flat drops either suddenly or more gradually at the outer edge to deeper waters, and here a chance

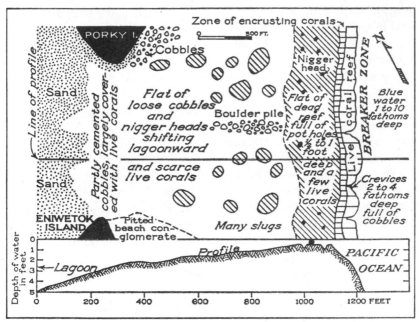

Fig. 170. Plan and profile of reef between Eniwetok and Porky islands, Marshall Group. (After Stearns, 1945, *Bull. Geol. Soc. Am.*, Vol. 56, Fig. 3, p. 787.)

is offered of observing coral growth in all its beauty and profusion. Either a sandy slope or a flourishing reef may be found. This slope may be anything between a few meters deep and a huge precipice down to oceanic depths. With some atolls the outer slope is 70° or more down to depths of 200 m, but there it grades into a scree, passing to a gently declining slope farther down. Some reefs have overhanging edges where the sounding lead drops scores of meters before striking bottom. Elsewhere the reef splits up into isolated knolls that lie at gradually increasing depths down to the limits of coral growth.

Lithothamnion Ridge. The slight ridge found towards the outer edge of many oceanic reefs was briefly described above; further details follow below (Fig. 173).

Negro Heads. Large blocks of coral torn from the outer face of the reef and tossed onto the flat by storm waves or tsunamic waves quickly become overgrown by a crust of black lichens; hence the name negro heads. They are a normal feature of exposed reef flats. Closer inspection has shown that some negro heads are remnants of large coral heads or reefs that grew during a relatively higher sea level, and now remain in the position where they were originally formed. In Indonesia a few normal negro heads have been found on reefs in the extreme northeast of the archipelago, where typhoons are known to occur, but in the inland seas only examples of the erosion type are known. The only exception is where tidal waves raised during volcanic eruptions have devastated the coast, for instance opposite Krakatau on Java and opposite Paloeweh on Flores.

Superficial examination of negro heads has sometimes led to the conclusion that basalt boulders occur on reefs, giving rise to faulty theories on the origin of the reef in question. Use of the geologist's hammer, however, easily proves the coralline nature of negro heads.

The curious observation has been made that in some instances negro heads are most frequent on the leeward side of reefs. Steers explained this phenomenon as the result of rare hurricanes, that approach from the direction opposite to that of normal winds. Off the leeward side of the reef in normally protected positions unwieldy knolls are able to develop with a mushroom shape. When suddenly exposed to the full force of huge storm waves they snap off and are thrown up onto the flat.

Sand Islands or Cays. On many reef flats or shallow reefs waves have built up smaller or larger sandy islands (Fig. 171). These generally present a flat surface slightly above high-tide level. In other cases there is a large admixture of coral fragments and the surface may show a number of concentric ridges formed by successive additions along the periphery of the island. Boulders and even huge blocks are sometimes encountered also. Sand cays may be semi-permanent, altering in shape and position with the monsoons, or vegetation may take possession and fix the sand. But sandy spits may remain under the influence of changing wind directions. It is not always possible to ascertain whether the island has been constructed under the prevailing conditions or has emerged through a relative fall of sea level. We will return to this problem when discussing the influence of the wind and relative emergence (pp. 441, 445).

Shingle and Boulder Ramparts. Commonly a narrow ridge of coarse detritus has been thrown up along part of the edge of the reef flat, especially on the side from which the prevailing winds blow. The height varies but seldom exceeds 1 or 2 m. The boulder zones or shingle ramparts are found close behind the lithothamnion ridge, where it is present. Narrow or broad tongues of shingle have developed at

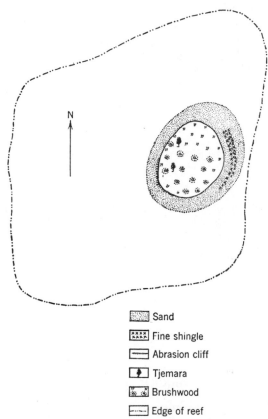

Sand	
Fine shingle	
Abrasion cliff	
Tjemara	
Brushwood	
Edge of reef	

Fig. 171. Mauang, a typical sand cay on a small reef patch off Makassar, Celebes. Scale 1:5000. (After Kuenen, 1933, Fig. 11, p. 13.)

right angles to the reef edge on some flats. More than one rampart may be found running parallel (Fig. 172).

An interesting record of changes which shingle ramparts have undergone in 17 years on Low Isles, Great Barrier Reefs, is given by Fairbridge and Teichert (1947).

Elevated Islands. Elevated islands are found on most reef flats throughout the coral seas. They rise to a few meters above high-tide level and consist either of sand and debris or of solid reef rock.

They have evidently been formed during a recent relatively higher stand of sea level. Erosion is nearly always occurring around part or the whole circumference, thus testifying to the ephemeral nature of these elevated islands.

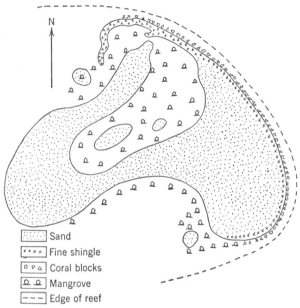

N

[::::]	Sand
[ʻ ˣ ˣ ʻ]	Fine shingle
[ᵒ ᵛ ᵟ]	Coral blocks
[Ω Ω]	Mangrove
[- - -]	Edge of reef

Fɪɢ. 172. Kawasang, a sand cay joined to a boulder rampart and enclosing a mangrove swamp. Paternoster Atoll, south of Celebes. Scale 1:20,000. (After Kuenen, 1933, Fig. 28, p. 19.)

THE INFLUENCE OF VARIOUS FACTORS ON CORAL REEFS

THE INFLUENCE OF LITHOTHAMNION

These calcareous algae cover all fixed and loose objects on parts of some reefs with a firm veneer of relatively resistant magnesian limestone. They fill up crevasses and cover over hollows and uncemented material, transforming the surface into a smooth, consolidated mass on which the breakers pound ineffectually. The activity of nullipores is restricted to depths of less than 6 to 7 m and reaches to a meter above high-tide level, as long as spray continually moistens the surface. Owing to the fact that nullipores grow very slowly in thickness, they are hardly able to fill up larger hollows between coral knolls. Hence, where algae take the upper hand, a curious buttressed and trenched shape develops at the edge of the reef. Accurate maps of this formation are contained in the report of the Funafuti expedition. On most reefs of the Pacific and Indian oceans the buttressed edges are found along most of the periphery. But in inland waters such as the Moluccan seas, or in lagoons of barriers and atolls, these forms are absent. In Indonesia they have been formed only along the oceanic coasts (Talaud and Schouten Islands in the northeast, on the south coast of Java, on the west coast of Sumatra, etc.). Evidently the heavy surf caused by oceanic swell is required for the growth of

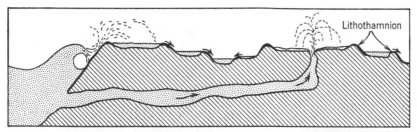

FIG. 173. Diagrammatic section of *Lithothamnion* ridge.

Lithothamnion encrustations and the formation of buttresses and trenches.

In horizontal projection the buttresses are several meters long and 1 to 5 m wide (see Fig. 167, p. 423). The trenches are from a few meters to less than a meter wide, with a depth of 2 to 3 m. Now and again a trench has become overgrown from the sides and closed by a roof, a tunnel thus being formed. The surf rushes in on the seaward side and is thrown back at the inner end. With a closed tunnel a water spout springs up through an opening at the inner end. Towards the outer end more and more interconnections between the trenches are found and the buttresses are divided into separate pillars.

At first sight the trenches might be explained as erosion forms, scoured by the waves in the rock of the reef. Several observations show, however, that they have been formed by growth. The covering with live nullipores, the formation of tunnels, the transverse connections at right angles to the rush of the waters, and finally the absence of sand or other erosion tools around the blow holes, all testify to the absence of mechanical wear.

The nullipores cause yet another remarkable feature on the surface of reefs, namely, shallow, rimmed pools, strongly resembling the terraced formations around geysers and hot springs and in tropical

streams with algal growths (Figs. 173 and 174). In all these cases
the growth of algae secreting lime or silica proves to be responsible.
The necessary condition is that, where the water flows over the rim
of a pool, the secretion of lime or silica takes place. This results in
the upbuilding of the lowest point of the rim and the closing of any
breach in the encircling rampart. The pools are circular around the
point where the water reaches the surface and are arranged in successively lower terraces as sections of a circle around the overflow
from the higher level.

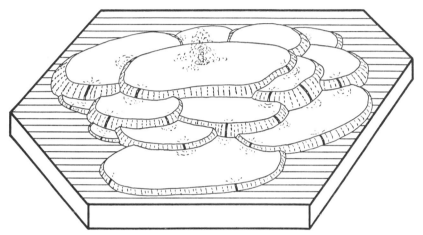

Fig. 174. Diagram of terraced pools on *Lithothamnion* ridge.

Figure 173 shows a diagrammatic section through a Lithothamnion
ridge with a blow hole. The highest pool on the left is fed by spray
from the surf. Figure 174 pictures the terraced arrangement. Pre-
sumably the water in the pools is insufficiently aerated to allow of
algal growth; otherwise the basins would soon be filled up. The
points of overflow offer optimal conditions for the plants.

Solution alone can never account for terraced pools, because then
the lowest point on the rim would be attacked most vigorously. Instead of being regenerated, any damaged point would be cut down
and tap the pool of its contents. But it might be that an elevated reef
undergoes abrasion mainly by solution and that live algae growing in
aerated water do not build up the limestone but do offer a certain
amount of protection from the solvent action. The entire surface
would then be gradually lowered, but the rims bearing a protective
cover of algae would lag behind and become raised above the floor

of the surrounding pools. The requisite conditions of life for such algae should be the same as those for *Lithothamnion*.

As pointed out earlier, nullipores build a ridge on most Pacific reefs and the surfaces generally show the terraced pools just described. Although these calcareous algae are important in strengthening the surface structures of a reef exposed to the full force of oceanic waves, the presence of nullipores is not, as some investigators hold, a necessary condition for the formation of sea-level reefs. The absence of these plants on most Indonesian reefs and on lagoon islands clearly shows that reefs may grow up to sea level without the aid of nullipores, provided wave action is somewhat restricted.

CEMENTING OF LOOSE PARTICLES

The cementing action of *Lithothamnion* has been dealt with above. Elevated reefs quickly become lithified to a firm mass by solution and

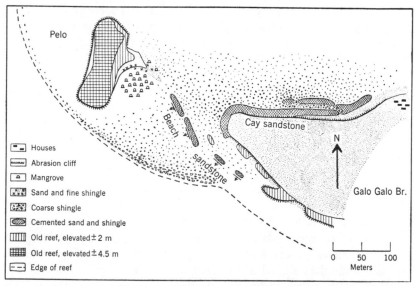

Legend:
- Houses
- Abrasion cliff
- Mangrove
- Sand and fine shingle
- Coarse shingle
- Cemented sand and shingle
- Old reef, elevated ± 2 m
- Old reef, elevated ± 4.5 m
- Edge of reef

0   50   100
Meters

FIG. 175. Sketch map of two coral islands on reef flat west of Morotai, Moluccas, showing elevated reef rock, cay sandstone, and dipping beach sandstone where island has been eroded. (After Kuenen, 1933, Fig. 49, p. 36.)

deposition caused by percolating rain water. Sand, shingle, and separate coral heads become firmly linked together and form a hard, rocky mass without stratification, and generally all fossil structures are lost by recrystallization. Together with this cementing the reefs become honeycombed in ever-increasing degree. Both spray from waves and rain water help in this process. The reef rock acquires a deeply pitted, extremely rough and sharp-edged surface, while internally a sponge-like structure develops. In spite of this gradual destruction elevated reefs preserve their original shape to a surprising degree, and the level or domed surface remains long after the internal structure has become highly cavernous.

A striking feature of many sandy coral beaches is the occurrence of beach sandstone (Kuenen, 1933; Sewell, 1935, 1936). This is a clearly stratified, generally dipping series of calcarenite (calcareous sandstone) beds, most often found between tide levels. Two types can be distinguished, beach sandstone and cay sandstone (Figs. 175– 178).

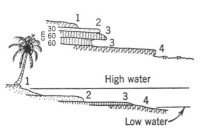

FIG. 176. Two sections of the beach of a sand cay with cay sandstone. Reef island west of Morotai, Moluccas: 1, sand with humus; 2, loosely cemented cay sand; 3, firmly cemented cay sandstone; 4, cemented reef limestone. (After Kuenen, 1933, Fig. 48, p. 35.)

Beach sandstone is characterized by dipping layers, generally 10 to 20 cm thick. It is of fairly uniform hardness, comparable to that of poorly cemented sandstone or inferior cement. It is situated between high and low tide and appears to have been cemented by the evaporation of sea water during low tide. The presence of organic matter in the beach sand is apparently favorable to the cementing action. Cases have been known in which beach sandstone has formed in one year's time. Displacement of the island or other alterations on the reef flat sometimes expose the beach sandstone to erosion. Where the sand cay is shifted right across the beach sandstone the strata finally emerge at the other side dipping towards the island. Here and there separate patches are found on the reef flat while the original island has been entirely washed away. The cause of the stratification has not yet been ascertained.

The *cay sandstone* is formed in horizontal strata that may attain a thickness of more than half a meter and reach above high-tide level. It varies from scarcely cemented to a firm limestone rock. Digging a hole in a sand cay frequently reveals the presence of a friable cay sandstone, evidently cemented by the action of fresh water. Where such a stratum is exposed on the beach by erosion of the island the same cementing influence is exerted as on the beach sandstone. Now, however, a more advanced stage of cementation is reached, thus producing a hard limestone.

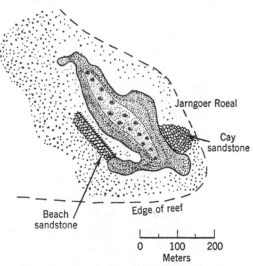

FIG. 177. Sketch map of Jarngoer Roeal, a sand cay near Jamdena, Moluccas, showing beach sandstone and cay sandstone. (After Kuenen, 1933, Fig. 65, p. 50.)

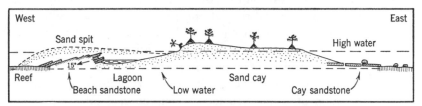

FIG. 178. Section through Jarngoer Roeal, showing dipping beach sandstone and horizontal cay sandstone. (Redrawn after Kuenen, 1933, Fig. 66, p. 50.)

MARINE EROSION OF CORAL LIMESTONE

Along many tropical coasts elevated coral reefs are found, and the degree to which these reefs are attacked by marine erosion is a question of some importance. On the one hand it may be assumed that the frequent terraces are mainly due to the growth of successive fringing reefs around the island while it was being raised by intermittent deformation of the earth's crust. On the other hand it is conceivable that the successive terraces were cut by abrasion in an even covering of reef rock.

Landing on the coast of an elevated limestone island one is frequently struck by the deeply cut notch at or just above high-tide level. A sandy patch with beach may later have been deposited in front of the notch, but generally the attack is in full swing.

The fact of erosion, therefore, cannot be doubted, but we must attempt to decide whether mechanical or chemical action is responsible. Investigation of sea water from the surface in tropical seas has led chemists to the conclusion that it is always saturated or even supersaturated with lime. Hence, they have concluded that solution of limestone is not possible. But it is exceedingly difficult to establish whether solution under natural conditions is really excluded. Such factors of a natural environment as overnight cooling, rain, percolation of humic acid from the island, and the pressure of waves have been absent from the laboratory experiments. The carbonic acid dissolved in the water may vary according to the temperature, and the possibility is not remote that solution takes place under special circumstances that have not been represented by the sampling of the water. Thus samples will not have been taken during rainstorms or at night, or carefully from a thin superficial layer. Hence the results arrived at by chemical analyses are not conclusive.

Fairbridge (1948) suggests that the main cause of this solution is the wide daily range in temperature that he was able to prove, and the postulated variation in carbon dioxide content of a thin layer of water on the reef. This would bring about precipitation by day from a supersaturated solution, and at night, with cooling and excessive liberation of carbon dioxide by algae, etc., the solution of more limestone.

Against the doubtful laboratory results the testimony of geological observations may be placed. These appear to establish beyond doubt the solvent action of tropical surface waters on reef limestone. The surface of the notch, especially the roof, is excessively rough and covered with sharp-edged pits a few centimeters deep. The markings are typical of solution. Abrasive materials in the form of sand and shingle are conspicuously absent. Moreover, mechanical action on insoluble rocks always results in smooth surfaces in the notches, and the tools are found in the immediate neighborhood.

Furthermore, notches in elevated reefs are found as deeply cut in localities protected from the force of the waves as in exposed positions. Large examples are found on the lagoon shores of elevated atolls such as Maratua in Indonesia. Mushroom-shaped pedestal rocks on reef flats are undercut no less deeply on the side facing away from the reef edge as on the side exposed to the full rush of the surf (Kuenen). On the coast of Togian, near Celebes, where limestone alternates with soft volcanics, the notch is restricted to the soluble rock, while the tuffs are almost unattacked (Umbgrove).

Several investigators have pointed out that erosion continues at great distances behind the outer edge of the reef, even where the reef flat is entirely above low-tide level. This proves on the one hand that not much detritus is produced or the corals on the reef front would be smothered, and on the other hand that where the force of the waves is broken the attack can nevertheless continue.

Sewell showed, however, that most coral islands in the Indian Ocean are found on the leeward side of atolls. This indicates that after they were formed by relative elevation those to windward were soonest swept away again. From this it may be concluded that wind and surf do activate the chemical erosion, probably by constant renewal of the solvent waters. But the main reason is that these islands were poorly consolidated and could be attacked by mechanical action as well. On some Pacific reefs the opposite situation is found with most islands to windward. According to Sewell, this is due to the addition of new detritus since the last emergence.

In this connection it may be pointed out that the elevated terraces on some Fiji islands were proved to have been formed partly by erosion of the emerged limestones and partly by the growth of fringing reefs. This is yet another example of coral growth and concomitant erosion.

The chemical erosion of reef limestone is frequently prepared for and supported by the solvent action of the groundwater. It is a well-known fact that rainwater containing carbonic and humic acid strongly attacks limestone, as has been emphasized above. A striking example was described by Kuenen from the elevated atolls of Maratua and Kakaban to the northeast of Borneo, where an elevated terrace a few meters above sea level had been transformed to a cavernous mass while the outer edge was much more compact on account of the absence of humic acid. Once the sea had succeeded in forming a breach in this outer rim the spongelike interior was soon washed away. A row of pedestal rocks remained for a while along the former outer edge of the terrace before finally falling a prey to the erosion (Fig. 179).

The foregoing discussion shows definitely that the marine erosion of elevated coral limestone is effected almost entirely by chemical solution. No conclusive evidence is yet available as to the absolute rate at which this action takes place. A tentative estimate has been made by Kuenen (1947). The terraces on Maratua and Kakaban, just mentioned, lie about 5 m above sea level and were probably developed by a world-wide sinking of ocean level some 3000 to 4000 years ago. In part the terraces had already been removed by solution and to a much smaller extent the surrounding reefs had grown out to seaward. The resultant reef flat is 200 m broad on the former and 75 on the latter island. From this it follows that about 0.2 m³ of rock per meter length of coast has been removed per annum. Further ob-

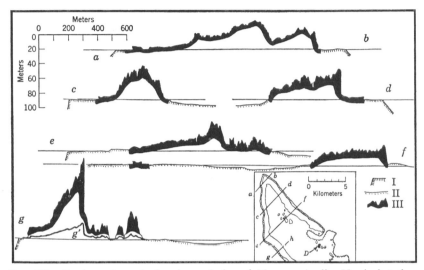

Fig. 179. Sections through the elevated rim of Maratua Atoll. Vertical 5 times horizontal scale, g′ = natural scale. I, living reef; II, sand; III, reef rock. D = site of borings. (After Kuenen, 1947, Fig. 2, p. 9.)

servations are needed before this figure can be relied upon and the variations in magnitude under different conditions evaluated.

THE INFLUENCE OF SEDIMENT ON CORAL GROWTH

Most reef-building corals can flourish only in clear water, partly owing to their requirement of light, partly to the adverse influence of settling sediment. Some species do possess to a remarkable degree the quality of being able to remove silt that has settled on their tissues. These occur in localities where sediment tends to accumulate. But a reef as a whole cannot thrive unless the turbidity of the water is very slight.

However, the injurious influence of silt should not be exaggerated. Ladd and Hoffmeister found flourishing reefs close to the mouth of

a large river on Fiji. Kuenen called attention to the universal occurrence of fringing reefs around recently elevated islands in the tropical
belt, where a relatively large amount of detritus must be supplied to
the coastal waters. Both volcanic and sedimentary rock islands are
represented. On several recently extinct or active volcanic islands
powerful fringing reefs are found throughout the Moluccan seas.
These observations appear to contradict Davis' contention that subsidence and the formation of sediment traps in drowned valleys must
precede the development of fringing reefs on volcanic islands.

That moderate subsidence provides conditions favorable to coral
growth can be admitted, but a relative rise of sea level is evidently
not essential.

Some writers are of the opinion that detritus is of such importance
in inhibiting coral growth that the shape of reefs is largely due to
this influence. Thus Wood Jones has maintained that the development of atolls and barrier reefs is possible only because of this property of corals. For, if the growth were not hampered by detritus, a
reef growing up around a subsiding island would remain in contact
with the coast and no lagoon would develop. But owing to the much
more favorable conditions at the outer edge of a reef, where the
detritus and terrestrial denudation products are washed away, the reef
is built up and strives to draw away from the coast as far as possible,
while the conditions for growth in the resulting depression to the
rear become continuously less favorable to coral growth. Umbgrove
pointed out that in the Togian Islands, near Celebes, knolls and other
lagoon reefs are most plentiful where the depth of the lagoon is great
and turbidity at its lowest. In shallower portions of the barrier lagoon
silt has apparently reduced the development of lagoon reefs.

It should not be overlooked, however, that another factor is in
operation which has a similar influence. Wherever the water is insufficiently agitated and renewed, scarcity of oxygen and plankton
will occur. Accumulation of silt and poor ventilation tend to coincide. Hence, it is generally impossible to say which of the two is of
greater importance. For instance, clear water may prevail along the
inside of atoll reefs, but this does not prove that poor ventilation
causes the common absence of corals in this area. It may be that
during storms sufficient detritus is churned up in the lagoon or washed
over the reef onto the inner slopes to kill corals.

It can hardly be doubted, however, that on many open tropical
coasts, where waves and currents must bring abundance of oxygen

and food, absence of coral reefs should be attributed entirely to turbidity of the coastal waters or to absence of a suitable firm foundation.

THE INFLUENCE OF WIND ON CORAL ISLANDS

On Coral Growth. The prevailing wind has a marked influence on the growth of a coral reef. Oxygen and nourishment are carried to the animals from the windward side. Hence, growth is rapid, but the growth forms tend to be compact. On the lee side conditions are less favorable because of shortage of food and oxygen and because of the supply of detritus. As a result, a smaller amount is annually added to the reef by growth than on the windward side, while branching, delicate growth forms and separate knolls prevail. Commonly growth is hampered to such a degree on the lee side of a reef that no live corals are found, only a barren waste of sand and shingle. It may be surmised that with depth the difference between the windward and lee slopes of a reef becomes less marked. The restriction of *Lithothamnion* and the buttressed edge of the reef flat to the windward side may here be recalled.

On the Shape of the Reefs. A prevailing direction of wind may have a strong modeling influence on the shape of the reef. The living reef tends to grow to windward, while detritus is dumped to leeward. Many other factors also play a part in determining the ultimate shape of the reef, and no fixed rule can be given. Some special cases may be described.

Wood Jones has given a report on the atoll of Cocos Keeling, which is like a horseshoe with the open end directed away from the advance of the trade winds (Fig. 180). The alternating monsoons may cause double horseshoes, such as those described by Krempf from the South China Sea. But these well-developed forms are exceptional. Many reefs appear to conform more or less accurately to the shape of the foundation on which they rest, with a tendency towards rounded outlines. However, there are also many atolls with an angular plan, such as Bikini and Kwajalein. It has not yet been ascertained whether this angularity is gradually developed from a more rounded shape, for instance by outgrowth in consequence of favorable ecological conditions at corners of the reef, or whether it is primary, the shape of the foundation having been influenced by faulting.

On the Sand Cays. The sandy islands thrown up on reef flats by waves are naturally strongly influenced in shape by the winds. Where the reef flat lies comparatively low the waves sweep the sand right across to the leeward side. But curiously enough it is frequently not carried off, but accumulates there to form a cay island. This may even occur on small flats that are less broad than neighboring reefs without sand accumulations.

Steers found a simple explanation for this apparent incongruous halting of the debris. The surf curves round the reef and the refracted waves roll in from the leeward side also, although with little force. The sand is stopped by these small waves shortly before reaching the leeward side of the flat.

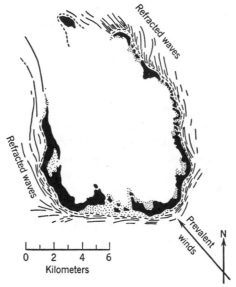

Fig. 180. Cocos Keeling, an atoll showing the effect of the prevalent winds. (Modified after Wood Jones, 1910, Fig. 62, p. 260.)

Sand cays may be small and barren, and then they tend to accommodate their shape to the varying directions of the wind. A crescent-shaped form resembling that of barchans may be assumed under the regime of strongly prevailing winds. Alternating monsoon winds are able to force the crescent into the opposite orientation twice yearly. On the reefs of oceanic atolls the spits joining to cays are generally bent backwards toward the lagoon and may even curve round to meet, thus enclosing a shallow pond. Islands covered by vegetation are, of course, less mobile, but barren spits are often developed that alter in position and shape with the time of year. It takes some time for the waves to shift the sand, and a change of direction for a few days will not influence a cay to any appreciable extent.

Sand cays are strongly developed in regions that are somewhat protected from the full force of oceanic swell and violent storms. Indonesia and the West Indies and the lagoon reefs of the Great Barrier Reefs are the classical regions of cays. On more exposed reefs most islands owe their existence to a relative fall of sea level. They consist of elevated reef rock with added accumulations of coarse detritus and some sandy material.

The action of wind and waves tends to heap up sand on the lagoon side of exposed atoll reefs in a high ridge on which sand dunes may develop. A remarkable feature of many islands in the Indian Ocean is the occurrence of vast accumulations of pumice, which may be attributed to the Krakatau eruption of 1883. Using this datum, average subsequent growth to an amount of several decimeters per year could be ascertained in some cays.

Cays are sometimes found to migrate across the reef flat in the direction of the atoll lagoon. The fact that this process is at present in full swing strongly indicates that the islands owe their formation to a comparatively recent alteration of conditions. It will be shown later that a recent world-wide sinking of ocean level, which probably occurred three or four thousand years ago, is responsible for the emergence of the reef flats and initiated the development of the cays. The consequences have not yet developed to a stable condition.

On Coarser Detritus. The influence of the wind on the accumulation of shingle and boulders is no less evident than in the case of sand, but different laws can be established. The larger weight and rough interlocking shape render the shingle less mobile than the sand. Hence, the coarser material tends to accumulate closer to the edge of the reef flat, where it is directly supplied by the living reef. Once it has been thrown up in ridges to the height of a few decimeters to 1 or 2 m these accumulations are relatively immobile.

Nevertheless these shingle ramparts are not permanent structures. Several cases have been described in which the ramparts migrate slowly away from the reef edge and are forced across the flat. Partly buried mangrove trees may testify to this movement. In other cases a new rampart is in course of formation closer to the edge, and half-buried remnants of the original rampart, consisting of blackened shingle, emerge below its inner slope.

The conclusion is warranted that the ramparts are destroyed in the course of time. Scattering of the shingle, solution and disintegration of the coral fragments, will gradually result in the disappearance of an old rampart and the formation of sand and silt that is swept away. Under favorable conditions a new rampart is then built up at the seaward edge of the reef flat.

Umbgrove showed that the position of the shingle ramparts is closely related to the direction of the prevailing winds. In the Bay of Batavia (Fig. 181) the ramparts are restricted to the side of the reefs, whence the prevailing and strongest winds also blow. On the Duizend Eilanden in the Java Sea the influence of both monsoons is

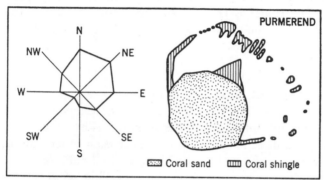

Fig. 181. The reef island of Purmerend in the Bay of Batavia, showing the distribution of sand and shingle under influence of prevailing winds. Scale 1:12,000. (After Umbgrove and Verwey, 1929, Fig. 1, p. 9.)

clearly visible, for here this investigator met with ramparts at opposite sides of the reef flats. Finally, in the Gulf of Tomini, Celebes, he found ramparts to be entirely absent in the remarkably calm waters of this bay.

Similar observations have been made elsewhere in Indonesia, the Great Barrier Reefs, and the West Indies (Steers and others). On oceanic reefs the ramparts are generally found to consist of large boulders or to be entirely absent, owing to excessive force of the waves.

Here and there the shingle accumulates in tongues at right angles to the edge of the reef flat. These ridges are low and flat but may attain considerable length. Probably they are formed more especially on reef flats that lie relatively low, allowing somewhat more scope to waves running across the surface.

On most reef flats, where one of the two types of debris (sand or shingle) accumulations is found the other is also present. The distance between the shingle and sand may be large, and they may lie at opposite sides of the flat. Elsewhere the two types are grown together, but generally a shallow lagoon with tidal waters lies between, either entirely enclosed or communicating with open waters.

Mangroves on coral reefs are generally restricted to the reef flats in little-exposed positions. They grow either in a narrow belt along the coast of the cay or in dense forests behind the rampart. In the Boö Islands east of Halmahera a sandy ridge close to the edge of the reef encircles an extensive mangrove swamp on several of the reefs.

It would lead us too far to describe the various shapes of coral islands. The reader is referred to the reports by the authors mentioned and the account and beautiful maps given by Spender of a few Australian islands.

THE INFLUENCE OF CURRENTS ON CORAL REEFS

It is not easy to distinguish between the action of currents and waves, more especially because the surface waters move to a large extent under the influence of the winds. When the two agencies have the same direction they will support each other's influence and only where powerful and clearly directed hydraulic or tidal currents occur that diverge strongly from the prevailing wind is there a possibility of judging in what measure each of the two helps to shape the reefs.

This case occurs, although not very distinctly, in the coral islands of the Sibutu Group to the north of Borneo (Fig. 182). Strong currents run between the Sulu and Celebes Seas through the straits between the islands on the ridge connecting Borneo with Mindanao. The atolls and reefs are strongly elongated in the direction of the currents, and the impression is gained that the coral structures have grown in the direction of the moving waters. Not only were the ends most favorable to coral growth, but also the dumping of sediment built out screes on which the reefs could advance, while the channels between the islands were swept clean and developed steep or overhanging edges so that outbuilding was hampered. The depth curves, below the range of corals, clearly show the deltalike bastions jutting out from the crest of the submarine ridge into the Celebes and Sulu Seas.

The Thousand Islands North of Java form a group of elongated coral islands pointing in the direction of the alternating monsoonal winds and currents (Fig. 183). The deep swales between the islands, that reach to considerable depths below the floor of the surrounding shelf sea, are evidently due to the scouring action of the currents. Hence the currents are mainly responsible for the oblong shape of these coral formations.

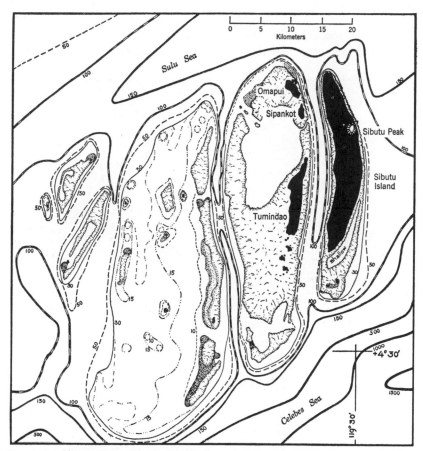

FIG. 182. Chart of the Sibutu Archipelago, north of Borneo, a group of oblong atolls grown on a submarine ridge under the influence of currents between the Sulu and Celebes seas. Slight tilting of the foundation has elevated Sibutu Island and partly drowned the large atoll to the west of Tumindao Atoll. (After Kuenen, 1933, Fig. 38, p. 26.)

THE INFLUENCE OF CHANGES IN LEVEL

Small Changes in Level (up to a few meters). Subsidence of a reef relative to sea level is in general favorable to coral growth. The corals succumb only under conditions where the movement is too rapid for the reef to follow the rising sea surface and turbidity obstructs the penetration of light. No observations on this theoretical possibility have been published.

A slight elevation with relation to sea level will strongly influence all but the deepest reefs. The greatest change is naturally brought about by emergence of the reef surface, by which the corals are killed. The more fragile colonies are directly broken away by the waves, and the more massive ones also will be planed off in the course

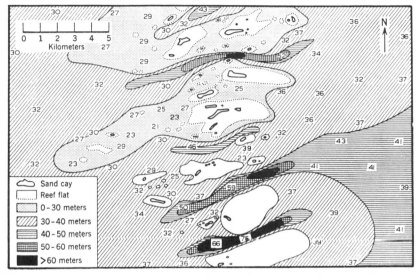

FIG. 183. Chart of the central part of the Thousand Islands in the Java Sea, showing deep swales between the reefs caused by currents. (Redrawn after Umbgrove, 1929, Plate I.)

of time. Finally a dead, rocky abrasion surface near low-tide level is formed. Shallow pools may fill up by growth. Very large colonies and knolls withstand abrasion for a long time and are gradually under-cut to form pedestal rocks. Ultimately the supporting pillar is cut through and the head rolls off onto the flat as a loose boulder, there quickly to be disintegrated.

On some Indonesian reefs Kuenen found such remains of emerged reefs (Fig. 184). The blocks had been thrown up close to the edge of the reef flat into a rampart, strongly resembling shingle ramparts but of much coarser texture. A crest of normal shingle crowned these *boulder ramparts*, while on the inner side facing the reef flat a few minute pedestals in the original position of growth still stood up a meter above the surrounding flat. The gradual elimination of the boulder rampart was obvious from the fallen and undermined trees growing on top and the spits curving away from the reef edge onto the flat at the ends.

The reef flats are generally situated at a higher level than the reef could have grown up to as a compact structure. Inspection shows that the surface cuts across dead colonies fixed in the rock. This is clear proof of the flat's having been formed by a negative shift of

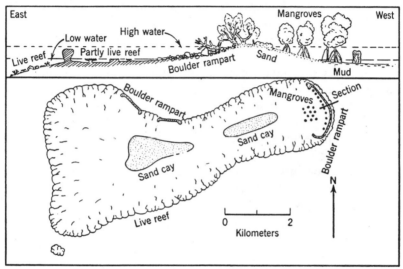

Fig. 184. Boulder ramparts on Pelokan, Sapuka Atoll, south of Celebes. The section is viewed from the north. (After Kuenen, 1941, Fig. 24, p. 118.)

the strand line. The sand cays and shingle ramparts lying on the surface of the flat must also have developed after the relative emergence. It would even appear that practically no cays and ramparts could have been formed but for the preceding emergence. This is beyond doubt true of all islands formed of reef rock that abound on the atolls and barriers of the coral seas. It is almost universally observed that all islands on a reef are being attacked by erosion and doomed to be devoured by the waves. It has already been mentioned that the islands on the windward side of the Maldive and Laccadive archipelagoes have disappeared. Although some reef islands are being added to on the lagoon side, the coasts are rapidly receding on the outer side. The resultant migration will probably end with their being pushed back across the reef into the depths of the lagoon. Even in the calm waters of the Moluccan seas coral islands are almost always found to be on the wane.

It was Gardiner who especially emphasized the importance to the development of coral islands of a relative rise of the reefs throughout the coral seas. The fact that they are often larger and closer together on the leeward side of atolls is a strong argument against their being due only to the action of waves and in favor of the opposite contention that waves may be temporarily forced to build islands on an emerged flat but will ultimately succeed, together with solution, in destroying all or the vast majority of resultant islands.

It is of interest to note that Darwin observed the destruction going on among the coral islands and attributed it to subsidence. This appeared to argue in favor of his theory of atoll and barrier formation. If he had pondered the question how these islands could first have been formed, he would soon have come to the conclusion that only a relative emergence could have caused the former period of construction. The exact opposite to what Darwin attempted to prove has taken place.

Daly later drew attention to the large number of coasts on which a subrecent emergence of nearly uniform amounts has left its mark in the shape of elevated notches and erosion terraces. He attributed them all to a recent world-wide sinking of ocean level by 5 or 6 m. Since then evidence has been added from many more localities, especially from practically all the reef groups investigated. Daly's postulate has thus been confirmed and may be accepted as practically established, especially when the less obvious but no less pertinent testimony of all reef flats that lie above the growth limit of reefs is added. It should be admitted, however, that subsidence of the land leaves much less evidence, and it might be claimed that an equal length of coast may have been drowned. In that event sea level should have remained stable and deformation of the crust would have caused the deleveling noted. This contention is unreasonable, however, in view of the fact that all the emerged beaches are found at roughly the same altitude above present sea level.

As soon as an attempt is made, however, to ascertain the exact amount of the depression of sea level, difficulties are encountered in spite of the fact that coral reefs are the best geological tide gauges available. The advantages offered by reefs for studying former stands of sea level are due to the following properties: (1) the solid reef cannot be built up above average sea level; (2) the reef can develop into a hard, coherent mass; (3) sharply chiseled notches are cut in elevated reef rock even in protected positions; (4) the reefs tend to grow up to low tide level; (5) erosion of emerged reefs generally ends when low water level is reached; (6) sand cays are built up to a small height above high tide and many of them possess a flat surface.

Uncertainties are introduced when the range of the tides is large, or where strong onshore winds pile up the water against the coast.

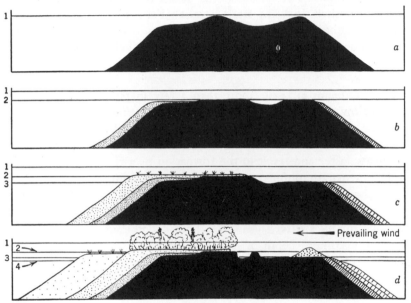

FIG. 185. Development of the islands in the Bay of Batavia by lowering of sea level in three successive stages, according to Kuenen. (After Kuenen, 1933, Fig. 85, p. 72.)

Moreover, many measurements have been only rough estimates, and datum level is not easily established during normal field explorations.

Kuenen studied many instances in Indonesia. He found that generally the movements, so well recorded on the reef-encircled coasts of these tropical seas, appear to have taken place in steps. Most cases were recorded on Moluccan islands, where recent diastrophic movements of the crust may have played a part. But the coral islands in the Bay of Batavia on the stable Sunda Shelf also provided excellent examples (Fig. 185). He therefore tentatively suggested a sinking of ocean level in three successive stages of 4–5, 1½–2, and ½–1 m. Similar results have been recorded by a number of workers from Indian and Pacific islands and from Australia (Teichert, 1947).

Later work by Stearns (1941) has confirmed and greatly extended these results, but it was also shown that great care should be taken in estimating the amounts. Thus benches may be cut as much as 4 m above high-tide level on exposed coasts. Stearns concluded from evidence over wide areas of the Pacific coral seas that there are two main levels of 8 and 1½ m above the present position of sea level.

Studies of recent eustatic changes of sea level are now being energetically pushed forward in Australia (Fairbridge and Gill, 1947) and many other parts of the world.

The time of the major retreat may be tentatively estimated at 3000 to 4000 years ago. We will return to these eustatic movements in Chapter 8.

Larger Changes of Level (more than a few meters). Where subsidence is slow the reef is able to grow upwards and remain in contact with the zone of optimal conditions for corals. It may be assumed, however, that, conditions being more favorable at the edges, corals will grow faster and result in the formation of a rim around a lagoon. In the next paragraph this aspect will be treated more in detail. Above it was shown that, for a reef as a whole, maximum rate of upgrowth is of the order of 1 m in a half to two centuries. The corals need not be killed off by swifter subsidence, provided the amount is not more than the maximum depth of coral life. Thus a much larger depression of the foundation may take place by intermittent swift stages divided by long periods in which the reef can regain its original level. As elevated islands show this type of intermittent movement with steps of several meters' height, a similar irregular subsidence should also have occurred here and there.

Subsidence exceeding in amount and rate the maximum that coral growth can compensate must lead to the drowning of the reef. Once the dead surface is carried below the limiting depth for corals, upgrowth cannot recommence, even when prolonged standstill follows. Several banks occur in the coral seas at moderate depths, but yet at too low a level for colonization. Nearly all show a low rim and are evidently drowned atolls. As it is highly improbable that they subsided more swiftly than their neighbors, the obvious explanation is that the reefs were killed at a certain moment and growth was not resumed in time to prevent drowning. When subsidence approximates to the maximum rate of upbuilding, a barrier or atoll may be drowned over most of its circumference, while a few patches succeed in keeping in contact with the zone of coral growth. This situation is represented by some reefs between New Guinea and Halmahera. An example is the drowned barrier of Waigeo (Fig. 186). The lagoon is of abnormal depth, averaging 150 m with a maximum of 200, while the rim lies at a depth of 50 to 100 m. Hence, upgrowth is no longer possible. But one patch shows only 30-m depth and is probably covered by living corals. At this point the crest of the barrier rises to 170 m above the lagoon floor.

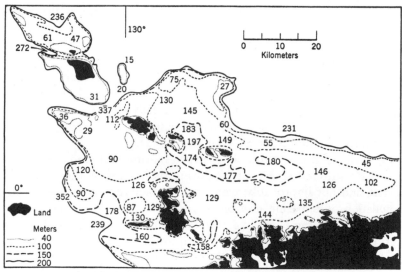

Fig. 186. The drowned barrier of Waigeo in the Moluccas. The lagoon floor is 170 m below the crest of the barrier. (After Kuenen, 1933, Fig. 100, p. 107.)

The result of greater elevation is the formation of reef-coated islands. These coatings tend to be comparatively thin and terraced. The part played by erosion in the cutting of these steps has already been discussed. The reef cap by its presence proves that elevation does not necessarily cause extinction of reef growth by sediment. The covering strongly diminishes the mechanical denudation of the non-coralliferous foundation and reduces the amount of detritus that might otherwise wash off the island and smother the reefs. But the elevation does cause the reefs to be thin, and where the movement is swift the coating is split up into a series of concentric and incomplete benches of reef rock with the foundation showing through in between.

Reef coatings are of course formed from fringing reefs. Elevated barriers and atolls also occur. A fine example of the latter is found in the islands Maratua and Kakaban to the northeast of Borneo (Figs.

179 and 196). The present situation closely approximates to the conditions experienced by all pre- or interglacial atolls during the low sea levels of the Ice Ages. Closer inspection is therefore needed. Chemical marine erosion and denudation of the emerged reef rock are in full swing. Part of the reef ring of Maratua has already completely disappeared, and the remaining crescent is facing early destruction. It is worthy of note that in spite of the elevation and erosion the entire structure is surrounded by a flourishing reef. Local sandy flats of the nature of cays have been thrown up against the elevated rim here and there, but it may be surmised that they will soon be cut away again. The rock is cavernous, and, although still showing roughly the original surface features of the atoll before emergence, the present remnants are greatly weakened and form an easy prey for destructive agents. The lagoons are quite shallow, and even in Kakaban, with an uninterrupted rim, the water rises and falls with the tide and evidently communicates freely with the outer world through crevasses and tunnels in the reef rock (Kuenen, 1933).

From this example it follows that pre-existing atoll and barrier rims must have suffered severe attack during the retreat of the Pleistocene oceans, and not improbably were entirely beheaded at sea level. But denudation and marine erosion were not active below the level of the oceans, and the encircling reefs continued to flourish and to protect the reef foundation and central islands of barriers from the mechanical force of wave attack. Only in the marginal belts of the coral seas, where the temperature of the surface waters sank below the minimum required by reef corals, did this protection disappear and allow the waves to attack islands and reef foundations, resulting in steep cliffs.

In this connection it is of interest to note that the depth of the Maratua and Kakaban lagoons is only 8 to 10 m. The deeper reentrant on the northeast side of Maratua is covered with a flourishing reef and is obviously in the course of being filled in, not of being excavated. Neither is the lagoon being degraded, for otherwise the corals in the reentrant would soon be smothered.

It is a pity that it has not been possible to ascertain how long ago the elevation took place; otherwise a measure of the rate of destruction could have been deduced and some insight gained of the amount of degradation emerged reefs must have suffered during the low levels of the ice age. The only indication is that derived from the recent sinking of ocean level mentioned earlier (p. 437). The amount of destruction arrived at is of the order that would be necessary to reduce an entire atoll to the lowered sea level in the time available during an ice age. But without further confirmation this conclusion is still highly speculative.

Examples of elevated atolls have been described among others from the Lau Archipelago. But Ladd and Hoffmeister showed that the limestone is generally of Tertiary age and consists of coral rock for a minor portion only. The basin-shaped surface appears to be due mainly to denudation, whereby the central hollow is formed by solution. Denudation processes are also responsible for the barrier-shaped rampart of coral limestone in Kisar northeast of Timor and the so-called Makatea of several Pacific islands (Kuenen, 1933).

THE FORMATION OF ATOLLS AND BARRIER REEFS

SUMMARY OF THE PRINCIPAL THEORIES

This inquiry may be preceded by a quotation from Hoffmeister and Ladd (1935): "Probably no single reef theory will explain all reefs. Certainly, recognition of the complexity of the problem is essential to its solution. It does not belong within the realm of any one subject, but requires the attention of scientists of many fields, each contributing his share." The present author is in complete agreement with this statement. In presenting the following summary he wishes the reader to realize that, in spite of the preference shown for certain views on the formation of atolls and barriers, the writer is the first to admit their speculative nature.

A large number of hypotheses have been put forward during more more than a century of intensive investigation and speculation on the mode of origin of atolls and barrier reefs, since Darwin first published his famous theory. Space is lacking to review all these, and the reader wishing a fuller account is referred to the masterly compilation given by Davis in his *The Coral Reef Problem.*

The more important theories can be placed in two groups: (1) explanations claiming no relative changes of level; (2) theories requiring a relative rise of sea level.

Several authors believed that the lagoons had been formed by solution of a solid mass of reef limestone. But it is now generally admitted that sedimentation and not solution is active in lagoons. Hence this explanation cannot be maintained.

Ladd and Hoffmeister have revived the conception of atoll formation without relative changes of sea level and term their explanation the antecedent-platform theory. Stearns, although he lays more emphasis on relative subsidence, also tends to give importance to this point of view.

The first authors mentioned postulate a swift marine erosion of volcanic cinder cones down to a level of 50 m or more below sea level. Afterwards a veneer of calcareous non-coralliferous deposits is laid down on these platforms until suitable depths are attained for colonization by reef-building corals. These will prefer the periphery of the antecedent platform on account of more favorable conditions and will grow up to form an atoll or barrier. The depth at which corals start to grow is estimated at 60 m, an amount that is rather large for many cases but that will be admitted for the sake of argument.

A number of grave objections can be raised against this conception that atolls develop without the intervention of changes of level.

1. No explanation is offered to account for the erosion of coarse volcanic debris, followed without change of conditions by the accumulation of fine-grained organic matter as "skeletons of algae and Foraminifera, together with the shells of molluscs and the spines of echinoids." One need but recall Shepard's demonstration of non-depositional environments prevailing on banks, even at considerable depths, in consequence of currents and waves, to realize that the primary postulate of the antecedent-platform theory is poorly founded.

2. The depth of most of the larger lagoons is 80 m, which is greater than the maximum depth at which corals can thrive. Moreover, a certain amount of recent sedimentation at present veneers the lagoon floor, and, if this cover were to be removed, most lagoons would be found to exceed by a considerable amount the limits for reef development.

3. The drowned morphology of barrier reef islands, the excessively steep submarine slope of many atolls, the results of boring on Maratua and Bikini, and several other phenomena are incompatible with a basement formed of non-coralliferous rock. These points will be discussed in detail presently when dealing with other theories, together with further arguments opposing antecedent platforms as atoll foundations.

Stearns has suggested that atolls may form on the crest of stationary or even on rising anticlines. He fails to explain why an atoll with lagoon is formed and not an extensive solid reef flat. The excavation of a lagoon by solution is not possible because, at present, no solution is going on in lagoons but, on the contrary, deposition of lime. As the difference in level between the lagoon floor and the surface of the sea is only a few dozen meters, local eminences as flat as a billiard table, and several dozen kilometers across, must be postulated on the anticlines—a fact neglected by Stearns' text. His diagrams indicate outward growth on screes as one of the processes involved. One can hardly believe that there was sufficient time for so slow a process. Besides, the greatly exaggerated vertical scale of these diagrams tends to obscure the abnormal shape of the anticlines postulated by Stearns, especially for atolls first formed on somewhat deeper anticlines during low levels of the Pleistocene.

The above discussion shows that atolls and barriers cannot be explained in the manner proposed by Ladd and Hoffmeister. It is admitted, however, that, if the postulated stratum of fine sediment is omitted, there may have been a few exceptional cases in which barriers or atolls with shallow lagoon, slight outer slopes, and cliffed islands formed on pre-existing platforms without intervention of subsidence after colonization started. But the overwhelming majority show features that cannot be thus explained and call for subsidence as the dominant factor in development. There may be antecedent platforms at great depth below the coral formations, and there are very probably platforms at glacial sea level cutting across most coral formations. To this extent the importance of antecedent platforms may be readily admitted. But this should not be allowed to obscure the evidence for subsidence that is so clear and so widespread.

Foremost among the coral-reef theories postulating a relative rise of sea level is the subsidence theory of Darwin. Darwin started from a fringing reef that grows upward during slow subsidence of the foundation (Fig. 187). As the corals tend to grow vertically upwards, and owing to the more favorable conditions on the outward side of the reefs, the periphery is gradually raised while a lagoon forms between it and the central island. Thus a barrier is developed which mounts until the island disappears, leaving an atoll. In this manner Darwin was able to arrange the major reef forms in a closely related series. The logical simplicity of this theory forms a strong attraction, and soon after it was propounded Dana added an important observation in confirmation. Nearly all the islands surrounded by barriers show deeply embayed shorelines, testifying to a submergence of a few hundred meters at least. Borings on Oahu, Hawaii, for instance, have since indicated a subsidence of at least 300 m.

Further arguments in favor of the subsidence theory can be enumerated. In the Moluccas a number of lagoons of abnormal depth amounting to 150 or even 200 m have been found. These call for subsidence to an amount of 150 m. The case of Waigeo may here be recalled (see p. 451).

Many atolls and barriers show abnormally steep submarine slopes. Down to depths of 200 m they sometimes approach the vertical, and declivities of 50° reaching to a depth of 600 m have been recorded. As the slopes around volcanic islands seldom exceed 35° the only logical explanation of the steep foundations is by vertical upgrowth

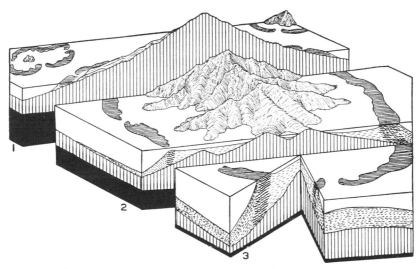

Fig. 187. Block diagram showing the development of barrier and atoll reefs from a fringing reef on a subsiding island according to Darwin's theory.

of coral reefs. In the Tukangbesi Group to the southeast of Celebes, rows of elevated islands and atolls alternate. The submerged slopes of the islands are much gentler than those of the atolls, a strong argument for attributing the atoll slopes to coral growth with screes lower down while the islands represent normal elevated portions of the sea floor (Figs. 188 and 189).

The most convincing evidence of all is found in the recently reported results of geophysical investigation of Bikini Atoll and a deep boring carried out there by the U. S. Navy and of a couple of borings undertaken by the Bataafsche Petroleum Maatschappij on the elevated atoll of Maratua already referred to. The deepest bore hole on Maratua was carried out 2 km inside the edge of the reef to a depth of 429 m below sea level on a cay in the lagoon (see Figs. 179, 190, and 196). It passed through an alternation of reef rock, reef detritus,

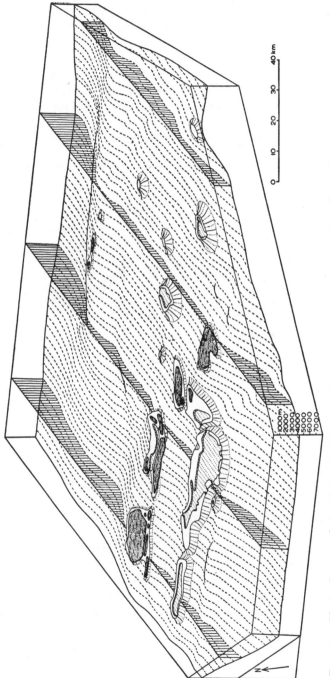

Fig. 188. Block diagram of the Tukangbesi Group.   Vertical 2 times horizontal scale.   (After Kuenen, 1933, Fig. 106, p. 126.)

and fine calcareous lagoon deposits. The last contrast strongly with the coarse terrigenous sand found on the surrounding insular terrace of Borneo and consist mainly of fine, chemically precipitated calcite needles identical with some recent lagoon sediments. Evidently this lime mud was deposited in the protected, badly ventilated waters of a deep lagoon. The bore hole reached to 550 m below the crest of the atoll rim and brings unequivocal evidence of subsidence to an

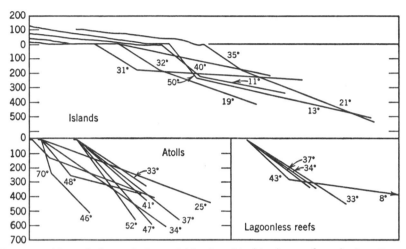

Fig. 189. Natural slope of elevated islands with fringing reefs and of atolls and reefs in the Tukangbesi Group southeast of Celebes. (After Kuenen, 1933, Fig. 88, p. 94.)

amount of at least 500 m during upgrowth of the atoll (Kuenen, 1947).

The seismic section of Bikini Atoll strongly indicated the presence of coral formation down to a more or less horizontal level at 600-m depth. Then followed either consolidated reef rock or volcanic ash, while the compact volcanic cone started at nearly 2000 m below sea level.

Later the results of a boring 1½ km inside the edge have been recorded that showed shallow-water deposits to a depth of 800 m. The fossils appear to be Tertiary, possibly Miocene below about 200 to 300 m. Calcareous sand is the dominant sediment.

It is specially telling that great thickness of coral formations in the foundation of atolls has been proved by two entirely independent methods and for an oceanic atoll and for one from a tectonically unstable region.

Stearns reported coralliferous limestone at depths of well over 300 m from a bore hole on Oahu, Hawaii, but it is not definitely proved that the rock was not a scree.

A second theory of relative subsidence has been proposed by Daly. He drew attention to the remarkable uniformity in reef breadth and lagoon depth of atolls, barrier reefs, and reefless banks of the coral seas. This strongly indicates a comparatively recent event of world-wide importance that has unified conditions of atoll and barrier growth. The theory of glacial control, as advocated by Daly, main-tains that during the ice age sea level sank repeatedly by an amount of about 100 m. The concomitant cooling of the seas killed off

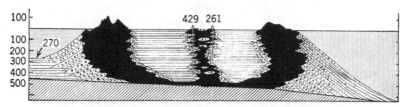

FIG. 190. Diagrammatic section through Maratua, showing interpretation of boring results. (After Kuenen, 1947, Fig. 3, p. 11.)

existing reefs and thus deprived islands and continental coasts of the equatorial belt of their protecting fringe of reefs. This result was strengthened by the churning up of vast quantities of mud that formerly lay beyond the reach of waves but could now be activated by the lowering of sea level. The turbidity caused further havoc among coral life. Erosion set in, and pre-existing banks were beveled off at glacial low level. Thus a vast number of foundations were smoothed and cleansed and prepared for colonization.

In later writings Daly laid more stress on the "sandpapering" of submerged banks and island shelfs formed by marine action on ancient volcanic islands. The adverse conditions of the ice age should then have prevented the establishment of corals during the cold periods, thus allowing the waves to smooth the platforms.

As soon as a milder climate returned coral larvae began to colonize these platforms. They came from the more favorable localities, the Moluccas for instance, where corals had hibernated during the cold spells. The conditions most favorable to coral life were offered by the outer edges of the platforms, where food and oxygen were most abundant and the water of special cleanness. Hence, corals here soon gained the upper hand of those established farther inwards. They were able to grow upward after the gradual return of sea level to its normal station. In this manner atolls and barriers became rooted at the periphery of the platforms that were gradually submerged to a uniform depth of about 80 m, much deeper than the limits of coral growth. Aggradation of the lagoon floors took place. Owing to the smaller area within atolls of lesser extent as compared to the circumference, the accumulation was greater. This explains the observed fact that, the smaller the lagoon, the less the depth at which the floor tends to lie.

The theory of glacial control evidently gives a satisfactory explanation of the extreme scarcity of atoll and barrier lagoons exceeding 80 to 90 m in depth and the relatively small and uniform volume of the encircling reefs, while the lesser depths of small lagoons is also accounted for.

Davis was much impressed by the morphological evidence of drowning encountered in barrier-reef islands. A wide experience in exploration and an exhaustive study of charts led him to accept the subsidence theory for explaining atolls and barriers, but to introduce an important modification. He showed that the straight shoreline and plunging cliffs, absent on barrier islands in the central coral seas, prevail on islands in the marginal belts towards the northern and southern limits of coral growth. He concluded that the zone of flourishing reefs was narrowed down by the cooling of surface waters during the glacial low levels. In the marginal belts thus abandoned low-level erosion succeeded in planing off preglacial reefs and in cliffing central islands. In short he concedes the principles of glacial control for these marginal belts, but not for the torrid central coral seas. His explanation of the uniformity of lagoon depths is that they represent base level for the waves. For wider lagoons this level should lie deeper on account of the larger waves raised. Any sediment introduced into a lagoon in excess of the ordained depth is churned up and carried to deeper spots or swept out through the leeward passes and scattered far and wide over the deep-sea floor.

Kuenen went yet a step further in combining the main elements of the two theories (1933), later proposing the "glacially controlled subsidence theory" (1947). His contention is that, although the arguments in favor of subsidence are almost irrefutable and go far toward proving the formation of the foundation of atolls and barriers by slow sinking of the substratum, no one can deny that all Tertiary reef structures must have suffered attack during glacial low levels (Fig. 191). Existing reefs therefore owe their present shape largely to glacial control, as Daly maintains. Stearns (1945) and others have also suggested without working out details that Darwin's and Daly's theories should be combined, even between Davis's marginal belts.

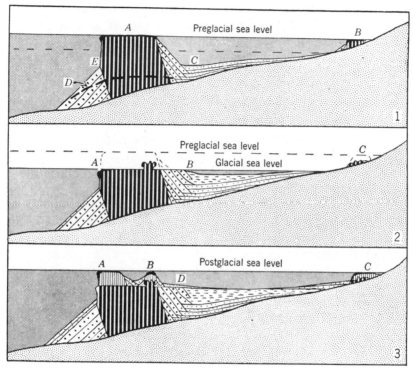

Fig. 191. Diagrams illustrating: 1. Growth of barrier in preglacial times by subsidence as swift as postglacial rise of sea level. *A*, barrier; *B*, fringing reef; *C*, deep lagoon; *D*, very deep passages; *E*, very steep outer slope.

2. Glacial control of a barrier formed by slow subsidence without a deep passage. *A*, abrasion behind a growing reef; *B*, infilling of deep lagoon; *C*, denudation of elevated fringing reef.

3. Postglacial growth of reefs. *A* and *B*, possibly a faro; *C*, fringing reef with boat channel; *D*, sediments veneering platform and forming a basin with greatest depth in center. No passages deeper than about glacial sea level. (After Kuenen, 1947, Fig. 11, p. 24.)

One of the main points in which Kuenen differs from Daly, however, is that he assumes as many coral structures before the ice age as at present and that he ascribes the destruction of the limestone exposed during low sea levels to chemical marine erosion and denudation. All emerged reef rock is supposed to have suffered, while the corals continued to flourish along the new coastline. Aggradation of deep lagoons could continue, while shallow emerged lagoon floors were being degraded. In this manner unification of lagoon depths was strongly promoted. Although proof cannot yet be given, Kuenen is inclined to assume that this glacial control of Tertiary reefs amounted to complete or far advanced leveling of all emerged reef rock. The mode of attack is described on p. 435.

The theory of glacially controlled subsidence thus attempts to combine the merits of the subsidence and glacial control theories. All the arguments in favor of the former pertain to the foundations: boring results, steep slopes below 100-m depth, subsided central islands of barrier reefs, etc. While allowing the chilling of the marginal belts and the mechanical erosion of islands there, the suppression of coral life in the central coral seas is denied in conjunction with the opinion of most paleontologists (Umbgrove, 1947) and the evidence against mud control offered by elevated reef-encircled islands. On the other hand the unification in lagoon depth and volume of present reefs is attributed to low-level erosion, and the absence of cliffed central islands is readily explained by continued protection from mechanical marine erosion.

Supposed glacial control by mechanical erosion leads to the following difficulties (Fig. 192). In order to reach the central area of wide platforms low-level erosion would first have had to cut down the outer parts well below sea level. An atoll like Suvadiva is 60 km across, and marginal depths of one or even a few dozen meters would be required to allow powerful waves to bevel the entire expanse in the short time available.

Two results would be expected if this had actually been the case. First the present floor of the lagoon should be domed and show smaller depths towards the center. But charts (Fig. 193) demonstrate that the opposite is true. Hence postglacial aggradation by sediment must be assumed to convert the domed into a shallower basined bottom. The eroded platform, then, is buried perhaps as much as several dozens of meters. The present shape and flatness are then due to the action of present waves in distributing debris. Daly's argument based on lagoon depths and flatness thus loses some of its appeal.

In the second place, coral starting to grow after the erosion would frequently have encountered more favorable sites some distance inwards from the deep margin of the platform. Conditions for reef growth cannot have reverted immediately to normal after the peak of glaciation. Halting and readvance of the retreating glaciers shows that climatic conditions improved only gradually. Hence, the re-establishment of reefs, if they had been suppressed, should in many cases have come long after sea level had started to rise. By then the margins of Daly's mechanically eroded platforms would have been

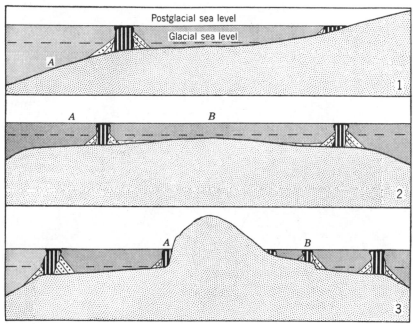

Fig. 192. Diagrams showing some consequences to be expected from mechanical glacial control: 1. Lagoons deeper than glacial sea level.* *A*, gradual slopes outside screes of coral debris. 2. Outward sloping platforms. *A*, reefs frequently set well inside edge of platform; *B*, lagoon shallower in center.* 3. Plunging cliffs at *A*, submerged cliffs at *B*.

* If assumed to be obliterated by later aggradation, present floor cannot prove existence of smoothed platform at glacial sea level.

too deep for colonization, or at any rate they would not have offered particularly favorable sites for reef establishment. Extensive terraces somewhat deeper than glacial sea level would jut out here and there beyond the periphery of the atoll and barrier reefs. However, in the central coral seas and wherever a distinct barrier or atoll reef is developed such platforms are conspicuous by their absence.

With the postulates of glacially controlled subsidence the continued protection of the platform below sea level by thriving coral growth not only accounts for the absence of greater marginal than central depths in wide lagoons but it also offers a logical explanation for the consistent external position of present reefs. The corals were already

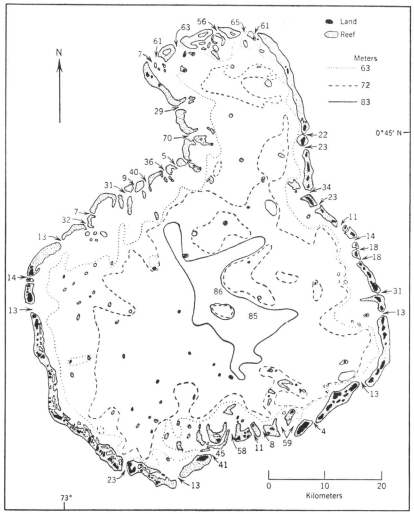

FIG. 193. Chart of Suvadiva Atoll. Note slight basin shape of lagoon floor. Depths in meters. (After Kuenen, 1947, Fig. 10, p. 22.)

established along the margins of the platforms, and the firm substratum of abraded reef rock offered an ideal foundation for colonization, far better than the abraded or aggraded lagoon floor farther inwards.

In the marginal belts, where killing of the corals by lowered temperature is admitted, one would expect the reefs to be rooted in general inwards from the edge of the platform. This is actually the case, as Davis showed. Either fringing reefs or bank-inset reefs are met with. Among dozen of examples of these conditions only two or three are known where the reefs are marginal to the platform.

Another objection to Daly's theory is that if coral life had been suppressed throughout the Pacific and re-established by larvae coming from the Moluccan Seas, as he supposes, this process would have taken a long time for all reefs lying upstream of this region with regard to surface currents. One should also remember the countless other types of organisms found in the communities termed "coral reefs." Re-establishment would have proved impossible in some areas. Moreover, the new fauna should be poor, because many forms of reef life cannot readily cross the open ocean. Coral species are not distributed universally, proving that migration is a very slow process. Many forms known from elsewhere appear to be absent from the Moluccas and could not have been supplied from this area in post-glacial times. These findings can hardly be reconciled with the postulates of Daly's theory.

Davis claimed that, if mechanical erosion had acted on the platforms around barrier islands, the islands should present plunging cliffs. Daly denies this contention because sea level was swinging up and down most of the time. But then, how are the plunging cliffs of the marginal belts to be explained? Moreover, the coastal features of barrier reef islands are so different from those of coasts in higher latitudes that uninterrupted protection of the former must be assumed.

Shepard pointed out that the breadth of lagoons is not greater on the windward side of barrier islands, as it should be if mechanical wave erosion had played an important part in developing underlying platforms. Likewise the more or less peripheral position of the islands within the Vanua Mbalavu Barrier (Fig. 194) cannot be satisfactorily accounted for by wave action. On the other hand a foundation with irregular topography subsiding within a fringing reef might show eccentric islands within a barrier at a later stage.

Taken together the evidence seems strongly opposed to the theory of glacial control by mechanical action of the waves, while these objections cannot be raised against the view that solution decapitated Tertiary and interglacial reefs during glacial stages.

The main objection that can be raised against the subsidence theory is the absence of deep passes through the atoll and barrier rims

(Kuenen, 1947). Large atolls generally show a dozen or more passages of varying depths a few of which are of the same order as the lagoon floor. Many of these interruptions of the rim, at any rate the deeper ones, are beyond the limits of coral growth and cannot be closed by upgrowth from the bottom. In the event of further subsidence the depth would continue to increase. Now, if the develop-

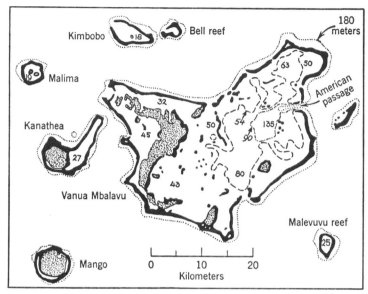

Fig. 194. Part of Lau Archipelago, Fiji, showing the deep American Passage. Depths in meters. (After Kuenen, 1947, Fig. 9, p. 21.)

ment of passes were a normal feature of atoll or barrier rims, as their profusion would lead one to suppose, the growth of these reef forms by subsidence should have led to the formation of countless gaps reaching to great depths. The lagoon floor behind these breaches should show abnormal depths on account of the loss of material through the gap to the outer world. Inspection of charts soon teaches that passes reaching below normal lagoon depths are extremely scarce. American Passage in the barrier of Vanua Mbalavu, Fiji, with a depth of 200 m is one of the very few exceptions in the tropical Pacific (Fig. 194). Opposite this passage the lagoon shows an abnormally deep area.

Two explanations can be offered for the almost complete absence of deep passes. Either the foundation was not formed by subsidence, in which case glacial control of non-coral islands would have to be assumed. Or preglacial absolute subsidence differed in some important respect, probably velocity, from the postglacial relative subsidence. Owing to this difference the ancient slow movement led to the formation of reefs without passes, while the recent swift movement caused them to develop profusely. Comparison with other earth movements would lead one to expect a preglacial subsidence of the foundation of not more than a few centimeters per century, probably considerably less, while the recent rise of sea level must have attained several tens of centimeters per century. The Bikini bore actually showed Miocene rock at a depth of only 300 m, indicating a subsidence of less than half a centimeter per century.

If these figures are accepted the following tentative explanation can be given. During slow Tertiary subsidence atolls and barriers grew up in uninterrupted rims. Whenever a portion of the reef was killed, ample time was available for repairing the gap by coral growth. Many instances can be given of present atolls and barriers without passes, so these gaps are evidently not a necessary consequence of tides or winds (Fig. 195). On the other hand postglacial rise of sea level approached the maximum at which a reef can grow upwards. Hence, if any portion of the rim lagged behind in consequence of death or the establishment of slowly growing species, it soon fell below the level of optimal development. Tidal and wind-driven currents would concentrate in these gaps and sweep debris away. The bottom would lag behind more and more in the construction of the rim and finally come to lie below the maximum depth at which corals can live.

The figures on the velocity of reef growth given on a former page accord satisfactorily with the view here expounded, for an addition of 50 to 200 cm per century under favorable conditions would leave only a small margin with a sea level rising at 30 to 40 cm per century. On the other hand it must be admitted that the two borings on the Great Barrier reefs of Australia are interpreted as indicating subsidence to an amount of 170 m in postglacial time and yet well-developed reefs have been able to form. However, this does not disprove that elsewhere under somewhat less favorable conditions the smaller rate of rising sea level could approach the limit for reef thickening.

Many barrier-reef islands are encircled by fringing reefs. This combination does not fit Darwin's theory, because further subsidence would cause a second barrier to form within the first. The total absence of multiple barrier reefs shows that fringing reefs within barriers must be a recent abnormal development which has affected the majority of barrier islands simultaneously. Glacial control again offers a satisfactory explanation. Faros can be likewise explained.

The above review tends to show that the theory of glacially controlled subsidence has advantages over its component elements when

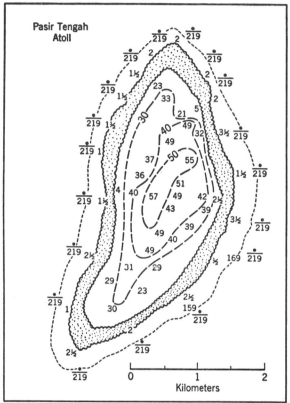

FIG. 195. An atoll of the Togian Group, Celebes, showing a rim without passages and basin-shaped lagoon floor. Depths in meters. (Modified from Umbgrove, 1939, Fig. 10, p. 151.)

these are applied separately. Yet one should keep in mind the want of quantitative data on chemical marine erosion, reef growth, etc. The weakest point is the assumption that exposed reefs were largely destroyed although the processes invoked may prove to act very slowly. It may also be that in some reef groups other theories offer a better explanation.

EVIDENCE FROM SOME CORAL REEF ARCHIPELAGOES

Important evidence in the problem of atolls and barriers can be gained by inspection of some coral-reef groups. The configuration and position on the morphology of the sea floor, as well as the geological structure of elevated islands, may indicate in what manner the foundations of the reefs were formed. A short treatment of some important archipelagoes will therefore be given.

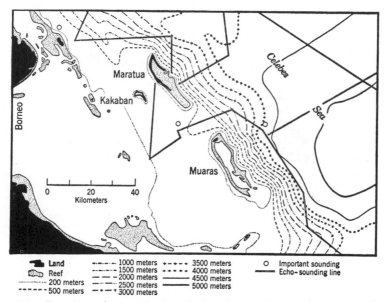

Fig. 196. Situation of the raised atolls to the northeast of Borneo. (After Kuenen, 1933, Fig. 95, p. 104.)

Maratua, Muaras, and Kakaban. These three raised atolls have been repeatedly mentioned on foregoing pages, but no account has been given of the geological history of the group. It is situated in the Celebes Sea to the northeast of Borneo (Fig. 196). Maratua is raised to 110 m above sea level and is partly abraded, presenting a crescentic rim, while Kakaban attains about 45 m in a complete ring. Muaras lies at sea level and appears to have been entirely eroded, except for one small island at the northwestern end. These reefs rise abruptly from an almost flat shelf that gradually dips outward from the mainland. An intermittent barrier reef is found along the 100-m line, but the atolls are situated farther out in water that is about 250 m deep.

Borings in the lagoon of Maratua (Fig. 190, p. 459) failed to attain the foundation of the coral structure at 550 m below the crest of the rim, that is, nearly 200 m lower than the adjoining sea floor. The following picture of the evolution can be suggested.

Originally the outer edge of the shelf lay at least 400 m higher than at present. During slow subsidence a fringing reef developed into a barrier that split up into two parts (Maratua and Muaras), while a lagoon reef also formed (Kakaban). Gradually the reefs developed

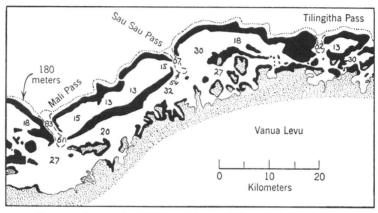

FIG. 197. Part of the barrier of Vanua Levu, Fiji, with large faros. Depths in meters.

into atolls as the great distance to the coast tended to equalize conditions all around the circumference of each reef. The curious barrier of Vanua Levu (Fig. 197), consisting of large atoll-like faros, may illustrate an intermediate stage of development. The reefs and atolls on the northwestern edge of the Sahul Shelf, rising from a platform at 540-m depth, also represent this stage of development (Teichert and Fairbridge, 1948). In the meantime accumulation of terrigenous deposits aggraded the shelf by an amount of 200 to 300 m. During the ice age an independent barrier took root farther in in shallower water. The final act was the upwarping of the edge of the submerged shelf whereby the atolls were raised to their present high station.

The Tijger Atoll. This atoll rises steeply from a deeply submerged ridge connecting Celebes with a group of islands to the south (Figs. 198 and 199). The atoll tops this geanticline like a chimneypot standing on a roof, but it is much broader than the crown of the ridge and has evidently spread outward on its own screes. Its small neighbor Taka Garlarang sprouts up abruptly from the side of the ridge, from a depth of more than 2000 m. It is hard to imagine tectonically

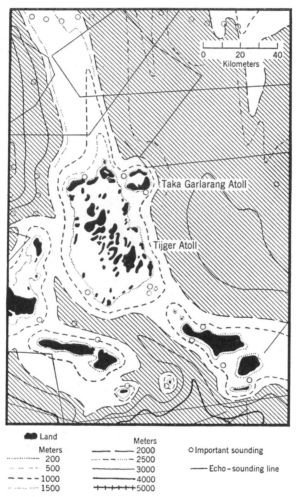

FIG. 198.   Chart of Tijger Atoll and Taka Garlarang Atoll south of Celebes. (After Kuenen, 1933, Fig. 93, p. 102.)

formed and abraded foundations to account for these atolls. Subsidence during upgrowth, however, offers a logical explanation.

The Sibutu Atolls. These reefs on the submarine ridge connecting Borneo with Mindanao have already been mentioned (p. 444). It is obvious that the basements of these reefs are of such a curious yet systematic shape that they can hardly be explained as eroded islands of tectonic or volcanic origin. A simple picture can be offered by assuming the growth of reefs on the ridge during very long periods of slow subsidence, allowing the atolls to grow outwards on their own screes under the influence of strong currents, as explained earlier.

The Maldive and Laccadive Archipelagoes. These coral formations contain many fine atolls. If one were to suppose that former islands had been base-leveled to form the foundations, it is difficult to account

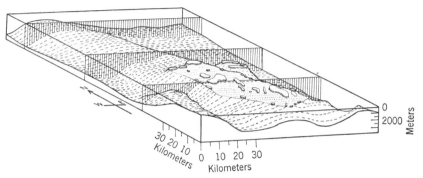

Fig. 199. Block diagram of Tijger Atoll and Taka Garlarang Atoll south of Celebes. (After Kuenen, 1938, Fig. 4, p. 96.)

for the regular shapes and fairly constant sizes, and especially the close juxtaposition with narrow deep passages in between. Neither tectonic nor volcanic activity tends to produce such forms. But growth on a gradually subsiding ridge again offers an adequate explanation of the configuration (Fig. 200).

The Fiji Islands. The Fiji Islands form the most complicated and richest group of reef islands of the world. Barrier reefs and atolls fringing reefs and elevated coral structures abound. Ladd and Hoffmeister described the elevated limestones at length and offered the suggestion that after marine erosion of pyroclastic cones the platforms were blanketed with fine-grained limestone, consisting of algae, Foraminifera, etc. On Numuka these rocks are 70 m thick and covered by at least 25 m of reef limestone. As the lower strata were deposited in shallow water a subsidence of about 100 m is proved.

It is difficult to imagine conditions under which these fine-grained deposits would cling to a submarine platform in shallow water. The small depth is proved by some isolated reef corals and reefs and by cross-bedding. But if we assume a protecting barrier and slow subsidence, as in Darwin's theory, the limestones could be interpreted as

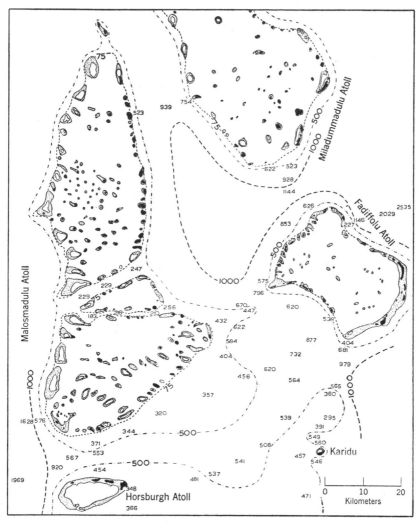

FIG. 200. Part of the group of Maldive atolls in the Indian Ocean. Note the deep channels dividing Malosmadulu Atoll into separate parts, and the faros. Depths in meters.

ancient lagoon deposits. Later elevation resulted in the chemical marine erosion of the rim and the terracing of the central island. The final attack took place during Pleistocene low levels, and the present barriers and atoll rims grew up in postglacial times. Figure 201 summarizes this suggestion. In some cases two types of limestone were deposited, testifying to two periods of subsidence with elevation be-

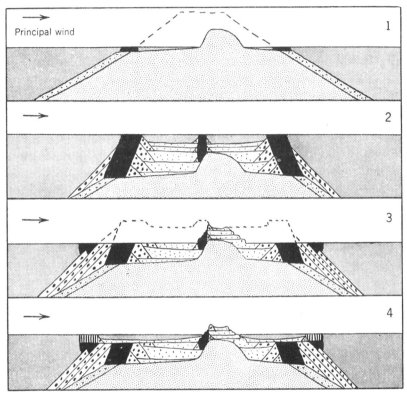

FIG. 201. Diagram showing development of barrier islands of the Lau Archipelago, Fiji, according to glacially controlled subsidence. 1. Marine erosion of volcanic island with reefs on the platform edges. 2. Slow subsidence, blanketing during Tertiary times of island by fine lagoon deposits, with some reefs and scree material. 3. Stepped elevation accompanied by erosion and final erosion at glacial sea level. 4. Postglacial growth of barrier reef and sedimentation on the platform. (After Kuenen, 1947, Fig. 4, p. 14.)

tween. In this picture the long period between the deposition of the limestones and the present is occupied by outgrowth of the atolls probably before they were elevated and by the elevation itself.

Davis attempted to bring all these forms into a logical and comparatively simple system by postulating a north-to-south geanticline wandering westward through the group. But field examinations, especially by Ladd and Hoffmeister, have shown that most of the so-called raised atolls and barriers consist of Tertiary limestones and that sub-aerial solution is responsible for the basin shape. Renewed testing of Davis's views is required.

DEGREE OF STABILITY OF REEF FOUNDATIONS

For the theory of glacial control, stability—at least during the Pleistocene—of reef foundations must be assumed, whereas the theory of subsidence calls for general instability. Which of the two conditions appears the more likely postulate?

This question has been much debated, but the opposing views do not really exclude each other. As soon as it is admitted that tectonic and epirogenic movements are very slow as compared to eustatic movements of the ice ages, the opposing arguments can be readily reconciled. The average velocity of the former appears very seldom to exceed 0.5 mm per annum and is generally much less. The rise of sea level during the melting of the Pleistocene ice caps averaged 2 to 3 mm and must have approached 10 mm as a maximum. Hence, while there are many indications of instability for atoll substratums the deduced movements were probably so slow that when they are contrasted with the glacial swings of sea level the reef foundations appeared to have been stationary or nearly so. Keeping this in mind, the evidence may now be shortly reviewed.

It was pointed out above that abnormally deep lagoons, many examples attaining 150 m or more in depth, form direct proof of a certain degree of instability. For regions such as the West Indies, Indonesia, the Fiji group, etc., elevated reefs form another, striking illustration of crustal unrest. To postulate stability of foundations for these parts of the world is highly questionable. Investigations of the geological history of Indonesia, especially of later years, have proved that many of the orogenic movements and the elevation of the terraced reef caps have occurred very recently, partly during the Pleistocene. Although the possibility cannot be entirely excluded that the tectonic and epirogenic movements may have been comparatively inactive of later times, the present author believes that all geologists conversant with the history of the Moluccas would deny this for the Indonesian coral formations. Moreover, such convincing examples of development through subsidence have been cited above that one can hardly doubt (and even Daly appears to admit, 1948) that Darwin's theory is applicable to the atolls and barriers of these archipelagoes.

The occurrence of important subsidences in the far-flung coral formations of the central Pacific and Indian oceans appears more open to doubt. Molengraaff invoked the intervention of isostatic sinking of volcanic cones that had been built up on the sea floor. Recent investigations of gravity appear to point to a considerable strength of the earth's crust, thus enabling it to bear the weight of a volcano for indefinite lengths of time. The elastic reaction to loading would naturally have been fully carried out long before the reefs established themselves on the volcanic cones. The possibility remains that over sufficient length of time the crust gives way under large local loads. Very slow subsidence might then take place. Thus, Stearns (1946) found coralliferous limestone in well logs on Oahu (Hawaii Group) as deep as 300 m below sea level. This is strong evidence in favor of considerable subsidence, if the limestone is a real reef and not a scree. Valley filling also testified to subsidence of at least 300 m since the Pliocene. If this movement is not due to isostatic adjustments, other causes must have operated, such as diastrophic movements.

In a former chapter the possibility of subsidence through the compaction and plastic deformation of the deep-sea sediments below a newly built pelagic volcanic edifice was mentioned. Tectonic activity of the ocean floor has long been denied. Now that the great topographic irregularity of the sea bottom has been proved, it has become probable that folding and block faulting are as active on the ocean floors as on the continents. Hence, tectonic activity including subsidence is a reasonable postulate for part of the atolls and barrier reefs.

Davis (1928) showed that platforms at a suitable depth for coral growth are practically absent in the cooler parts of the ocean. "But, when the relative abundance of banks of moderate depth in the narrow marginal belts of the coral seas is discovered and still more when the considerable number of banks in the coral seas is recognized, the assumption that no volcanic islands have ever been formed in the blank areas of the cooler seas of the Pacific and Indian oceans seems unreasonable. For it is altogether improbable that the climatic boundary should also be the boundary between areas in which volcanic islands have not been formed and areas in which they have been formed" (p. 164). He concludes that volcanic islands were also formed in the cooler seas, but that everywhere they subside slowly. In the warmer seas coral growth has maintained contact with the surface and the existing platforms consequently owe their origin to reef development.

This deduction of Davis' has recently found support. Hess discovered several hundred deeply submerged flat-topped cones, his guyots (see p. 103). Most of them lie within the belt of coral growth, but several occur in cooler parts of the northern Pacific. It is reasonably certain that atolls are similar cones crowned with a limestone mass. For Bikini and Eniwetok this has actually been proved (Emery, 1948; Emery et al., 1949). The explanation offered by Hess is that any volcanic cone is quickly planed off by waves after extinction. The relative rise in sea level due to oceanic sedimentation then carries the beheaded cone gradually downwards. The guyots would be the pre-Cambrian representatives from periods when no lime-secreting organisms existed to build up the cone, while cones erected later were capped by organic lime, finally by reef corals. In this manner he explains the curious absence of guyots with depths less than about 1000 m. This hypothesis is highly attractive in its simplicity, but the rate of subsidence would be excessively small. The writer is inclined to assume that sedimentation cannot account for a rise of more than half the observed amount. Tentatively it may be suggested that a period of swifter, compactional subsidence of newly built volcanic cones amounting to several hundreds of meters precedes the depression by sedimentation (see also pp. 399 and 400).

Shepard is of the opinion that atolls may have grown up from the average level of guyots, some 1300 m, during the melting of huge ice sheets belonging to the early Pleistocene (see next chapter). One might call this "super glacial control." This would imply upgrowth at a rate of at least 20 mm per year in uninterrupted rims. Then, after the last lowering of sea level, upgrowth at about one-tenth of that rate took place, yet leaving many gaps in the rims to account for the passages. This picture is most unsatisfactory. Moreover, the Bikini bore hole shows that most of the material is of Tertiary age and was not built up during the Pleistocene.

We thus arrive at the conclusion that instability of reef foundations is highly probable in tectonically active regions. In many others there is not much evidence to go by, but little can be said against the postulate as a probability. On the other hand the universal but limited "stability" required by the theory of glacial control can hardly be denied for the short period necessary. Even swift diastrophic shifts should have caused movements of no more than a few dozen meters during the Pleistocene, generally even less. The stability required does not exclude such movements. Perhaps the very deep Indonesian lagoons belong to the few exceptions where diastrophism somewhat exceeded normal values.

For many oceanic reef foundations even long-continued stability is probable, apart from the influence of sedimentation, just mentioned. The borings on Bikini, for instance, reached Miocene fossils at depths of 280 m or even less.

Bibliography

ARMSTRONG, H. E., et al. *The Atoll of Funafuti*, Royal Soc. London, 428 pp., 1904.

DALY, R. A. A Recent Worldwide Sinking of Ocean Level, *Geol. Mag.*, Vol. 57, pp. 246–261, 1920.

The Changing World of the Ice Age, 271 pp., Yale University Press, 1934.

Coral Reefs—A Review, *Am. J. Sci.*, Vol. 246, pp. 193–207, 1948.

DARWIN, C. *The Structure and Distribution of Coral Reefs*, 2nd ed., 278 pp., Smith, Elder, London, 1874.

DAVIS, W. M. *The Coral Reef Problem*, Am. Geogr. Soc., 596 pp., 1928.

EMERY, K. O. Submarine Geology of Bikini Atoll, *Bull. Geol. Soc. Am.*, Vol. 59, pp. 855–860, 1948.

EMERY, K. O., J. I. TRACEY, and H. S. LADD. Submarine Geology and Topography in the Northern Marshalls, *Trans. Am. Geoph. Union*, Vol. 30, pp. 55–58, 1949.

FAIRBRIDGE, R. W. Notes on the Geomorphology of the Pelsart Group of the Houtman's Abrolhos Islands, *J. Royal Soc. Western Australia*, Vol. 33, pp. 1–43, 1948.

FAIRBRIDGE, R. W., and E. D. GILL. The Study of Eustatic Changes of Sea Level, *Austr. J. Sci.*, Vol. 10, pp. 63–67, 1947.

FAIRBRIDGE, R. W., and C. TEICHERT. The Rampart System at Low Isles, 1925-45, *Rept. Great Barrier Reef Comm.*, Vol. 6, 1, pp. 1–16, 1947.

FLINT, R. F. *Glacial Geology and the Pleistocene Epoch*, 589 pp., John Wiley & Sons, New York, 1947.

GARDINER, J. ST. *Coral Reefs and Atolls*, 181 pp., Macmillan, London, 1931.

HESS, H. H. Drowned Ancient Islands of the Pacific Basin, *Am. J. Sci.*, Vol. 244, pp. 772–791, 1946.

HOFFMEISTER, J. E., and H. S. LADD. The Foundations of Atolls, *J. Geol.*, Vol. 43, pp. 653–665, 1935.

A Criticism of the Glacial-Control Theory, *J. Geol.*, Vol. 44, pp. 74–92, 1936.

The Antecedent-Platform Theory, *J. Geol.*, Vol. 52, pp. 388–402, 1944.

Geology of Lau, Fiji, *B. P. Bishop Museum Bull.*, Vol. 181, 399 pp., 1945.

KUENEN, PH. H. Geology of Coral Reefs, *The Snellius Expedition*, Vol. 5, part 2, 126 pp., Brill, Leyden, 1933.

Submarine Slopes of Volcanoes and Coral Reefs in the East Indian Archipelago, *C. R. Congr. Intern. Géogr. Amsterdam* 1938, T. II, Sec. II^b, pp. 93–98.

Kruistochten over de indische Diepzeebekkens, 220 pp., Leopold, The Hague, 1941.

Two Problems of Marine Geology, Atolls and Canyons, *Verh. Kon. Ned. Akad. v. Wet. Amsterdam, afd. Nat.*, D1.43, 3, 69 pp., 1947.

Reports of the Great Barrier Reef Committee, Vols. I–V, 1925–1942.

SAVILLE KENT, W. *The Great Barrier Reef of Australia*, 387 pp., Allen, London, 1893.

SEWELL, R. B. SEYMOUR. Studies on Coral and Coral Formations in Indian Waters, *Mem. Asiatic Soc. Bengal*, Vol. 9, pp. 461–540, 1935.

An Account of Addu Atoll, An Account of Hornsburgh Atoll, *John Murray Exp.*, Vol. I, 3 + 5, pp. 63–93, 109–125, 1936.

SPENDER, M. A. Islands Reefs of the Queensland Coast, *Geogr. J.*, Vol. 76, pp. 193–214, 273–297, 1930.

STEARNS, H. T. Decadent Coral Reef on Eniwetok, Marshall Group, *Bull. Geol. Soc. Am.*, Vol. 56, pp. 783–788, 1945.

An Integration of Coral-Reef Hypotheses, *Am. J. Sci.*, pp. 245–262, 1946.

STEERS, J. A. The Queensland Coast and the Great Barrier Reefs, *Geogr. J.*, Vol. 74, pp. 232–257, 341–370, 1929.

The Coral Islands and Associated Features of the Great Barrier Reefs, *Geogr. J.*, Vol. 89, pp. 1–28, 119–146, 1937.

The Coral Cays of Jamaica, *Geogr. J.*, Vol. 95, pp. 30–42, 1940.

STEERS, J. A., et al. Sand Cays and Mangroves in Jamaica, *Geogr. J.*, Vol. 96, pp. 305–328, 1940.

TEICHERT, C. Contributions to the Geology of Houtman's Abrolhos, Western Australia, *Proc. Linn. Soc. N. S. Wales*, Vol. 71, pp. 145–196, 1947.

TEICHERT, C., and R. W. FAIRBRIDGE. Some Coral Reefs of the Sahul Shelf, *Geogr. Rev.*, Vol. 38, pp. 222–249, 1948.

TRACEY, J. I., H. S. LADD, and J. E. HOFFMEISTER. Reefs of Bikini, Marshall Island, *Bull. Geol. Soc. Am.*, Vol. 59, pp. 861–878, 1948.

UMBGROVE, J. H. F. (*a*) The Influence of the Monsoons on the Geomorphology of Coral Islands, *Proc. Fourth Pac. Sci. Congr. Java*, Vol. 2, pp. 49–54, 1929.

(*b*) De koraalriffen der Duizend Eilanden (Java-zee), *Wet. Med. Dienst Mijnbouw Ned.-Indië*, No. 12, 47 pp., 1929.

De koraalriffen van Emmahaven (W. Sumatra), *Leid. Geol. Med.*, Vol. 4, pp. 9–24, 1931.

De atollen en barrière riffen der Togian Eilanden (summary in English), *Leid. Geol. Med.*, Dl. 11, pp. 132–187, 1939.

Coral Reefs of the East Indies, *Bull. Geol. Soc. Am.*, Vol. 58, pp. 729–778, 1947.

UMBGROVE, J. H. F., and J. VERWEY. The Coral Reefs in the Bay of Batavia, *Fourth Pac. Sci. Congr.*, Exc. A2, 30 pp., 1929.

VERWEY, J. Coral Reef Studies, *Treubia*, Vol. 13, pp. 169–198, 199–215, 1931.

WOOD JONES, F. *Coral and Atolls*, 392 pp., Lovell Reeve, London, 1910.

WOODS, H. *Palaeontology, Invertebrate*, 477 pp., Cambridge University Press, 1946.

Geomorphology
of the Sea Floor

Submarine geomorphology is concerned with a number of topographic features, some of which have already been considered on previous pages. Thus the major forms such as oceanic deeps and smaller basins, the continental terraces, ridges, troughs, etc., were treated in earlier chapters. The blanketing effect of sedimentation, already discussed, is likewise a geomorphological phenomenon. Two subjects remain, however, to which more detailed attention will be given in the present chapter: submarine valleys and submarine volcanic slopes.

SUBMARINE VALLEYS

Many oblong depressions exist in the sea floor. In Chapters 2 and 3 the deep-sea troughs were briefly discussed. But besides those larger topographic forms a number of smaller depressions are found that can be conveniently classed as "submarine valleys." It is no simple matter, however, to give a satisfactory definition of submarine valleys. Between dendritic systems of trenches that are almost identical with land valleys on the one hand, and the deep-sea troughs, basins, and inland seas on the other hand, there appear to occur all manner of transitions. It is the same on land, where many factors have operated to form a great variety of valleys: river and ice action, tectonic processes, wind action, volcanic activity, etc. Here we will exclude all major depressions obviously formed by tectonic processes of the nature of folding or trough faulting, and confine our attention to the forms that strongly recall erosion valleys on dry land.

Submarine erosion valleys may be conveniently classed in two types: shelf channels and submarine canyons.

SHELF CHANNELS

The shelf channels are of three different kinds. One class resembles river valleys; another, glacial troughs; the third is due to tidal scour.

Drowned River Valleys. Various shelves are crossed by winding channels of moderate depths, which are evidently the seaward continuations of land river valleys. The best-known example of a simple valley is the Hudson channel that runs in a slightly winding course from

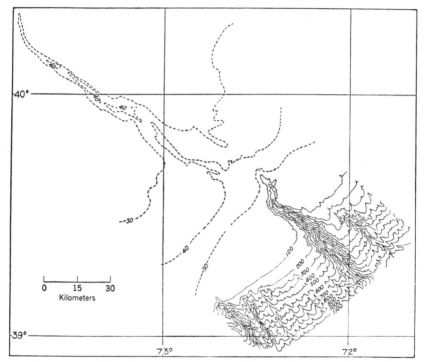

FIG. 202. Chart of the Hudson channel and Hudson Canyon. (Redrawn from Veatch and Smith, 1939; see also Fig. 217, p. 494, and Fig. 224, p. 506.)

near Sandy Hook, south of Long Island, to a position roughly lat. 39° 40′, long. 72° 40′ (Fig. 202). The head is rounded and shallow, but soon the channel deepens to 70 m and the deepest swales attain as much as 100 m. The adjacent shelf is about 40 m deep. Towards the lower end the channel broadens from 7 to 25 km, but the deep portion is generally less than 4 km wide. It also appears to bifurcate on a delta before becoming lost approximately at the 80-m line (45 fathoms) of the shelf (Fig. 224, p. 506). There is at present no direct continuation into the Hudson Canyon that starts immediately out-side the 80-m line and cuts across the remainder of the shelf, attaining a depth of 1000 m where the steep continental slope begins at the 180-m line. Half a dozen less conspicuous channels are reported from the Atlantic shelf of North America. Similar submerged river valleys are known from the North Sea where the Elbe and Rhine channels can be roughly traced for a few hundred kilometers to depths of about 100 m (Lewis, 1935).

Although not nearly so well established by soundings as the Hud-son channel, the pattern of branching channels on the Sunda Shelf between Sumatra and Borneo is the finest example of a shelf channel-system known. It was described and called the Sunda river by Molen-graaff. Our Fig. 203 is based on the most recent data available and shows the depth lines and the channels. A distinction has been made between inferred river valleys and channels that are attributed to tidal scour (Umbgrove, 1929).

While the channel system of the Java Sea is somewhat obscured, probably owing to recent sedimentation (except close in to the Borneo shore), the southern China Sea displays a wonderful set of long wind-ing valleys, starting off the mouths of many important rivers and joining in the center to form a huge north-running channel. This channel can be traced as far north as the Natuna Islands, where the steep slope into the basin of the China Sea begins. The greatest depth attained is 120 m, while the shelf is about 50–80 m deep. The available data indicate a relative rise of sea level since the channel was cut amounting to about 90 m.

Apart from a few doubtful connections, both with present rivers and between channels, a surprisingly consistent dendritic pattern is encountered that strongly recalls a lowland river system. A remark-able characteristic is the almost complete absence of basins along the course of the channels, the bottom grading outwards at a very low angle.

The channels out on the open shelves cannot be attributed to tidal erosion. Not only are the observed velocities of currents too low to have a scouring effect, but also there is no reason why narrow stretches of the sea floor should be more seriously attacked than the neighbor-ing areas. The dendritic pattern of some systems is further strong evidence against the influence of tidal and other marine currents. Tidal currents, moreover, are known to change their direction and to swing round gradually during the tidal cycle.

Diastrophic origin is likewise ruled out, partly by the winding

FIG. 203. Chart of the Sunda Shelf with drowned river.

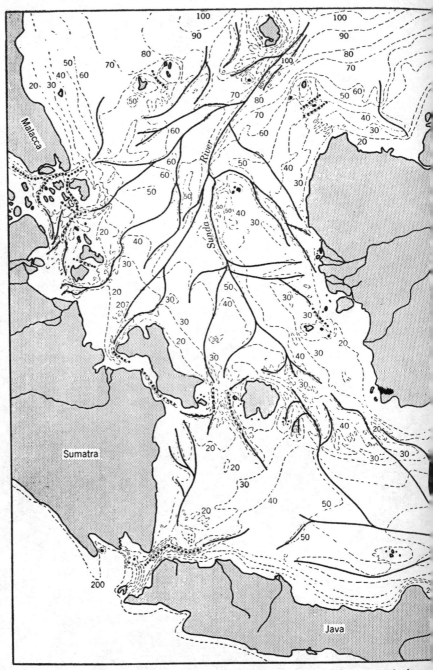

FIG. 203. Chart of the Sunda Shelf with drowned river

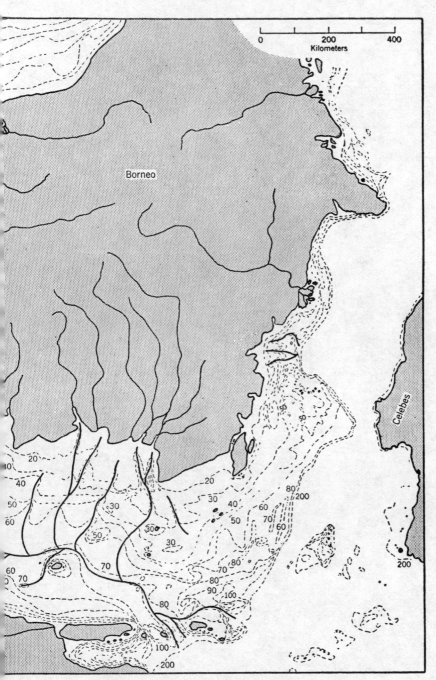

nels and swales deepened by tidal scour (dotted lines).

course, partly by the dendritic pattern, and also by the evident link with lowland rivers on the adjoining land.

The explanation offered by Molengraaff (1922) for the Sunda River and by others for the Hudson and other channels is that during the glacial lowering of sea level the shelf was laid dry and the rivers

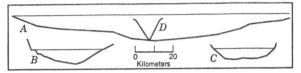

FIG. 204. Transverse sections of glacial troughs: *A*, South Norwegian trough (Fig. 206). *B*, Frederick Sound, Alaska; *C*, Porsanger Fiord, Norway. For comparison, *D*, the Congo Canyon at the edge of the shelf, is added. Vertical scale 10 times horizontal.

crossed it to the new shoreline. The lowering of sea level is generally assumed to have attained 70 to 100 m below present level, and this amount accords closely with the evidence from the shelf channels. Very important data in favor of this explanation come from the fresh-water fish fauna of the Sunda Islands. While the rivers of western

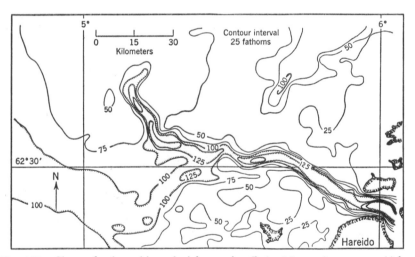

FIG. 205. Chart of a branching glacial trough off the Norwegian coast. (After Shepard, *J. Geol.*, 1931, Fig. 6, p. 349.)

Borneo show few species and genera in common with the rivers draining to the east, their fauna is intimately related to that of the Sumatra rivers. At present 500 km of sea water separate these two islands, but they should have joined during the Pleistocene stages of low level, their streams then forming the branches of one master drainage system.

It is of interest to note that the shelf channels are a few dozen kilometers wide, evidently representing shallow valleys, not actual streambeds. The streambeds may have been filled in by sedimentation during the rise of sea level and later, or it may be that they will be detected later by more accurate surveys.

Channels Due to Tidal Scour. Many deep swales in shallow regions are evidently due to tidal scour (see, for instance, Fig. 111, p. 231).

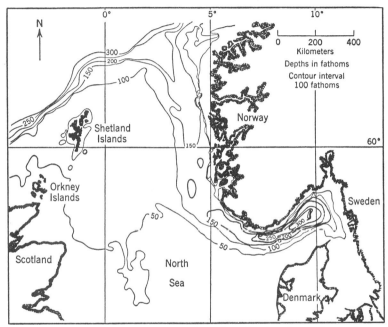

Fig. 206. Chart of the South Norwegian Trough, showing a large depression close to its origin south of Oslo. (After Shepard, 1931, *J. Geol.*, Fig. 9, p. 352.)

This most obviously happened with deep swales between islands, where strong tidal currents run in and out. Examples are found between the islands along the southeastern shore of the North Sea and off the east coast of the United States. Submarine deltas at both ends or at one end testify to the deposition of materials eroded from the channels and brought in from the sides by drifting.

The same explanation appears to hold for a number of isolated channels between islands of the Sunda Shelf. They have been marked with a dotted line on the map (Fig. 203). These end fairly abruptly both ways, and the deepest portions are generally situated about in

Fig. 205. The three canyons of Georges Bank, drawn by Shepard. Contour[

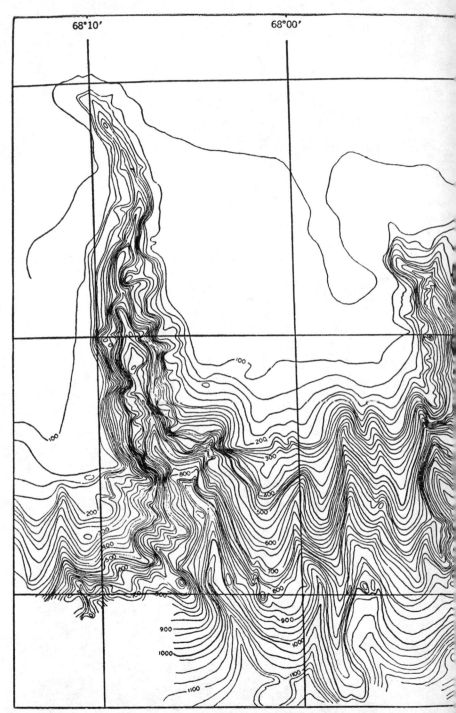

FIG. 207. The three canyons of Georges Bank, drawn by Shepard. Contour i

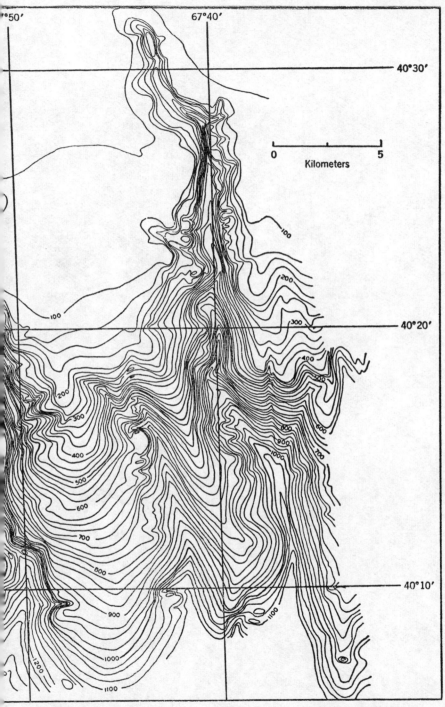

°50' 67°40'

40°30'

0 ———— 5
Kilometers

100

200

300   40°20'

400

100   500

200   800   600

300   900   700

400   1000

500

600   40°10'

700

800

900   1100

1000

1200   1100

al 25 fathoms.   (After Stetson, 1936, *Bull. Geol. Soc. Am.*, Vol. 47, Plate 3.)

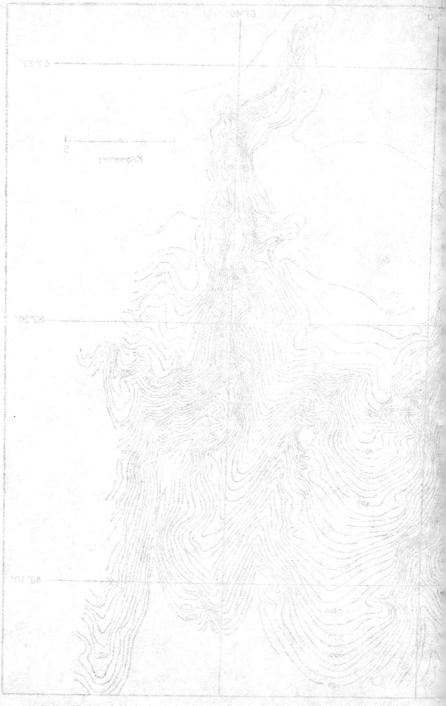

the middle. As some of these tidal channels link up with the dendritic system on beyond, however, it appears likely that they originated by river erosion and have merely been deepened by the action of the tides since.

Drowned Glacial Troughs. Shepard (1931) and Holtedahl (1929) pointed out that off coasts that were glaciated during the Pleistocene a different type of shelf channel is met with. The walls are relatively steep and straight, and the base is broad (Figs. 204, 205, and 206). The transverse section is similar to that of fiords. The longitudinal profile is undulating, with the deepest parts frequently in the inner portions. Most of these troughs are seaward continuations of estuaries, especially of the fiord type. Coalescing and branching troughs, deep-rimmed depressions, and hanging valleys on the side are all met with. Evidence of the presence of moraines within the troughs and along the border has been discovered. Holtedahl is of the opinion that faults have played an important part in locating both fiords and drowned glacial troughs.

The evidence in favor of glacial erosion is overwhelming, and one can hardly doubt that Shepard's interpretation is correct.

There remains one aspect that is in need of further elucidation. Though it is easily understood why glaciers should cut troughlike depressions out of pre-existing river valleys, the cutting of troughs on the continental shelf needs some explanation. Why did the ice coming out of the fiord onto the flat shelf not spread out to form a piedmont glacier? Nansen assumed that valleys had been cut across the shelf prior to glaciation. As sea level was lowered before the glacier reached the coast, there is much to be said for this suggestion. Most troughs are wider than the fiords with which they connect. Hence, there evidently was a certain tendency to expand beyond the narrow valley.

SUBMARINE CANYONS

Data on Submarine Canyons. Submarine valleys of great depth cutting the continental slope became known towards the end of the nineteenth century, and an explanation by the drowning of rivers was offered. More general interest, however, was not excited until Shepard took up the subject in the early thirties. This investigator has also been most active in the collecting of data and the testing of theories to explain these intriguing features of the sea floor. Although the hydrographic surveys of many countries have published charts of the continental slopes exhibiting these deep gashes that are now generally called *submarine canyons*, the U. S. Coast and Geodetic Survey has contributed by far the greatest number of soundings on which accurate charts have been constructed (Fig. 207). Other oceanographers and geologists who should be mentioned are Stetson, who investigated canyons off the east coast of the United States, and

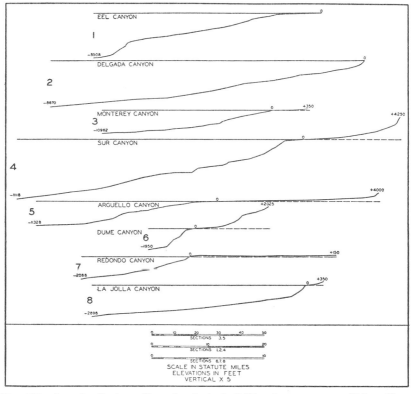

Fig. 208.   Longitudinal profiles of principal Californian canyons.   (After Shepard and Emery, 1941, *Geol. Soc. Am. Spec. Paper* 31, Plate 12, p. 70.)

Veatch and Smith, who compiled a set of contoured charts for the whole eastern coast. Johnson reviewed all available data up to 1938. He and several others mentioned below offered hypotheses concerning the origin.

The wealth of information now available renders a detailed regional description out of the question. But thanks to the publications cited anyone interested can easily gain access to all the facts that have been established so far.

A typical canyon starts as a steep, narrow gorge cutting across the continental shelf for a few dozen kilometers and running straight down the continental slope to great depths (Figs. 208–210). At the edge of the shelf the bottom may lie many hundreds to a thousand meters below the adjoining sea floor. The walls are steep, in some cases locally exceeding 100% slope, and may rise more than 1000 m on both sides. The transverse section is V-shaped, and in ground plan a moderately sinuous course is followed. Longitudinal profiles

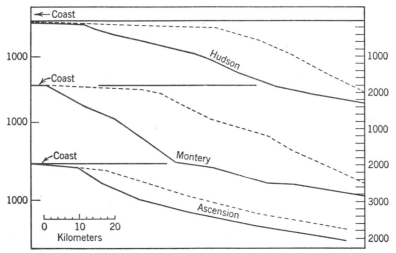

FIG. 209.   Longitudinal sections of two west coast and one east coast canyons, with approximate shape of adjoining slope.   Vertical 10 times horizontal scale, depths in meters.   (After Kuenen, 1947, Fig. 1, p. 38.)

generally show the steepest gradients at the head, where 15% is not uncommon. Thence the slope decreases to some 5%, while the lower reaches show only 3–4% or even less. Many profiles are remarkably adjusted, but there are also canyons along which steeper gradients occur here and there, even at great distances below sea level. Anything approaching a waterfall or even a rapid, however, has never been found. Tributaries, generally heading well into the shelf or beginning at the top of the continental slope, come in, forming a dendritic pattern (Fig. 215). Only one or two examples of hanging tributaries are known; nearly all enter at grade. Down to depths of 1000 or 2000 m the canyons retain the above characteristics. Owing to technical difficulties in sounding, the lower reaches are less well known. Moreover, the relative depth of the canyons decreases. On the east coast of the

United States they can still be traced to well over 2000 m, as far out as the surveys have been carried, but the number of sounding lines is insufficient to establish the true pattern.

Veatch and Smith show on their charts of the continental slope off the east coast a valley system that is similar in pattern to that of youthfully dissected continental areas (Fig. 211). Shepard has criticized

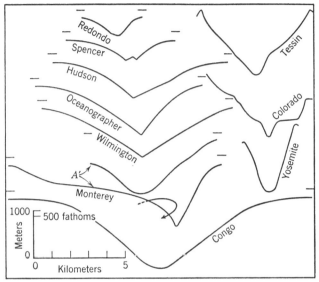

FIG. 210. Transverse sections of submarine canyons measured at the edge of the continental terrace (100 fathoms). Redondo and Monterey on the west coast. For comparison, three land valleys are added. Vertical scale is 2½ times horizontal scale. Note asymmetrical profile of Monterey Canyon in bend, steep on outward side; the other section is across a straight portion upstream from point *A*. (See Fig. 232.) (After Kuenen, 1947, Fig. 14, p. 67.)

their contouring of the soundings and is not convinced that a normal valley system exists. It must be admitted that this criticism is justified. We need but take their sheet III[A] to see that the direction of the gullying is oblique to the slope and follows the course of the parallel sounding lines (Fig. 212). Ridges are assumed between these lines, but, wherever a transverse row of depth determinations crosses the main system, saddles in these ridges have had to be introduced. In the outer portions, where a network of sounding lines occurs, the regularity of the valley system is suddenly lost. Still the exaggeration of intervening ridges is evident from the consistent saddles where they are crossed by the sounding lines.

Figure 213 shows two sets of sections not down but across the continental slope. The upper two were drawn along the same line, one on the Veatch-Smith contours and one on a sounding line run afterwards. These two are much alike, but there is a marked tendency to exaggerate in Section I based on the contours. The lower two were constructed along a row of soundings, used by these authors, and along a parallel line a few kilometers up the slope where only sound-

Fig. 211. Dendritic pattern of canyons off east coast of the United States according to chart of Veatch and Smith. (After Kuenen, 1947, Fig. 13, p. 66.)

ing lines parallel to the valleys were available, that is, at right angles to the section. The entirely unwarranted exaggeration of the relief by the contours as shown by the dotted line is brought out in a striking manner.

Until more detailed surveys are made, the true nature of the relief must remain unknown, and in discussing submarine canyons only the major, well-established features can be taken into account. It is to be deplored that the authors, according to their own admission, set out to draw the contours on the postulate that a valley pattern prevails. The result is consequently biased, and their charts should not be used without full allowance for this fact.

Along the west coast of the United States several canyons fade out toward the floor of the basins off southern California at about 1000-m

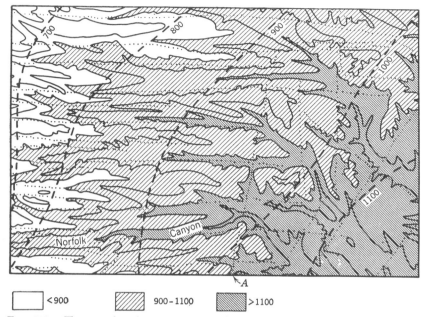

<900	900-1100	>1100

FIG. 212. Topography shown on part of chart by Veatch and Smith of the continental slope off the east coast of the United States. Note that the valleys are constructed parallel to sounding lines (soundings shown by dots) and, oblique to the general trend of the contours (shown, in fathoms, by thick, dashed lines). Saddles where sounding lines cross the ridges are also shown.

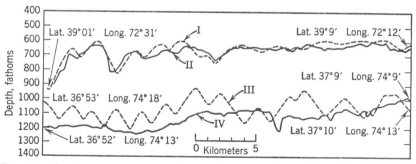

FIG. 213. Sections across the continental slope roughly parallel to the east coast of the United States. I, according to Veatch and Smith. II, same locality according to subsequent sounding line. III, elsewhere according to Veatch and Smith. IV, along sounding line shown on their chart 6 km down the slope. Note the exaggeration of the relief by the dotted sections based on contours. (After Kuenen, 1947, Fig. 2, p. 40.)

depth.   More to the north they can be traced to at least 2500 m, but
farther out they lose their original character and are continued in
shallow, troughlike depressions of the sea floor.   These troughs
strongly resemble the basins of the neighboring ocean floor.   Shepard
points out that the direction also accords well with the supposed
diastrophic nature of these outer troughs.   The manner in which the

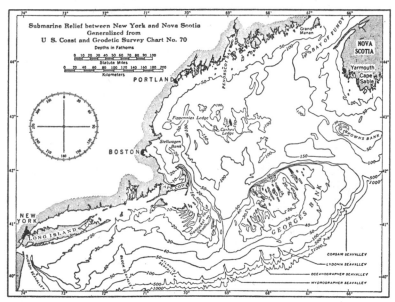

F𝐈𝐆. 214.   Chart of the Georges Bank and surroundings, showing relation of
canyons to hinterland.   (After Smith, 1941, *Scientific Monthly*, Vol. 53, p. 406.)

narrow canyon enters obliquely, often at the side and not at the head
of the trough, is further evidence that the outer portions are not the
products of erosion but merely tectonic depressions into which the
canyons debouch.

Some of the canyons off California, where the shelf is generally
narrow, head in close to the beach (Fig. 215).   Others start on submarine banks with or without an island, but significantly no examples
of typical canyons are known on banks that remain below depths of
100 m.

Most of the eastern continental slope of North America is serrated
and, according to Veatch and Smith, shows practically no flat-topped
ridges between the furrows (Fig. 216).   But it has just been shown
that their interpretation is doubtful.   On the other hand it appears

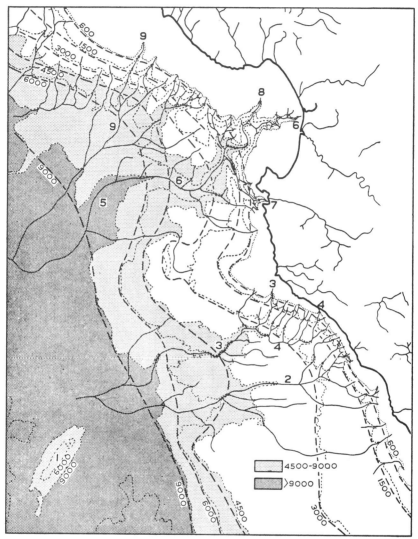

Fig. 215. Chart of dendritic canyons off the California coast. Inferred original shape of contours before canyons were cut is also shown. Data from chart by Shepard. Depths in feet. 1, Davidson Seamount; 2, Lucia Canyon; 3, Sur Canyon; 4, Partington Canyon; 5, Monterey Trough; 6, Monterey Canyon; 7, Carmel Canyon; 8, Soquel Canyon; 9, Ascension Canyon.

that considerable stretches of the Californian slope are entirely free of canyons or smaller valleys. There are also parts where shallow depressions cut down the slopes, but where no major valleys are present worthy of the name of canyon.

Comparison of Figs. 207 and 215 and of the original charts brings out clearly that the canyon system off California is less regular in

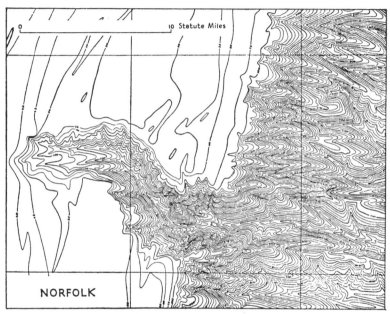

FIG. 216. Chart of the Norfolk Canyon and vicinity according to Veatch and Smith. Outside the 100-fathom isobath the contour interval is 25 fathoms. (After Daly, 1942, *The Floor of the Ocean*, Fig. 66, p. 120, University of North Carolina Press.)

pattern than that off the east coast. This may be attributed to the greater irregularity of the continental slope on the western side of North America, but it appears doubtful whether there is any fundamental contrast in the nature of the valleys. Figure 210 brings out the similarity in transverse section of the canyons on both slopes, and Fig. 209 in longitudinal profile.

Outside the United States there are no areas explored with sufficient accuracy to show the nature and number of submarine canyons. Nevertheless more than a hundred examples have become known, and apparently the occurrence of canyons may be considered the rule rather than the exception. One of the best-known examples is that of the Congo, which is exceptional in that it runs directly into the estuary of that river.

Dredging and coring operations by Stetson in the eastern canyons and by Shepard in the Californian gorges have brought to light many

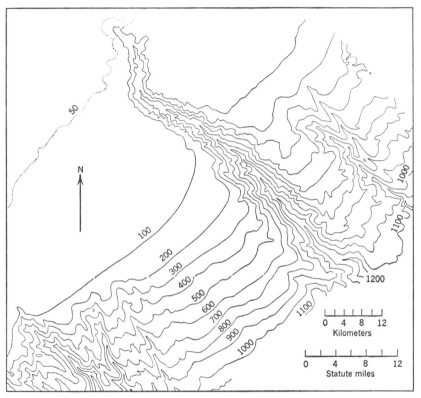

Fig. 217. Chart of Hudson Canyon, based on chart by Veatch and Smith. (See Fig. 202, p. 481, and Fig. 224, p. 506.)

significant facts. The walls are cut through slightly to moderately consolidated rocks. Hard sandstone and even granite were encountered, and the covering by recent sediment is generally slight. Carmel Canyon, a tributary to Monterey Canyon, is entirely cut through granite. The age of the outcropping rocks is generally Mesozoic or Tertiary including Pliocene strata.

Terry (1941) presented a certain amount of evidence that the submarine valley of David Bay off southwestern Panama with its canyon-shaped tributaries is very young. It appears not improbable that the V-shaped gorges are cut in rocks as young as the Pleistocene.

In an east coast canyon a fill of post-Pleistocene mud was found on the bottom with a cold-water fauna in the lower end of a long core. This shows that this valley was cut before the close of the ice age and has continued to receive a slow deposition of sediment since then. In the Californian coring operations similar conditions were met with in the examples heading well out from the coast. But in the canyons arising close to the shore the bottom consisted of sand, gravel, or hard rock, sometimes with a thin coating of mud. It should be noted that the absence of recent fine sediment was not restricted to the upper reaches, but continued out beyond the edge of the shelf to depths of at least 1700 m. Bourcart reports that down to 600-m depth a submarine canyon (so-called "rech") in the Mediterranean off the Pyrenees contains rounded pebbles and strongly corroded littoral molluscs, indicating cold-water conditions. This shows that transport by a powerful current took place to great depths during the last cold stage of the Pleistocene.

No attempt will be made here to classify submarine canyons or to make a distinction between "canyons," "valleys," "gullies," "trough-valleys," etc.—terms that have been proposed by various authors to denote different types of deeply submerged valley formations. As

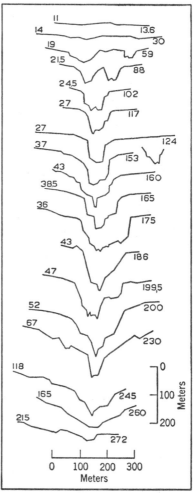

Fig. 218. Transverse profiles of Scripps Canyon from beach out to confluence with La Jolla Canyon. No vertical exaggeration. Note the comparison with a profile of an adjacent land canyon. Depths in meters; on the right, deepest sounding in axis of canyon. (Redrawn after Shepard and Emery, 1941, *Geol. Soc. Am. Spec. Paper* 31, Fig. 20, p. 61.)

yet no sharp distinction can be made among these types. It is worth while pointing out, however, that the peculiar "Mississippi Trough" differs in many respects from the normal type of submarine canyon. It is much wider and less regular in shape, and it presents a flat bottom. Shepard has suggested that salt domes played a part in developing the

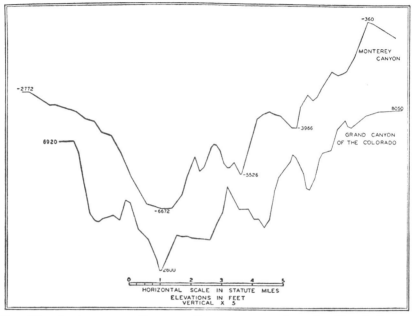

Fig. 219. Section across Monterey Canyon compared to the Grand Canyon. Same scale and spacing of observation points. Vertical 5 times horizontal scale. (After Shepard, 1948, *Submarine Geology*, Fig. 72, p. 216, Harper and Brothers.)

topographic forms, and that it was partly filled by mud from the Mississippi after having been cut as a normal canyon. Several authors have attributed the formation to a great submarine slide (Fig. 220).

Hypotheses on the Formation of Submarine Canyons. Several attempts have been made to explain the formation of submarine canyons. Shepard has carefully weighed with commendable impartiality the evidence *pro* and *con*, coming to the conclusion that several agencies have probably played a part in originating, altering, and maintaining the canyons, but that as yet no definite decision can be made as to what factor was chiefly responsible. On the whole he favors stream erosion during a vast lowering of sea level in early Pleistocene times. The present author, on the other hand, is strongly inclined to reject this explanation and to adhere to another hypothesis, namely, the action of turbidity currents, especially during the ice ages.

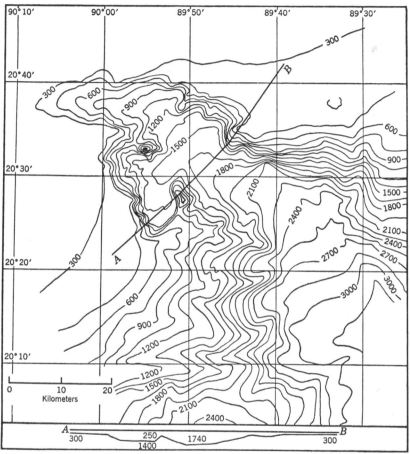

FIG. 220. Chart of the Mississippi Trough. Contour interval 150 feet. In section: vertical 5 times horizontal scale. (Simplified after Shepard, 1937, *Bull. Geol. Soc. Am.*, Vol. 48, Fig. 2, p. 1351.)

Only the main arguments can be given, because Shepard lists about one hundred for and against the various theories and even then many more could be introduced. First a number of suggested causes will be dealt with, that appear to the present author to be ruled out as the main factors responsible. For the latter reason it is deemed superfluous to sum up the points in favor of these views.

Diastrophic Origin. Several authors have suggested that submarine canyons have been developed mainly by faulting and local subsidence by which narrow troughs were produced. The chief opposing considerations are: the dendritic and sinuous pattern, the graded longitudinal profiles, the direction transverse to the tectonic trends of the adjoining coast (California), the evident linking with major aggrading rivers on the adjoining land, the restricted time of formation (late Pliocene to late Glacial), the great number off the east coast of the United States that is tectonically inactive.

Although diastrophism is hereby ruled out as the main cause, it may have helped to locate canyons, to alter their course, and to form the broad troughs out towards the ocean floor. Thus Shepard points to the evident structural control of Monterey Canyon. The present writer is strongly inclined with Lawson and others to attribute the cutting of Carmel Canyon to a pre-existing fault zone across the granite mass into which this gorge is incised. The direction is in accord with the strike of the many faults in the neighboring Santa Lucia Range, and on the opposite wall of Monterey Canyon complicated features indicate some abnormal influence in action. Besides, the time available for the cutting is extremely short even if subaerial erosion by an extension of Carmel River is assumed.

Shepard places the deep valley off San Clemente Island in a separate class, calling it the San Clemente "Rift" Valley. It lies in the direct continuation of the submarine escarpment that cuts off the bank around this island on the northeastern side. Pointing to the abnormally straight course and the position, he argues that a tectonic origin is highly probable, although the nature of the faulting cannot be ascertained.

The singular, broad depressions in the Bahamas have many points in common with submarine canyons, but the major depressions can be more readily explained by diastrophic processes. On the other hand the regular outward grading and sharp V-shaped trench along the floor of the "Tongue of the Ocean" might be due to some type of erosive current. (See Hess, 1933.)

Warping of the Continental Borderland. Various authors have assumed great changes of level in the areas now forming the continental slopes, so as to drown canyons that had previously been excavated by subaerial rivers. Daly and Umbgrove have raised objections to these views. As long as canyons were thought to be exceptional features and to be limited to a few incidental gorges off the mouths of some major rivers, this explanation held the attraction of simplicity.

Now that canyons have been found by the dozen, are known from all over the world, and will evidently be found to be more the rule than the exception, the conception of valleys drowned by warping has lost most of its appeal. Not only must one assume that most continental slopes were drowned to an extent of a few thousand meters in very recent times, but before the period of high stand, sedimentation was proceeding. From this it follows that up to the end of the Tertiary the continental slopes were roughly in the same position as at present and a temporary emergence during the cutting of the canyons has to

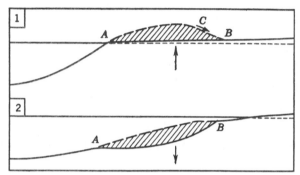

Fig. 221. Diagram showing the peripheral welt (1) which must have existed if submarine canyons (2) had been formed by warping of the continental border.

be assumed. No one could attribute such swift, regular, and universal uplifting followed by a downward movement of like extent to normal diastrophism.

Bourcart assumes periodic movements of the nature of flexures along the continental border. However, as many canyons are incised 1000 m deep into the continental slope, one is forced to assume a coastal borderland of at least that height above sea level at the time of canyon cutting, and, as the portion of rivers now visible on dry land was not incised, the elevated area formed a narrow welt (Fig. 221). Under these conditions erosion products should have been carried off this ridge towards the land and the drainage system would have been drastically influenced. All evidence of such developments being absent, Bourcart's hypothesis must be abandoned.

Du Toit attempted to give an explanation by marginal uparching of the continents in connection with his theory of continental wandering. But several of the enumerated objections, such as the short period of formation and the absence of geomorphological evidence for recent upbulging of the hinterland, appear to rule out this possibility also.

Artesian Spring Sapping. Johnson proposed attributing submarine canyons to the action of submarine springs, pointing to the development of valleys by a similar process on land. The following reasons can be given for discounting this process (see Rich, 1941). The artesian head required to force the fresh water out on the submarine slopes is large and is not provided for in low coastal plains back of many canyons, even less for the furrows on Georges Bank or the banks along the California coast with no dry land in the neighborhood. Furthermore, the structures necessary for carrying the water out and down from the continents would have to be exceptional. As the outflowing fresh waters would rise directly upward through the heavier sea water, they could have no influence apart from dissolving the materials on the continental slope. Mechanical erosive action is out of the question here, whereas on land it does most of the work. Weathering is also important on land, but the absence of changes in temperature of frost and of humic acid reduces submarine weathering to the minimum (see p. 236). The importance of the external agents in forming spring-sap valleys on land is shown by the absence of great subterranean solution channels before the stream emerges, except in limestone country. In other words, the erosive action does not start before the spring water comes out into the open. On the sea floor these subaerial agents are excluded. Only a very small proportion of the rocks along the continental slope are soluble. Hence, a spring cannot be expected to form a large depression. At most, submarine springs could develop sink holes.

No reason can be given why, when assuming artesian spring sapping, nearly all canyons reach the edge of the shelf. They would begin to form where the aquifer crops out, but some should have failed to cut back as far as others and should end abruptly in a cirque-shaped head around the mouth of the spring (Fig. 222). What reason can be given for the Pleistocene age of the canyons? Why are there tributaries, and why do they enter at grade?

One could continue to sum up objections to the spring sapping hypothesis, which evidently fails to explain any of the major characteristics and meets all manner of insurmountable obstacles. It is more profitable to turn to other suggestions. The following three are considered by the present author to contain elements that are of importance both for the formation and further modeling of the submarine canyons without, however, constituting the main action responsible.

Mudflows and Landslides. The sliding of sedimentary deposits on steep submarine slopes is proved by fossil evidence, by observations in the Californian canyon heads, and also by dredgings and soundings showing hard bottom in regions where deposition takes place on adjoining flatter portions of the sea floor (see Chapter 4). We know very little about the influence either of slope or of the nature of the deposits. Neither are we informed about what happens to the materials set in motion. It does not appear unlikely that a slide may involve a certain amount of the sea water, may change to a mudflow, and finally to a turbidity current. Another uncertainty is about the shape of the depression left when a slide has taken place.

Yet there is no reasonable argument against the assumption of many authors that sliding in one form or another has played a part, both in

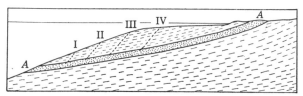

FIG. 222. Diagram illustrating the artesian spring sapping hypothesis. I–IV, successive positions of spring heads if the postulates of that hypothesis are granted. *A*, aquifer. (After Kuenen, 1947, Fig. 3, p. 44.)

forming initial depressions that other factors have altered to the present canyons, and in keeping the canyon walls and head free of recent sediment.

To assess quantitatively what the action of gravity sliding has been is as yet beyond us. It may even prove to have been a major factor in setting up turbidity flows able to erode the bottom of canyons. It also appears likely that the minor tributaries starting some distance down the slope and the furrows in the walls of major canyons owe their shape to density flows set up by slumping or even to slumping alone. We shall return to this mechanism when discussing the action of turbidity currents.

Tsunamis. Bucher invoked the action of tidal waves formed by earthquakes, so-called tsunamis, as the principal agents in canyon formation. There is much to be said for and against this opinion. The main objections are that these great waves are oscillatory and would carry nearly as much sediment up as down the slope, even if we are prepared to admit that the engendered currents are sufficiently powerful to erode the continental slopes to any marked degree. Once gullies were formed, one would expect the intervening, shallower portions of the slopes to be more severely attacked than the floors of the canyons. The dendritic pattern is a further obstacle, and the evident link between canyons and land rivers is also hard to explain.

Two other important facts are difficult to account for: (1) that the canyons were cut since the late Pliocene, and (2) the development in regions where tsunamis are at present unfrequent (southern Atlantic, California coast, Shepard and Emery, 1941).

Bucher suggested that the Pleistocene was perhaps a particularly seismic period. Little can be brought forward in support of this *ad hoc* postulate. Even then the available time is so short that an almost uninterrupted string of seismic waves would have been required to effect such gigantic work of erosion.

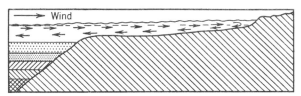

Fig. 223. Diagram illustrating the hydraulic currents caused by onshore winds that cannot sweep down the slope in consequence of density stratification of the ocean. (After Kuenen, 1947, Fig. 4, p. 46.)

The present author is inclined to assume that tsunamis may play an important part in the production of slumping (see p. 247), but only when a canyon has once been formed by other agents and steep walls are already present.

Hydraulic and Tidal Currents. Davis attempted to explain the mock valleys, as he called them, by hydraulic currents. Onshore winds pile the sea water up against the coast, and an outflow along the bottom must take place. These or other throughgoing currents, however, cannot be held responsible on account of the density stratification in the oceans. The warm surface waters are unable to force their way down beyond the edge of the continental shelf, because they would have to replace heavier cold water (Fig. 223).

Nevertheless, it is probable that an important part is played by the hydraulic effect of onshore winds in starting suspension currents, as will be explained below.

Tidal currents and eddies have been measured close to the bottom both on the east and west coasts of the United States in and around the canyons. The maximum velocities found were only a few dozen centimeters per second, and water samples have entirely confirmed the inability of such currents to churn up even fine sand or mud.

Neither was the direction closely correlated to the shape of the canyons. Again, the limited geological time in which cutting was effective rules out normal currents as agents in the development of the canyons. Several objections raised against the hypotheses already discussed apply to this view also.

Effects Due to the Ice Ages. One of the most significant facts discovered about submarine canyons is the short period during which they must have been formed. Many instances of Miocene strata cropping out along the walls have been encountered during dredging operations, and even Pliocene deposits have come to light. Evidently the formation of the canyons may have begun earlier and furrows may have developed by sliding, diastrophism, etc., in earlier periods. But there can be no doubt that, during the Pleistocene, excavation suddenly became universal and proceeded at great speed. Whereas in earlier periods deposition was the rule on the continental slopes, the ice ages saw a reversal of conditions and erosion in gullies became widespread off the Californian and the Atlantic coasts of North America.

No less significant is the return to deposition since the last cold stages of the Pleistocene. Not only does this prove a time limit to the period of active erosion, but it also is conclusive evidence that deposition is the normal phenomenon beyond the edge of the shelf and in depressions.

The question thus arises of the cause of abnormal conditions on the sea floor during the Pleistocene. This period does not appear to have been exceptional in diastrophic or any other internal respect. Neither can the general cooling of the oceans have resulted in erosional processes on the sea floor. There was probably increased erosion on the continents, but it is hard to see how this could have called forth directly an excavation of furrows on the continental slopes. *All other causes being thus eliminated, we are forced to attribute the canyons to the lowering of sea level during the ice ages.* This having been ascertained with great probability one is left with two possible explanations. Either the sea level was lowered sufficiently to leave the sea floor dry, thus allowing normal subaerial erosion to cut the canyons, or a submarine type of current was engendered in consequence of a moderate fall of ocean level.

Excessive Lowering of Sea Level. Soon after beginning his prolific studies on the problem of submarine canyons, Shepard came to the conclusion that only subaerial excavation by rivers could account for their formation. Although he later admitted that slumping, diastrophism, and suspension currents may have played a part, he remains of the opinion that the action of rivers must be considered the chief cause. The following are the main facts on which he bases this conclusion. The dendritic pattern, the entrance of tributaries at grade, the smooth outward sloping floor without counterslopes, the V-shaped cross section, the location off the mouths of rivers, the youthful development, the hard rocks in the walls are all readily explained by river action during the Pleistocene.

Shepard then attempts to show that glacial lowering of sea level, generally believed to have attained not more than 100 m below the present position, may have gone much further. By assuming greater extent and thickness of the ice caps than most authors are prepared to accept, and by postulating an ice cap over the arctic basin, resting partly on the sea floor, he is able to increase the estimate for lowering to 1100 m. These calculations are meant to apply to pre-Wisconsin ice caps, while the last extension of the glaciers caused a lowering of perhaps 70–80 m. As the largest possible amount is only about half of the very minimum necessary to expose the narrow, V-shaped parts of the canyons a further isostatic effect is required. The continents being thrown out of adjustment with the ocean floor by the relief of water pressure from the latter, a subcrustal flow of materials outward should have taken place. This would have caused the continental slopes to bulge upward, allowing the rivers to cut into an additional 1000 m of the bared slopes. After return of the waters to the oceans the slopes subsided to their former position, carrying the outer portions of the canyons down to their present level of 2000-m depth.

Shepard's theory is well argued, and considerable evidence is advanced in support of the high estimate for the ice caps. Yet the result is hardly convincing. We must assume either a much longer duration or a far more rigorous climate for the earlier glaciations if we are to account for the volume of the ice caps having been at least 20 times as large as of the Wisconsin (Würm). In the size of the successive Alpine glaciers and the Scandinavian and North American ice caps, clearly established by the outer limits of their deposits, no great differences in order of magnitude is shown (double the volume is the maximum). Neither does the amount of erosion, deposition of drift, etc., or the formation of terraces differ drastically. The faunas and floras indicate similar climatic conditions for the cold periods. Evidence thus appears to be against a much larger extent of the older glaciations.

If we attempt to gauge the effect of lowering sea level by more than 1000 m the consequences on many features of geological history appear to be profound. All major rivers should have cut deep trenches across the shelf and far back into the present mouths. Only the Congo now shows such features, and the number of infilled estuaries of great depths, such as the buried channel of the Mississippi, is limited. This is especially important in view of the great number of moderately deepened river valleys, indicating a sea level not more than 100 m below the present position (see p. 536).

All the Lesser Sunda Islands would have been joined to the Asiatic continent by a large depression of sea level. The present distribution of faunas is indicative of a gradual decrease of Asiatic forms going eastwards and concomitantly of Australian forms going westward. The present limited possibilities of migration would account for these facts, whereas a complete joining should have more or less unified the faunas.

The material eroded from the submarine canyons must have been deposited somewhere. Yet no indications of deltas are found at the lower ends of the narrow gorges, that is at roughly 2000-m depth. During the sinking of the sea surface the supposed rivers must have been cutting continuously into the deposits washed out and laid down at the mouths of the forming canyons. Thus the amount of debris to be removed gradually increased as lower and lower levels were reached. The downward movement cannot have ended abruptly, and a certain amount of coarse material should have accumulated before the direction of movement was reversed.

During the waning of the ice sheets, erosion in the uncovered portions of the canyons would have continued and large amounts of sediment would have had to be disposed of at the lower end of the river. This process should have caused a considerable filling of the bottom of the gorge as the water rose. The narrow shape without a broad, flat floor can hardly be reconciled with this deduction. The nature of the wall rocks and lack of time for intensive weathering coupled with the steep gradient would have resulted in a large percentage of coarse material among the sediment brought down out of the river mouth. This could not have been removed by sliding or slumping. We will return to the canyon shapes later on.

There is undoubtedly a strong link between submarine canyons and rivers on land. Nearly all the larger canyons known occur on the deltas or off the outlets of major rivers: the Congo, the Indus, the Ganges, the Columbia, the São Francisco of Brazil, a buried channel of the Mississippi, the Hudson Canyon in the direct continuation of the Hudson Shelf Channel but separated from it by a submerged delta on the shelf (Fig. 224), Monterey Canyon off the Salinas River, Cap Breton Canyon off an old mouth of the Adour River, the three canyons of the Morobe area, New Guinea, off the three major rivers of the region recently described by Sprigg (Fig. 225).

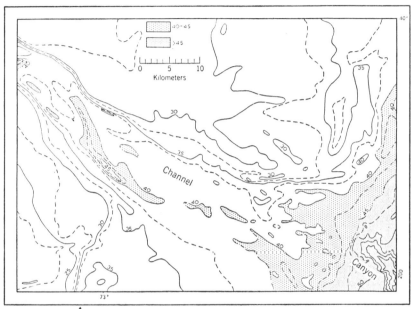

Fig. 224. Chart of the lower end of Hudson Channel ending on a submarine delta, based on chart by Veatch and Smith. Depths in fathoms. Note that there is no direct connection with the head of the submarine canyon. (See also Fig. 202, p. 481, and Fig. 217, p. 494.)

But the relation is not a very close one. There are many large rivers without a canyon. Many canyons occur where only small streams reach the coast, or where only doubtful glacial melt water streams can be postulated (Georges Bank). Thus the largest Portuguese canyon, the Nazaré, is located off a small river, and there is little to be said in support of Shepard's suggestion that the Tagus may have reached the coast at this point during the Pleistocene. The correlation between the size of the river and the size of the adjoining canyon is poor. Canyons also tend to come in groups, often quite close together, where there is only one river on the land. In other cases the canyon has a forked head, only one of the two gorges showing a relation to a land river.

Moreover, with only few exceptions the canyon head is situated a few or even many kilometers out from the coast. The topography of many canyon heads is definitely against the supposition that they

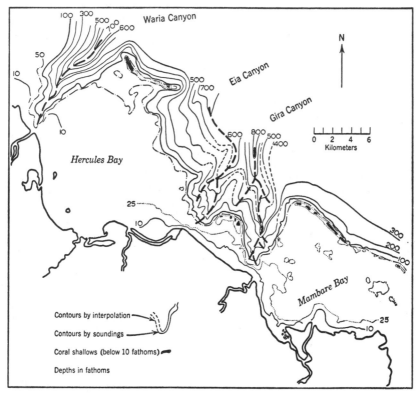

FIG. 225. Chart of three canyons off the northeastern coast of New Guinea. (Redrawn from Sprigg, 1947, Fig. 2, p. 300.)

formerly extended to within the present coastline but have since been infilled by river deposits. The canyon usually narrows and shoals gradually towards its head and sometimes ends in a sharply cut small furrow. Had a much deeper and broader gorge been silted up, one would expect a rounded head and a flat bottom (for instance, like the Mississippi Canyon). The ending is evidently a primary unaltered erosion form. Where the wall rock is consolidated the same conclusion can be drawn. This point is strong evidence against the hypothesis of river cutting, because in that event the river could not have failed to sink a deep valley across the shelf.

Shepard has also sought for other sources of evidence showing that sea level stood much lower in comparatively recent times. He mentions the widespread occurrence of rounded gravel and shallow-water shells in canyons and elsewhere. The present writer believes that turbidity currents of high density may also account for these phenomena, while rafting, winnowing by currents on seamounts, and subsidence may be responsible in other localities.

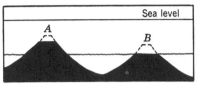

FIG. 226. Diagram of the formation of guyots by low-level marine planation, as postulated by Shepard. *A* should have been eroded while *B* was being beheaded.

Guyots are also held by Shepard as evidence of a low sea level, because they are evidently beheaded volcanoes, and many have flat tops at about 1300-m depth. However, the depth varies between 1000 and 1700 m, and probably the range will expand with increasing knowledge of the sea floor. While the deeper-lying guyots were being beheaded, the more lofty ones evidently escaped erosion, for there are no terraces on the slopes corresponding to the wave action that found time to smooth off their neighbors to a perfectly level bank 10 to 20 km across (Fig. 226).

If, on the other hand, we assume develeling since the truncation, which must have occurred less than half a million years ago in Shepard's scheme, the deduced movements are exceedingly swift (at least 1 mm per year) and surprisingly large. Moreover, sea level must have stood for a long time at its extreme level to truncate also lava flows, plugs, etc. Finally, if such swift develeling is common, guyots or at least the sinking ones must represent young volcanic cones, for all pre-Pliocene ones would have disappeared (see also p. 477).

Then, in the case of Bikini the drilling has demonstrated that the atoll structure commenced to grow at least as early as the Miocene. Hence the guyot below was beheaded long before the Pleistocene.

The alternative view put forward by Hess is that guyots are of all ages and tend to subside very slowly, the deeper ones having been submerged farther than the shallower ones (see p. 397). This picture accounts more satisfactorily for the observed facts.

Two possibilities can be suggested for the conditions in the Mediterranean during excessive lowering of sea level. If precipitation and runoff were in excess of evaporation, the sea should have been ponded at sill depths in the Straits of Gibraltar at 400 m. For about two-thirds of the time of lowered sea level Mediterranean waters thus should have stood at 400 m below the present position. During this long time considerable deltas should have been built by the major rejuvenated rivers. But nowhere does the 500-m line project appreciably beyond the 200-m line, not even on the Nile delta. Moreover, the submarine canyons of this inland sea descend at least 500 m below still depths.

The other possibility is that evaporation remained in excess of precipitation. Then the surface of the Mediterranean would have sunk below sill depths. Even if one is prepared to grant this possibility, still more serious objections are presented by the Japan Sea. Here, in this colder climate, precipitation must have remained in excess of evaporation, and ponding at less than 200 m would result. There are canyons, however, in this basin also, passing more than 1000 m below sill depths.

The outcome of this review is that even if the highest possible values are assumed for glacial lowering of sea level only half the minimum depth to which canyons are cut can be attributed to this cause. The remainder must be explained by assuming a highly speculative upbulging of the continental slopes. Even then many features of the canyons themselves can hardly be reconciled with logical deductions. Some further points will be mentioned in the next paragraph. To all these objections must be added the evidence from geology and biology against any major reduction of sea level.

Turbidity Currents. Soon after the problem of submarine canyons had again excited the interest of geologists Daly proposed an ingenious mechanism by which submarine cutting might be explained. During the moderate lowering of glacial sea level great quantities of mud on the continental shelves are supposed to have been churned up by storm waves.

When sediment is taken up in suspension the specific gravity of the water is increased. Thus the density of water to which 1% of silt is added becomes roughly 1.017, while for sea water the density is raised from 1.026 to 1.040. Hence, the turbid water of the shelf during storms would have formed a heavy suspension. This weighted water would act just as though the density had been increased by greater salinity, and it would tend to flow out from the shelf and to run down the continental slope to the floor of the ocean. In this manner rivers of muddy water were set up that could have eroded the bottom and cut the submarine canyons.

In Chapter 4 the nature of turbidity currents was briefly discussed, and it was pointed out that with high densities they develop remarkable powers of transport. It was also shown in Chapter 5 that they might be responsible for the development of graded bedding and for the transport of deep-sea sands to their area of deposition. In the present connection the possibility of their having played a part in the erosion of submarine canyons will be discussed.

The experiments in tanks, by Bell and Kuenen, demonstrated the following properties of turbidity flows. The formula for calculating

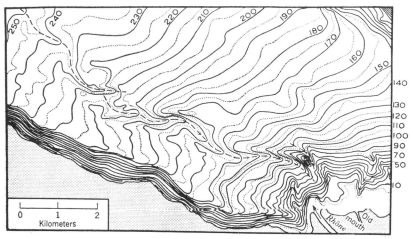

Fig. 227.   Chart of channel on Rhône Delta in Lake Geneva. (Redrawn from chart by Delebecque, in Collet, 1925, Fig. 42, p. 189.)

the velocity of flow in rivers also holds for turbidity currents, but with increasing density allowance must be made for higher viscosity. The flow collects in slight indentations of the slope and draws in turbid waters flowing down the slope along the sides of the trench. The flow, even when showing a very slight effective density, runs along the bottom, and, although turbulent mixing with surrounding clear water is active, the currents continue for large distances as separate bodies. Owing to their momentum they do not come to a standstill when they reach horizontal areas but continue for a long way and can even ascend slopes if they happen to encounter them.

Turbidity currents of low velocities are known to occur in reservoirs and lakes. In lakes they form trenches on the deltas, but possibly more by lack of deposition than by erosion (Fig. 227). In reservoirs no trenches appear to develop. It is frequently argued that these cases demonstrate that turbidity currents have no erosive power. Daly and Kuenen showed, however, that the greater slope and larger dimensions of the supposed glacial flows down the continental slopes warrant the assumption of greater velocity.

There is known to exist a threshold value for velocities of a current necessary to erode the bottom. The fact that lacustrine turbidity currents are generally below this minimum is no evidence against the erosive power of faster currents.

The mechanism of turbidity current during the ice age is thought to have been roughly as follows. During onshore storms, when glacial sea level had been appreciably lowered, a heavy suspension of mud, silt, and sand was churned up in shallow waters along the coast. The piling up of waters against the beach set up a hydraulic current along the bottom, carrying the suspension out to the edge of the shelf. This is an important aspect, for otherwise the churned-up sediment would have had time to settle again before reaching the canyon head. Evidence in support of this contention is given below in connection with the relation between headlands and canyon sites (p. 515).

Where the slope was perfectly even, the suspension flowed down it in a fairly thin sheet, causing little erosion on account of the low velocity even on steep inclines. Wherever a slight depression at the edge of the shelf or in the slope allowed any accumulation of the suspension the resulting greater depth of heavy waters caused a greater velocity. This again resulted in suction and the drawing-in of more heavy water off the surrounding bottom. In this manner sufficient velocity was developed to start erosion, except on very low grades. Eroded material was then added to the current, and the greater turbidity helped to accelerate the flow. Given a lead, the canyon eroded itself because all the material building up the continental terrace possessed potential energy.

Towards the bottom of the continental slope the declivity decreased. The velocity became less, and the coarser sediment dropped to the bottom. Gradually the density current became lighter and slowed down, while the last remnants spread out over a wide area of the deep-sea floor.

The current ran straight down the slope, but wherever slight initial irregularities occurred, due to slumping, diastrophism, etc., the direction was altered and a sinuous course developed. Tributaries formed, partly through surface irregularities, partly owing to local slumping of the walls, or along weak zones of faulting. The turbidity flow being, after all, a type of current, it is not surprising that a system of dendritic, graded furrows was developed.

Although most of the material removed by the currents from the walls was comparatively fine grained and only slightly consolidated, hard strata had also to be eroded. This would happen more easily than might at first sight appear probable, on account of undercutting and breaking off along joints. The large blocks tumbled to the bottom of the gorge.

The action of slumping became of much greater importance as soon as the turbidity flows had developed steep slopes on the canyon walls and head. The slump first resembled a mud flow on land. But, whereas the mud flows and slides along without change of consistency, the submarine slumps tended to become diluted and to develop truly turbulent flow. Taking into account the marked longitudinal slope of submarine canyons it is legitimate to suppose that a slide down a canyon wall continued along the bottom out to the deep sea as a turbidity current and owing to its high power of transport it swept away the larger fragments of hard strata that had tumbled down the slopes previously and collected along the axis of the gorge. Assuming a thickness of 4 m on a slope of 3° and a density of 2, the computed velocity is 3 m per sec. Such a current can carry along boulders weighing some 30 tons.

If all the sediment required to set up the flows had to come from the shelf an area of some 100 km² is needed for each larger canyon. Taking into account the longshore movement of the silty waters during an obliquely directed storm and the fact that even the Californian shelf is hardly anywhere narrower than 4 km, the available material at the start of the Pleistocene was probably considerable. Add the vast amount supplied by the rejuvenated rivers during glacial periods of low sea level, and it becomes evident that the volume of sediment required for setting up the flows was available. The main source, however, was in the canyons themselves.

Sprigg, who is strongly inclined to attribute canyon cutting to turbidity currents, claims that the mud-laden river waters were of greater density than sea water and submerged straightway at the outlet. The turbidity currents were thus generated directly by the parent rivers.

It is a well-established fact that during the lowering of sea level rivers deepened their channels, and it may be inferred that a high proportion of fine sediment was carried to the coast. The possibility may therefore be granted that the density of the river water can sometimes have exceeded that of sea water and that turbidity currents were thus generated beyond the mouth. The present writer is therefore inclined to assume that the tendency of canyons to occur off river outlets is partly due to this phenomenon. On the other hand the link between rivers and canyons is not so close, as one would expect if Sprigg's suggestion were the principal process involved. Some of the criticism of Shepard's hypothesis applies also to this explanation. Hence the extra sediment is held to have been supplied indirectly by rivers during low sea levels and to have been first deposited before being churned up by waves or set in motion by slumping.

One of Shepard's many important discoveries is that slumping takes place at the head of some Californian canyons. By careful repetition of lines of soundings he found that sudden deepening up to amounts of nearly 20 m may occur. In one place a hump that was found to have settled on the floor had later disappeared, evidently having slid out to sea.

At Redondo a slide was actually witnessed from the pier that had recently been extended to the head of Redondo Canyon. Numerous people fishing along the pier with a calm sea and no wind felt their leads being pulled out to sea and had to put out more line to get bottom. After a short interval boiling masses of mud appeared in the water. In about an hour the deepening had ceased but not until depths had increased from 3 to 12 m. Shepard also points out that, where great masses of sand and silt are yearly introduced into the heads of canyons close inshore, slumping of some sort must be continually keeping these depressions from being filled in.

There can be small doubt that the movement in these cases was of the nature of slumping. But some features indicate that the slumps tend to change to turbidity currents. More than once, where sudden deepening was actually witnessed, currents have been seen to flow into the head of the canyon. This proves that a large volume of water was passing down the canyon away from the coast. If only sediment had taken part in the movement, no extra water would have been sucked into the canyon. Thus evidence is found that the slumping results in a flow of watery mud or muddy water.

Then, during a local northwest blow rapid deepening to the amount of 8 m has been observed in Redondo Canyon. Here the churning-up of sediment and a turbidity flow are indicated as the causes of the erosion.

Shepard's finding may here be recalled that, while canyons heading well out to sea have received a fill of recent fine sediment apparently ever since the last glacial stage, the gorges that run in close to the shore have hard rocky bottoms or coarse deposits along the floor, with only a thin film of mud on top. He rightly draws the conclusion that some type of sliding intermittently sweeps out the latter group of canyons.

A strong case can be made for the contention that turbidity currents are the chief agent in this process. Neither the depth, slope, nor shape of the canyons shows systematic differences in these two groups. The only difference that can logically be claimed as the cause of the inshore type being swept out is the smaller depth of the surrounding sea floor and the shorter distance to the zone of breakers. In other words, the fact that mud and sand are occasionally churned up around the head of a canyon might well be the cause of non-deposition farther out. A turbidity current is then set up into the canyon and sweeps it out. This conclusion is supported by the observation that the sweeping is not restricted to the inshore parts but continues far out to sea beyond the line along the steep heads of offshore canyons with unswept floors.

It is true that sliding could also account for the phenomena, but the slope is rather small. Although it is known that a body of mud can slide on a slope no larger than that of a canyon bed, it may be doubted that it can remove all mud on so slight a declivity without having changed to a turbulent current.

Whether the sweeping out is attributed to a pure slide or to a turbulent current, the difference between the two groups of canyons at any rate shows that the lowering of sea level during the ice age must have brought all types under more favorable conditions for erosion.

Further Aspects of Turbidity Currents. It was shown above that the explanation of submarine canyons is to be sought in the effects of the ice age and that either a great lowering of sea level or turbidity currents may be the main cause. A number of objections against a great depression of sea level that must have amounted to more than 1000 m have already been enumerated. In the following an attempt will be made to show that the hypothesis of turbidity currents can account for some remarkable features of the canyons that are inconsistent with the alternative explanation by subaerial currents.

In the first place, there is the formation of some canyons in positions where no hinterland exists that could have provided large volumes of

water for river erosion (Georges Bank off the east coast of the
United States, Spanish and Delgada canyons off California, Tanner
Canyon off Tanner Bank to the southwest of San Clemente Island,
Nazaré Canyon off the Portuguese coast).

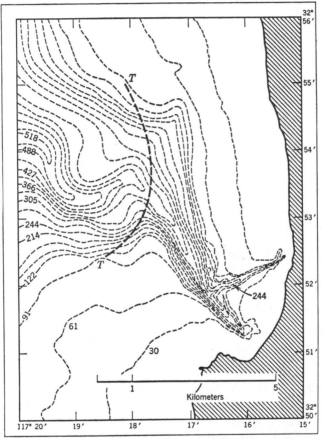

FIG. 228. Chart showing position of La Jolla and Scripps canyons to the north
of a cape on the California coast. Based on chart by Shepard and Emery, 1941,
Plate 9, p. 64. *T–T*, approximate original edge of shelf. Depths in meters.

In the second place, many canyons off California are located to
the north of headlands (Fig. 228). During onshore gales that struck
the coast obliquely the suspension would migrate along the beach to
the next obstacle encountered and pile up there (see Fig. 229). The
outflow would thus tend to occur close to headlands, especially on
the northern side, provided the main direction of storms was slightly

to the north of a line at right angles to the general trend of the coast-line as it is at the present day.

In the third place, the forked head of many canyons is easily accounted for by considering how the suspension is drawn in from the sides off the shelf. Had the erosion been due to a river crossing the shelf from the hinterland only a single trench would be expected.

According to Shepard (1941, p. 86), "The extraordinary thing about this pairing is that in all cases except La Jolla Canyon the head of the southern member of the pair approaches closer to the coast than does the northern member. Also in all cases the southern member is the larger. Furthermore in most of these cases the southern canyon is found directly north of either a point or of the termination of one of the short coast ranges. Finally, in the majority of cases both canyons head into a broad indentation of the coast." These characteristics are readily explained by the supposed development of turbidity currents where the waters were piled up by oblique storms. Once the canyon had deeply indented the shelf a tributary was formed to the north by inflow off the shelf, but it failed to develop as far as its older partner through lack of time and sediment. It is most unlikely that any other theory could explain these rules more satisfactorily.

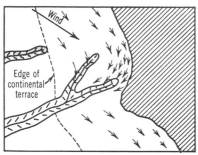

FIG. 229. Diagram illustrating the two types of offshore and inshore canyons on the west coast of the United States. The inshore type is continually swept out by slumping and turbidity currents. Development north of headland is due to ponding of muddy waters against obstruction to longshore currents, due to oblique winds. (After Kuenen, 1947, Fig. 7, p. 56.)

To the mind of the present writer one of the most significant points in choosing between submarine and subaerial erosion is concerned with the disposition of materials excavated from the canyons. Shepard mentions three canyons (Coronado, Redondo, and Dume) in front of which a deltalike bulge of the continental slope is revealed by the soundings. Either theory could explain the occasional occurrence of deltas where conditions were favorable to deposition. But, as already pointed out above, a more general development would be expected if subaerial erosion had cut out the canyons. Moreover, the canyon usually continues down along the side of the "delta"—a feature that does not accord with the view of delta building during lowered sea level (Fig. 230).

With turbidity currents, however, the exceptional deltas might be due to preglacial slumping or local circumstances in connection with slope, relatively coarse materials, etc. But there is no need to expect

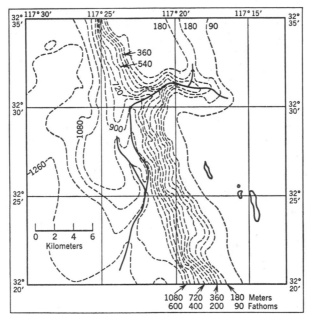

FIG. 230. Chart showing delta-shaped bulge at lower end of Coronado Canyon with the channel passing down the side of the "delta." The delta may be due to a major slump, later furrowed by turbidity currents. If it were a delta formed during excessive lowering of sea level, it should lie deeper, as the San Diego Trough, into which the canyon flows, would not have been ponded. (Based on chart by Shepard and Emery, 1941, Plate 8, p. 62.)

deltas as a general phenomenon. The current should continue beyond the area where its erosive power has ceased in consequence of decreasing slope. The finer sediment would be carried far out and spread over a wide area of the ocean floor. Sand may accumulate to form levees in the region where cutting power is gradually giving way to deposition. Thus the natural ending of a canyon due to the action of turbidity currents would be to become gradually broader, flatter, and shallower and to grade into depressions formed on the ocean floor by other agents. The outward slope, however, should continue as far as the amount of materials carried along was still sufficient to build a graded bed.

The lower ends of the canyons, as far as has been ascertained, conform satisfactorily to the deductions above. On the other hand, with the hypothesis of greatly lowered sea level, deltas should be the rule and the canyons should have broad flat bottoms, as pointed out earlier.

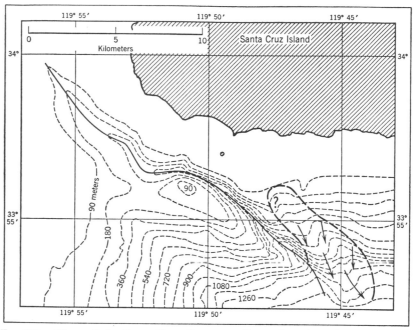

Fig. 231. Chart of the Santa Cruz Canyon ending rather abruptly on the slope at "ponding level" of Santa Cruz Basin. Note absence of delta and slight indication of slump smothering lower end of canyon. (Based on chart by Shepard and Emery, 1941, Plate 17, p. 88.)

Shepard maintains that some canyons end above the floor of basins into which they debouch. They die out at the level at which lowering of sea level would have caused ponding of the waters. The Santa Cruz Canyon is an example. On the one hand there is no indication of the delta, at this level, that should have resulted from ponding. On the other hand there are features on the adjoining slope that might indicate a slump that smothered the former, lower end of the canyon where it passed below sill depths (Fig. 231).

Another argument of considerable weight in choosing between subaerial and submarine erosion is the degree of angularity of the canyons.

Shepard has repeatedly emphasized the complete similarity between submarine gorges and the canyons formed by running water on land. There is, however, one respect in which the two forms show a significant difference. Water is able to flow on land around relatively sharp bends on account of gravity that holds it down even where a strong centrifugal force is developed in a sharp turning. A turbidity

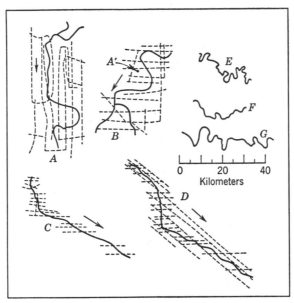

F_{IG}. 232. Comparison of sinuous submarine canyons with subaerial canyons, drawn to the same scale. *A*, Eel Canyon; *B*, Monterey Canyon; *C*, Washington Canyon; *D*, Hudson Canyon; *E*, San Juan River; *F*, *G*, Colorado Marble Canyon. The dotted lines denote sounding lines. Note the sharper bends in subaerial canyons. (After Kuenen, 1947, Fig. 10, p. 61.)

flow, on the other hand, has a very small effective density; consequently in a sharp bend it would be forced high up against the outer wall by its inertia and jump right out of a shallow canyon. Therefore only slight curves can be followed by a turbidity flow, and where faults would tend to induce a sharp turning the current will round off the bend and erode a wide curve.

When the submarine canyons are compared to subaerial canyons a remarkable difference immediately catches the eye. In Fig. 232 the two most sinuous canyons off California and the east coast are drawn to the same scale as two land canyons. The sounding lines are indicated to show the large number of data on which the shapes of the marine canyons are based. When the great depth of the submarine canyons is taken into account it is obvious that, although minor irregularities need not come out in a chart, the major curves are accurately known. If forms comparable to those of the land canyons existed, these should cause abrupt turns in the depth curves. It appears safe to conclude that the submarine canyons nowhere present the sharp turnings of the land canyons. Even a much larger river than the supposed stream in Monterey Canyon can twist and turn in quite sharp bends, as exemplified by Colorado Canyon. The structural control of Eel and Monterey canyons is expressed only in wide bends. Kneebends like the one in Niagara gorge have not been developed. The greater slope of the continental terrace may be held responsible for the generally straight course of the canyons. But the examples shown in our figure clearly demonstrate that this is not a rule without exceptions. Had the agents cutting the submarine canyons been able to form sharp bends there would doubtless have been found examples by now.

Daly suggested that quite possibly a few of the California trenches were actually river-cut far back in geological time, then drowned, afterwards more or less completely filled with sediment, and, finally, recently re-excavated by turbidity currents. Although this is a reasonable suggestion the difficulty is to account for the outcropping of Tertiary rock high up on the walls. The correlation with the shapes of the coastline would also remain obscure. Is it likely that some canyons are of a different origin from others off the same stretch of coast? It is not an impossible but hardly a satisfactory explanation.

The most weighty argument that has been brought forward against the hypothesis of turbidity currents is that they cannot have developed sufficient erosive power to cut into the continental slope. This point must therefore be treated in some detail. Dredging in the east-coast and west-coast canyons has shown that the majority of rock encountered is less consolidated than rocks, in general, encountered on land. The absence of percolating groundwater, the principal agent in the induration of sediments below the land surface, readily explains this difference.

Two sets of observations bear out this conclusion. In the first place, geophysical investigations of the Atlantic continental shelf by seismic methods have demonstrated that the materials building up the continental terrace are poorly or moderately consolidated. Below a few hundred meters of unconsolidated sand, mud, and gravel, a thick

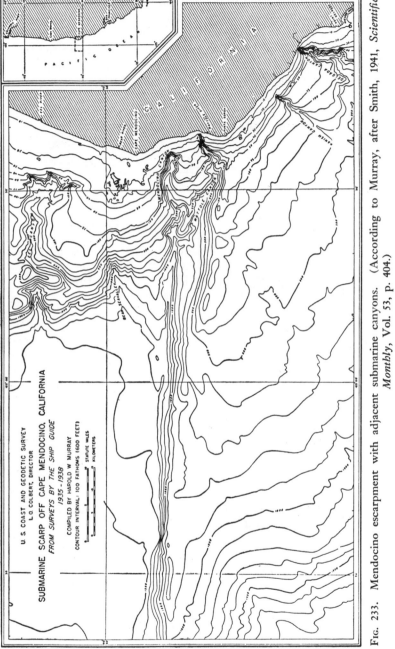

U. S. COAST AND GEODETIC SURVEY
L. O. COLBERT, DIRECTOR

SUBMARINE SCARP OFF CAPE MENDOCINO, CALIFORNIA
FROM SURVEYS BY THE SHIP GUIDE
1935 - 1938

COMPILED BY HAROLD W. MURRAY
CONTOUR INTERVAL: 100 FATHOMS (600 FEET)

Fig. 233. Mendocino escarpment with adjacent submarine canyons. (According to Murray, after Smith, 1941, *Scientific Monthly*, Vol. 53, p. 404.)

wedge of semi-consolidated sediments, possibly interbedded with thin layers or lenses of hard rock, was deduced.

In the second place, the absence of "waterfalls" along the course of the canyons and of steep cliffs of great height, either on the canyon walls or where faults are inferred on the continental slope, forms strong evidence for the comparative weakness of the rocks.

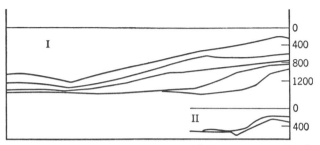

Fig. 234. True-to-scale sections of submarine "fault escarpments" off California, showing that slumping appears to have lessened the declivity in spite of hydrostatic support. I, Gorda Scarp; II, San Clemente Scarp. Depths in fathoms. (After Kuenen, 1947, Fig. 5, p. 54.)

The scarps of what are probably submarine faults are all of moderate steepness, although the fault planes must in most cases have been much nearer vertical. Thus the steepest parts of San Clemente, Catalina, and Coronado escarpments show slopes of 30–40% (1:3.3 to 2.5). The steeper sections of Gorda Escarpment are 26% (1:3.8); the average is only 4.3% (1:23) (Figs. 233 and 234).

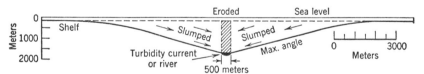

Fig. 235. Transverse section (natural slope) of the Congo submarine canyon at edge of shelf, showing small proportion of eroded matter as against slumped matter.

In this connection the transverse sections of the canyons also bear testimony to the comparative instability of the walls. Whether subaerial or submarine streams excavated the gorges, only the central portions can have been directly eroded by the flowing water. The remainder must have slumped down into the gorge, just as a river valley is widened by weathering and creep (Fig. 235). If this were not so, the walls would have remained perpendicular. The slopes, however, are moderate and evidently represent the maximum angle of repose of the material. Geological evidence shows that the cutting of the Colorado Canyon occupied a much longer period (probably 10 times) than the excavation of the submarine canyons. As the slope of the walls is almost identical, while the time available in the case of the Colorado to weather back the slopes was so very much longer, the Colorado wall rocks must be considerably more resistant.

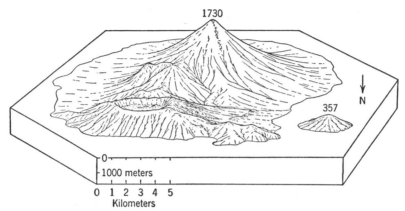

Fig. 236. Block diagram of the extinct volcanic islands of Tidore and Maitara in the Moluccas.

When the hydrostatic support of the submarine slopes is taken into account, the weakness of the rock becomes even more obvious.

In fact, in the case of submarine canyons there was hardly any time even under the theory of subaerial erosion for normal weathering and creep, so that the action of gravity alone must account for the widening of the gorge.

Yet in another respect the profiles of the canyons do not conform to Shepard's views. Under his hypothesis the time available for weathering back the walls should have been much longer for the upper reaches than for the lower ends, and the lower ends should be not only shallower but also narrower and steeper walled if weathering and not collapse had widened water-worn gorges. This is not the case, for in general the steepest walls are encountered near the heads of the canyons. Hence collapse must have produced the transverse sections. Figure 235 shows how slumping of the walls is supposed to have widened the canyons while the turbidity currents excavated the floor.

Against these deductions a considerable amount of evidence of hard rock cropping out on the canyon walls must be noted. This evidence was gained partly by submarine photography, mainly by sampling. Thus Carmel Canyon is stated to have been cut in granite. But there

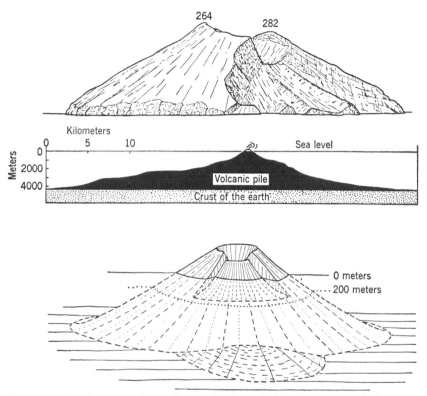

Fig. 237. Sketch, true-scale section, and schematic block diagram of the active volcanic island of Gunung Api, north of Wetar in the Banda Sea. (Kuenen, 1941, Fig. 32, p. 146; Fig. 33, p. 150.)

are reasons for supposing (Lawson) that a fault zone had crushed and weakened the rock beforehand, thus greatly facilitating erosion. We need but look at the abnormal direction of this gorge, closely according with the direction of faults in the adjoining Santa Lucia Range, the complicated physiography of the wall of Monterey Canyon, opposite the lower end of the tributary Carmel Canyon, and the structural control of the whole system of furrows as emphasized by Shepard to be convinced of the high probability of faulting having aided in locating Carmel Canyon and preparing the rock for facile erosion. La Jolla Canyon also appears to coincide with a fault on the coast. In other cases the existence of a fault is demonstrated by the contrasted nature of the opposite walls proved by dredging. The slope is then found to be much steeper on the hard-rock side.

When seeking for evidence on the origin of the canyons it should be kept in mind that evidence from depths less than 100 m is questionable, because of the emergence during the glacial lowering of sea level.

Concluding Remarks on the Origin of Submarine Canyons. On the foregoing pages the problem of submarine canyons was discussed at some length. The following main conclusions were reached.

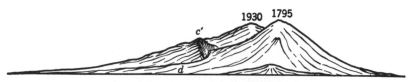

Fig. 238. Sketch of the active volcanic island of Sangean north of Sumbawa, seen from the south southwest.

That the formation was almost entirely brought about during the ice ages appears to be firmly established. This rules out most proposed agents as constituting the main cause and can be explained only by attributing the excavation to the influence of lowered sea level. Diastrophic action, especially faulting and the development of troughs, has played a part, but only a minor one. Slumping and sliding are of importance, both in forming initial furrows and in widening the canyons from vertical trenches to open valleys. Probably turbidity flows were engendered by this mechanism. Tsunamis may have caused some of these slides. Spring sapping and excessive lowering of sea level are not believed to have played a part.

The main cause is sought in turbidity flows, weighted by mud and sand. During the ice ages this action was greatly strengthened owing to the sinking of ocean level by 80 to 100 m below present level, so that virtually the canyons were developed and modeled during this period. It brought all canyons into even more favorable positions for the action of turbidity flows than the present inshore canyons of California. These canyons are being continually swept out by this mechanism at the present day. The chief points in favor of turbidity flows are: absence of sharp turnings and waterfalls, the almost universal absence of deltas at the lower end, the forked heads and preferred position close to the north of promontories (California), the only partial correlation with rivers, the passage far below sill depths and absence of deltas in the Mediterranean and Japan Seas, the close adherence of the heads to the shelf and shallow banks, and the formation during the Pleistocene.

The main point of doubt is whether the rocks forming the continental terrace are so poorly consolidated that they can have been swiftly eroded by currents of a few meters per second. This doubt is so serious, in view of the many places in which hard rock has been encountered on the canyon walls, that the hypothesis of turbidity currents cannot be definitely accepted, in spite of its many outstanding merits. But the swiftly accumulating mass of data may bring conviction one way or another in the near future.

SUBMARINE VOLCANIC SLOPES

An analysis of the submarine slopes of volcanoes will reveal some interesting facts that prove to be of considerable value in explaining the subaerial shapes of cones.

The slopes of simple volcanic cones rising from a deeper sea floor differ according to the length of time the volcano has been dormant and the type of activity (explosive, mixed, or effusive). An ancient cone, such as St. Helena, is cliffed and presents an island terrace built out onto the pre-existing slope. Most of the volcanic islands of the Moluccas, on the other hand, have been active up to a recent date. The absence, moreover, of oceanic swell and stormy weather in these inland seas reduces the erosive activity of waves. Hence, the profiles show little in the nature of cliff and terrace. By analyzing the profiles of these composite, andesite volcanoes Kuenen (1935) came to the following conclusions. The submarine slopes down to a depth of 200 m vary between about 10° and 40° and average roughly 25°. The height of the cone above sea level does not influence this slope, but, when the higher parts of the slopes are steep, the submarine slopes also tend to show a stronger declivity. Evidently the influences that govern the slopes of volcanoes, such as viscosity of the lava, size and shape of the ejectamenta, and type of eruption, tend to form the same declivities above and below the water.

When, on the other hand, the lower subaerial slopes are considered quite different results are obtained. It is found that the higher the volcano the lower is the declivity of the dry foot. This means that the beautiful concave profiles are developed most strikingly on high cones. Yet, as we saw, this does not hold for the submarine slopes.

By plotting against each other the height of the cone and the angle formed at sea level between the dry and wet parts of the slope (Fig. 239) a clear picture is obtained. It is found that the low cones up to 600 m are steeper above water. Gradually the angle decreases to zero and then changes in sign. With increasing height the angle again grows in absolute value until at 2000 m it approaches 25°. This means that for volcanoes of more than 2000 m the bottom of the dry slope is almost zero and the angle with the submarine slope attains the same value as the declivity of the sub-marine slope.

The explanation of these findings is not far to seek. The observed sudden and considerable increase of slope below sea level in high volcanoes cannot be explained by variations in the distance particles are scattered during eruptions. The distribution of the amount of material is governed by influences in the atmosphere from which it drops in regularly decreasing quantities farther away from the vent. There is no reason why the amount would suddenly change beyond the coastline.

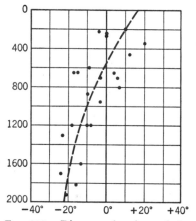

Fig. 239. Diagram showing relation between height of volcanic cones above sea level and angle between submarine and subaerial slope, in the Moluccas.

The influence of erosion, on the other hand, is intimately connected with the position of sea level; indeed, it cannot extend below it. The fact that the submarine slopes are of the same order of steepness as the top of the dry part proves that the low declivity just above sea level is due to erosion and deposition.

With a small cone the rate of vertical growth is large in comparison with the speed of denudation. But as the cone grows in height the amount of material required to add each meter increases. Even if we assume that the rate of production is not adversely influenced by increasing height, the time required to add 1 m to a cone twice as high is no less than four times as long. As the amount of precipitation per unit of surface remains the same or even increases, the influence of erosion during the addition will be four times as large. Hence it may be concluded that the higher a volcano becomes the greater the influence of denudation on the shape will become. In other words:

the study of submarine slopes reveals that the concave profiles of larger subaerial volcanoes are due to erosion and deposition, and not, as has been suggested, to collapse.

A test of the above deductions is found in the shape of the submarine profiles. Here the fact that the slopes are almost straight down to near the sea floor is in accordance with the view that concavity is due to subaerial influences.

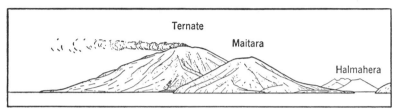

FIG. 240. Sketch of Ternate (1715 m) and Maitara (357 m), two volcanic islands west of Halmahera, Moluccas, seen from the south.

So far the submarine slopes of volcanic cones outside Indonesia have not yet been analyzed. Obviously the nature of the volcanic action and the resulting products—lava of various degrees of viscosity, fine or coarse efflata, the rate of growth, etc.—will influence the submarine declivity and the shape of the profiles.

In conclusion, the growth of a composite volcano on a comparatively deep sea bottom may be visualized. At first the cone grows in

FIG. 241. Sketch of Paluweh (875 m), a deeply eroded, active volcanic island, north of Flores, Moluccas, seen from the northeast.

steepness, height, and volume. Soon the upper portion assumes the natural slope. The growth will continue upward and outward, until over the whole pile the natural slope predominates. With the varying force of eruptions and the range in size of ejectamenta a slight concavity may result. When the cone emerges above sea level the dry part will be slightly steeper on account of the higher angle of repose for dry material. With increasing height of the subaerial part, erosion gains in relative importance. On an average (in Indonesia) it will compensate for the difference between the wet and dry material when the cone rises to 600 m. The upper part loses more and more of the fine volcanic materials through the washing out by rain. The lower parts are built up in ever-increasing degree by water-borne

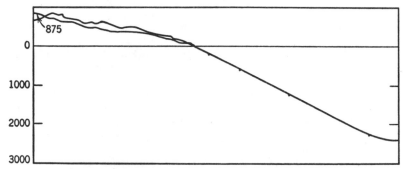

FIG. 242. Two sections through the volcanic island of Paluweh with submarine slope based on four soundings (see Fig. 241).

material. The submarine slopes are fed by a decreasing quantity of direct ejectamenta and more and more by products of denudation. Waves tend to spread this deltalike addition to the submarine slopes evenly around the entire circumference. The particles added to the

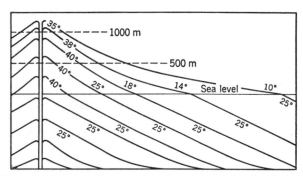

FIG. 243. Diagram showing the growth of a composite volcanic cone from the sea floor to above sea level.

submarine slopes will also become progressively finer in proportion to the decreasing slope of the dry "foot" of the volcano. In Fig. 243 an attempt is made to show diagrammatically the successive stages of development.

Bibliography

BAILEY, E. B. American Gleanings, 1936, *Trans. Geol. Soc. Glasgow*, Vol. 20, pp. 1–16, 1938.

BELL, H. S. Density Currents as Agents for Transporting Sediments, *J. Geol.*, Vol. 50, pp. 512–547, 1942.

BOURCART, J. Sur les rechs, sillons sous-marins du plateau continental des Albères (Pyrénées-Orientales), *Comp. rend. acad. sci.*, Vol. 224, pp. 1175–1177, 1947.

BUCHER, W. H. Submarine Valleys and Related Geologic Problems of the North Atlantic, *Bull. Geol. Soc. Am.*, Vol. 51, pp. 489–512, 1940.

COLLET, L. W. *Les lacs*, 320 pp., Gaston Doin, Paris, 1925.

DALY, R. A. Origin of Submarine Canyons, *Am. J. Sci.*, Vol. 31, pp. 401–420, 1936.
The Floor of the Ocean, 177 pp., University of North Carolina Press, 1942.

DAVIS, W. M. Submarine Mock Valleys, *Geogr. Rev.*, Vol. 24, pp. 297–308, 1934.

DUTOIT, A. L. An Hypothesis of Submarine Canyons, *Geol. Mag.*, Vol. 77, pp. 395–404, 1940.

HESS, H. H. *Interpretation of Geological and Geophysical Observations*, The Navy-Princeton Gravity Expedition to the West Indies, 54 pp., 1933.

HOLTEDAHL, O. Some Remarkable Features of the Submarine Relief on the North Coast of the Varanger Peninsula, Northern Norway, *Avh. Norske Vid. Akad. Oslo*, I Mat.-Nat. Kl., Vol. 12, 14 pp., 1929.
The Submarine Relief off the Norwegian Coast, Norske Vid. Akad. Oslo, 43 pp., 1940.

JOHNSON, D. W. Origin of Submarine Canyons, *J. Geol.*, Vol. 1, 1938, Vol. 2, 1939. (Also: Columbia University Press, 126 pp., 1939.)

KUENEN, PH. H. Geological Interpretation of the Bathymetrical Results, *The Snellius Expedition*, Vol. 5, Geological Results, part 1, 123 pp., Brill, Leyden, 1935.
Experiments in Connection with Daly's Hypothesis on the Formation of Submarine Canyons, *Leidsche Geol. Med.*, Vol. 8, pp. 327–351, 1937.
Density Currents in Connection with the Problem of Submarine Canyons, *Geol. Mag.*, Vol. 75, pp. 241–249, 1938.
Two Problems of Marine Geology, Atolls and Canyons, Verh. Kon. Ned. Akad. Wet. Afd. Nat. 2e Sect., Vol. 43, 3, 69 pp., Amsterdam, 1947.
Turbidity Currents of High Density, *Int. Geol. Congr., 18th Session*, 1948.

LEWIS, R. G. The Orography of the North Sea Bed, *Geogr. J.*, Vol. 86, pp. 334–342, 1935.

MOLENGRAAFF, G. A. F. Geologie, in *De Zeeën van Ned. Oost Indië*, pp. 272–357, Brill, Leyden, 1922.

RICH, J. L. Review of Johnson's book, *J. Geol.*, Vol. 49, pp. 107–109, 1941.

SHEPARD, F. P. Glacial Troughs of the Continental Shelves, *J. Geol.*, Vol. 39, pp. 345–360, 1931.
"Salt" Domes Related to Mississippi Submarine Trough, *Bull. Geol. Soc. Am.*, Vol. 48, pp. 1349–1362, 1937.
Non-Depositional Physiographic Environments off the California Coast, *Bull. Geol. Soc. Am.*, Vol. 52, pp. 1869–1886, 1941.
Imaginary Submarine Canyons, *Science*, Vol. 98, pp. 208–209, 1943.
Submarine Geology, 348 pp., Harper, New York, 1948.

Shepard, F. P., and C. N. Beard. Submarine Canyons; Distribution and Longitudinal Profiles, *Geogr. Rev.*, Vol. 28, pp. 439–451, 1938.

Shepard, F. P., and K. O. Emery. Submarine Topography off the California Coast, *Geol. Soc. Am. Spec. Paper*, No. 31, 171 pp., 1941.

Smith, P. A. Submarine Valleys, *U. S. C. G. S. Field Eng. Bull.*, No. 10, pp. 150–158, 1936.

The Submarine Topography of Bogoslof, *Geogr. Rev.*, Vol. 27, pp. 625–636, 1937.

Lands beneath the Sea, *Sci. Monthly*, Vol. 53, pp. 393–409, 1941.

Sprigg, R. C. Submarine Canyons of the New Guinea and South Australian Coasts, *Trans. Roy. Soc. S. Austr.*, Vol. 71, pp. 296–310, 1947.

Stetson, H. C. Geology and Paleontology of the Georges Bank Canyons, Pt. 1, Geology, *Bull. Geol. Soc. Am.*, Vol. 47, pp. 339–366, 1936.

Stetson, H. C., and J. F. Smith. Behavior of Suspension Currents and Mud Slides on the Continental Slope, *Am. J. Sci.*, Vol. 35, pp. 1–13, 1938.

Terry, R. A. Notes on Submarine Valleys off the Panamanian Coast, *Geogr. Rev.*, Vol. 31, pp. 377–384, 1941.

Umbgrove, J. H. F. De Koraalriffen der Duizend Eilanden (Java-Zee), *Wet. Med. Dienst Mijnb. Ned. Indië*, No. 12, 47 pp., 1929.

The Pulse of the Earth, 358 pp., Nijhoff, The Hague, 1947.

Veatch, A. C., and P. A. Smith. Atlantic Submarine Valleys of the United States and the Congo Submarine Valley, *Geol. Soc. Am. Spec. Paper*, No. 7, 101 pp., 1939.

Eustatic Changes
of Sea Level

One is accustomed to look upon sea level as an unalterable datum level and to ascribe all changes in height above or depth below it to movements of the solid crust. Thus engineers and historians have long studied the problem of the "sinking of the Dutch coast" under the assumption that the observed submergence is due to subsidence of the coast. The geologist, however, is well aware that several processes take place that cause world-wide changes of sea level. He applies the term eustatic to such movements. The principal agents bringing them about are: (1) alteration in the shape of the sea basins (sedimentation, isostatic and orogenic movements of the sea floor); (2) alteration of the amount of water on the continents (growth or decay of lakes and glaciers); (3) alteration of the total mass of water on the surface of the earth (the production of water by volcanoes and from other internal sources, the absorption of water by minerals during weathering).

However, the local submergence or emergence of a coastline can also take place through the intervention of orogenic, epirogenic, or isostatic adjustments. Although the neighboring sea floor will also be affected the consequent eustatic movements will be negligible. Obviously, therefore, a eustatic movement can seldom be deduced from local shifts of the strand line and can be demonstrated only by world-wide emergence or submergence of the coastlines or other more general indications.

The problems of eustatic shifts can be conveniently studied from three aspects: recent movements, glacial and postglacial movements, ancient stratigraphically demonstrated movements.

RECENT EUSTATIC MOVEMENTS

The position of mean sea level with relation to the land can be determined by means of tide gauges and mareographs (accurate, self-registering instruments with damped readings). A single station, however, cannot give us information on eustatic movements, because the readings are influenced by several factors of which mean sea level is but one. Some of these disturbing influences can be eliminated by calculating the average of a number of years. For instance, the influence of variations in barometric pressure, wind, and tides can be ruled out when the mean of some 10 years is compared with that of a different decade. Sinking or rising of the foundation of a tide gauge, however, whether in consequence of local compaction or of deformations of the earth's crust, is more difficult to assess. Precision leveling may help to detect such movements, but it is only recently that the technique has become sufficiently accurate to warrant conclusions. The amount of trustworthy data is still very small, and it will be many years before this line of approach to our problem can be followed with confidence.

The safest manner in which eustatic shifts can be ascertained is by studying the results of reading tide gauges distributed over the entire earth. Local diastrophic movements up and down will then compensate each other and their influence will be ruled out. (The number of tide gauges that may possibly be sinking through local compaction is luckily small.) This method has been followed by Gutenberg (1941) mainly on data provided by Proudman (1940). He found an average secular rise of sea level of 12 cm, roughly during the period from 1880 to 1930. Kuenen (1945) averaged the readings from 11 Dutch stations for the period of 1832 to 1942. From geological, archeological, and precision leveling data he deduced a secular sinking of the crust of 5 cm. Combining these two results he constructed a curve for the eustatic rise. Over the same period as roughly covered by Gutenberg, Kuenen found a secular rise of 12 to 14 cm in striking accordance with the figure given by the former investigator.

Moreover, Kuenen attempted to correlate the irregularities of the curve for Holland with the facts known about the recession and advance of glaciers. It appears that the amounts deduced for the eustatic shift are in agreement with the probable reduction of ice during the same period. Thus Thorarinsson estimated that the rise of sea level since 1890 in consequence of shrinking of mountain glaciers alone attained 5 (possibly 12½) cm per 100 years. However, he and Ahlmann held that the Greenland and Antarctic ice caps are so cold that a slight rise of temperature would not affect their volumes. But a relatively small reduction, partly in consequence of less precipitation, partly because of a faster flow in the tongues leaking down into the sea, is also to be expected. If the reduction of these vast masses were, relatively, only one-tenth of that on mountain glaciers this would add another 15 cm to the rise of sea level. Hence a rise during the last half century of 20 cm per 100 years, increasing to double or treble that value over shorter periods, appears to be a fair estimate from observation and deduction on ice volume.

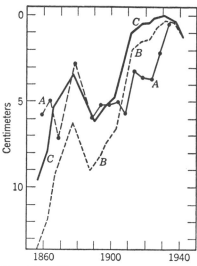

FIG. 244. Changes in mean sea level in centimeters deduced from tide gauges. For explanation see text.

Furthermore the eustatic sinking between 1880 and 1890 could be correlated by Kuenen with the general advance of glaciers noted in the Alps around 1890. Indications were found of a renewed sinking of ocean level between about 1935 and 1942.

In Fig. 244 the line B shows the results of 11 Dutch tide gauge readings; C represents the deduced eustatic changes obtained by reducing B by 5 cm per century. The line A was constructed from the data given by Proudman, using the same stations as Gutenberg. There are more than 20 stations for the years following 1890 and 12 for the years from 1880 to 1890, but only 3 to 6 for the years 1860 to 1880. In view of the small number of stations and the many disturbing factors the degree of correlation is satisfactory. Both appear to show the influence of the glacial advance of 1890. On the evidence of these lines one might conclude that the subsidence of the Dutch coast is on an average not 5 but 7 or 8 cm per 100 years.

It is to be expected that, with a growing amount of data on the volume changes of glaciers and land ice, coupled with an ever-increasing knowledge of tide gauge readings, we may comparatively soon be able to establish a close correlation between sea level and ice volume. It may even prove possible to trace a connection with meteorological influences and ultimately to predict changes of sea level at least roughly for many years in advance. But the last task will have to await a trustworthy theory on climatic variations and cannot be hoped for in the near future.

GLACIAL AND POSTGLACIAL SWINGS OF SEA LEVEL [1]

The repeated great advances of glaciers and land ice during the Pleistocene cannot have occurred without corresponding reductions of sea level, as all the water bound up in the state of ice is obtained from the oceans. This is not the place to discuss the problem of the number of ice ages, held by most to have been four, but by others five or even six.

The Foraminifera in long bottom samples from the oceans provide the most trustworthy evidence on climatic variations of the Pleistocene, because all stages are represented in chronological sequence, the one above the other in a bottom sample of sufficient length. This line of investigation has only recently been taken up in earnest but is now being energetically pursued. Soon we may hope to have a detailed chronology of climatic variations of the last million years from cores 10 to 20 m long. Results up to the present have shown a highly complicated succession of warmer and colder periods for the last 200,000 years. The matter that concerns us here is the degree of lowering of sea level sustained. This problem can be attacked from two directions. One is to estimate the volume of the glaciers; the other, to find morphological evidence of former lower and higher sea levels.

The volume of the Pleistocene glaciers has been calculated by several investigators. The area occupied by ice is the best-known quantity, but the thickness can be guessed only very roughly, although there are several indications. The figures arrived at can hardly claim to be more than an estimate, showing the order of magnitude. Generally a volume is arrived at that corresponds to a lowering of sea level of some 50 to 150 m below the present position. Shepard, on the other hand, holds that sea level may have been lowered by as much as 1100 m (Chapter 7). Although he set out to find a maximum, and glaciologists do not appear to agree with him, the fact that so high a figure was found possible certainly demonstrates how

[1] For a recent useful summary see Flint (1947).

uncertain the outcome of such calculations still is. A complication is introduced by probable isostatic reaction of the ocean floor to unloading. This would reduce the lowering of sea level by 10 to 30%. For the time being we must content ourselves with the result that with respect to present level a lowering of the order of 90–110 m for the greatest and 60–80 m for the last advance of the land ice is the most probable, but that considerably higher figures are not excluded.

Morphological evidence tends to confirm the former lower estimates. It has already been pointed out that the drowned shelf channels must be looked upon as glacial continuations of rivers. This line of evidence must be correlated with the last advance of the glaciers and shows a sea-level lowering of about 70–80 m. Umbgrove held that the Sunda River (Fig. 203, between pp. 482 and 483), where depths of more than 100 m are found in the lower reaches, testifies to a lowering of that amount. However, he overlooked the fact that a large river may be a few dozen meters deep near its mouth. Bearing this in mind, the original estimate of 70 m given by Molengraaff, though on the conservative side, appears near the truth. About 90 m is the figure best fitting the present bathymetrical data of the northern Sunda Shelf. For the Hudson trench 70 m may be deduced from the charts (Fig. 224, p. 506).

It has been contended that crustal movements may have greatly altered the level of the Sunda channels subsequent to their development. To the mind of the present author this is not probable, however. Admittedly crustal movements have taken place in this area up to at least the end of the Tertiary. This follows from the observation that the region north of Java has delivered denudation products to the geosynclines of this island as late as the Pliocene.

But the present morphology appears to point to stability at the prevailing level, at least during and since the last glacial lowering of sea level. When the length of the Sunda River, which is more than 1000 km, is compared with the perfectly even outward grade, and when the absence of counter slopes except close to the former coastline in the north (and in narrows with tidal scour at the present day) is noted, the evidence in favor of complete crustal stability is formidable. An elevation or depression of a few dozen meters without destroying the slope or warping a channel of such length would indeed be a very surprising type of earth movement.

Similar evidence of a lower base level in recent times is found in large river valleys of many parts of the world. The bedrock floors are now found under a fill of drift at 50 to 70 m below sea level. The mouth, at the time, must have lain far out towards the edge of the shelf. Hence a sea level at least as deep as the bed within the present coastline is indicated.

Another line of evidence on the amount of lowering of glacial sea level is provided by coral reefs, especially the lagoon floors of atolls and barrier reefs. But, as indicated in Chapter 6, a certain amount of sedimentation has taken place since the lagoon floors were leveled during the eustatic lowering, and diastrophic or other crustal movements may also have intervened. At any rate present depths of lagoons, and perhaps more forcibly the depths of reef-free banks that in general accord well with the deeper lagoons, point to a lowering of 80 m or thereabouts and are thus in harmony with other indications. Again it is the last glacial advance that must be chiefly concerned in this result.

Complications arise through the attraction exerted by the great masses of ice around the poles. These draw up the water from their surroundings, owing to their center of gravity lying above sea level. In consequence of the isostatic sinking of the crust under their weight, however, the effect is limited.

The isostatic reactions to loading and unloading cause deformations that lag behind the cause. Consequently strand lines are formed that afterward rise or sink according to the nature of the deformations. In considering former stands of sea level these reactions of the crust must be taken into account, and polar regions cannot be used in determining the extent of Pleistocene eustatic movements. The complicated history of the Baltic Sea, ably expounded by Daly (1934) on the basis of work by Scandinavian geologists, forms a typical illustration.

The outcome of these various modes of approach is that the last ice age saw a lowering of sea level of perhaps 70 to 80 m, while foregoing eustatic shifts were of the order of 100 to 120 m. These figures must be viewed with circumspection, and future investigations may lead to their revision. It is highly improbable, however, that mistakes of more than 50% are involved.

To Daly we owe another interesting and important exposition on a postglacial eustatic shift. As pointed out on p. 448, Daly drew attention to the occurrence of a large number of coasts where a comparatively recent elevation of a few meters is proved by well-preserved strands, caves, etc. (1934). The number is so large and the uniformity of elevation so pronounced that he postulated a eustatic sinking of ocean level of 5 or 6 m. In the thirty-odd years following Daly's first paper many further instances have been recorded by a number of investigators the world over, so that this recent shift is now well established. Several factors play a part in causing slight variations in the resulting elevation. Crustal warpings, deformation of the ocean level, and variations of the level at which the coastal terrace is cut during its formation are among the more important. It is therefore no argument against the eustatic nature of the cause that one finds only an imperfect correlation of the recently emerged strand lines.

Johnson (1933), following Bartrum and others, claimed that marine erosion tends to form a bench sloping upwards towards the sea cliff reaching a height roughly 2 m above high-tide level. His main argument was that benches at that level are still swept by storm waves. Most investigators hold, however, that the inner edge is normally at about high-tide level. Where a bench is found at a higher level they assume relative elevation. The present writer agrees with the latter view, although admitting that the cliff behind a slightly elevated platform can still be reached by storm waves at high tide and will be slightly notched if suitable rocks occur. It may also be granted that the level of the inner edge of the erosion platform varies according to local conditions. In the author's opinion, however, an elevated platform will be gradually destroyed by weaker waves and by storm waves during lower tide levels. These waves have battering rams at their disposal in the form of debris and must attack at a lower level than high tide waves and with greater success. On the elevated bench debris is practically absent. Most recently elevated terraces are seen to be suffering attack from seaward at a lower level.

Johnson reasoned as if the force of attack increased upwards to a maximum and were zero immediately above, whereas actually there is a swift but gradual decrease above the level of maximum assault. Hence slight elevation does not lift the bench right beyond the reach of waves. This happens only when uplift has been sufficient.

The time of the movement was estimated by Daly to be probably some 3000 to 4000 years ago. Detailed field work in the Netherlands and in eastern England has shown a recent eustatic depression of the same order of magnitude as deduced by Daly. Here the time can be fixed at roughly 3000 to 3500 years ago.

The cause of this shift has not yet been ascertained. Daly pointed out (1934) that the return of water to the oceans on the melting of the Pleistocene ice must cause an overburden on the ocean floors. He suggested that a lag has occurred in the isostatic compensation, resulting finally in a sudden sinking of the crust below the increased weight of water. Another possibility is a minor increase of volume of the land ice in consequence of climatic influences. It cannot be said which of these two suggestions is the more probable.

From many areas elevated beaches are recorded at considerable height above present sea level. Even when leaving out of account those caused by isostatic elevation since the disappearance of Pleistocene ice caps, a considerable number remain. On an ice-free earth, ocean level would stand 20 to 50 m higher than at present, according to various estimates of present glacier volume. It has therefore been suggested that in interglacial periods the land ice was reduced to the minimum and that the elevated beaches outside the direct sphere of influence of the ice are due to an ocean level at its maximum height.

The clearest evidence so far obtained comes from the Atlantic coast of southern United States. Here two elevated, wave-cut scarps, the Suffolk and Surry scarps, have been traced for many hundreds of miles at altitudes of 7–10 and 30–33 m respectively above sea level. The Surry scarp is tentatively attributed by Flint to the Yarmouth (the last but one), the Suffolk to the Sangamon (the last), interglacial age. The Surry scarp appears to be represented in many other coastal areas of the world. It would correspond roughly to the expected altitude of sea level on an ice-free world. A critical treatment of the whole subject is needed before a definite opinion can be formed. Again, there are many complicating factors, as Daly pointed out (1934).

In the foregoing discussion evidence from depressed shorelines has not been considered. Morphological evidence of submerged shorelines is very poor. Only one such feature has so far been clearly identified, the Franklin Shore, a gentle scarplike break in the seaward slope of the shelf off eastern North America. It extends for at least 300 km from a depth of 75 m in the vicinity of Chesapeake Bay to 100 m off Philadelphia (Veatch and Smith, 1939). Less obvious examples have been reported from the Rhône Delta in the Mediterranean and from Alaska.

Beach deposits may also indicate ancient, submerged shorelines. Bourcart has compiled evidence on this problem. He believes that when dredging is carried out systematically a clear picture may eventually be obtained because the evidence is not destroyed so quickly as that of elevated shorelines. All along the eastern coasts of the Atlantic coarse boulders have been dredged far out to sea, consisting of many different types of rock. The growth of organisms on all but one side testifies to their not being shifted under present conditions. They appear to occur in narrow strips parallel to the coast. Bourcart interprets them as ancient beach conglomerates. In many cases they are associated with a break in slope. While most occurrences belong to the edge of the present continental terrace and can be attributed to Pleistocene changes of sea level, there are also occurrences in depths of 200 to 500 m and even more. Bourcart believes that they may be the consequence of a Late Pliocene regression but prefers to assume warping of the continental border. Although there is much to be said for this opinion, the fact that the boulders are not covered by recent sediment needs explanation. Until this question has been solved we must reserve a definite conclusion on the meaning of these boulder tracts. According to Stearns (1945) an intermediate level at 20-m depth is also indicated on Pacific coasts. This might represent a stage in the retreat of the land ice, when sea level must have remained approximately stable for some length of time.

In conclusion attention may be drawn to a paper by Hoffmeister and Wentworth (1939), who point out the complicated processes at work in the production of benches on rocky coasts and the difficulties encountered in ascertaining the height of sea level at the time such features were developed. In some benches wave attack dominates; in others, solution or organic activity plays a major part. The nature of the rock undergoing erosion is highly variable, and in consequence the level at which the bench is cut or the beach is thrown up varies within wide bounds. The authors cited have found, from experience, that prolonged application to the subject in the field essential to the collecting of trustworthy data.

One serious omission in this otherwise excellent discussion is that of benches formed at low tide level in limestone, especially coraliferous limestone, by means of solution in the upper stratum of the sea (chemical marine erosion). The great importance of this activity, which gradually cuts off the emerged part of elevated atolls and other limestones, was discussed in Chapter 6.

EUSTATIC SHIFTS DEMONSTRATED BY STRATIGRAPHY

Several investigators have shown that, besides local shifts of the strand line, world-wide transgressions and regressions have also occurred in a rhythmic sequence throughout the history of the earth (Suess; Schuchert; Stille; Grabau; Umbgrove, 1947). Kuenen (1939) and others have attempted to gain insight into the nature of these eustatic movements.

The first question is the size of the shifts that are thus found expressed in the stratigraphical column. As the continents were never perfectly flat and were continually subject to minor undulations, it is obvious that a lowering or raising of sea level by a few meters before the Pleistocene would now pass entirely unnoticed.

It can be shown from the hypsographic curve (Fig. 89) that under present conditions a eustatic rise of 50 m would flood one-seventh to one-eighth of the land; a rise of 100 m, as much as one-fourth to one-fifth; and a rise of 200 m, nearly one-third. But at present the continents show an abnormally high relief in consequence of the short time elapsed since the Tertiary mountain-building processes. Moreover, following a eustatic rise, marine planation would add to the area flooded by the ocean waters. Consequently at most periods in the earth's history a rise of 50 m would have caused a transgression over one-fourth of the continents and one of 100 m over one-third.

The area covered by transgressions is hard to estimate, but consultation of paleogeographic maps shows that seldom more than a third of the continents was submerged (Fig. 245) and that the present period is one of regression. It appears safe to conclude that, apart from extreme cases, sea level swung upward, as compared to the continents, less than 100 but more than 25 m to cause the transgressions. The most extensive transgressions will have resulted from a somewhat larger rise of level, but probably not more than 200 m. It is not known how far regressions went, but the available evidence is in favor of assuming that sea level seldom sank much lower than at the present time. Otherwise there should be periods practically without marine deposits anywhere on the continents. In the following it will be assumed that the mechanism we are investigating must be able to account for eustatic movements of at least 50 m.

Penck (1934) and Joly (1925) also made estimates of the amount of eustatic movements. Penck believed the amplitude to be of the order of 500 m, Joly indicating shifts of even 1000 m. Neither of these two authors, however, based their conclusions on established facts. Thus Joly overlooked the fact that the present relief of the continents is abnormally strong, and Penck merely argues that transgressions cannot have attained the height that would follow from complete base leveling of the continents. His calculation is erroneous, moreover. The average height of the continents is somewhat over 800 m, their area three-tenths that of the earth. Hence complete base

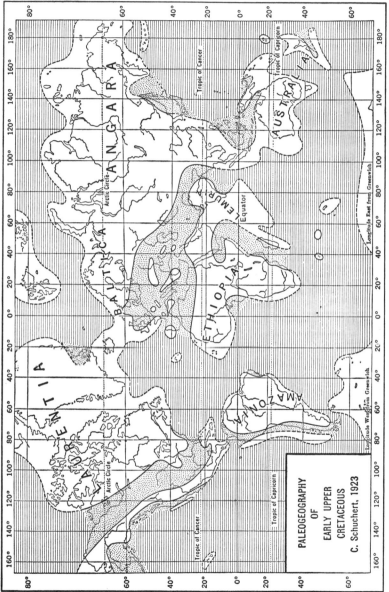

Fig. 245. The great Middle Cretaceous transgression (dotted) of the oceans (ruled) over the lands. This was probably the greatest submergence that ever befell the continents. (After Schuchert, 1924, *Textbook of Geology, Part II, Historical Geology*, Fig. 191, p. 555, John Wiley & Sons.)

leveling, whether isostasy is maintained or not, would cause a eustatic rise of only 250 m. Neither the distribution of depths nor the position on the sea floor of the denuded material would influence this figure.

The smallness of the figure is surprising. Sea level might, of course, rise more than this amount with respect to the level of the continents, if the sea floor were to be raised and the land to be depressed with respect to each other by some internal cause. But external agents, that is base leveling of the land and sedimentation in the sea, could not result in a larger shift of sea level than the 250 m mentioned.

Umbgrove points out that the eustatic movements of the Pleistocene amounted to three times the value assumed by the present writer for earlier eustatic movements. He concludes that a larger amount should be assumed for the earlier swings of sea level. But Umbgrove, like Joly, does not bear in mind that for most of the geological past the continents were much flatter than at present and at a slightly lower level in consequence of there being no land ice. During those times smaller swings of sea level would result in far greater transgressions and regressions than those of the Pleistocene. In the Pleistocene sea level started to sink from an already regressive stage when shallow seas were at the minimum. On the comparatively steep slopes of the emerged continents a further reduction of sea level could bring about but minor changes in coastal configuration.

The next step in our inquiry must be to calculate the amount of water that would have to be added to the sea to cause a transgression, or subtracted for a regression. For a rise of 50 m, roughly 20×10^6 km³ is required. This amount must be added to or abstracted from the volume of water, or the cubic content of the ocean basins, in about 20 to 30 million years to explain the pulsations deduced by stratigraphers for the Paleozoic Era.

Having ascertained roughly the magnitude involved in the average eustatic variations of the past, we are now in a position to consider how this change in volume may have been brought about. Several explanations can be suggested.

VARIATIONS IN THE AMOUNT OF WATER ON EARTH

Water is delivered to the surface from consolidating igneous rocks and is chemically bound by weathering of minerals. The output of volcanic rock at present is somewhat less than 1 km³ per year. If 10% of the area of the earth, or 50,000,000 km², has been intruded by batholiths since the Cambrian (a liberal estimate), with a depth of

10 km, then the average volume of intrusions would be 1 km³ per year. For all igneous rocks together this is 2 km³ per year as a high estimate. The highest estimates of the water content of magmas is well below 10% by weight (see Gilluly, 1937), and of this no more than 6% can have been liberated. Part of this water is not juvenile, but taken from the pore space of migmatized sediments. Let 5% by weight be juvenile; then the total output of juvenile water would be 0.25 km³ per year.

It is true that batholiths may be more than 10 km deep, but the lower parts would probably consist of basic magma with a small percentage of water that cannot escape in consequence of the high pressure. It appears that we are quite safe in assuming that no more than $\frac{1}{4}$ km³ is liberated per year from intrusives and extrusives. From this amount must be subtracted what is bound up again by hydration during weathering of rocks. Although this amount may be less, it is of the same order of magnitude. It appears impossible to assume that the yearly increase of free water is more than $\frac{1}{5}$ km³. The writer is inclined to believe that it is of the order of $\frac{1}{25}$ km³. Yet we need at least 1 km³ per year to explain a eustatic rise in 20 million years. The first conclusion, therefore, is that juvenile waters may play a subordinate part in raising sea level and loss through hydration in lowering it, but that they can never explain more than a fraction of the total phenomenon.

Some investigators have assumed there is loss of water to interstellar space, but it appears highly improbable that this attains appreciable amounts. For one reason, the stratosphere is characterized by extremely low vapor pressure.

VARIATIONS IN THE AMOUNT OF WATER IN THE OCEANS

The most extreme assumptions on variations in the humidity of the atmosphere could not explain eustatic movements of as much as 1 m.

Many rhythms occurred between ice ages, when no land ice was found anywhere on earth. Hence the eustatic movements were not caused by the formation of ice. Moreover, the rhythm is about 1000 times slower than that of ice ages. Evidently the position of the water on earth is not the varying factor we are in search of. The extent of lakes is too small to be of any consequence.

The general conclusion from the first two points is that eustatic movements must be attributed to changes in the cubic content of the sea basins. Bucher (1933) arrived at the same conclusion along different lines.

The change in cubic content of the ocean basins can be due either to external or to internal causes. The only possible external cause would be sedimentation.

SEDIMENTATION

Suess attributed transgressions to the influence of sedimentation, his contention being that the dumping of sediments into the sea must cause a rise of level. Grabau (1936) is less explicit. When considered more in detail the process is found to be complicated. To start with, a distinction must be made between sedimentation in the deep sea and that in geosynclinal troughs, as the effects are opposite in the two locations.

Sedimentation in Geosynclines. The normal type of geosyncline is a large trough, the bottom of which sinks while sedimentation continually keeps the hollow brim full. Whether we ascribe the sinking to horizontal or vertical forces, or to the combined action of isostasy coupled with alterations in the paramorphic zone, and whether the water depths show marked variations or not, the outcome must always be loss of water from free circulation. This loss is in the pore space of the detrital rocks. All that sedimentation does from our point of view is to reduce the inflow of water into the newly forming depression.

To prove this contention it should be borne in mind that alterations in the shape either of the emerged part of the continents or of their parts submerged in the sima have no influence on the level of the continent. They merely form a shifting of the load. But when a deformation takes place such that the sea can flood the new depression, the continent will sink deeper into the sima in the neighborhood. The consequent slight rise of the sima elsewhere merely floats up the crust with respect to the center of the earth but not with respect to the surface of the sima. The result is that the area covered by water is enlarged, and, owing to the constant total amount, the depth of the oceans is decreased. This finally results in a decreased sinking of the remainder of the continents into the sima. As net outcome of the whole process there results a slight increase of freeboard of the continents outside the geosynclinal area (Fig. 246).

To cause a loss of 1,000,000 km³ of water, a volume of 5,000,000 km³ of sediments is required (assuming an average pore space of 20%). A geosyncline with an average depth of 5000 m and an area of (2500 × 400 =) 1,000,000 km² is needed for this amount. In other words, we require 20 such geosynclines forming in 20 million years to cause one major regression! Obviously this is very much above the rate of sedimentation between two major transgressions. A rough estimation is that on an average $\frac{1}{25}$ km³ water has yearly been abstracted from the oceans by geosynclinal subsidence. However, compaction and uplift of the geosynclinal prisms later return this water to the oceans. In the long run no appreciable change results.

Sedimentation in the Deep Sea. On the ocean floor sedimentation has the opposite effect. In consequence of the great area one has to

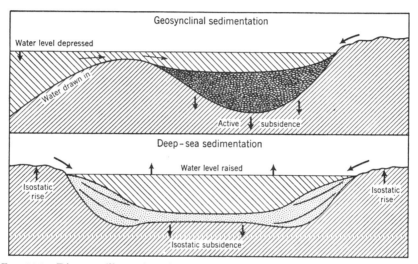

Fig. 246.   Diagram illustrating the opposed effects on sea level of geosynclinal development and deep-sea sedimentation.

assume that sedimentation takes place without loss of isostatic equilibrium. Sediments deposited in the deep sea will cause a rise of sea level, but most of this rise is compensated by isostatic depression of the floor coupled with isostatic rise of the continents and flow of sima towards them. At an estimate that many would consider too high, oceanic sedimentation is of the order of magnitude of $\frac{1}{3}$ km³ per year (solid). If we add sedimentation on the continental slopes the total amount is about $\frac{1}{2}$ km³ per year (see Chapter 5). The amount of isostatic sinking depends on the specific gravity allotted to the sediments and to the subcrustal material. It probably lies between $\frac{3}{4}$ and $\frac{9}{10}$. Sedimentation outside the continents will therefore raise sea level by $\frac{1}{8}$ to $\frac{1}{20}$ (or even less) km³ per year. In the time available there could result a difference of 1,000,000 (or less) to 2,500,000 km³ instead of the 20,000,000 required. The volume of the sediments deposited in epeiric seas was small in comparison and may be neglected.

Again we find an amount that is much too small. As, moreover, geosynclinal and oceanic sedimentation are opposed, their influence must be negligible. Combined with juvenile water the net rise would probably be less than 10 m in the available time. Even if the causes investigated so far have any influence, it must be so small that it can safely be neglected.

The conclusion to be drawn from our estimates is that external influences are entirely inadequate to cause the rhythms.

BASIN FORMATION

Umbgrove pointed out that the deep basins of Indonesia, the West Indies, and the Mediterranean have probably sunk away in "recent" times and that the formation of these new receptacles might constitute a cause of regression.

A rough estimate of the volume of water contained in these basins and troughs within the Indonesian archipelago is 6,000,000 km³. As there were basins there before the recent subsidence, and as elevation has also taken place, the whole of that amount is not available for causing a regression. The maximum estimate would be 5,000,000 km³. This would cause a eustatic shift of only 13 m.

The total volume of all the Indonesian and West Indian basins, the Mediterranean, and the East Asiatic basins is roughly 27,000,000 km³. It does not appear improbable that some are to sink still further, as many are characterized by strong positive anomalies of gravity. On the other hand they are not pure gain. If we assume, for the sake of argument, that they are all of recent origin, then their combined influence would cause a eustatic depression of sea level of 60 to 80 m. We have at last found an influence that is at least of the correct order of magnitude.

It is a different question, however, whether this mechanism can be relied upon to explain repeated eustatic movements. In the first place it must be assumed that there was not a corresponding rise of the ocean floor elsewhere. In the case of oceanic deep-sea troughs one would expect such a rise of neighboring parts of the sea floor, and for this reason these troughs have not been added to the estimated volume of the possible recent sinkings. In other words, most of the mass abstracted from below the floor of the basins must have flowed in below the continents, causing them to rise if a fall of sea level was to result. In the second place the youth of all or most of the basins enumerated would have to be admitted. In the third place only a possible cause of regressions is given.

One might postulate some other mechanism to explain the transgressions, in which event the subsidences would be permanent and constitute a loss to the area of the continents. We would then need similar extensive subsidences for each of the regressions of the geological past. No continental mass would then have remained, because there are no indications in stratigraphy that true ocean bottom has ever been transformed into continental masses.

The other possibility would be that the floor of the basins pulsates up and down, pumping the waters on the continents and sucking it off again! Although we are not sure how the basins are formed, the down-and-up movement of their floor does not appear probable.

Suess attributed regressions to sinking of the entire sea floor in consequence of contraction of the earth. As the principle of isostasy has been firmly established the substratum must be in a plastic state. A contraction would therefore affect the continents in like manner as the ocean floor. The mechanism proposed by Suess has no physical foundation.

OROGENIC PROCESSES OF THE OCEAN FLOORS

Koszmat (1936) attributed the major influence to orogenic processes of the ocean floor. If the elevation is isostatically uncompensated one would have to assume an anomaly of some 40 milligals over an area of 30,000,000 km^2, or $\frac{1}{12}$ of the sea floor. Horizontal compression could never bring this about. If isostatically compensated as a bulge with a root of sial, the formation would not affect the position of sea level. This may be illustrated by the Mid-Atlantic Rise. Its elevation from the general level of the ocean floor would cause a eustatic rise of 42 m, according to Penck. But as it is isostatically compensated it is not an arching bulge of sima lifting the waters onto the continents, and ready to sink away again and thus cause a regression. It is a floating mass, and if it has been formed by horizontal compression it would not influence sea level at all.

INTERNAL CAUSES ACTING BELOW THE CRUST

Joly assumed a rhythmic variation of the state of subcrustal matter. The expansion could not alter the area of the earth more than 1%, and therefore no direct influence on the depth of the oceans could be expected. But during periods of high temperature the continents would sink isostatically, and vice versa. It is beyond the scope of this book to enter into the merits of this hypothesis. For those who are inclined, like the present author, to reject Joly's hypothesis, yet another cause must be sought for. Possibly the conception of convection currents in the substratum affords an explanation.

The investigations of gravity at sea by Vening Meinesz have shown that there exists a general positive anomaly over the oceanic basins with a deficiency over the continents. The difference is of the order of 30 milligals, corresponding to the attraction of a layer of rock about 300 m thick. The strength of the crust is insufficient to bear this weight, and Vening Meinesz finds that the existence of convection currents in the substratum is the only hypothesis that can account for the phenomenon.

It is obvious that, if this mechanism of convection currents includes variations in magnitude, these currents may be sufficient to cause major eustatic movements. To work out this line of thought in detail is a separate problem that will not be attempted by us.

Our review of possible explanations of the eustatic swings of the past has led us to the unexpected conclusion that even the lesser shifts cannot be accounted for by processes operating either in or at the surface of the crust. As external processes and diastrophism are inadequate, we are forced to assume that only some pulsating, subcrustal influence, such as alternating convection currents, can be of sufficient magnitude to explain the rhythmic rise and fall of sea level during the geological past.

A few words may be added on the position of sea level through longer periods. When a folded geosyncline is raised and gradually eroded, the contained water is brought back into circulation. Part of the water in the migmatized zones is given off as "juvenile" magnetic exhalations.

In the long run the sedimentation in the deep sea and the addition of truly juvenile water might cause a small rise of sea level. Our estimates would lead to an addition of about $\frac{1}{7}$ km^3 per year, or 175 m since the beginning of the Cambrian. This increase is shown on the diagram, Fig. 77, p. 130.

On the other hand orogenesis is generally supposed to thicken the continents, thus giving them more freeboard. Intrusion of differentiated acid magma would have the same influence. The fact that since at least the beginning of the Paleozoic the continents have remained on the average at the same level as compared to sea level proves that the net outcome of all these processes must be to compensate each other. To correspond with a deepening of the oceans by 175 m, the continents would have to thicken roughly 1000 m, assuming constant elevation above sea level.

It is scarcely probable that this balance is due merely to chance. But the processes involved are to a certain extent self-regulating. The higher the continental blocks stand with relation to sea level, the faster denudation cuts them down. The lower they lie and the farther they are covered by transgressive seas, the slower the delivery of sediment to the oceans must be. Consequently, as long as orogenic and volcanic processes continue to rejuvenate the relief of the land and together with magmatic processes to thicken the continental blocks, so long the level of the continents will remain a certain but moderate amount above that of the oceans. It is therefore not surprising to find that the opposed factors raising sea level and thickening the continents have tended to strike a balance throughout the ages of geological history.

Bibliography

BOURCART, J. La marge continentale. Essai sur les régressions et transgressions marines, *Bull. soc. géol. France*, pp. 393–474, 1938.

BUCHER, W. H. *The Deformation of the Earth's Crust*, 518 pp., Princeton University Press, 1933.

DALY, R. A. *The Changing World of the Ice Age*, 271 pp., Yale University Press, 1934.

FLINT, R. F. *Glacial Geology and the Pleistocene Epoch*, 589 pp., John Wiley, New York, 1947.

GILLULY, J. The Water Content of Magmas, *Am. J. Sci.*, Vol. 33, pp. 430–441, 1937.

GRABAU, A. W. *Palæozoic Formations in the Light of the Pulsation Theory*, Vol. I, 680 pp., University Press, Peiping, 1936.

GUTENBERG, B. Changes in Sea Level, Postglacial Uplight and Mobility of the Earth's Interior, *Bull. Geol. Soc. Am.*, Vol. 52, pp. 721–772, 1941.

HOFFMEISTER, E., and C. K. WENTWORTH. Data for the Recognition of Changes of Sea Level, *Proc. 6th Pac. Sci. Congr.*, pp. 839–848, 1939.

JOHNSON, D. Supposed Two-Meter Eustatic Bench of the Pacific Shores, *C. R. Congr. Int. Géogr., Paris*, Vol. 2, pp. 158–163, 1933.

JOLY, J. *The Surface-History of the Earth*, 192 pp., Clarendon Press, Oxford, 1925.

KOSZMAT, F. *Paläogeographie und Tektonik*, 414 pp., Bornträger, Berlin, 1936.

KUENEN, PH. H. Geology of Coral Reefs, *The Snellius Expedition*, Vol. 5, Geological Results, part 2, 126 pp., Brill, Leyden, 1933.

Quantitative Estimations Relating to Eustatic Movements, *Geol. en Mijnb.*, Vol. 1, pp. 194–201, 1939.

De Zeespiegelrijzing der laatste Decennia, *Tijdschr. Kon. Ned. Aardr. Gen.*, Vol. 62, pp. 159–169, 1945.

MARMER, H. A. Is the Atlantic Coast Sinking? The Evidence from the Tide, *Geogr. Rev.*, Vol. 38, pp. 652–657, 1948.

PENCK, A. Theorie der Bewegung der Strandlinie, *Sitzb. Preusz. Akad. d. Wiss. Phys.-Math. Kl.*, pp. 321–348, 1934.

PROUDMAN, J. Monthly and Annual Mean Heights of Sea Level, up to and including the Year 1936, *Ass. d'Océanogr. Phys. Publ. Sci.*, Vol. 5, 255 pp., 1940.

SCHUCHERT, C. A Textbook of Geology, Part II, *Historical Geology*, 2nd ed., 724 pp., John Wiley, New York, 1924.

STEARNS, H. T. Shore Benches on North Pacific Islands, *Bull. Geol. Soc. Am.*, Vol. 52, pp. 773–780, 1941.

Eustatic Shore Lines in the Pacific, *Bull. Geol. Soc. Am.*, Vol. 56, pp. 1071–1078, 1945.

UMBGROVE, J. H. F. *The Pulse of the Earth*, 358 pp., Nijhoff, The Hague, 1947.

VEATCH, A. C., and P. A. SMITH. Atlantic Submarine Valleys of the United States and the Congo Submarine Valley, *Geol. Soc. Am. Spec. Paper* 7, 101 pp., 1939.

Index

Pages in italic type indicate illustrations.